CONCORDIA UNIVERSITY CHICAGO

3 4211 00186 9174

S0-BJP-210

WITHDRAWN

ANNUAL REVIEW OF PHYSIOLOGY

EDITORIAL COMMITTEE (1978)

T. E. ANDREOLI
R. M. BERNE
W. R. DAWSON
I. S. EDELMAN
A. P. FISHMAN
W. J. FREEMAN
J. GERGELY
A. KARLIN
S. M. McCANN
S. G. SCHULTZ

Responsible for the organization of Volume 40
(Editorial Committee, 1975)

R. M. BERNE
W. R. DAWSON
I. S. EDELMAN
W. J. FREEMAN
E. KNOBIL
S. M. McCANN
S. G. SCHULTZ
R. R. SONNENSCHEIN

Production Editor   R. L. BURKE
Indexing Coordinator   M. A. GLASS
Subject Indexers   V. E. HALL
                         F. M. HALL

ANNUAL REVIEW OF PHYSIOLOGY

ERNST KNOBIL, *Editor*
University of Pittsburgh School of Medicine

RALPH R. SONNENSCHEIN, *Associate Editor*
University of California, Los Angeles

I. S. EDELMAN, *Associate Editor*
University of California School of Medicine, San Francisco

VOLUME 40

1978

KLINCK MEMORIAL LIBRARY
Concordia Teachers College
River Forest, Illinois 60305

ANNUAL REVIEWS INC.   4139 EL CAMINO WAY   PALO ALTO, CALIFORNIA 94306

ANNUAL REVIEWS INC.
Palo Alto, California, USA

COPYRIGHT © 1978 BY ANNUAL REVIEWS INC., PALO ALTO, CALIFORNIA, USA. ALL RIGHTS RESERVED. The appearance of the code at the bottom of the first page of an article in this serial indicates the copyright owner's consent that copies of the article may be made for personal or internal use, or for the personal or internal use of specific clients. This consent is given on the condition, however, that the copier pay the stated per-copy fee of $1.00 per article through the Copyright Clearance Center, Inc. (P. O. Box 765, Schenectady, NY 12301) for copying beyond that permitted by Sections 107 or 108 of the US Copyright Law. The per-copy fee of $1.00 per article also applies to the copying, under the stated conditions, of articles published in any Annual Review serial before January 1, 1978. Individual readers, and nonprofit libraries acting for them, are permitted to make a single copy of an article without charge for use in research or teaching. This consent does not extend to other kinds of copying, such as copying for general distribution, for advertising or promotional purposes, for creating new collective works, or for resale.

REPRINTS The conspicuous number aligned in the margin with the title of each article in this volume is a key for use in ordering reprints. Available reprints are priced at the uniform rate of $1.00 each postpaid. The minimum acceptable reprint order is 10 reprints and/or $10.00 prepaid. A quantity discount is available.

International Standard Serial Number: 0066-4278
International Standard Book Number: 0-8243-0340-7
Library of Congress Catalog Card Number: 39-15404

Annual Reviews Inc. and the Editors of its publications assume no responsibility for the statements expressed by the contributors of this Review.

PRINTED AND BOUND IN THE UNITED STATES OF AMERICA

122407

PREFACE

This volume of the *Annual Review of Physiology* is the last to be published in the format which has become familiar to generations of readers since the series began 40 years ago. Volume 41 will usher in a new era under the seasoned editorship of Isadore Edelman, who served this enterprise long and well as an Associate Editor. The realities of the ever increasing diversity and specialization of Physiology, a field which has evolved from a single, encompassable discipline to an amalgam which no single mind can truly master, have dictated the sectionalization of forthcoming volumes. Each section will be planned and edited by its own Associate Editor, who will be a specialist in the area of Physiology addressed by his section. This major change should significantly increase the utility of the *Annual Review of Physiology* to its vast and varied readership by improving, extending, and deepening coverage of the field. As retiring Editor, I anticipate with great pleasure and satisfaction that the future volumes of this series will surpass their antecedents in excellence, influence, and responsiveness to the rapidly advancing frontiers of Physiology in its many aspects.

I shall be joined in retirement by Ralph Sonnenschein who has been a guiding light of the *Annual Review of Physiology* during his dedicated and extraordinarily competent service as Associate Editor in the course of the past 15 years. Three successive Editors are in his profound debt for his awesome knowledge, unflagging devotion, unwavering support, and undeviatingly great good sense. I, for one, never would have assumed Julius Comroe's mantle had Ralph Sonnenschein not agreed to stay on and lead the way. The *Annual Review of Physiology* and all those who have profited from the last 15 volumes of this series will join me in extending to him heartfelt thanks and all good wishes.

ERNST KNOBIL
EDITOR

ANNUAL REVIEWS INC. is a nonprofit corporation established to promote the advancement of the sciences. Beginning in 1932 with the *Annual Review of Biochemistry,* the Company has pursued as its principal function the publication of high quality, reasonably priced Annual Review volumes. The volumes are organized by Editors and Editorial Committees who invite qualified authors to contribute critical articles reviewing significant developments within each major discipline.

Annual Reviews Inc. is administered by a Board of Directors whose members serve without compensation.

BOARD OF DIRECTORS
1978

Dr. J. Murray Luck
Founder Emeritus, Annual Reviews Inc.
Department of Chemistry
Stanford University

Dr. Joshua Lederberg
President, Annual Reviews Inc.
Department of Genetics
Stanford University Medical School

Dr. James E. Howell
Vice President, Annual Reviews Inc.
Graduate School of Business
Stanford University

Dr. William O. Baker
President
Bell Telephone Laboratories

Dr. Sidney D. Drell
Deputy Director
Stanford Linear Accelerator Center

Dr. Eugene Garfield
President
Institute for Scientific Information

Dr. William D. McElroy
Chancellor
University of California, San Diego

Dr. William F. Miller
Vice President and Provost
Stanford University

Dr. John Pappenheimer
Department of Physiology
Harvard Medical School

Dr. Colin S. Pittendrigh
Director
Hopkins Marine Station

Dr. Esmond E. Snell
Department of Microbiology
University of Texas at Austin

Dr. Harriet Zuckerman
Department of Sociology
Columbia University

Annual Reviews are published in the following sciences: Anthropology, Astronomy and Astrophysics, Biochemistry, Biophysics and Bioengineering, Earth and Planetary Sciences, Ecology and Systematics, Energy, Entomology, Fluid Mechanics, Genetics, Materials Science, Medicine, Microbiology, Neuroscience, Nuclear Science, Pharmacology and Toxicology, Physical Chemistry, Physiology, Phytopathology, Plant Physiology, Psychology, and Sociology. In addition, two special volumes have been published by Annual Reviews Inc.: *History of Entomology* (1973) and *The Excitement and Fascination of Science* (1965).

Annual Review of Physiology
Volume 40, 1978

CONTENTS

INDEXES

Author with rare gourmet mushroom (*Sparassis*)—just another childhood hobby.

Ann. Rev. Physiol. 1978. 40:1–17
Copyright © 1978 by Annual Reviews Inc. All rights reserved

RHAPSODY IN SCIENCE ❖1183

P. F. Scholander

5508 N.E. 180th Street, Seattle, Washington 98155

Dear readers, I find it quite shocking to have reached a stage in life when I am supposed to be retrospective. Like a vulgar streaker I shall expose myself in the limelight. I frequently ask myself how has it been possible to live such an exciting and happy life being such an irregular and irresponsible person?

My Norwegian mother was an accomplished pianist. I have just noticed in her copy of Speemans' encyclopedia, *Goldenes Buch der Musik* (1909), that she underlined the following advice to prospective musicians (which in my opinion applies to scientists as well): "Nur dem kann ich raten, Künstler zu werden, der aus reiner Liebe zur Kunst selbst, aus innerem Drang und Bedürfnis—unbekümmert um glänzenden Erfolg—ihr sein Leben weihen will und darin sein Genügen und sein Glück findet."[1]

GROWING UP IN SWEDEN

Emotion has certainly been a strong ingredient in my life, whether in music or science. As a small boy I crawled underneath my mother's Steinway when she practiced, smothered by the waves of emotion in the music of Bach, Grieg, Sinding. . . . Once when I was about two years old I walked on the ice of a little pond, and I can still see in detail the reeds I passed, namely *Scirpus lacustre,* then twice as high as I, now only half my size. Music comes early, and I believe also fondness for nature.

As an adolescent I was exclusively interested in natural history. I loved zoology, Brehm's *Tierleben,* Seton Thompson, botany, physics, and as-

[1]Only such a person can I advise to become an artist, who from pure love of art itself, through internal urge and need—unconcerned about spectacular successes—desires to devote his life to it and therein to find his fulfillment and his happiness."

0066-4278/78/0301-0001$01.00

tronomy (Arrhenius, Jeans, Eddington, etc). While in school I flunked history, but an unusual faculty let me make up for it by merits in the sciences. I might have been stopped dead right there, but my teachers *protected* me. There is one thing I realized very early. I had a curiosity that *craved* research of any kind, and could not think of anything else. I was deadly afraid of winding up as a school teacher and decided that the surest way of avoiding that would be to go into medicine.

MEDICAL SCHOOL IN OSLO, WITH ARCTIC EXPEDITIONS (1924–1939)

During the first years in the medical school in Oslo, reading Latin, philosophy, anatomy, I felt dreadfully wanting in active research, so one winter day I threw my fetters and went out to look at some little plants growing on the bark of trees. Consulting a book on lower plants, I recognized that these were lichens, which I could easily identify. In a spruce forest I found little yellow tufted lichens, which turned out to be the very common *Cetraria pinastri.* It so happened that one specimen had little round fruiting bodies along its powdery margin, and this was stated to be *extremely rare.* I was struck as if by lightning, sped across town to the Botanical Museum, and there met the famous lichenologist Professor Bernt Lynge. I showed him my insignificant treasure and he said: "This is most exciting, and I will give you working space right here. If you stick with this hobby, I'll send you to Greenland. I cannot go because of my rheumatism."

This was a fantastic welcome, the like of which I had never experienced. It changed my whole life. Lynge certainly knew his fishing, and he hooked me like a young trout on a "Professor" fly.

As a consequence I spent three summers (1931–1933) on arctic expeditions to NE Greenland, SE Greenland, and Spitzbergen. The latter was a glaciological expedition and came about because the camp of Andrée, the famous Swedish polar balloonist, had just been found on White Island. The great Swedish glaciologist, Hans Ahlmann, saw his chance to finance a Swedish-Norwegian expedition, ostensibly to put up a commemorative plaque in honor of Andrée. His main purpose, of course, was to map and study the inland ice of Northeast Land. I was asked to serve as botanist and medical man. This gave me my first extensive contact with outstanding men in the geophysical sciences.

A Generous Gift of Ph.D. in Botany

On these botanical summer expeditions going through the pack ice I saw a great many seals, polar bears, and diving birds; intrigued by Starling's textbook in physiology, I decided I would take up diving as a research project if and when I ever got through medical school. My textbooks have always been full of derogatory marginal notes about explanations I did not believe. This somewhat irreverent attitude toward the accepted doctrines made my grades mediocre to say the least.

Finished at last with medical school, where I came out at just about the bottom of my class, I moved up to the Botanical Museum and through the help of my outstanding friend, curator Johannes Lid, I completed my project with vascular plants and wrote two regional floras, one on Greenland and one on Spitzbergen. With Lynge and Dahl I coauthored two lichen floras on Greenland.

To my utter surprise I was approached by Professor Jens Holmboe, head of the Botany department, who told me that my plant work would qualify me for a Ph.D. in Botany if I would take exams in plant histology and physiology. Reading the plant physiology I became fascinated by the old problem of sap rising in trees. At that time it was accounted for by the cohesion theory of Dixon, which predicted that the hydrostatic pressure in the sap would be negative by easily −30 to −40 atm. It seemed to me that this would be utterly impossible to accept without clear experimental demonstration, which was not at hand. (But see below.)

Two years after barely squeezing through my medical exams, I subjected myself to the quite formal Ph.D. ritual. This involved two public lectures, one proposed by the faculty and the other by myself. The latter was on lichens and their striking symbiosis with specific algae. As is the case with many other symbiotic conditions, in Tridacnas, corals, and even rumen, it is still unclear how the nonsymbiotic spawn of the host gets infected with the appropriate clone of the symbiont.

Studies in Diving Animals

Having a Ph.D. made things very much easier for me. I got a developmental grant and a big laboratory in the physiology department of the medical school, originally planned for lab courses but until then never used. Harald Erikson (a medical student) and I got hold of several seals and, using Haldane and van Slyke apparatuses and a seal in harness in a bathtub, we got some preliminary information on the physiology of diving. It became immediately clear that in order to follow this in detail we needed recording instrumentation. This took us about a half year to construct and gave us a running record of all essential respiratory data. In addition, arterial samples and EKGs were taken. After a couple of years we had a good picture of what happens during diving: the tremendous bradycardia, the great change in blood distribution, etc.

ROCKEFELLER FELLOW WITH LARRY IRVING (1939–1943)

On his own initiative, my friend and mentor Bernt Lynge went down to Copenhagen and contacted the great physiologist, August Krogh, who invited me to his lab and arranged with Larry Irving for the Rockefeller Fellowship that took me to Swarthmore. Larry had already done distinguished work on diving physiology, and together we greatly expanded the field at Swarthmore. The Second World War approached and Larry went into the Air Force. I followed later, after having spent some time at the Fatigue Lab with Professor Jack Roughton, working out a microtechnique for the measurement of blood- and respiratory-gases—always in collaboration with the great glassblower and friend, Jim Graham. One day I asked Jack, "If I were to fake the oxygen content of water by adding oxyhemoglobin to it, what chance would you give me that the oxygen transport through the solution would be increased?" He said, "Two per cent." I took his reply with a grain of salt and filed the problem for a later time.

While working out the carbon monoxide micromethod, I was all the time in the grip of the Arctic allure. I thought I might influence Larry in that direction, and suggested that we study the old problem of monoxide poisoning in tents and snow-houses. (It had been suggested that Andrée's party very likely died from monoxide poisoning.) We made an expedition to Mt. Washington and found that the flame of a kerosene stove in a poorly ventilated tent or snowhouse will go out at some 3% CO_2, and even at 1.5% a match or candle will not burn, but no monoxide is formed. However, the minute you cook on the flame monoxide pours out and rises rapidly in the blood.

Little did I know then how susceptible Larry was to the Arctic lure; as everybody now knows, he wound up with great honors in the Alaska Hall of Fame after founding the Arctic Institute for Biology at the University at Fairbanks.

IN THE UNITED STATES AIR FORCE (1944–1947)

Covered Life Rafts in the Aleutians

Commissioned as Captain in the Air Force on Larry's research team, I spent some time looking at the difficulties our pilots had in the Aleutians. Their main problem was exposure, and so we devised a covered, four-man life raft, which we took to Attu in March. A folded tent was sealed along the sides. It could be erected on a paddle front and aft and could be closed at the top. Its occupants sat on an air mattress, dry and warm. Tied by a floating line several hundred feet behind a standby vessel in the mouth of a southern fjord in Attu, we tested two rafts for four days and nights. Half of the time we spent in storms with 80 mph gusts and mountainous waves. In my tent were Sir Hubert Wilkins, the arctic explorer, and Dr. George Sutton, the well-known ornithologist, plus a young Navy man. Everything went fine and we all enjoyed Sir Hubert's long tales of his great admiration for his old friend Frederick Cook, whose negative celebrity was undeserved.[2]

Altar Wine and Rescue from the Sky

Shortly after this successful demonstration, a telegram notified Sir Hubert that a B-47 had crashed near Cold Bay at the tip of the Alaskan peninsula. Would he please lend his arctic experience to the rescue efforts? We flew in and passed over the crash site, which was at the edge of a 3000 foot mountain plateau. One survivor had been seen. Tractors and dog teams had tried in vain to reach the site. There was general turmoil at headquarters. Clearly somebody had to jump down there. I had plenty of experience in snow and ice, and called for a pilot. Somebody told me that jumping had been vetoed by the camp commander, to which I snarled "Go to bloody hell!" Risking his career, a young pilot called Estes volunteered, as did a medical doctor, John Weston, and a priest whose name I cannot recall. We located some emergency chutes, raced to the B-17, and in ten minutes were flying over the site. None of us had ever jumped before. Once down, I was dragged at a good clip by the wind. Pulling in the shrouds, I stopped but had some trouble getting my leg straps unbuckled. It occurred to me that my friends might be in danger. I raced downwind and caught one after the other as they were helplessly dragged along by the wind. Throwing myself on top of them, I got them loose from their harnesses.

It took me two hours to walk up to the crashed plane. It was upsidedown and contained three survivors. Two men had perished. The doc administered medical aid, while I took on the cooking. I was greatly helped by the fact that the plane was filled with cases of altar wine, for this was a supply plane for Passover, or "Hangover" as we called it. Appropriately, our priest was the bartender, and I hope all that sanctified altar wine will give me a sorely needed Brownie point for the hereafter. Finally, a bush plane from Anchorage got us all out of there.

Our covered raft fell into oblivion, but was reinvented in a brilliant edition some ten years later by the British and was universally adopted.

Meanwhile, the war had ended. It turned out that our short stay in the Aleutians counted as foreign service; I had been there two days (!) more than required for United States citizenship, which I was gallantly offered.

[2]See: Mowatt, F. 1968. *Polar Passion.* Boston: Little Brown.

Accepting it involved an oath of allegiance, and I was deathly afraid of being asked to recite the second verse of "The Star Spangled Banner," which I simply could not learn.

POINT BARROW AND STUDIES IN COLD

Larry had now really been taken by the polar passion and had started a laboratory at Point Barrow where the Navy was engaged in petroleum research. He asked me to give him a hand, which of course I did. With splendid help from Otto Hebel of Swarthmore we got a quonset hut well insulated and heated for exacting physiological work. Before winter freeze-up we marked suitable habitats with flags, locating animals and plants under the snow cover.

Mammals and Birds

Our work on warm-blooded animals concentrated on measurements of insulation, metabolic rate, and body surface temperatures. It turned out that mammals larger than the fox could sleep with basal oxygen consumption at temperatures as low as $-30°$ to $-40°C$, which were the coldest we could produce. The smaller ones, like weasels or lemmings, started to shiver at $+15°C$; below that, they increased their heat production essentially proportional to the deviation from their internal temperature of $+37°C$, as would be expected from Newton's law of cooling. By comparison, tropical animals in Panama had a critical temperature only a few degrees below the body temperature and also followed Newton's basic law. Arctic and tropical birds did the same. It goes without saying that the animals adjusted their insulation by raising or lowering furs or feathers, curling up with the nose under the tail, etc. In the appendages of aquatic animals (seals, whales, water fowl), arteriovenous countercurrent systems are common heat savers.

Cold-blooded Animals and Plants

In contrast, the cold-blooded animals and plants showed a rather regular Q_{10} sequence that went from 2 to 4 between $0°$ and $10°C$ and then decreased with increasing temperature. Our arctic material badly needed tropical material for comparison. I secured it in Cuba, and it turned out that findings from these specimens were practically identical to those from the arctic material. This line of inquiry was promptly discontinued.

Freezing the Living Engine

However, another aspect was much more attractive. Going out to the little flags that marked our desired pools, we cut out vertical slices of the ice. When we melted their surfaces with our warm hands we found that quite a few insect larvae (chironomids, i.e. gnats) were frozen there. Within several hours of thawing, they started to crawl around and feed. While thawing, they changed from an opaque yellow to a transparent red, so they had obviously been completely frozen. We therefore ran a series of experiments to discover to what extent the metabolic rate would vary with the ice-content in the larvae and the lichens. This required a flotation technique where the specimen initially sank to the bottom of a vial containing, say, $-5°C$ kerosene. Heavy bromo-benzene of exactly the same temperature was added until neutral buoyancy was attained. The density of the mixture was then equal to that of the object and was easily determined by simple pycnometry. The procedure was repeated at $0°C$. The difference in density gave the ice content, provided the sample was gas-free, which was checked by melting it under a microscope. It turned out that at $-5°C$ some 90% of the water was already frozen in most material.

Putting the frozen samples in the smallest possible amount of air, either singly or packed together in an airtight glass vial, one could wait until enough change had taken place in the gas composition to tell the story. It turned out that below freezing temperature the Q_{10} was between 20 and 50. At $-20°C$ one had to wait 1880 hr to get a significant gas change. If we now consider that these animals or plants readily survived in a melted state for a month or ten days at $0°C$, one may extrapolate that at $-40°C$ they would survive for several million years. Whether or not such extrapolation holds is another story.

Gas Penetration Through Ice

In securing our frozen chironomid larvae our attention was attracted by the fact that right under the ice surface there regularly appeared a great many gas bubbles. Puncturing these with a micropipette through a little pool of cold mercury, we could micro-analyze a few mm^3 of the gas. It turned out to contain large amounts of CO_2, and not a trace of oxygen; the rest was nitrogen and undoubtedly methane. This gas had been sitting for 7–8 months under a sheet of ice only a fraction of a millimeter thick. Its retention suggested a very high impermeability of ice to gases.

A series of experiments was made to check this. Ice sheets 0.1 mm thick were cast between flat hydrophobic surfaces and floated on cold mercury. A known volume of a gas, e.g. oxygen, was introduced under the sheet and its surface area measured. We could now go in with a curved micropipette after a certain period and sample the bubble for microanalysis. We were never able to detect any penetration of oxygen or nitrogen; as far as CO_2 was concerned, at $-10°C$ it penetrated ice at least 70,000–80,000 times more slowly than water. Later more accurate checks performed by Hemmingsen gave figures for CO_2 ten times slower than mine. This right away gave us the idea that the air trapped in glacier ice when the snow compacts (visible as tiny bubbles) carries a permanent record of the composition of the atmosphere, provided that no melting has occurred.

WOODS HOLE OCEANOGRAPHIC INSTITUTE (1949–55)

Supercooling in Fish

The productive period at Pt. Barrow resulted in a huge volume of material to be written up. I moved to the famous library at the Marine Biological Laboratory (MBL), and was soon invited by Dr. Alfred Redfield to join the Oceanographic Institute.

Dr. David Nutt of Dartmouth had told me that the Hebron fjord in Labrador maintained its winter temperature (–1.9°C) all year at the bottom, even though the temperature of the surface layer in the summer would regularly reach +5° to +10°C. Now, an oceanic fish usually has a freezing point depression of about –0.5° to –0.8°C, somewhat like ours. The question then is, what happens in fishes living at or near the freezing point of sea water? Do they raise their osmolality? Do they supercool, or what? Through several expeditions, summer and winter, we found that at the bottom of the Hebron fjord the fishes retain their normal freezing point depression of about –0.8°C all year round, and are supercooled by about 1°C at all times. At the surface they are supercooled only in the winter.

At Woods Hole we found that several species of local fishes could be supercooled to –3°C and survive perfectly well. But, if the supercooled water was *seeded with ice* the fishes froze and died almost instantly. Even in sea water at –1.5°C, i.e. warmer than the freezing point of sea water, a fish touched by a piece of ice would freeze and die. In other words it is the absence of seeding that protects the Labrador fish from freezing at the bottom. A summer fish there with its freezing point at only –0.8°C will freeze when touching ice in a vat of sea water cooled to its freezing point. Shallow water fish swimming about in the winter ice at Hebron double their freezing point depression and then are not seeded by touching the ice. In contrast to marine fish, marine invertebrates are always nearly isosmotic with the sea water and therefore do not freeze unless they are exposed to severe winter air by low tide (and even then some survive). Recently these early data on arctic fish and invertebrates have been expanded qualitatively as well as quantitatively, mainly by the beautiful work of Dr. Arthur DeVries and collaborators. They have shown that in essence the antifreeze in antarctic fish is provided by mucoproteins that stabilize against nucleation and ice propagation.

Sap Rising in Grapevines as Part of Ocean Circulation

Ever since my preparations for the Ph.D. in botany in Oslo I had been bugged by the problem of sap rising in trees. No direct measurements were available to confirm Dixon's brilliant cohesion theory of sap rising, which essentially said that water evaporating from the leaves pulled sap in continuous strings under tension up from the ground. Strasburger had shown that trees 20 m tall that had been sawed off at the base under water would transport poisons like copper sulfate or picric acid up into their leaves. Obviously no living pumps could be involved.

While in Woods Hole at the Oceanographic Institute I noticed that when native grapevine twigs were broken off before the leaves were out, sap dripped from the plant. In other words, at that time the sap pressure was surely positive. A micromanometer was constructed that could be clamped airtight to a branch, and it measured the positive pressure. By removing it, carefully sealing the puncture, and clamping it at various heights, one obtained very accurately a perfectly normal hydrostatic gradient of 0.1 atm per 1 m elevation, regardless of the general pressure, which might easily be up to + 5 atm. In other words, there was no mysterious lifting force in the xylem, no "wiggling hairs" or "matric potential." With the leaves out, measurement became impossible; the pressures were clearly negative. For instance, if the base of a vine were cut off under water and connected airtight with a burette, the vine drew up water. Even if the burette was filled to the brim and closed vacuum tight, the drinking rate remained the same, indicating high negative pressure. It could be demonstrated that no air leaked into the burette from the cut.

My colleague John Kanwisher and I spent much spare time working on the grapevines. To the rest of the faculty this hardly seemed a fitting job for an Oceanographic Institute. But the day was saved when Alfred Redfield pointed out that evaporation from the ocean falls as rain and is drawn up by the vines. The rising of sap is, indeed, a neglected part of this grand circulation.

The reader will discover that we return several times to this intriguing old problem below.

UNIVERSITY OF OSLO (1955–1958)

Hunting Reindeer in the Cold

We were intrigued by our experience with cold acclimation in arctic and tropical warm-blooded animals, and it was natural to take a look at how humans manage it. Our first task was to define a reasonable standard for cold stress, avoiding such extremes as putting naked people in a barrel of ice water. We were surprised to find that lying naked on a sofa at +20°C gives humans a very uncomfortable night of shivering. The cold is hardly bearable after four o'clock in the morning. We found that a similar stress could be obtained by sleeping naked in a single-blanket sleeping bag at 0°C. That these standards were about the same was determined by checking oxygen consumption (the sleeper's head being enveloped in a ventilated hood connected with a spirometer), and by measuring rectal and skin temperatures during the entire night. The advantage in using 0°C as the outside temperature is that it is relatively easy to find in nature.

Using the bag apparatus in the mountains of Norway, we subjected a group of students dressed in summer clothing to autumn temperatures around 0°C (and gave them reindeer hunting as a reward). They spent their nights sleeping naked in the single-blanket bag under an open rain shelter, no fires permitted. After five or six days they had no trouble; when checked in the lab test, they slept warm all night, with bouts of shivering that raised their basal metabolic rate to 150%.

Silly Bugger White Man

We were now prepared to tackle the aborigines of Australia. We were greatly aided in this by the great pioneer in the field, Sir Stanton Hicks, of Adelaide University, who some 20 years earlier had led several expeditions to central Australia for this purpose. Members of our group were Hugh Le Messurier (Adelaide), Ted Hammel (Yale), Sandy Hart (Ottawa), John Steen (Oslo), and myself. Our work essentially supported and extended Sir Stanton Hicks' findings.

We arrived at our destination (150 miles west of Alice Springs in central Australia) in their midwinter. Frost formed on the ground at night. We found that the natives slept naked on the sand between two little brush fires. As the sun rose, the aborigines gathered around a big fire to chat and warm up. We had an excellent interpreter with us, and arranged the test as a competition between the natives and the "silly bugger white man." We began by lying down next to them naked on the sand behind their little brush windbreak and between two little fires. Sleeping was very difficult for us. While they stoked their little fires a dozen times during the night, we had to do it thirty or forty times. They got a kick out of our awkwardness.

After that we introduced them to the bag test. The outside temperature was just about 0°C. They accepted the hood and a series of skin thermocouples with no trouble, but how Hammel ever talked these young spear-throwing warriors into accepting the intimacy of a rectal thermocouple I shall never understand. Again we placed one of ourselves next to the subject, identically equipped. We suffered through the night shivering and chilling, raising our basal rate to 150%. In contrast, the aborigines slept through the bag test with a normal basal rate, but with leg temperatures going down to around 10°C. In other words, they had learned to adapt the economical way, by accepting peripheral cooling.

Eskimos and Lapps reacted in the test as we do; by virtue of their warm clothing and bed gear they, like us, live in a tropical microclimate. But Hammel's similar studies of the few surviving Indians in Tierra Del Fuégo and of cold-hardy tribes in the Kalahari desert, found essentially the same phenomenon we found in the Australian aborigine. It is interesting that when Hammel tested the latter in scorching hot midsummer in a 0°C cold van at Darwin, they retained their cold-hardy, economical winter reaction.

Search for Ancient Atmosphere in Norwegian Glaciers

Our studies at Point Barrow of the frozen aquatic larvae had given us data on the virtually complete gas-tightness of ice, even in sheets only a tenth of a millimeter thick. This suggested the possibility of finding ancient atmospheres preserved in the gas bubbles so characteristic of glacier ice. The technique was worked out in collaboration with the famous Danish isotope glaciologist Willy Dansgaard, on a glacier in the Norwegian mountains. We mined large pieces of ice and transported them by snowmobile. One ^{14}C dating required vacuum distillation of 20–30 tons of ice. The CO_2 was collected in KOH. With the technique in good order and the project recommended by such outstanding colleagues as Hans Ahlmann, Carl Rossby, and Harald Sverdrup, we were funded through the Arctic Institute of North America to go after the Greenland ice. (All Norwegian ice samples had been contaminated by melting of the glacier. The composition of the gas samples, instead of reflecting that of the atmosphere, reflected the gross differences in solubility coefficients of CO_2, argon, and nitrogen.)

Expedition to Greenland Glaciers (1958)

The expedition was organized with a laboratory built on the deck of the sealer "Rundöy." Senior scientists were Willy Dansgaard (Copenhagen), David Nutt and Larry Coachman (Dartmouth), and myself. We made our first attempt to obtain ice from a desirable iceberg by boarding it with instrumentation. In less than an hour it capsized. Dansgaard and his two assistants were nearly lost. We never boarded an iceberg again, but stayed with the ship at a safe distance. We towed ton-sized pieces, which had fallen off the berg, to our ship where they were split (by a narrow, long loop of steampipe) into pieces that could be hoisted onboard. On deck they were split further to fit into our two 150-liter vacuum boilers. Laboring day and night, we could process a single sample of 0.2 gr ^{14}C as CO_2 in two to three days. The technique worked fine; but as it turned out, there were slight differences in the gas compositions from adjacent 2–3 kg pieces. Even in

Greenland, every locality displayed contamination of the gases by melting. That melting does occur was later confirmed by the United States Air Force. Landing on the Greenland Ice Cap in the summertime, observers frequently found pools of meltwater at almost any altitude and latitude. This, however, would not invalidate our ^{14}C and oxygen-isotope data. From these Dansgaard could estimate whence our samples came. Our oldest iceberg was caught at latitude 73°N. It was about 3000 yrs old and had formed at about 3000 m altitude, which placed it some 300 km inland. It became quite clear from our findings that if one wishes to try for a sample of the old atmosphere trapped in a glacier, one must seek it in the coldest part of our globe, namely in the antarctic ice cap.

SCRIPPS INSTITUTION OF OCEANOGRAPHY (1958–   )

Facilitated Oxygen Transport with Baird Hastings

Since my lab at Scripps was not yet ready when I joined the Institution in 1958, I had a great time with Baird in his roomy lab suite at Scripps Clinic and Research Foundation in La Jolla. I had already spent a most fruitful time in his lab at Harvard Medical School, where I had worked out an ultrasensitive respirometer for single cell divisions. Now I was eagerly getting into facilitated O_2 transport through hemoglobin solutions, a phenomenon I and my students had discovered in Oslo five years earlier with an instrument designed in collaboration with Jim Graham (see above). Using essentially the original technique, I did a comprehensive series demonstrating enhanced diffusion of oxygen through hemo- and myoglobin, along with some other heme pigments (also in vitro).

As was to be expected, my sloppy handling of mercury demanded plastic replacements of the brass fixtures in half a dozen of the sinks. However, I was redeemed when my boss tripped aboard one of Scripps' ships, spilling all the mercury out of a van Slyke apparatus! Nobody knows what that did to the engine room.

Reverse osmosis in mangroves

Speculation about rising sap as a case of reverse osmosis naturally focused attention on mangroves. The interesting thing about mangroves is that they grow in sea water; thus the substrate is known, at least if they are not growing in estuaries. Therefore, if the cohesion theory were right, the trees would require at least –25 atm sap pressure in order to pull fresh water out of the sea. In the daytime when the process would be driven by evaporation, at least –40 to –50 atm would be expected. We found that mangrove sap is indeed very close to being fresh water; some carries a little salt, which is excreted by the leaves.

Finally on a Baja California expedition the problem of measuring the negative pressure was solved. Using a small portable lathe aboard ship, I made a little pressure chamber of about 100 cc capacity. The chamber could hold 140 atm nitrogen pressure and it had an airtight seal in the lid for letting through the stem of a mangrove seedling. The idea was to try a reverse osmosis experiment with a seedling replanted in sand and sea water in a beaker that could be placed inside my "bomb."

I was called away to Scripps for a few days. While I was away Hammel and Hemmingsen got the idea of putting a mangrove twig in the pressure chamber with the cut end sticking out. When they applied nitrogen pressure, the sap suddenly appeared at the cut end. The balancing pressure could be accurately determined; it was between 30 and 50 atm, and was characteristic for each different bush. Next the technique was expanded to produce pressure-volume curves: in steps, more and more sap was extruded and measured together with the new balancing pressure. It turned out that the extruded sap was almost completely saltfree, often containing less than 0.01% sodium chloride, even in salt-secreting mangroves that normally had 0.1% salt in the ascending xylem sap. Later on, after shooting down high twigs from Douglas fir and Redwoods (from triangulated heights), we found within $\pm$ 10% that there was a normal gravitational gradient in the negative hydrostatic pressure. As with the grapevines, there was no active pumping.

THE RESEARCH VESSEL *ALPHA HELIX* (1966–)

My contacts with a great many marine-oriented scientists here as well as abroad, along with my own experience, convinced me that there did not exist a vessel that made even the slightest attempt to cater to the needs of modern experimental biology. It became quite clear to me that something ought to be done about it. I was introduced by Larry Irving to marine biology as a general and fundamental tool in the Marine Biological Laboratory at Woods Hole. Its history of numerous contributions to fundamental biological and medical knowledge is impressive. Modern advances in biomedical science depend more than ever upon access to precisely the kind of material that exhibits most clearly what we are after, regardless of what plant, animal, or microbe is involved. It seemed to me highly appropriate to propose that a specially built ship be acquired to serve as a transportable biological laboratory for modern experimental research.

In support of this proposal was the attractive possibility of generating on these expeditionary efforts an interdisciplinary and international cooperation, where each member was isolated from his routine academic chores, and where all shared the enormous privilege of having uninterrupted time with selected colleagues otherwise not available. Not least of all, I felt such expeditions would be a legacy passed on from the senior to the young—an opportunity like those I had myself so richly experienced.

A national advisory board headed by Baird Hastings was constituted in 1963 with a dozen highly distinguished senior members. As a result, the *Alpha Helix* was funded and built. To myself and hundreds of colleagues from various disciplines and countries who have had the privilege of using this facility, the research vessel *Alpha Helix* stands as a proud landmark of *nonpolitical U.S. generosity,* as a gift to international friendship and scientific cooperation. During its ten years of operation it has visited many parts of the globe, from the tropics to the arctic and antarctic. It is presently (for the second time) a guest in the Amazon, joining in most fertile cooperation with scientists from our great South American hosts. Its scientific productiveness has been prodigious.

Some of Our Work on the Alpha Helix

The first place we took the *Alpha Helix* (1966) was to the Great Barrier Reef, into sheltered waters between the Flinders Islands north of Cairns, in Queensland. One of our programs was a continuation of inquiry into water relations in mangroves, a study in reverse osmosis. It showed that seedlings transplanted in sand and sea water, when given ample time to heal the damaged root, did indeed respond to pressure in the "bomb" by filtering out essentially fresh water. Another thing of fundamental interest, found by our renowned colleague Dr. Stanley Miller in wilted (i.e. turgor free) twigs of the mangrove *Lumnizera,* was that when such a twig was put in an accurately thermostated pressure bomb the balancing pressure *varied with temperature.* Going down from 27°C to 3°C and then back up to 37°C, using seven steps in all, he found that within a few per cent plus or minus the balancing pressure was indeed proportional to the absolute temperature —i.e. was of kinetic origin. This was later superbly confirmed by Hammel on a conifer and was the last information from plants necessary to convince us that the purely thermodynamic description of osmosis (such as that pioneered by G. N. Lewis) based on the *activity* construct could be transcribed into an easily visualized *kinetic mechanism* accessible to direct experimental verification.

Negative Interstitial Fluid Pressure in Animals

In April, 1967, while we were working on supercooling in fish in the Bering Sea, the *Alpha Helix* got stuck in the ice for a week. I used the time to pay attention to a simple physical problem. I had long wanted to examine the physical meaning, if any, of what plant physiologists and others call "matric potential;" to determine, in other words, whether there is any anomaly in the hydrostatic gradient in a vertical matrix through which water can move. I let starch (from the galley) sediment in a cylinder. By stuffing a cotton tuft in one end of a fine plastic tube and a standard glass capillary in the other, I made a wick probe. The wick, pervious only to water, was placed at the thixotropic bottom sediment and the capillary was mounted vertically. An identical wick probe was placed in the clear water surface. Of course the meniscuses in the identical capillaries stayed level, in accordance with the Second Law. When starch was added so that it pushed against the water surface, capillarity turned the water pressure negative and both wicks registered this. Again, of course, the depressed meniscuses stood at identical levels—i.e. connecting the capillaries could not maintain a perpetual motion. In a submerged matrix (homogeneous or not) the inside hydrostatic pressure of motile water at equilibrium must, level by level, be exactly the same as that of the outside water.

In preparing for our Amazon expedition (1967) at Scripps, a colleague happened to use our laboratory to do some work on iguana lizards. It struck me that the sharp skin folds so characteristic of these animals indicated that there must be a negative fluid pressure in the subcutaneous tissue to hold these folds together; otherwise edema would develop. Why should one not check this with the simple wick method which worked so well in all sorts of nonliving matrixes? At this time I was not aware of Dr. Guyton's pioneer work, claiming negative tissue fluid pressure, and the strange controversy raised by this simple concept. Anyhow, a wick stuck under the skin of an iguana sure enough registered a few cm negative water pressure. We worked out the proper technique for this simple approach and took it with us on the expedition.

Down in the Amazon we confirmed our finding in a number of organs and animals. Together with Stanley Miller, student Alan Hargens and I had a great deal of fun comparing a big water snake (anaconda) with a big land snake (boa constrictor). Putting these three-meter-long snakes on a tilt table, with one subcutaneous wick in the neck and one in the tail, we found that the anaconda compensated beautifully against hydrostatic pressure changes when tilted head up or head down—an ability, one may respectfully point out, that is not vital in a submerged animal. Head down, the boa also compensated beautifully against positive changes; but head up, as when climbing a tree, he developed edema (positive pressure) in his tail. It appears the Powers That Be must have gotten their wires crossed.

THE SOLVENT TENSION THEORY OF OSMOSIS

Dixon's cohesion theory of the ascent of sap is closely related to a proposed kinetic explanation of the osmotic process. The "solvent tension theory" has been proposed very clearly several times, starting with Hulett (1901), who accounted for all colligative properties by solvent tension. Later it was stated by Herzfeld (1935), Mysels (1959), and others. This kinetic concept lent itself to conclusive experimental verification, as first demonstrated by the brilliant work of Perrin on the Brownian motion (1909).

If solute molecules like sugar are deposited on the bottom of a beaker of water they will rise by thermal motion; if stopped by a semipermeable membrane fastened across the beaker they are reflected, exerting a *pressure on the membrane*. If the membrane is removed they proceed, putting drag on the water until they are stopped by another barrier, namely the free surface; and as Professor Theorell in Stockholm commented, "They are blind and don't know what the hell they hit!" Being reflected this time by the surface, they exert their *pressure on the surface* and hence leave the solvent under tension. Based on equipartition of energy, this is the simple reason for the lowered vapor pressure over a solution, expressed in Poynting's relation.

This is a *kinetic*, easily comprehended *physical explanation*, which takes into consideration everything known about osmotic processes. As already pointed out by Hulett, and lately in great detail by Hammel, solvent tension is the direct cause of all colligative properties. Using magnetic solutes one can superimpose a known magnetic force upon the thermal force; the two forces are exactly additive with respect to osmotic pressure. The same additive effect can be obtained by the buoyancy effect of heavy and light solute molecules in a reversing osmometer.

In contrast we have Lewis' thermodynamic activity concept. Useful as a mathematical construct to keep the numerical aspects of the colligative properties in order, it was never designed to give insight into the physical mechanism. Nevertheless, it has bred an array of free-for-all concepts like water concentration, molfraction component of hydrostatic gradient, the abolition of gravitational gradients by chemical potential, etc. No wonder then that one can point to thermodynamic inconsistencies in the presently popular "water concentration theory." Take a rigid semipermeable cylinder submerged in a jar of water. At equilibrium the *solution* in the cylinder registers say +24 atm on a gauge that accepts solute and solvent. It is now assumed that the *water* pressure in the solution is +24 atm as registered on the gauge. If that were so, the water in the solution would be compressed and heavier than the outside water and would maintain a perpetual motion by sinking through the solution. On the contrary, the solvent pressure (and its vapor pressure) in such a system is identical layer by layer inside and outside.

COSMOLOGICAL VISTAS

When I first read about it I became fascinated by Mach's postulation of the relativity of mass. Of course I had already been thrilled by Cavendish's elegant measurement of the universal gravitational constant, where in a sense he overpowered locally the gravity of the earth. It so happened at this time that our institution needed a simple ultracentrifuge; a standard Beckman L with a little window in the lid was ordered. As an extra item we ordered a 4 kg rotor with a flat upper surface upon which z-bent capillaries could be fastened, à la Briggs, for studying cohesiveness of fluids by submitting them to G forces. The window was above the rotor edge.

With a brilliant young student, Bent Schmidt Nielsen, I often discussed the thrill of doing a relativistic experiment focused on Mach's principle. Imagine a battery-driven centrifuge in absolutely empty space. In such a circumstance it would be meaningless to ask which rotates around the other, the rotor or the housing. This seemed to open a possibility that a large spinning mass might induce an ever-so-slight centrifugal force in a closely adjacent smaller mass. Right or wrong the notion filled us with surges of cosmological elation.

So, returning from our exciting expedition to the Great Barrier Reef in Australia (1966), we fitted a half-meter-long brass tube, vacuum tight, through the window fixture in the centrifuge lid. The tube was closed at the bottom with a thin brass plate that could be lowered to within a fraction of a millimeter of the spinning rotor. Inside the tube a 200 gr brass weight was suspended as a pendulum with a flat base almost touching the bottom plate. The pendulum was damped by a dashpot and the optical readout by a galvanometer mirror was easily sensitive to 0.01 mg. We elevated the cylinder and started the rotor. Once full speed was attained, we lowered the cylinder to within a fraction of a millimeter of the rotor spinning in high vacuum. The nearness was made audible by the scraping of a thin steel string (a violin's E string) attached near the bottom plate. The first time this was tried we stood on a ladder rather than in the direct firing line, in case the rotor should blow out as it did for Svedberg in Uppsala, where it shot a big hole in the wall. Everything went well. The stability of the system was admirable and the effect of the rotating mass upon the pendulum was absolutely and completely *nil,* luckily for us.

Ten years later I had the pleasure of showing the remnants of this my greatest experiment to my colleague, the renowned astrophysicist Dr. William Thompson of the University of California at San Diego. He calculated that the theoretical displacement of our pendulum should have been on the order of $2.5 \cdot 10^{-11}$Å!! The experiment was a resounding fiasco, but so what? My reward? A wonderful *Appassionato* with the *Cosmos!*

Ann. Rev. Physiol. 1978. 40:19–41
Copyright © 1978 by Annual Reviews Inc. All rights reserved

MEMBRANE CATION TRANSPORT AND THE CONTROL OF PROLIFERATION OF MAMMALIAN CELLS

♦1184

J. Gordin Kaplan

Department of Biology, University of Ottawa, Ottawa K1N 6N5 Canada

INTRODUCTION

The cell membrane has a critical role in the control of cell synthesis and metabolism in general, and in the control of cell proliferation in particular; this has been the subject of a number of recent volumes (22, 73, 123). I review here one small aspect of this imposing subject: the relation between cation flux across the membrane and the activation of the cell responses leading to DNA synthesis and cell division.

A cascade of morphological, physiological, and biochemical changes follows the initial triggering of cell activation and precedes the DNA synthesis and division; however, not all of these phenomena need be in the train of causally related events which will ultimately lead to mitosis (Figure 1). Some may be outside the mainline sequence (shown in line A); some may be in parallel, but dead-end (line B); others may be in parallel for considerable time and then converge on the mainline sequence (line C). Still other events may occur in parallel but be required at all stages in order for the mainline sequence to proceed (line D). It is, of course, vital in studying the role of events like cation fluxes, which are proximal in time to the initial stimulation, to establish their relation to the time-distal events of proliferation. Otherwise, one risks committing the logical error of *post hoc ergo propter hoc,* nowhere more frequently encountered in the biological sciences than in that branch which deals with the mechanism of activation of quiescent or metastable cells, such as eggs after fertilization or stimulated mammalian cells in culture.

19

0066-4278/78/0301-0019$01.00

It is obvious that a review dealing with transport of cations such as K^+, which have in the cell such profound and pleiotropic effects, must be highly selective. In particular, I do not deal with the structure and reaction mechanism of the sodium-potassium pump itself, which have been well reviewed recently (51, 52, 104), nor do I treat the related subject of the cyclic nucleotides, whose role, by no means certain, in control of proliferation has been recently discussed both pro (16, 43, 130) and con (13). Limitations of space also require that I limit myself to proliferation of a few cell types (mammalian lymphocytes in primary culture and established mammalian cell lines) and prevent my reviewing the rapidly growing literature on the role of Ca^{2+} in control of growth. The role of the cation pump in animal cells and tissues has been reviewed (7, 37) and the relation of cation transport to a variety of immunological reactions has been considered in two meticulous reviews by Lauf (68, 69). Reviews dealing with lymphocyte membranes (27) and with the physiology and molecular biology (82, 83) of lymphocyte transformation are also available, as is an excellent general treatment for the nonspecialist of all aspects of the chemistry, physiology, and pathology of cell membranes (137).

FLUXES OF MONOVALENT CATIONS IN LYMPHOCYTE TRANSFORMATION

Function of the Membrane Cation Pump

Ten years ago, the cardiotonic steroid ouabain, a specific inhibitor of the $Na^+K^+ATPase$ (EC3.6.1.3.) (131), was shown to be a potent inhibitor of the transformation of human lymphocytes (106). Virtually all parameters

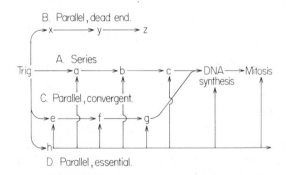

Figure 1   Schematic representation of events intervening between the initial triggering and S phase and mitosis. A more accurate representation of the cascade of events that follow cell activation will be found in Figure 1 of Reference 26. The small letters represent events and not precursors in a biosynthetic pathway.

of the activated state were affected at whatever stage the drug was added: morphological (blast transformation), physiological (increased respiration), and biochemical (biosynthesis of protein, DNA, and RNA) (106, 107). The inhibition was found to be completely reversible, either by washing the cells free from ouabain or by adding excess K^+ to the medium. Inhibition was observed within the same range of concentration of the cardiac glycoside regardless of how the lymphocytes were stimulated, whether by plant mitogens, the mixed lymphocyte reaction (MLR), specific antigen (141), or by treatment with the oxidizing reagent $NaIO_4$ (142). These early results have been repeatedly confirmed (60, 62, 98) and have been reviewed (57).

The conclusion was thus reached that continuous functioning of the $Na^+K^+ATPase$ was a *conditio sine qua non* of stimulating the lymphocytes and of maintaining them in the activated state (107). The fact that ouabain blocks the transformation of lymphocytes no matter at which stage it is added indicates that the enhanced function of the $Na^+K^+ATPase$ is parallel and essential (Figure 1,D) to the mainline events which link stimulation to mitosis. Quastel & Kaplan speculated that an indispensable requirement of activation might be an increased rate of cation pumping by the membrane ATPase (105, 141). In fact the mitogen phytohemagglutinin (PHA) was found to cause an increase in the $Na^+K^+ATPase$ of human lymphocytes assayed in membrane fragments (6). On the other hand, Novogrodsky reported that rise in the ATPase activity of rat lymphocyte microsomes was due to a Na^+ and K^+ independent, Mg^{++}-ATPase (99).

Ouabain was found to inhibit not only thymus-dependent (T cell) lymphocytes but also the bone marrow (or bursa equivalent) dependent B cells: Antibody-producing cells of the pig spleen were unable to cause plaque formation with sheep red cells if the splenocytes had been treated with ouabain (95, 111). Human lymphocytes, presumably B cells, stimulated to undergo blastogenesis by treatment with purified antiserum to human heavy immunoglobulin chains, were as sensitive to ouabain as were the T cells that respond to mitogen or in the MLR (57). Proliferation of spontaneously dividing lymphoid cells, whether the peripheral blood lymphocytes of patients suffering from acute leukemia (109) or a variety of human lymphoblastoid cell lines (57), were as sensitive to ouabain as fresh peripheral blood lymphocytes. The proliferation of cells of mouse lymphoblastoid established lines were also found to be inhibited by ouabain (28–30). Splenic and peripheral blood lymphocytes of rodents were found to be more resistant to the cardiotonic steroid, requiring three or more orders of magnitude higher concentration of the drug than did human cells; rabbit lymphocytes were intermediate in sensitivity (111, 112).

A variety of known inhibitors of the $Na^+K^+ATPase$ blocked DNA and RNA synthesis of human lymphocytes at concentrations comparable to those at which they inhibited the enzyme in vitro (105). The ionophore valinomycin was also found to inhibit DNA and RNA synthesis, 50% inhibition being produced at approximately $10^{-9}M$; this was attributed to its action as a mitochondrial uncoupler (105). Recently, the claim has been made that this ionophore inhibits by acting at the lymphocyte membrane and not by acting as an uncoupler (31). Further work is required to elucidate the mechanism of action of valinomycin. Another recent report shows that the $Na^+K^+ATPase$ inhibitor harmaline, which binds to the (internal) sodium sites of the pump unlike ouabain which competes with K^+ for its site, inhibits the proliferative response of human lymphocytes (103). Unfortunately this report contains no evidence that harmaline blocks blastogenesis by virtue of its primary interaction with the cation pump. Such a demonstration is especially necessary, even if difficult, in cases like this where one cannot reverse the blockade by adding an excess of the cation whose reduced transport one supposes to be the causal factor in inhibition.

At first glance, these data, showing that inhibition of the $Na^+K^+ATPase$ causes reversible arrest of virtually all the biosynthetic reactions of the cell, might seem in conflict with Edelman's compelling conclusion that active cation transport via the pump is an important thermogenic factor (37, 38); this conclusion was based partly on the assumption that ouabain blocks only that fraction of aerobic energy production which would otherwise go exclusively to support uphill transport of monovalent cations. There is no conflict: Edelman's measurements were completed within 30 min of adding ouabain to various rat tissues, whereas it requires at least one hour of incubation with the drug before inhibition of the protein synthesis of lymphocytes becomes detectable and two hours before synthesis of DNA and RNA is noticeably affected (107). Presumably this long lag is due to the time required for depletion of cell K^+ to below the threshold(s) at which its concentration is too low to support the activity of the various enzymes and organelles that require K^+.

While most of the effects of ouabain are completely reversible regardless of the duration of incubation of lymphocytes with this drug, certain effects, in particular the capacity of B lymphocytes to stimulate in the MLR and to proliferate in response to antigens, are irreversibly lost after incubations of greater than 24 hr in the presence of $10^{-6}M$ glycoside (21, 32, 140–142); prolonged incubation with $10^{-7}M$ ouabain has the opposite effect: Treated cells become superstimulators in MLR causing twice as many responding cells to proliferate (21, 32). Clinical application of this phenomenon should be attempted; it has been reviewed recently (58).

K^+ Influx: The Number and Turnover of Pump Sites

Within an hour or two of adding the mitogen phytohemagglutinin to a suspension of human lymphocytes, an increase in influx of ^{42}K was noted, rapidly reaching a rate about double that of the resting cells (108). It was subsequently shown by Averdunk that the increased rate of uptake of ^{42}K was manifest within 30 sec of adding PHA to cultures of lymphocytes (4). Increase in K^+ influx following PHA stimulation to about double the control rate has been confirmed in recent experiments by Segel & Lichtman (128). Corresponding increase in the rate of Na^+ exit following PHA treatment was also shown (6).

Analysis of the kinetics of ^{42}K transport demonstrated that it was the V_{max} of transport which changed after PHA treatment, rather than the K_M (105); furthermore, the change in rate of transport occurred even in the presence of concentrations of actinomycin D and cycloheximide which were found to inhibit virtually all RNA and protein synthesis (105). These data were taken to indicate that stimulation with PHA did not cause the synthesis of new pump sites but rather resulted in the appearance at the membrane of previously formed but unexposed or unassembled pump protein. The original paper on this subject by Averdunk (4) supports this interpretation, since it confirmed that mitogen increased the V_{max} of ^{42}K transport without change in its K_M.

Test of the hypothesis that stimulation caused a rapid increase in the number of cation pump sites at the lymphocyte surface was undertaken by studying the binding of ^3H-ouabain before and after treatment with mitogens (6, 110). The two published studies come to somewhat different conclusions and Lauf, the coauthor of one, has written a judicious analysis of the conflicting evidence in his comprehensive review (69). In brief, Quastel & Kaplan reported an increase in the number of ouabain binding sites following stimulation; at saturation the number rose from 1.25 to 2.3 $\times$ 10^5 per cell. They noted a correspondence between the fraction of ouabain binding sites occupied at a given concentration of the glycoside and the degree of inhibition of K^+ transport at that concentration (110). Averdunk & Lauf, on the other hand, found that stimulation caused the rate of ouabain binding to increase and not the maximum number of binding sites which, measured in the presence of NaN_3, was reported to be 3 $\times$ 10^4 per cell; they are aware of the apparent contradiction between these results and Averdunk's previous confirmation of the mitogen-induced change in V_{max} and constancy of K_M of transport (4). When binding was measured at 37°C in absence of NaN_3, a greater number of binding sites was seen, and these increased after stimulation (6)—results more compatible with those of

Quastel & Kaplan (110). Cook and his colleagues, in studies of the binding of ouabain and turnover of ouabain binding sites in HeLa cells (24), have called attention to the difficulties in measuring specific binding due to accumulation of the glycoside within the cells. Other discrepancies between the Ottawa (Quastel & Kaplan) and Durham (Averdunk & Lauf) groups are discussed by Lauf (69); obviously further work is required to reconcile them.

It has been known for many years that transport of certain amino acids into a variety of cells and tissues depends on co-transport of Na^+ via the cation pump (reviewed in 123a); inhibition of the latter by ouabain was shown to block active uptake of amino acids (123a). Stimulation of lymphocytes of man (93a) and of rat (135a) by mitogens caused increased uptake of the nonmetabolized amino acid, α-aminobutyric acid. Part of the inhibitory effect of ouabain on protein synthesis thus might be due to indirect block of uptake of one or more essential amino acids. However, experiments of van den Berg & Betel suggested strongly that the increased uptake of several amino acids was not caused by the increased Na^+K^+-ATPase activity since the former was not sensitive to inhibitory concentrations (5 mM) of ouabain.

Efflux and Cell Concentration of K^+

The initial studies of ^{42}K transport in PHA-stimulated lymphocytes indicated that efflux from cells preloaded with the radionuclide increased by only 25% over control rates; since the uptake of ^{42}K went up by about double, it was concluded that stimulation caused an increase in intracellular K^+ concentration, $[K^+]_c$ (108). This conclusion, based doubtless on inadequate techniques of measurement, is now known to be incorrect; a recent study in fact claims that after stimulation of human cells $[K^+]_c$ goes down by about 17% (97, 98; see also 5).

The confusion caused by these paradoxical data has to a large extent been dispelled by a series of studies from the laboratory of Lichtman, Segel and collaborators (81, 125–128). PHA stimulation of human lymphocytes was found to cause the cell membrane to become leaky to ions, and to K^+ in particular, such that washing with various media caused reduction of $[K^+]_c$ which was recovered in the supernatants (126). While it was possible that this might account for the first results of Negendank (97), he was able to show subsequently that his observation of mitogen-induced loss of $[K^+]_c$ was not an accidental result of washing the cells (98). It is interesting that plant lectins cause various cell lines, such as Ehrlich ascites cells, to lose intracellular K^+ as shown in studies from Nachbar's laboratory (3, 3a). Loss of cell K^+ is directly correlated to the degree of agglutination produced by the lectin, concanavalin A (53).

Other studies showed that PHA caused an increase in the rate of exit of

$^{42}K^+$ and ^{86}Rb from rat thymic and human lymphocytes (125); yet the $[K^+]_c$ remained unchanged for 24 hr following PHA treatment (127). The last paper of the series resolves the paradox by demonstrating a PHA-induced increase in the K^+ leak flux, which rose from 19 to 38 mmole l^{-1} cell water $\times$ hr and, in the same batch of cells, an increased pump flux, from 20 to 38 mmole l^{-1} cell water $\times$ hr; $[K^+]_c$ was again found to remain constant (128). A similar balanced increase in K^+ influx and efflux after concanavalin A stimulation of rat thymocytes has been reported by Iverson (53a). Hamilton & Kaplan, using a rapid micromethod involving spinning unwashed human lymphocytes that had been preloaded with ^{86}Rb, through a n-butyl phthalate–corn oil mixture (6), obtained comparable results: the leak flux of ^{86}Rb calculated as K^+ rose following PHA stimulation from 4.2 ± 0.7 fmoles cell^{-1} $\times$ hr to 9.9 ± 1.3 fmoles cell^{-1} $\times$ hr; efflux of ^{86}Rb was insensitive to ouabain (49). Hence, initiation of the proliferative response by mitogen involves a rapid and balanced increase in the rates of K^+ uptake and exit, the net result being that $[K^+]_c$ is kept constant. The 17% decrease in $[K^+]_c$ noted by Negendank (98), not accompanied by either increased Na^+ influx or by osmotic shrinkage of the cells, could either be a small but genuine loss of K^+ from cell water, an artifact, or, as seems probable, a loss of K^+ from a cell compartment external to the osmotic barrier; the existence of this compartment was shown by the discovery of a fraction of cell-bound ^{42}K exchangeable for K^+ or Rb^+ and removed by trypsin treatment but not by washing with Na^+ or sucrose (113).

Speculation as to the physiological and evolutionary significance of biochemical mechanisms, an exercise which has been called molecular theology (87), is risky, but on occasion heuristic. What is the molecular theology of the exactly balanced increase in K^+ influx and efflux following activation of lymphocytes? Two explanations have been proposed. The first supposes that $[K^+]_c$ homeostasis is maintained by balanced pump and leak fluxes during the first day or two of transformation; thereafter, as the huge volume increase (an order of magnitude or more) of blast formation occurs, $[K^+]_c$ homeostasis requires that the ratio of pump to leak flux increase. According to this hypothesis, homeostasis is achieved by reducing K^+ efflux while maintaining the high level of K^+ influx (56).

The other hypothesis envisages that this spinning of metabolic wheels is physiologically significant by virtue of its effect on the level of key intracellular nucleotides such as ATP, ADP [energy charge (2)], or cyclic AMP (cAMP). The evidence in favor of a reduction in cAMP levels as being necessary for cell proliferation has been recently reviewed (16, 43, 130). Compensated increase in K^+ pump flux might be a by-product of enhanced Na^+K^+ATPase activity, causing reduction in intracellular substrate available for adenyl cyclase and thus a reduction in the concentration of cAMP within the cell (49). A possible competition of Na^+K^+ATPase and adenyl cyclase for a common peripheral pool of ATP has been suggested as a possible growth-control mechanism (19, 47, 61). This hypothesis requires that ouabain treatment should increase cAMP levels. In fact, recent work from Paraf's laboratory has shown that in mouse plasmacytoma cell lines, ouabain did increase cAMP levels by as much as double in certain strains (76). Genetic data have caused these authors to interpret the phenomenon as being due to physical linkage of the cyclase and $Na^+K^+ATPase$ by means of a phospholipid-mediated interaction; they do not consider the more obvious possibility of interaction via competition for common substrate. In the case of a hamster cell line (BHK), no change in ATP levels was observed at inhibitory concentrations of ouabain and a rather surprising decrease in ATP levels occurred at extremely high ($10^{-3}M$) concentrations (93). It is possible that a compartmented peripheral pool of ATP, common to both the cyclase and the ATPase, is affected by ouabain and glycoside-induced change in this pool was concealed by the much larger cellular pool of ATP. Since the first report of inhibition of lymphocyte blastogenesis by cAMP and by dibutyryl cAMP (105), this phenomenon has been reported by several other authors [see, for example, (138a) and discussion following]. Unfortunately, the later authors have failed to note the *caveat lector* of Quastel & Kaplan (105), who showed that this inhibition was nonspecific since it was also caused by a variety of adenosine nucleotides.

There are several interesting phenomena that might be explained on the basis of an effect of ouabain acting via the $Na^+K^+ATPase$ primarily at the level of a (the) pool of intracellular ATP or of a derivative such as ADP or cAMP. In addition to examples to be cited below, there is the case of depression of glycolysis by ouabain in Ehrlich ascites tumor cells. Although this was shown to be due to inhibition of the $Na^+K^+ATPase$, it was not related to a lack of internal K^+ (122). There is also the report of a ouabain-induced stimulation of the migration of guinea pig alveolar macrophages occurring despite concomitant inhibition of pump-mediated Na^+, K^+ exchange (78).

$Na^+K^+ATPase$ IN NORMAL, MUTANT, AND TRANSFORMED CELL LINES

$[K^+]_c$ Cation Pump Activity, and Regulation of Proliferation in Mammalian Cell Lines

That growing cells of all types of organisms require and accumulate K^+ has been known for many decades; the review of Steinbach should be consulted for early references (134). Lubin has devoted intensive research to elucidating the role of this ion in the biosynthesis of macromolecules in bacteria

(84); his review summarizes this field as of 1964 (85). The state of knowledge of the role of K^+ in protein synthesis as of 1970 is summarized in a review of that date (102).

In his pioneering work on design of tissue culture media, Eagle showed that low concentration of K^+ in the medium limited the growth of cells in culture (36). Lubin and others demonstrated that ouabain could inhibit the proliferation of mammalian cells in culture (86, 114). Cation transport in Ehrlich ascites tumor cells had been studied by Hempling (50); it was then shown that ouabain could reversibly inhibit the growth of these cells in culture (91). Workers at the Carnegie Institution of Washington attempted to implicate $[K^+]_c$ as a controlling element in the regulation of cell division of hamster (BHK) cells (92, 121, 133); they were at least successful in proving that ouabain inhibited growth and DNA synthesis in these cells (93). However, attempts to reveal differences of the $[K^+]_c$, or compartmentalization or transport of this ion (e.g. as between growing and nongrowing chick-embryo fibroblasts in culture) were unsuccessful (115).

A number of studies have correlated the degree of inhibition of growth caused by ouabain with the extent to which it alters cation movements and $[K^+]_c$. In HeLa (cervical) and Girardi (heart) human cell lines, increasing the $[Na^+]_c$ and decreasing the $[K^+]_c$ with ouabain caused a reduction in rate of growth proportional to the concentration of glycoside (67). The time course of dissipation of the Na^+ gradient caused by varying concentrations of ouabain was parallel to that of inhibition of protein synthesis in a line of mouse lymphoblasts (19); incorporation of labelled thymidine was unaffected during this same period. However, prolonged incubation in ouabain did inhibit multiplication of the cells (19); the authors did not observe the recovery of cell function in the presence of ouabain that was reported in another mouse lymphoblastoid line by Cuff & Lichtman, who observed gradual reappearance of normal growth rate, $[K^+]_c$, and rate of uptake of ^{86}Rb (29); this unique observation is well worth further study. It is possible that this phenomenon is due to resynthesis of new pump sites following internalization of ouabain-receptor complexes as studied by Cook and his collaborators in HeLa cells (24, 25, 136).

New light on the relation between K^+ and growth has been shed by recent data from Lubin's laboratory (72). By means of varying ouabain concentrations in the medium, these authors were able to alter within wide limits the $[K^+]_c$ of a line of human fibroblasts. Growth and protein synthesis were unaffected until $[K^+]_c$ fell to below 60–80% that of normal; below this, protein synthesis fell in proportion to further reductions in $[K^+]_c$. DNA synthesis was also inhibited, but not RNA synthesis. Thus, below a threshold value of $[K^+]_c$, this parameter becomes limiting for cell growth (72).

Phenomena, all previously reported in connection with the activation of human lymphocytes by mitogens (references cited in previous sections of this review), have also been recently reported in the case of mouse 3T3 fibroblasts stimulated by addition of serum: There was increased uptake of ^{86}Rb; ouabain inhibited uptake but not exit of this K^+ congener; the increase in uptake was not sensitive to cycloheximide; the enhanced uptake was characterized by an increased V_{max} and an unchanged K_M; ouabain inhibited DNA synthesis reversibly (119).

Finally, it is worth reminding readers of the important studies of the Barths, who studied the influence of the metal cations on differentiation in vitro of explants of tissue from frog embryos; they found in particular that K^+ controlled the induction of undifferentiated ectoderm into notochord, a key stage in further differentiation of neural tissue (12).

Variation in Cation Pump Activity During the Cell Cycle

Alteration in the cell content and rate of transport of Na^+ and K^+ as a function of cell cycle was first demonstrated in a line of synchronized mouse lymphoblastoid cells by Jung & Rothstein (55). Cell cycle–related fluctuations in both Na^+ and K^+ content and fluxes were observed; the authors were able to correlate the change in ionic levels with the observed variations in rates of uptake and exit (55). The regular but complex pattern of cation regulation during the cycle was not a simple function of any easily measured variable such as cell volume or cell surface and was attributed to specific, cell cycle–related, internal events (55).

Cuff & Lichtman were able partially to synchronize their mouse lymphoblast cells by 12 hr exposure to ouabain; analysis of the fraction of cells in each of the stages of the cycle during ouabain blockade revealed a progressive increase in the percentage blocked in S phase. They thus attributed the ouabain-induced arrest of the lymphoblasts to a block in S phase (30). It is not clear whether this conclusion conflicts with the considerable body of data showing that, in mitogen-stimulated, nonsynchronized, human peripheral blood lymphocytes, ouabain inhibited protein and RNA synthesis and blocked the cells reversibly at all stages, including those well before any of them entered S phase (141, 142). This could reflect a species difference, a consequence of the transformation of the lymphoblastoid line, or a mistake in interpretation. Other workers, using the same established line of murine lymphoblasts (L5178Y) as Cuff & Lichtman (30) demonstrated that during the cell cycle there were parallel changes in binding of ^3H-ouabain and in uptake of ^{86}Rb (11a).

The $Na^+K^+ATPase$ activity of virus-transformed hamster fibroblasts was observed to increase several times over normal during the late inter-

122407

phase stage (45); Pasternak has recently reviewed the work of his laboratory and of others dealing with the overall patterns of change in surface membranes during the cell cycle (100). He points out that it is not clear whether the number of pump molecules undergoes change during the cycle or whether the activity per site varies via some unknown regulatory mechanism. An attempt to localize changes in pump and total fluxes of K^+ during the cell cycle of synchronized Ehrlich ascites tumor cells has recently been described (94); the properties of the $Na^+K^+ATPase$ of these cells had previously been described by Colombini & Johnstone (22a). Regular cycle-related variations in $K^+–K^+$ exchange and in K^+ pump and leak fluxes were observed and it was concluded that these were physiological events associated with the cycle (94). However, there are still no firm data showing which biochemical and physiological events of the cell cycles are regulated by these putative cycle-related variations in cation pumping. In any case, one should not lose sight of the possibility mentioned above that changes in activity of the pump may reflect not so much changing requirements for cation but rather for ATP, ADP, or cyclic nucleotides.

Function of the Cation Pump in Transformed Cell Lines and in Contact Inhibition

In the quest to understand the transformation of normal cells into tumor cells and the presence of density-dependent inhibition of growth in the former but not in the latter, numerous groups have investigated the effect of transformation on ion transport and on the activity of the Na^+K^+-ATPase. Unfortunately, no clear pattern emerges from these often contradictory experiments. The first such report claimed that transformation of the mouse fibroblast 3T3 line by SV40 caused the specific activity of the $Na^+K^+ATPase$ of the membrane fraction to decline (143); two other early papers found the same effect (44, 101). However, Sheinin & Onodera found that the $Na^+K^+ATPase$ of membrane fragments from 3T3 cells transformed by a variety of oncogenic viruses rose to about double in one case and was essentially unaffected by the others (128a). A meticulous study by Kasarov & Friedman revealed that mouse 3T3 fibroblasts as well as rat fibroblasts transformed by a wide variety of tumor viruses, including SV40, possessed four- to five-fold greater $Na^+K^+ATPase$ activity measured in homogenates than did the untransformed cells (61). An interesting finding was that this enzyme, which represented about 5% of the total ATPase of the normal cells, constituted 20–25% of that of the transformed cells. An increase in the $Na^+K^+ATPase$ as a consequence of viral transformation of hamster fibroblasts in culture was reported; this paper also demonstrated reciprocal changes in the activities of the adenyl cyclase and Na^+K^+-ATPase of this cell line (45).

Several other groups have also observed large increases in the Na^+K^+-ATPase of transformed 3T3 cells (39, 63, 64). The first of two interesting papers by Kimelberg & Mayhew correlated the 5.5-fold increase in the enzyme after SV40 transformation with a 2.5-fold increase in the uptake of ^{86}Rb; this was true of 3T3 cells transformed with SV40 and of BHK cells transformed by Rous sarcoma virus and SV40 (63). They also reported a discontinuity in the Arrhenius plots of the Na^+K^+ATPase from transformed cells not seen in enzyme from the untransformed; they speculated that there might be a relation between the increased cation transport and enzyme activity of transformed cells and a possible phospholipid phase change in their membranes (63). However, difficulties in relating the temperature dependence of in vitro preparations of the ATPase to that of K^+ transport in vivo have recently been pointed out (40). Their second paper showed that the rate of pump-mediated ^{86}Rb transport was a good indicator of protein synthesis and total protein content of these cells: When cell growth, measured by total protein, ceased, there was a decline in rate of cation uptake. They also reported that the increase in activity of the Na^+K^+ATPase of the transformed 3T3 cells was due to a 2.5-fold increase in the V_{max} without change in K_M (64), an effect like that reported for the K^+ transport of transformed human lymphocytes (105). This finding was independently confirmed by Banerjee & Bosmann (10). However, another paper from this group showed that ^{86}Rb uptake and ^3H-ouabain–binding of chick-embryo fibroblasts decreased in parallel with the degree of their transformation by a group of oncogenic viruses related to Rous sarcoma virus; the decrease seemed to be related to the transformation and not merely to viral infection (11). It is now crucial to explain the completely opposite response to transformation shown by the chick-embryo fibroblasts in primary culture and the established lines of mouse fibroblasts.

Several investigations of a possible relation between density-dependent inhibition of growth and the activity of the cation pump have been published. Both the Na^+K^+ATPase and a 5' nucleotidase of a mouse plasmacytoma strain which undergoes contact inhibition declined precipitously when cells of this strain came into confluence; on the other hand, in a strain that does not show contact inhibition, these enzymes did not decline when cells came into contact (77). Later work by this group showed that the K^+ flux and $[K^+]_c$ of either strain were not significantly different from those of the other (33). A recently published study shows that K^+ pump flux in 3T3 cells goes down sharply after growth to high cell density but the same change does not occur in SV40 transformed 3T3 (132). On the other hand, the rate of K^+–K^+ exchange goes up by 100% in both transformed and untransformed lines at high cell densities (132).

A report has appeared that correlates the activity of a membrane-bound

ATPase (assayed cytochemically) of several clones of cultured rat hepato-cyte lines with their tumorigenicity (59). The fact that this activity was apparently ouabain-resistant led the authors to the conclusion that it was not the $Na^+K^+ATPase$; however, the ouabain concentration which they used (Karasaki, personal communication) was too low by several orders of magnitude to permit such a conclusion (112).

There are some interesting studies of the effect of ouabain on the trans-forming viruses themselves. Nagai and co-workers showed that the glyco-side, at concentrations low enough to produce no noticeable effects on the host chick-embryo cells, inhibited markedly the multiplication of Sendai virus (HVJ) by retarding the rate of synthesis of viral macromolecules; high K^+ in the medium reversed the inhibition (96). These data were interpreted to indicate that viral multiplication requires an increase in $[K^+]_c$ to a higher threshold level than in the uninfected cells (96); however, this hypothesis, which was advanced by Quastel & Kaplan to account for their data on the effect of ouabain on lymphocyte transformation and the increase in K^+ influx consequent to it, has been proved incorrect (49, 56, 128). Nagai's data may also prove more compatible with an hypothesis according to which viral multiplication depends on altered levels of an intracellular nucleotide. The synthesis of picorna virus protein in mouse ascites cells caused a drastic decline in the ability of these cells to take up ^{86}Rb and a concomitant rise in $[Na^+]_c$; this rise in $[Na^+]_c$ caused a switch-off of synthesis of host protein (20). It was not clear whether the increase in $[Na^+]_c$ was caused by an inhibition of host $Na^+K^+ATPase$ or whether it was due to increased mem-brane leakiness resulting from the transformation.

An interesting study of the effect of ouabain on the action of interferon has shown that the antiviral action of interferon on the human cell line BSC 1 was blocked by ouabain, which inhibits the cation pump of these cells; ouabain had no effect on the action of interferon on viral multiplication within mouse L cells, which are ouabain-resistant (71).

Bernstein and collaborators have reported the striking finding that oua-bain added to the medium in which Friend erythroleukemic mouse cells are cultured can switch-on the synthesis of hemoglobin as effectively as can dimethylsulfoxide, the agent generally used for this purpose (15). The fact that the concentration of ouabain required was inversely related to the $[K^+]$ of the medium suggested to the authors that the $[K^+]_c$ might be involved in the switch mechanism; however, as discussed above, this inter-esting phenomenon might rather reflect a ouabain-induced alteration in the level of a critical nucleotide, such as ATP or cAMP. Another hypothesis to consider is that terminal differentiation of the Friend cell requires re-duced function of the cation pump. The former explanation might also apply to the recent report that ouabain, at concentrations which vary inversely to the $[K^+]$ of the medium, can act as a mitogen in the case of lymphocytes of the mouse spleen (120). Ouabain, as well as the ionophore gramicidin and veratridine, caused the induction of DNA synthesis and mitosis in the normally nondividing, mature neurons of the central nervous system of the chick when these were dissociated into culture medium from 7–10 day embryo spinal cords (23). These drugs have in common the fact that they cause reduced $[K^+]_c$ and increased $[Na^+]_c$. This phenomenon was taken to support the hypothesis of these authors that intracellular cation concentrations generate transmembrane potentials that have a regulatory role in the triggering of cell division (23); however, it is consistent with other hypotheses as well, such as the one just mentioned.

Isolation of Ouabain-Resistant Clones

Demonstration of the dependence of cell proliferation on the functional $Na^+K^+ATPase$ (86, 91, 106) led to attempts to use ouabain as a selective agent in the isolation of mutant cell lines. The first reports were those of Mayhew, who isolated ouabain-resistant (Oua^R) clones from Ehrlich acites [human carcinomata (90)], and of Sheinin & Onodera, who obtained a Oua^R variant from the 3T3 fibroblast line (128a). A number of Oua^R mutants from mouse, hamster, and human lines have been obtained by the Toronto group (9, 89); their work has been recently reviewed (8). Analysis of the Oua^R mutants in the rodent lines revealed that the molecular basis of resistance was an alteration in the affinity of the membrane receptor ($Na^+K^+ATPase$) for the drug. With human cell lines, the Oua^R mutant clones were invariably cross-resistant to two other inhibitors of the ATPase, digitoxin and digoxin; HeLa mutants selected for resistance to these digitalis derivatives were also cross-resistant to ouabain. However, different patterns of resistance revealed the existence of two categories of mutant clones, one being more resistant to ouabain than to the digitalis alkaloids and the other being as resistant to digitalis as to ouabain but less resistant to digoxin (8). The Oua^R character was co-dominant—that is, phenotypically apparent in the hybrid. Thus this type of mutant clone should be of utility in studying the ouabain receptor and the role of the cation pump under a variety of conditions of culture.

Other groups of workers have isolated Oua^R clones from rat myoblasts (88), HeLa cells (118), Balb/3T3 hybrids (54), and from mouse and human lymphoblast lines (1). From a line of human diploid lymphoblasts, Lever & Seegmiller have isolated Oua^R clones that appeared spontaneously with a frequency of 10^{-6} per cell per generation; this frequency increased greatly after mutagenesis with ethylmethyl sulfonate, which causes single base substitutions in DNA. Mutation frequency diminished after mutagenesis with the frameshift mutagen ICR-191, suggesting that this agent caused production of nonfunctional cation pump sites in mutated cells (79). These findings have been confirmed in studies of the induction of Oua^R clones in mutagenized lymphoma cells; X rays were found to act like ICR-191 (41a). As in the case of the clones isolated by Baker et al (9), the Oua^R clones from the lymphoblastoid lines displayed an uptake of K^+ (or ^{86}Rb) and a $Na^+K^+ATPase$ activity that were relatively resistant to ouabain (79). There was a linear relation between the concentration of the potent carcinogen-mutagen 4-nitroquinoline-1-oxide used to treat Fischer rat embryo cells and the number of Oua^R colonies isolated; exactly the same curve was obtained when the cells had been pre-infected with murine leukemia virus (95a).

Two interesting papers have come from Paraf's laboratory dealing with Oua^R clones isolated from plasmacytoma lines (75, 76). Such clones yielded microsomal preparations whose $Na^+K^+ATPase$ was ouabain-resistant. However, cross-resistance to ouabain was noted in clones that had been isolated using as selective agents dibutyryl cAMP, theophyllin, and concanavalin A (75). They then showed that the effect of ouabain to augment cAMP levels and adenyl cyclase activity, which I have discussed above, was absent in the Oua^R clones (76). It was the pleiotropic effect of the mutation to Oua^R that caused the authors to hypothesize a phospholipid-mediated interaction between the adenyl cyclase and the $Na^+K^+ATPase$ (76). In fact, ouabain has been shown to cause a conformational change in the $Na^+K^+ATPase$, detected by a drug-induced shift in the heat capacity–versus-temperature profile, indicating a greater heat stability of the enzyme-ligand complex (48). Since it is known that the enzyme spans the lipid bilayer (66), it is not unreasonable that the conformational change caused by ligand binding might provoke a perturbation of the bilayer that might, in turn, affect adjacent membrane proteins.

Finally, it is worth noting that a mutation in man which causes a pleiotropic membrane defect results, among other things, in red cells that lack all of the rhesus antigens (rh_{null}). Such erythrocytes have several abnormalities, including an increased K^+ transport, increased ouabain binding due to more pump sites on the surface, and an increased activity of the $Na^+K^+ATPase$ (70). Among the pleiotropic effects of hereditary stomatocytosis is a marked increase above normal of both total and ouabain-sensitive transport of Na^+ and K^+ (35). Analysis of these and other inborn errors of cation transport should yield valuable information as to the contribution of the cation pump to normal cell function. Utilizing such mutant cells to make hybrids with normal cells or with the Oua^R clones described above should permit isolation of hybrids with a spectrum of membrane states with respect to function of the cation pump and its sensitivity to inhibition by the cardiac glycosides.

INTERACTION OF CATION TRANSPORT WITH OTHER CELL PROCESSES

Insulin

In addition to the interactions of the active cation transport system with the parameters of cell stimulation, transformation, and proliferation that I have described above, there are other, perhaps less direct interactions, that may be no less vital in the initiation of the reactions leading to the stimulated state and thence to proliferation. Some of these interactions involve insulin and its receptors. It is indeed interesting that stimulation of human lymphocytes with concanavalin A caused the appearance of previously hidden insulin receptors and that the binding of insulin to leukemic lymphoblasts is quantitatively similar to that of the concanavalin A–transformed cells (65). Insulin itself promotes growth of cells in culture (129, 135), and concanavalin A has a number of insulin-like properties, including the inhibition of the adenyl cyclase activity of isolated membrane preparations (65).

Insulin was found to stimulate the ATPase activity of human lymphocyte membrane preparations in vitro and of ^{86}Rb uptake by intact cells (47), although the magnitude of the stimulations was marginal by comparison with that produced by the same concentrations of insulin in the case of glucose transport. It was then shown that the activating action of insulin on liver glycogen synthetase in amphibia was completely blocked by ouabain (17); the authors proposed that the primary action of insulin at the membrane level is on the Na^+K^+ATPase, causing increased influx of K^+. This hormone has also been found to expose cryptic Na^+ pump sites at the cell surface of frog muscle (46) and to stimulate the Na^+K^+ATPase of rat muscle sarcolemma, when the muscle tissue had itself been exposed to insulin before isolation of the membranes (18). Finally, insulin was shown to increase active Na^+ transport in toad bladder by (a) unmasking latent pump sites, and (b) in the long term promoting protein synthesis, perhaps of new pump sites (139).

Ca^{2+}

Perhaps even more important than these interactions with insulin and its receptor are those between the transport of the monovalent and of the divalent cations, especially Ca^{2+}. That these two membrane transport processes are coupled in some way is indicated by the fact that the cardiotonic effects of ouabain, known for almost a century, are mediated through increased $[Ca^{2+}]_c$ in the myocardial cells (41, 74). There is evidence that ouabain indirectly inhibits a Mg^{2+} membrane transport system (14). Lew & Ferreira found that in red cells there was a direct proportion between levels of $[Ca^{2+}]_c$ (obtained by balancing influx in the presence of the Ca^{2+}

ionophore A23187 with efflux via the membrane Ca^{2+} pump) and the rate constant for equilibration of ^{42}K across the membrane (80). These authors concluded that $[Ca^{2+}]_c$ controls the permeability of a K^+-selective channel in this cell (80).

It is known that the membranes of normal and tumor cells become leaky to cytoplasmic K^+ when the cells are incubated in media of low $[Ca^{2+}]$ (42). Ca^{2+} decreased the ^{86}Rb efflux from preloaded Ehrlich–Lettré tumor cells, both in presence and absence of ouabain; it was concluded that Ca^{2+} acted by reducing the rate of passive diffusion (leak flux) of K^+ and its congener possibly by the formation of Ca^{2+}-phospholipid complexes at the membrane (138). When Ca^{2+} was taken up by red cells in presence of A23187, intracellular K^+ was rapidly lost; this was also interpreted in terms of an interaction between Ca^{2+} and a membrane component (116). The ionophore caused a similar leak of K^+ from isolated mitochondria (34, 117). One may conclude that the action of Ca^{2+} on the K^+ leak flux was completely different from normal when measured in presence of the ionophore A23187. These findings should also give pause to those tempted to attribute the biological effects of the ionophore exclusively to increased uptake of Ca^{2+} into the cytoplasm; elsewhere, I have warned of possible misinterpretations arising from this (56).

Recently Schwartz has shown that there may be a link between Ca^{2+} transport and the cation pump. He has presented data which show that Ca^{2+} can bind directly to the phospholipid portion of the $Na^+K^+ATPase$ of the sarcolemma of cardiac muscle and suggests that it is via this membrane protein that Ca^{2+} enters the cell (124). Na^+ and K^+ altered the affinity of the phospholipid moiety for Ca^{2+} and so did ouabain (124). Schwartz calculates that his purified preparations of $Na^+K^+ATPase$ under approximately physiological conditions bind enough Ca^{2+} to account for contraction, provided that all of it were transported to the sarcoplasmic reticulum (124).

An interesting relationship between inner-face membrane proteins that bind Ca^{2+} and Mg^{2+} and the monovalent cation pump was observed in studies of purified membrane vesicles isolated by Paraf's group from mouse plasmacytoma cells (144). The chelator EDTA caused release of 35% of the total membrane protein from such vesicles; their $Na^+K^+ATPase$ activity was unchanged but its sensitivity to ouabain increased 350-fold in inside-out vesicles. This fact and other data suggested that inner-face proteins, whose mass was approximately 30,000 daltons, modify the ouabain-sensitivity of the $Na^+K^+ATPase$; the original sensitivity was not reconstituted by adding this material back to the inside-out vesicles but was recovered fully if Ca^{2+} and Mg^{2+} were then added (144). Since the ouabain-binding site is at the external face of the membrane, this curious modification of ouabain-sensitivity of the cation pump must be transmitted across the membrane, presumably as a result of a conformational change produced by the binding of divalent cations to inner-face proteins.

CONCLUDING REMARKS

Applying the parable of the blind men and the elephant to cation transport and cell proliferation explains at least to a first approximation why some workers see the Na^+ gradient as the crucial factor, others trans-membrane potential, and so on. Examples of mistaking a tail or a trunk for the elephant abound in the references cited above; and, I add with humility, my own work is no exception. Although sightless description of elephants and molecules is indeed part of the human condition, one should be careful to bear in mind that the function of the cation pump produces many related effects that might be called its primary colligative properties. These include: energy-dependent, uphill transport of Na^+ and K^+ in opposite directions across the membrane; contribution to the membrane potential, the stoichiometry of Na^+-K^+ exchange being electrogenic; hydrolysis of intracellular ATP; production of ADP. Enhanced or reduced function would thus produce a number of primary effects. For example, inhibition of the pump by means of ouabain would result in: reduced ion transport; increase in $[Na^+]_c$; decrease in $[K^+]_c$; decrease in membrane potential; increase in ATP and decrease in ADP levels (assuming no compensation by other ATP-forming or utilizing systems); reduction in oxygen consumption and oxidative phosphorylation, as well as conformational change in the pump molecule due to the ligand-induced allosteric transition. Secondary changes might include: inhibition of enzymes requiring K^+ as a co-factor; disaggregation of ribosomes into subunits caused by the low $[K^+]_c$; inhibition of protein synthesis; inhibition of Na^+-dependent uptake of certain amino acids; inhibition of DNA and RNA synthesis, which at some point depend on protein synthesis to make the required polymerases and factors; increase in $[Ca^{2+}]_c$; activation of enzymes requiring higher Ca^{2+} levels; increase in adenyl cyclase activity due to higher substrate concentration; increased cAMP levels; perturbation of phospholipid in the bilayer adjacent to the transmembrane pump molecules, etc. Each of these secondary effects will of course produce a cascade of others. Examining this little list makes one wonder at the temerity of those of us who have attributed to one or another of these primary or secondary effects that pivotal role in the coupling of pump function to proliferation.

This is not to say that achievement of a reasonable certainty about which is (are) the major primary or secondary effect(s) of pump function is impossible but it will require an experimental sophistication not usually encountered. For example, attribution of a key role to cAMP levels in linking the enhanced pump function of the stimulated state with the subsequent DNA synthesis and mitosis cannot be justified by showing only decreased cell concentration of cAMP, since this could be a parallel dead-end phenomenon (Figure 1, line B). At the very least, it is necessary to demonstrate that increasing the level of cAMP within the stimulated cell, by one experimental method or another, results in a reversible block of the chain of events leading to S phase.

Given the far-reaching cascade of effects consequent to function of the cation pump, it is not surprising that its continuous activity is essential to a variety of events involved in cell stimulation and proliferation, as well as to viral replication and interferon action. It was less easy to anticipate that one of the relatively early events in the proliferative response of cells in primary or continuous culture would be a greatly increased activity of the $Na^+K^+ATPase$, due, initially at least, to a greater availability or enhanced function of pump sites and not to synthesis of new ones. That the increased activity of the cation pump in stimulated lymphocytes was accompanied, or perhaps preceded, by a correspondingly greater K^+ leak flux, was, frankly, a surprise.

Critical unanswered questions abound. Is the increased pump activity in transformed cell lines, such as 3T3 mouse fibroblasts, also accompanied by increased K^+ efflux? What is the explanation of the striking difference between mouse and chick fibroblasts in this respect? Is the increased membrane permeability following lymphocyte activation specific for K^+? If so, what is the mechanism that produces such a selective membrane change? What is the causal relation between this change and the switching to high gear of the pump? Put more generally, what is the mechanism of K^+ homeostasis? Are additional, preformed pump sites exposed at the cell surface after stimulation, or is there increased activity per site, or both? Is K^+ homeostasis maintained during transformation of lymphocytes into lymphoblasts and, if so, how? What is the physiological significance of balanced increase in K^+ influx and efflux after stimulation? How does cell contact switch off the cation pump? What are the internal events in the cell cycle that influence the function of the $Na^+K^+ATPase$? I hope that many of these questions will have been answered when my successor prepares the next review of this field for the *Annual Review of Physiology*.

ACKNOWLEDGMENTS

I offer my apologies to the many colleagues who sent me reprints and manuscripts dealing with the role of Ca in cell proliferation; I had naively supposed that I would be able to deal with this subject as well in the space

38   KAPLAN

allotted. I apologize also to those whose work I should have cited in this review but did not, through ignorance or inadvertance. I am grateful to my secretary, Mrs. Anne Brown, who kept me afloat on the sea of paper that drifted in and out of my office during the preparation of this review, and to the National and Medical Research Councils of Canada for their support of the work of my laboratory.

Literature Cited

1. Adelberg, E. A., Callahan, T., Slayman, C. W., Hoffman, J. F. 1975. *J. Gen. Physiol.* 66:A17
2. Atkinson, D. 1969. *Curr. Top. Cell. Regul.* 1:29–43
3. Aull, F., Nachbar, M. S. 1973. *J. Cell. Physiol.* 83:243–50
3a. Aull, F., Nachbar, M. S., Oppenheim, J. D. 1976. *J. Cell. Physiol.* 90:9–14
4. Averdunk, R. 1972. *Hoppe-Seyler's Z. Physiol. Chem.* 353:79–88
5. Averdunk, R. 1976. *Biophys. Biochem. Res. Comm.* 70:101–9
6. Averdunk, R., Lauf, P. K. 1975. *Exp. Cell Res.* 93:331–42
7. Baker, P. F. 1972. In Ref. 52, pp. 243–68
8. Baker, R. M. 1976. In Ref. 24, pp. 93–103
9. Baker, R. M., Brunette, D. M., Mankovitz, R., Thompson, L. H., Whitmore, G. F., Siminovich, L., Till, J. E. 1974. *Cell* 1:9–21
10. Banerjee, S. P., Bosmann, H. B. 1976. *Exp. Cell. Res.* 100:153–58
11. Banerjee, S. P., Bosmann, H. B., Morgan, H. R. 1977. *Exp. Cell Res.* 104:111–17
11a. Banerjee, S. P., Hakimi, J., Bosmann, H. B. 1976. *Biochim. Biophys. Acta* 433:200–204
12. Barth, L. J., Barth, L. G. 1974. *Biol. Bull.* 146:313–25
13. Baserga, R. 1976. *Multiplication and Division in Mammalian Cells.* New York: Marcel Dekker. 239 pp.
14. Beauchamp, R. S., Silver, S., Hopkins, J. W. 1971. *Biochim. Biophys. Acta* 225:71–76
15. Bernstein, A., Hunt, D. M., Crichley, V., Mak, T. W. 1976. *Cell* 9:375–81
16. Berridge, M. J. 1975. *J. Cyclic Nucleotide Res.* 1:305–20
17. Blatt, L. M., McVerry, P. H., Kim, K.-H. 1972. *J. Biol. Chem.* 20:6551–54
18. Brodal, B. P., Jebens, E., Öy, V., Iversen, O.-J. 1974. *Nature* 249:41–43
19. Buckhold-Shank, B., Smith, N. E. 1975. *J. Cell Physiol.* 87:377–88

20. Carrasco, L., Smith, A. E. 1976. *Nature* 264:807–9
21. Christen, Y., Sasportes, M., Mawas, C., Dausset, J., Kaplan, J. G. 1975. *Cell Immunol.* 19:137–42
22. Clarkson, B., Baserga, R., eds. 1974. *Control of Proliferation of Animal Cells.* New York: Cold Spring Harbor Laboratory. 1029 pp.
22a. Colombini, M., Johnstone, R. M., 1973. *Biochim. Biophys. Acta* 323:69–86
23. Cone, C. D., Cone, C. M. 1976. *Science* 192:155–58
24. Cook, J. S. 1976. In *Biogenesis and Turnover of Membrane Macromolecules,* ed. J. S. Cook, pp. 15–16. New York: Raven Press
25. Cook, J. S., Vaughan, G. L., Proctor, W. R., Brake, E. T. 1975. *J. Cell. Physiol.* 86:59–70
26. Cooper, H. L. 1975. In *Immune Recognition,* ed. A. S. Rosenthal, pp. 411–415. New York: Academic
27. Crumpton, M. J., Snary, D. 1974. In *Contemporary Topics in Molecular Immunology,* ed. G. L. Ada, 3:27–56. New York: Plenum
28. Cuff, J. M., Lichtman, M. A. 1975. *J. Cell. Physiol.* 85:209–15
29. Cuff, J. M., Lichtman, M. A. 1975. *J. Cell. Physiol.* 85:217–26
30. Cuff, J. M., Lichtman, M. A. 1975. *J. Cell. Physiol.* 85:227–34
31. Daniele, R. P., Holian, S. K. 1976. *Proc. Natl. Acad. Sci. USA* 73:3599–3602
32. Dornand, J., Kaplan, J. G. 1976. *Can. J. Biochem.* 54:280–86
33. Ducouret-Prigent, B., Lelièvre, L., Paraf, A., Kepes, A. 1975. *Biochim. Biophys. Acta* 401:119–27
34. Duszynski, J., Wojtczak, L. 1977. *Biochem. Biophys. Res. Commun.* 74:417–24
35. Dutcher, P. O., Segel, G. B., Feig, S. A., Miller, D. R., Klemperer, M. R. 1975. *Pediatr. Res.* 9:924–27
36. Eagle, H. 1955. *Science* 122:501–4
37. Edelman, I. S. 1976. In Ref. 24, pp. 169–77

38. Edelman, I. S., Ismail-Beigi, F. 1974. *Recent Prog. Horm. Res.* 30:235–57
39. Elligsen, J. D., Thompson, J. E., Frey, H. E., Kruuv, J. 1974. *Exp. Cell Res.* 87:233–40
40. Ellory, J. C., Willis, J. S. 1976. *Biochim. Biophys. Acta* 443:301–5
41. Fisch, C., Surawiez, B. 1969. *Digitalis.* New York: Grune & Stratton
41a. Friedrich, U., Coffino, P. 1977. *Proc. Natl. Acad. Sci. USA* 74:679–83
42. Gilbert, I. G. F. 1972. *Eur. J. Cancer* 8:99–105
43. Goldberg, N. D., Haddox, M. K., Nicol, S. E., Acott, A. S., Glass, D. B., Zeilig, C. E. 1976. In *Control Mechanisms in Cancer*, ed. W. E. Criss, T. Ono, J. R. Sabine, pp. 99–108. New York: Raven Press
44. Graham, J. M. 1972. *Biochem. J.* 130:1113–24
45. Graham, J. M., Sumner, M. C. B., Curtis, D. H., Pasternak, C. A. 1973. *Nature* 246:291–95
46. Grinstein, S., Erlij, D. 1974. *Nature* 251:57–58
47. Hadden, J. W., Hadden, E. M., Wilson, E. E., Good, R. A. 1972. *Nature New Biol.* 235:174–76
48. Halsey, J. F., Mountcastle, D. B., Takeguchi, C. A., Biltonen, R. L., Lindenmayer, G. E. 1977. *Biochemistry* 16:432–35
49. Hamilton, L., Kaplan, J. G. 1977. *Can. J. Biochem.* 55:774–78
50. Hempling, H. G. 1958. *J. Gen. Physiol.* 41:565–83
51. Hokin, L. E. 1976. *Trends Biochem. Res.* 1:233–37
52. Hokin, L. E., Dahl, J. L. 1972. In *Metabolic Transport*, ed. L. E. Hokin, pp. 269–315. New York: Academic
53. Inoue, M., Utsumi, K., Seno, S. 1975. *Nature* 255:556–57
53a. Iverson, J.-G. 1976. *J. Cell Physiol.* 89:267–76
54. Jha, K. K., Ozer, H. L. 1976. *Somatic Cell Genet.* 2(3):215–23
55. Jung, C., Rothstein, A. 1967. *J. Gen. Physiol.* 50:917–32
56. Kaplan, J. G. 1977. In *Regulatory Mechanisms in Lymphocyte Activation*, ed. D. O. Lucas, pp. 51–74. New York: Academic
57. Kaplan, J. G., Quastel, M. R. 1975. In Ref. 26, pp. 391–403
58. Kaplan, J. G., Quastel, M. R., Dornand, J. 1976. In Ref. 24, pp. 207–20
59. Karasaki, S., Okigaki, T. 1976. *Cancer Res.* 36:4491–99
60. Kasakura, S. 1969. In *Proc. 4th Leucocyte Culture Conf.*, ed. O. R. McIntyre, pp. 564–570. New York: Meredith Press
61. Kasarov, L. B., Friedman, H. 1974. *Cancer Res.* 34:1862–65
62. Kay, J. E. 1972. *Exp. Cell Res.* 71:245–47
63. Kimelberg, H. K., Mayhew, E. 1975. *J. Biol. Chem.* 250:100–4
64. Kimelberg, H. K., Mayhew, E. 1976. *Biochim. Biophys. Acta* 455:865–75
65. Krug, U., Krug, F., Cuatrecasas, P. 1972. *Proc. Natl. Acad. Sci. USA* 69:2604–8
66. Kyte, J. 1974. *J. Biol. Chem.* 249:3652–60
67. Lamb, J. F., McCall, D. 1972. *J. Physiol.* 225:599–617
68. Lauf, P. K. 1975. *Biochim. Biophys. Acta* 415:173–229
69. Lauf, P. K. 1977. In *Transport across Biological Membranes*, ed. D. C. Tosteson, H. H. Ussing, G. Giebisch, Vol. I: *Fundamental Concepts and Model Systems*, ed. D. C. Tosteson. New York: Springer. In press
70. Lauf, P. K., Joiner, C. H. 1976. *Blood* 48:457–68
71. Lebon, P., Moreau, M.-C. 1973. *C. R. Acad. Sci. Paris* 276:3061–64
72. Ledbetter, M. L., Lubin, M. 1977. *Exp. Cell Res.* 105:223–36
73. Lee, E. Y. C., Smith, E. E., eds. 1974. *Biology and Chemistry of Eucaryotic Cell Surfaces.* New York: Academic. 366 pp.
74. Lee, K. S., Klaus, W. 1971. *Pharmacol. Rev.* 23:193–261
75. Lelièvre, L., Charlemagne, D., Paraf, A. 1976. *Biochim. Biophys. Acta* 455:277–86
76. Lelièvre, L., Paraf, A., Charlemagne, D., Sheppard, J. R. 1977. *Exp. Cell Res.* 104:191–97
77. Lelièvre, L., Prigent, B., Paraf, A. 1971. *Biochem. Biophys. Res. Commun.* 45:637–43
78. Leu, R. W., Eddleston, A. W. L. F., Good, R. A., Hadden, J. W. 1973. *Exp. Cell Res.* 76:458–61
79. Lever, J. E., Seegmiller, J. E. 1976. *J. Cell. Physiol.* 88:343–52
80. Lew, V. L., Ferreira, H. G. 1976. *Nature* 263:336–38
81. Lichtman, M. A., Jackson, A. H., Peck, W. A. 1972. *J. Cell. Physiol.* 80:383–96
82. Ling, N. R., Kay, J. E. 1975. *Lymphocyte Stimulation.* New York: American Elsevier. 398 pp. 2nd ed.
83. Loeb, L. A. 1974. In *Biology of Lymphoid Cells*, ed. A. A. Gottlieb, pp. 103–32. New York: Academic

84. Lubin, M. 1964. *Fed. Proc.* 23:994–1001
85. Lubin, M. 1964. In *The Cellular Functions of Membrane Transport*, ed. J. F. Hoffman, pp. 193–211. Englewood Cliffs, N.J.: Prentice-Hall
86. Lubin, M. 1967. *Nature* 213:451–53
87. Lue, P. F., Aitken, D. M., Kaplan, J. G. 1976. *Biochimie* 58:19–25
88. Luzzati, D. 1974. *Biochimie* 56:1567–69
89. Mankovitz, R., Buchwald, M., Baker, R. M. 1974. *Cell* 3:221–26
90. Mayhew, E. 1972. *J. Cell. Physiol.* 79:441–51
91. Mayhew, E., Levinson, C. 1968. *J. Cell. Physiol.* 72:73–76
92. McDonald, T. F., Sachs, H. G., Orr, C. W., Ebert, J. D. 1972. *Dev. Biol.* 28:290–303
93. McDonald, T. F., Sachs, H. G., Orr, C. W. M., Ebert, J. D. 1972. *Exp. Cell Res.* 74:201–6
93a. Mendelson, J., Skinner, A., Kornfield, S. 1970. See Ref. 105, pp. 31–37
94. Mills, B., Tupper, J. T. 1975. *J. Cell Physiol.* 89:123–32
95. Milthorp, P., Quastel, M. R., Kaplan, J. G., Vogelfanger, I. J. 1974. *Cell. Immunol.* 14:128–33
95a. Mishra, N. K., Pant, K. J., Wilson, C. M., Thomas, C. O. 1977. *Nature* 266:548–50
96. Nagai, Y., Maeno, K., Iinuma, M., Yoshida, T., Matsumoto, T. 1972. *J. Virol.* 9:234–43
97. Negendank, W. G. 1976. In *Leucocyte Membrane Determinants Regulating Immune Reactivity*, ed. V. P. Eijsvoogel, D. Roos, W. P. Zeijlemaker, p. 127. New York: Academic
98. Negendank, W. G., Collier, C. R. 1976. *Exp. Cell Res.* 101:31–40
99. Novogrodsky, A. 1972. *Biochim. Biophys. Acta* 266:343–49
100. Pasternak, C. A. 1976. *Trends Biochem. Sci.* 1:148–51
101. Perdue, J. F., Kletzien, R., Miller, K., Pridmore, G., Wray, V. L. 1971. *Biochim. Biophys. Acta* 249:435–53
102. Pestka, S. 1970. In *Membranes and Ion Transport*, ed. E. E. Bittar, 3:279–96. New York: Wiley-Interscience
103. Politoff, A. L., Ryser, H. J.-P., Pelikan, E. W. 1977. *Fed. Proc.* 36:988
104. Post, R. L., Taniguchi, K., Toda, G. 1975. *Molecular Aspects of Membrane Phenomena*, ed. H. R. Kaback, H. Neurath, G. K. Radda, R. Schwyzer, W. R. Wiley, pp. 92–103. New York: Springer
105. Quastel, M. R., Dow, D. S., Kaplan J. G. 1970. In *Proc. 5th Leucocyte Culture Conf.* pp. 97–123. New York: Academic
106. Quastel, M. R., Kaplan, J. G. 1968. *Nature* 219:198–200
107. Quastel, M. R., Kaplan, J. G. 1970. *Exp. Cell Res.* 62:407–20
108. Quastel, M. R., Kaplan, J. G. 1970. *Exp. Cell. Res.* 63:230–33
109. Quastel, M. R., Kaplan, J. G. 1971. *Lancet* 1:801–2
110. Quastel, M. R., Kaplan, J. G. 1975. *Exp. Cell. Res.* 94:351–62
111. Quastel, M. R., Milthorp, P., Kaplan, J. G., Vogelfanger, I. J. 1974. In *Lymphocyte Recognition and Effector Mechanisms*, ed. K. Lindahl-Kiessling, D. Osoba, pp. 493–500. New York: Academic
112. Quastel, M. R., Vogelfanger, I. J. 1971. *Cell. Immunol.* 2:504–8
113. Quastel, M. R., Wright, P., Kaplan, J. G. 1972. In *Proc. 6th Leucocyte Culture Conf.*, ed. M. R. Schwarz, pp. 185–214. New York: Academic
114. Quissell, D. O., Suttie, J. W. 1973. *J. Cell. Physiol.* 82:59–64
115. Raab, J. L., Humphreys, T. 1974. *Exp. Cell Res.* 89:407–10
116. Reed, P. W. 1976. *J. Biol. Chem.* 251:3489–94
117. Reed, P. W., Lardy, H. A. 1972. *J. Biol. Chem.* 247:6970–77
118. Rosenberg, H. M. 1975. *J. Cell. Physiol.* 85:135–42
119. Rozengurt, E., Heppel, L. A. 1975. *Proc. Natl. Acad. Sci. USA* 72:4492–95
120. Ryser, H. J.-P., Politoff, A. L. 1977. *Fed. Proc.* 36:989
121. Sachs, H. G., Stambrook, P. J., Ebert, J. D. 1974. *Exp. Cell Res.* 83:362–66
122. Scholnick, P., Lang, D., Racker, E. 1973. *J. Biol. Chem.* 248:5175–82
123. Schultz, J., Block, R. E., eds. 1974. *Membrane Transformations in Neoplasia.* New York: Academic. 297 pp.
123a. Schultz, S. G., Curran, P. F. 1970. *Physiol. Rev.* 50:637–718
124. Schwartz, A. 1976. *Fed. Proc.* 35:1279–82
125. Segel, G. B., Gordon, B. R., Lichtman, M. A., Hollander, M. M., Klemperer, M. R. 1975. *J. Cell. Physiol.* 87:337–44
126. Segel, G. B., Hollander, M. M., Gordon, B. R., Klemperer, M. R., Lichtman, M. A. 1975. *J. Cell. Physiol.* 86:327–36
127. Segel, G. B., Lichtman, M. A., Hollander, M. M., Gordon, B. R., Klemperer, M. R. 1975. *J. Cell. Physiol.* 88:43–48

128. Segel, G. B., Lichtman, M. A. 1976. *J. Clin. Invest.* 58:1358–69
128a. Sheinin, R., Onodera, K. 1972. *Biochim. Biophys. Acta* 274:49–63
129. Sheppard, J. R. 1972. *Nature New Biol.* 236:14–16
130. Sheppard, J. R. 1977. In Ref. 56, pp. 35–50
131. Skou, J. C. 1960. *Biochim. Biophys. Acta* 42:6–14
132. Spaggiare, S., Wallach, M. J., Tupper, J. T. 1976. *J. Cell. Physiol.* 89:403–16
133. Stambrook, P. J., Sachs, H. J., Ebert, J. D. 1975. *J. Cell. Physiol.* 85:283–92
134. Steinbach, H. B. 1962. *Perspect. Biol. Med.* 5:338
135. Temin, H. M. 1967. *J. Cell. Physiol.* 69:377–84
135a. van den Berg, K. J. 1974. *The Role of Amino Acids in the Mitogenic Activation of Lymphocytes.* Rijswijk, Netherlands: Org. Health Res. TNO. 103 pp.
136. Vaughan, G. L., Cook, J. S. 1972. *Proc. Natl. Acad. Sci. USA* 69:2627–31
137. Weissman, G., Claiborne, R., eds. 1975. *Cell Membranes.* New York: HP Publishing Co.
138. Wenner, C., Hackney, J. 1976. *Arch. Biochem. Biophys.* 176:37–42
139. Wiesmann, W. P., Sinha, S., Klahr, S. 1976. *Nature,* 260:546–47
140. Wright, P., Kaplan, J. G. 1976. *Cell. Immunol.* 25:197–206
141. Wright, P., Quastel, M. R., Kaplan, J. G. 1973. In *Proc. 7th Leucocyte Culture Conf.,* ed. F. Daguillard, pp. 87–104. New York: Academic
142. Wright, P., Quastel, M. R., Kaplan, J. G. 1973. *Exp. Cell Res.* 79:87–94
143. Yoshikawa-Fukada, M., Nojima, T. 1972. *J. Cell. Physiol.* 80:421–30
144. Zachowski, A., Lelièvre, L., Aubry, J., Charlemagne, D., Paraf, A. 1977. *Proc. Natl. Acad. Sci. USA* 74:633–37

Ann. Rev. Physiol. 1978. 40:43–66
Copyright © 1978 by Annual Reviews Inc. All rights reserved

RELATIONSHIP OF RENAL ❖1185
SODIUM AND WATER TRANSPORT
TO HYDROGEN ION SECRETION

Jose A. L. Arruda

Section of Nephrology, Veterans Administration West Side Hospital, Chicago, Illinois 60612 and Section of Nephrology, University of Illinois Abraham Lincoln School of Medicine, Chicago, Illinois 60612

Neil A. Kurtzman

Section of Nephrology, University of Illinois Abraham Lincoln School of Medicine, Chicago, Illinois 60612

INTRODUCTION

In recent years it has become increasingly clear that the kidney's regulation of volume homeostasis via its control of salt and water reabsorption is inextricably linked with its regulation of hydrogen ion secretion. The purpose of this review is to outline some of the processes that control hydrogen ion secretion both in the proximal and distal nephron and to detail how these functions are related to volume regulation. This report further outlines the difficulty sometimes encountered in assessing hydrogen ion secretory capacity. Such difficulties arise because salt and water reabsorption may influence parameters usually thought to reflect hydrogen ion secretory ability only. In other words, the demands of volume regulation, both on the bulk reabsorption of salt and water in the proximal tubule and on the reabsorption of salt in the ascending limb of the loop of Henle with its concomitant influence on water transport in the collecting duct, may alter tests of urinary acidification so that they seem to indicate acidification defects when none may actually exist.

43

0066-4278/78/0301-0043$01.00

FACTORS INFLUENCING BICARBONATE REABSORPTION

It has generally been believed that bicarbonate reabsorption is effected solely as the consequence of hydrogen ion secretion (65, 66, 68, 89). While this view may not be accurate and has been strongly challenged by Maren (53), we will assume for the purposes of our discussion that bicarbonate is reabsorbed solely by hydrogen ion secretion. Whether sodium bicarbonate is reabsorbed directly as sodium bicarbonate is not immediately germane to our subject (50).

Effective Arterial Blood Volume

The state of effective arterial blood volume is the most potent factor controlling bicarbonate reabsorption (40, 42–44, 46, 62). When volume is expanded, sodium reabsorption is inhibited and secondarily depresses bicarbonate reabsorption. Conversely when volume is contracted, sodium reabsorption is enhanced and so is that of bicarbonate. Classically bicarbonate reabsorption is considered to be essentially complete until the plasma level (in the human) reaches a value of about 26 mEq l^{-1} (renal bicarbonate threshold) and to be maximal above 28 mEq l^{-1} (bicarbonate Tm) (58, 59). The observation that no Tm is observed when bicarbonate reabsorption is measured in volume-contracted subjects required modification of this concept. As now used, bicarbonate Tm defines the maximal level of bicarbonate reabsorption observed under the particular set of circumstances in which it is measured, not the maximal rate possible (42). For example, bicarbonate Tm will be higher in normal subjects than in volume-expanded subjects. It has been suggested that chloride deficiency stimulates bicarbonate reabsorption (6, 29, 34–36, 55, 76). Since chloride's depletion almost invariably equals salt depletion it will almost inevitably be associated with contraction of effective arterial volume. Accordingly it is likely that chloride depletion enhances bicarbonate reabsorption through contraction of extracellular volume (42–44, 46).

Several studies have recently demonstrated that the absolute rate of absorption of sodium is highly correlated in a linear fashion with the absolute rate of bicarbonate reabsorption (1, 64, 66, 82). Since the measurement of the maximal rate of bicarbonate reabsorption invariably requires the infusion of large amounts of sodium bicarbonate, the assessment of bicarbonate reabsorption is made difficult by the concomitant volume expansion which occurs during the performance of a bicarbonate titration study (42–44, 46). In order to exclude the effect of volume on bicarbonate reabsorption when comparing two different subjects or two different groups of subjects, bicarbonate reabsorption per unit glomerular filtration rate

(GFR) has been plotted against fractional chloride excretion (1, 42–44, 46). If bicarbonate reabsorption in two differing groups of subjects is different at the same rate of chloride excretion (and inferentially the same level of volume), it has been reasoned that bicarbonate reabsorption is different in these two groups owing to some factor other than volume. This technique is sometimes cumbersome and sometimes inaccurate in that chloride excretion may increase because the reabsorption of chloride is inhibited at a site of the nephron where bicarbonate is not reabsorbed; also, it may be impossible to get an overlap in chloride excretion in the two groups being studied. It has been suggested that the ratio of absolute bicarbonate reabsorption to absolute sodium reabsorption is relatively unaffected by volume expansion. Over chloride excretory rates from 1–20%, this ratio remains relatively unchanged (64). Thus, the ratio can be used to assess the state of bicarbonate reabsorption independent of the effects of volume.

The mechanism whereby volume expansion or contraction influences the rate of bicarbonate reabsorption must still remain speculative. It is likely, however, that the exchange of sodium for hydrogen is unaffected by the state of effective arterial blood volume. It is likely that changes in volume result in the changes in the Starling forces in the peritubular capillaries of the proximal tubules, which result either in increased or decreased back diffusion of sodium bicarbonate into the lumen of the proximal tubule (78). Thus when effective arterial blood volume is decreased, the Starling forces are such that back diffusion is minimized and sodium bicarbonate reabsorption is enhanced. The opposite is likely true when volume is expanded.

Glomerular Filtration Rate

It has been known for many years that there is a direct correlation between GFR and absolute bicarbonate reabsorption; i.e. an increase in GFR is accompanied by a parallel increase in absolute bicarbonate reabsorption; conversely, a decrease in GFR leads to a decrease in absolute bicarbonate reabsorption (58, 59). Bicarbonate reabsorption expressed as mEq l^{-1} GFR, however, is constant. Acute or chronic reduction of GFR is associated with a decrease in absolute bicarbonate reabsorption; again, Tm/GFR remains constant (9). Thus there is good glomerulotubular balance for bicarbonate.

Aldosterone and Bicarbonate Reabsorption

Patients with adrenal insufficiency commonly develop mild metabolic acidosis. Bicarbonate reabsorption measured in dogs with selective aldosterone deficiency, produced by adrenalectomy and replacement of glucocorticoids, is incomplete at low plasma bicarbonate concentrations (15–24 mEq l^{-1}); bicarbonate reabsorption is normal when the plasma concentration exceeds 24 mEq l^{-1} (44). It thus appears likely that aldosterone exerts no effect on proximal hydrogen ion secretion, but does play some role in the regulation of distal nephron proton secretion (21, 31, 44).

Potassium

Several studies have shown that renal bicarbonate reabsorption is inversely proportional to the level of body potassium stores (67). That is to say, bicarbonate reabsorption is depressed in potassium-loaded animals and increased in potassium-depleted animals. This fact has been demonstrated by the infusion of potassium chloride or potassium bicarbonate into bicarbonate-loaded animals. The infusion of potassium salts and sodium bicarbonate leads to extracellular volume expansion (40, 46). It is possible therefore that potassium loading results in depressed bicarbonate reabsorption as a consequence of volume expansion rather than as a result of a direct effect of potassium on bicarbonate reabsorption (46). The demonstration that hypokalemic metabolic alkalosis could be corrected by the administration of sodium chloride alone (this is the same as stating that bicarbonate reabsorption falls) casts doubt on the role of potassium as a regulator of bicarbonate reabsorption (36). Recently, however, it has been demonstrated that potassium exerts a regulatory role over bicarbonate reabsorption independent of any effect attributable to volume. Kurtzman, White & Rogers studied bicarbonate reabsorption in three groups of dogs: one with potassium depletion, a second with hyperkalemia, and a third normokalemic group (46). Bicarbonate reabsorption fell in all three groups following volume expansion with isotonic saline. The higher the fractional chloride excretion, the lower the bicarbonate reabsorption in all three groups. At any given level of fractional chloride excretion, however, bicarbonate reabsorption was higher in potassium-depleted than in normal animals, and higher in normal animals than in those that were potassium-loaded. When salt excretion was very low, and by inference volume markedly contracted, there was no difference in bicarbonate reabsorption amont the three groups. These workers concluded that volume expansion depressed bicarbonate reabsorption to the same degree in potassium-loaded, normal, and potassium-depleted animals but that, independent of volume, the state of body potassium stores affected bicarbonate reabsorption (46). It also became clear that volume contraction was such a major stimulus to bicarbonate reabsorption that it could completely overcome the depressive effects of potassium loading on bicarbonate reabsorption (46).

Effects of Carbon Dioxide Tension and Carbonic Anhydrase

Bicarbonate reabsorption is directly proportional to the blood carbon dioxide tension. Rector et al showed that bicarbonate reabsorption increased curvilinearly as plasma carbon dioxide tension was raised to levels as high as 450 mm Hg (70). Kurtzman (43) performed similar experiments in volume-expanded dogs; he showed that elevation of carbon dioxide tension led to a decrease in salt excretion as well as to an increase in bicarbonate reabsorption; he postulated that this effect was the result of vasodilatation induced by hypercapnia and that the vasodilatation resulted in a decreased effective arterial blood volume. Thus the effect of acute elevation of carbon dioxide tension on bicarbonate reabsorption was thought to be the result of two factors: the high carbon dioxide tension per se, and the contraction in volume. This study and a subsequent one (90) demonstrated that the major effect of acute hypercapnia is mediated by changes in volume rather than changes in intracellular pH induced by high carbon dioxide tension (43). This belief was reinforced by the demonstration that when the vasodilatation and its accompanying drop in blood pressure were reversed by the infusion of norepinephrine, chloride excretion increased and bicarbonate reabsorption fell, although not quite to control levels.

Carbonic anhydrase exerts an easily demonstrable effect on bicarbonate reabsorption (52, 53, 65). The inhibition of the enzyme causes a marked decrease in the maximal capacity of the kidney to reabsorb bicarbonate. To date, however, there has been no convincing evidence presented that the enzyme plays an important role in mediating changes in the rate of bicarbonate reabsorption.

Parathyroid Hormone and Phosphate Depletion

Both parathyroid hormone and phosphate depletion depress bicarbonate reabsorption (3, 7, 18, 20, 26, 32, 63). Phosphate retention may increase bicarbonate reabsorption, but definitive evidence for such an effect is lacking.

Glucose

Patients returning to a normal diet after long fasting commonly develop metabolic alkalosis (83). Glucose loading elevates bicarbonate reabsorption in these patients. More recently, glucose infusion has been shown to enhance bicarbonate reabsorption in normal dogs (84). This seems to be a direct effect of glucose since insulin administration has no effect on bicarbonate reabsorption. Recently it has also been shown in man that glucose loading enhances distal hydrogen ion secretion as reflected by an increase in acid excretion (25).

Calcium and Vitamin D

Both hypocalcemia and hypercalcemia have been reported to affect bicarbonate reabsorption (18, 23). Hypercalcemia enhances the capacity of the kidney to reabsorb bicarbonate, while hypocalcemia depresses bicarbonate reabsorption. Vitamin D also has a stimulatory effect on bicarbonate reabsorption. Infusion of 25-hydroxycholecalciferol into the renal artery of dogs enhances bicarbonate reabsorption (57, 81).

Chronic Renal Failure

Two recently published studies have convincingly demonstrated that in dogs with chronic renal failure bicarbonate reabsorption is markedly enhanced (1, 73). For some time it has been thought that chronic renal failure is associated with a depression in bicarbonate reabsorptive capacity. This is likely due to the fact that chronic renal failure results in volume expansion. Volume expansion depresses bicarbonate reabsorption regardless of other events (1, 40). The two new studies of bicarbonate reabsorption in the presence of renal failure corrected for volume expansion showed that at any level of volume bicarbonate reabsorption was significantly greater in dogs with renal failure than in normal animals. None of the known mechanisms that affect bicarbonate reabsorption could be successfully invoked to explain this observation (1, 73). These studies seem to indicate that there is at least one additional ill-defined regulator of bicarbonate reabsorption. Regardless of the mechanism involved, total hydrogen ion secretory capacity per nephron is increased in the presence of chronic renal failure.

ACID EXCRETION

As a consequence of normal metabolism there is a daily production of approximately 1 mEq kg^{-1} body weight of hydrogen ions (4, 65, 66). These hydrogen ions result from the metabolism of sulfoproteins and phosphoproteins, which yield sulfuric acid and phosphoric acid, respectively. Small amounts of acid may be generated under normal circumstances from the incomplete oxidation of fat from carbohydrates. The acids formed as a consequence of normal metabolism are neutralized by the buffers in extracellular fluid; this process results in the consumption of bicarbonate and the other extracellular buffers present. It is obvious that there must be a way of replenishing the extracellular bicarbonate used to neutralize the endogenously produced acid. The kidney is charged with the responsibility of excreting hydrogen ions resulting from normal metabolism. To maintain acid-base homeostasis the kidney must not only reabsorb virtually all of the bicarbonate filtered, but must secrete an additional amount of hydrogen ions to equal the amount generated as a consequence of metabolism. Thus once bicarbonate reabsorption is complete, for each mEq of hydrogen ion secreted by the kidney, one mEq of bicarbonate is added to the blood. In this fashion the kidney regenerates the bicarbonate consumed in neutralization of endogenous acid. The net amount of acid excreted by the kidney per day equals the daily production of acid. The kidney secretes hydrogen ions through three main mechanisms: (*a*) reabsorption of bicarbonate, (*b*) excretion of titratable acid, and (*c*) excretion of ammonium.

The integrity of the proximal hydrogen secretory apparatus has long been measured by use of the bicarbonate titration curve described by Pitts and co-workers (58, 59). Distal acidification has been assessed by measuring the effects of acid loading on urinary pH, ammonium excretion, and on the excretion of titratable acidity (4). The infusion of sodium sulfate under conditions of salt depletion and the administration of mineralocorticoid has also been used to assess distal acidifying capacity (75). The administration of sodium sulfate results in a decrease in urine pH and an increase in ammonium excretion.

Recently interest has been rekindled in the use of urinary carbon dioxide tension in the assessment of distal acidification. Pitts et al demonstrated that alkalinization of the urine results in an increase in urinary carbon dioxide tension considerably above that observed in plasma (58, 59). Since carbonic anhydrase is not present on the luminal epithelial surface of the distal nephron it was initially postulated that the carbonic acid formed, as the result of the addition of hydrogen by the nephron to bicarbonate, dehydrated slowly such that carbon dioxide was formed after the urine had left the nephron. The formation of carbon dioxide in the lower urinary tract (beyond the papilla), where the surface-to-volume relationships are such that carbon dioxide could not diffuse back into blood, was thought to be the mechanism responsible for the phenomenon (59). This explanation may not be adequate, however, since the uncatalyzed dehydration of carbonic acid is sufficiently rapid to allow for formation of carbon dioxide before the urine has left the nephron.

This fact caused the postulation that hydrogen ion secretion, presumably in the collecting duct, was partitioned by bicarbonate and the other urinary buffers (61, 65, 69, 71). This partition would allow for the urinary buffers other than bicarbonate to release hydrogen ions in the lower urinary tract where it could react with bicarbonate to form carbon dioxide. The likely candidate for such a urinary buffer was phosphate (37, 38).

$$H^+ + HPO_4^= \xrightleftharpoons{pK = 6.8} H_2PO_4^-$$

As can be seen from the above reactions, the pK of the phosphate buffer system of 6.8 is sufficiently low that when the urine is maximally alkaline, pH 8.0, the amount of acid phosphate present in the urine is so small that this buffer system cannot function as a major source of hydrogen ions (2).

This observation is supported by reports from our laboratory that demonstrate that phosphate administration to animals with a highly alkaline urine has no effect whatsoever on urinary carbon dioxide tension (2).

When phosphate is infused into an animal whose urine pH is close to the pK of the phosphate buffer system, there is a highly significant linear correlation between urinary phosphate concentration and urinary carbon dioxide tension (2). This holds true for animals with acidification defects. If the acidification defect is of the gradient type (that is to say hydrogen ion secretory capacity is intact but the secreted hydrogen or resulting carbonic acid back-diffuses) then the administration of phosphate will likewise result in an increase in urinary carbon dioxide tension (2, 4). If, however, the capacity to secrete hydrogen ion is markedly impaired, then phosphate administration when the urine has a pH of about 6.8 has no effect on urinary carbon dioxide tension.

The observations that phosphate plays little or no role in the setting of the urinary carbon dioxide tension when the urine is maximally alkaline and that both humans with acidification defects and animals with experimentally induced acidification defects show no rise in urinary carbon dioxide tension present a serious conceptual problem (2, 30, 54, 72, 86). Why does the urinary carbon dioxide tension go up with bicarbonate loading? One could postulate that there is another buffer present in the urine with an appropriate pK which allows for the partition of the secreted hydrogen ions between bicarbonate and the buffer. Whether this buffer substance exists, and if so what it is, are not currently known.

Another problem concerning the explanation for the elevation of urinary carbon dioxide tension following bicarbonate loading may reside in the fact that all workers in the field have started with the assumption that the high carbon dioxide tension is in some way related to the capacity of the collecting duct to secrete hydrogen ions (2, 11, 12, 30, 54, 72, 77, 86). Almost totally ignored has been the fact that bicarbonate in aqueous solution reacts with bicarbonate according to the following set of chemical reactions (10, 22).

$$2H_2O \rightleftharpoons H_3O^+ + OH^- \qquad K_w = 1.01 \times 10^{-14} = [H_3O][OH^-] \qquad 1.$$

$$HCO_3^- + H_2O \rightleftharpoons H_3O^+ + CO_3^= \qquad K_2 = 6.0 \times 10^{-11} = \frac{[H_3O^+][CO_3^=]}{HCO_3^-} \qquad 2.$$

$$HCO_3^- + H_2O \rightleftharpoons H_2CO_3 + OH^- \qquad K_b = 3.1 \times 10^{-8} = \frac{[H_2CO_3][OH^-]}{HCO_3} \qquad 3.$$

$$CO_2 + H_2O \rightleftharpoons H_2CO_3 \rightleftharpoons H_3O^+ + HCO_3^- \quad K_1 = 3.5 \times 10^{-7} = \frac{[H_3O^+][HCO_3^-]}{CO_2} \quad 4.$$

$$HCO_3^- + HCO_3^- \rightleftharpoons H_2CO_3 + CO_3^= \qquad K = \frac{K_2}{K_1} = \frac{[CO_2][CO_3^=]}{[HCO_3^-]^2} \quad 5.$$

$$\Updownarrow$$

$$CO_2 + H_2O$$

The $[P_{CO_2}]$ of an ideal solution at 25°C and zero ionic strength containing 0.3M $NaHCO_3$ can be calculated in the following way from the 5th equation above:

$$K = \frac{K_2}{K_1} = 1.71 \times 10^{-4} = \frac{[CO_2][CO_3^=]}{[HCO_3^-]^2}.$$

Let $x = [CO_2] = [CO_3^=]$. Then,

$$1.71 \times 10^{-4} = \frac{x^2}{[0.3-2x]^2}, \text{ or } 1.31 \times 10^{-2} = \frac{x}{0.3-2x}.$$

Therefore: $x = 0.00383M$ $CO_2 = CO_3^=$; and therefore: $P_{CO_2} = 3.83$ mM of $CO_2 \div 0.03 = 127.7$ mm Hg.

The above calculations are applicable only to an ideal solution at 25°C. Since urine is not an ideal solution, these calculations are at best an approximation of the carbon dioxide tension resulting from a solution of bicarbonate in urine. If one takes into account the effects of temperature (37°C) and the ionic strength of blood, $K_1 = 7.9 \times 10^{-7}$ and $K_2 = 1.66 \times 10^{-10}$, and therefore $K = 2.1 \times 10^{-4}$ (15). Using this new value for K the carbon dioxide tension of a 0.3M solution of sodium bicarbonate is 141 mm Hg.

Thus the concentration of bicarbonate that occurs in the collecting duct as the result of water abstraction in that segment of the nephron must contribute a large fraction of the carbon dioxide tension observed during bicarbonate loading (65, 71, 89). It is even conceivable that all the elevation in carbon dioxide tension observed during bicarbonate loading may be the result of the concentration of bicarbonate rather than the result of hydrogen ion secretion in the collecting duct (5). New studies are required to determine with precision to what extent urinary carbon dioxide tension during bicarbonate loading reflects hydrogen ion secretion and to what extent it is the result of urinary concentration. The failure to consider the contribution of bicarbonate itself to urinary carbon dioxide tension in almost all previously reported studies of urinary acidification requires that these studies be reassessed (2, 30, 54, 72, 86).

Disequilibrium pH

In order to support the hypothesis that the reabsorption of filtered bicarbonate by the kidney was mediated in both the proximal and distal tubules by hydrogen ion secretion, it was necessary to examine the fate of the carbonic acid that resulted from the addition of hydrogen ions to filtered bicarbonate. Rector and co-workers hypothesized that were carbonic anhydrase available on the luminal epithelial surface, the carbonic acid formed by hydrogen ion secretion would be immediately dissipated into carbon dioxide tension and water (68). If, on the other hand, carbonic anhydrase were not available, carbonic acid would accumulate at a rate considerably in excess of that which would be observed at equilibrium. These workers believed, as have all others in this field, that luminal carbonic acid resulted solely from hydrogen ion secretion (11, 12, 33, 68, 89). By measuring the pH of distal nephron urine in vivo and comparing it with the measured equilibrium pH, it could be determined if carbonic acid were in equilibrium (68, 89). If the intraluminal pH were lower than the equilibrium pH (an acid disequilibrium pH) then this would indicate that hydrogen ion secretion resulted in the formation of carbonic acid at a rate faster than it could be dissipated in the absence of carbonic anhydrase. The finding of no disequilibrium pH in the proximal tubule and an acid disequilibrium pH in the distal nephron, along with the observation that carbonic anhydrase inhibition resulted in the formation of an acid disequilibrium pH in the proximal tubule while carbonic anhydrase administration eliminated the acid disequilibrium pH in the distal nephron, was felt to demonstrate conclusively that hydrogen ion secretion was the mechanism whereby bicarbonate was reabsorbed in both these segments of the nephron (49–51, 68, 89).

Another important observation felt to support this hypothesis as regards the distal nephron was that infusion of carbonic anhydrase to animals undergoing bicarbonate diuresis resulted in a fall in urinary carbon dioxide tension from a value considerably in excess of that of blood to a value approximately equal to that of blood (56). This observation was interpreted as indicating that carbonic acid accumulated in the distal nephron because of the absence of its catalyst; the infusion of the enzyme carbonic anhydrase allowed carbonic acid to come into equilibrium while the urine was still within the nephron, such that the carbon dioxide formed as a result of this equilibrium could back-diffuse to the blood (68, 89). The interpretation of this observation was again based on the assumption that all the carbonic acid formed was the result of hydrogen ion secretion. We would like to examine the distal nephron disequilibrium pH and its physiologic significance in light of information recently acquired.

Basically this disequilibrium pH in the distal nephron has been measured as follows (68, 89): A pH-microelectrode is used to measure intratubular pH in vivo. A urine sample collected from the distal nephron is removed and allowed to equilibrate with 5% carbon dioxide. Following this equilibration the pH is measured again. At equilibrium the Henderson-Hasselbalch equation may be used to calculate the intratubular bicarbonate concentration. Using this bicarbonate concentration, and knowing the blood carbon dioxide tension of the animal from which the urine was obtained, one can calculate the pH that would have been measured in vivo in the distal nephron if carbonic acid were in equilibrium. Note that this technique assumes that intratubular carbon dioxide tension is equal to that of blood. This method has been used to show that the measured pH in the distal nephron is below the equilibrium pH. The two sets of observers who have measured distal nephron disequilibrium pH have reported different values (68, 89). This technique is so difficult technically and fraught with so many potential errors that its results should be considered qualitative rather than quantitative.

Brodsky & Schilb have described in detail the limitations of the pH disequilibrium technique (12). They point out that the work demonstrating a disequilibrium pH has not used the technique of a sealed system. As mentioned above, the work as performed assumes that intraluminal carbon dioxide tension is equal to that of blood. To the extent that intraluminal carbon dioxide tension is greater or lower than blood carbon dioxide tension, a significant error will be introduced into the calculation of intraluminal equilibrium pH. Brodsky & Schilb propose that the proper technique for measuring disequilibrium pH is first to measure intraluminal pH (12). Following this tubular urine should be collected in a sealed, gas-tight system and its equilibrium pH measured in this sealed system. The direction of the pH change observed at equilibrium as compared to the in vivo measured pH would indicate the presence and direction of a disequilibrium pH.

An alternative method for measuring disequilibrium pH accurately would be to measure intraluminal pH and carbon dioxide tension simultaneously. Advances in microelectrode techniques have progressed to the point where this proposal is in the realm of technical feasibility (13). Following these measurements urine would be removed from the nephron and equilibrated against gas containing the same carbon dioxide tension measured in vivo. After equilibration, pH would be remeasured. This second pH measurement would accurately detect both the presence and direction of a disequilibrium pH. Both these proposed techniques for measuring disequilibrium pH have an additional advantage over those actually employed. The techniques already used to measure disequilibrium pH would be markedly affected were there a barrier to the diffusion of carbon dioxide in the distal nephron. If such a barrier existed, the intratubular formation of carbon dioxide would result in an intraluminal carbon dioxide tension considerably in excess of that observed in blood. Were this tubular urine equilibrated against a carbon dioxide tension equal to that of blood, its pH would rise and an acid disequilibrium pH would be observed. This acid disequilibrium pH would be observed even though carbonic acid were in equilibrium with carbon dioxide. It would be solely the consequence of lowering the carbon dioxide tension. If the pH were measured in a sealed system or in urine equilibrated against a carbon dioxide tension equal to that measured in the luminal tubule, a barrier to the diffusion of carbon dioxide would not influence measured pH.

As has been mentioned, the general assumption has been made that all the carbonic acid formed in the nephron is the result of hydrogen ion secretion. The final site of urinary acidification is not the distal tubule but is the collecting duct (65). No data concerning the presence or absence of a disequilibrium pH in the collecting duct are available. The observation (based on clearance studies) that bicarbonate loading results in a urinary carbon dioxide tension higher than that of blood has been interpreted as indicating that carbonic acid must be off equilibrium in the collecting duct (30). When urine leaves the nephron, equilibrium is achieved and urine carbon dioxide tension rises. The collecting duct is not only the site of final acidification of the urine, it is also the site of final concentration of the urine. During bicarbonate loading, urine bicarbonate concentrations in excess of 200 mEq l^{-1} may be observed (89). It is unlikely in such a circumstance that the concentration of bicarbonate entering the collecting duct is much in excess of 70 mEq l^{-1} (89). Thus the high concentration of bicarbonate observed in the final urine is the result of water abstraction in the collecting duct (89). As has been demonstrated above, the increase in concentration of bicarbonate results in an immediate increase in the concentration of carbonic acid. Thus during bicarbonate loading much of the carbonic acid generated may result from water removal rather than from hydrogen ion secretion. It is even conceivable that during bicarbonate loading, hydrogen ion secretion in the collecting duct is totally abolished and all the carbonic acid formed in that segment of the nephron results from water removal. Thus two factors may influence the concentration of carbonic acid in the collecting duct, and thus may influence the disequilibrium pH that might be observed: namely, hydrogen ion secretion, and urinary concentration.

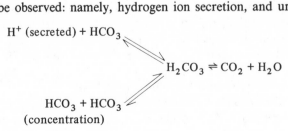

In vitro the addition of bicarbonate to water raises the carbon dioxide tension (10, 22). The pH and carbon dioxide tension of a stirred bicarbonate concentration solution is stable for a period of time considerably in excess of the time in which urine is in the collecting duct. Thus it is likely that intratubular carbon dioxide tension in the collecting duct during bicarbonate loading may be considerably in excess of blood carbon dioxide tension. This excess, if present, may be the result of bicarbonate concentration, not hydrogen ion secretion. Diffusion of carbon dioxide across the collecting duct epithelial surface might not dissipate the high carbon dioxide tension because the high concentration of bicarbonate would immediately result in its regeneration. The only available evidence suggests that carbon dioxide tension in the collecting duct is high during sodium bicarbonate administration (87). It should be emphasized that in this study intratubular carbon dioxide tension was calculated rather than measured directly. Alternatively, it is possible that carbon dioxide diffusion across the collecting duct might be sufficient to lower the intraluminal carbon dioxide tension to that of blood. Were this the case, when urine left the nephron the high concentration of bicarbonate would now generate a high carbon dioxide tension.

The observation that carbonic anhydrase administration lowers urinary carbon dioxide tension during bicarbonate loading and dissipates the acid disequilibrium pH does not have the significance attributed to it (56, 68). Carbonic anhydrase will catalyze the dehydration of carbonic acid regardless of how it was generated. Addition of carbonic anhydrase to a solution of bicarbonate and water results in an immediate dissipation of high carbon dioxide tension present before its addition. Following the addition of carbonic anhydrase in vitro, the carbon dioxide tension decreases to the level of blood carbon dioxide tension (40mm Hg). Thus the presence of carbonic anhydrase in the collecting duct might allow a high intraluminal carbon dioxide tension to equilibrate with that of blood. All that can be made of this observation is that carbonic acid (in the collecting duct) is allowed to reach equilibrium rapidly or else a new equilibrium is established. It does not necessarily indicate hydrogen ion secretion.

Thus when the intraluminal bicarbonate concentration is high (bicarbonate loading or acetazolamide administration), carbonic acid concentration may be increased and be off equilibrium as the result of either hydrogen ion secretion or water removal. The observation that a disequilibrium pH is present when intraluminal bicarbonate concentration is much lower (provided the measurements are made as described above) would likely signify hydrogen ion secretion. This situation would be analogous to the observation made in clearance studies that phosphate administration has no effect on urinary carbon dioxide tension in highly alkaline urine but that administration of phosphate to animals whose urine pH is close to the pK of phosphate (6.7) results in an increase in urinary carbon dioxide tension that is directly related to the urinary phosphate concentration (2); under this circumstance the urinary bicarbonate concentration is too low to account for the high carbon dioxide tension observed.

Even if the measurement of a disequilibrium pH is performed perfectly there are still difficulties in its interpretation. Hydrogen ion secretion in the distal nephron may occur, but nonionic diffusion of carbonic acid may prevent the establishment of a disequilibrium pH (68). If bicarbonate is reabsorbed in this segment of the nephron as bicarbonate, such reabsorption would tend to establish an alkaline disequilibrium pH (12). To the extent that bicarbonate reabsorption were counterbalanced by hydrogen ion secretion one might eliminate the effect of the other. The concentration of bicarbonate in and of itself may generate enough carbonic acid to cause a disequilibrium pH.

Factors Controlling Distal Nephron Acidification

Aldosterone, which plays a pivotal role in the regulation of salt and water homeostasis, also plays a major role in acid-base balance (48). The hormone has as its major site of action the distal nephron. Recent studies suggest that it acts solely on the collecting duct (27, 28). When aldosterone is present in supernormal amounts, acid excretion increases (provided there is accompanying potassium depletion) and metabolic alkalosis results (45, 79). When the hormone is present in decreased amounts or is absent, acid excretion diminishes and metabolic acidosis develops (21, 31, 44).

The maximal urine–blood pH gradient is achieved in the collecting duct (65). A variety of factors govern this segment of the nephron's capacity to secrete hydrogen. Aldosterone is undoubtedly one of them (21, 31). There are, however, a variety of ways whereby aldosterone may influence the collecting duct's ability to secrete hydrogen ion.

When aldosterone is absent, salt will be wasted in the urine and volume contraction will result (21, 31, 48). This volume contraction will decrease distal delivery of sodium by virtue of its stimulatory effect on proximal tubular reabsorption and its tendency to reduce GFR. If distal delivery of sodium is diminished, sodium for hydrogen exchange must diminish and urinary acidification must be impaired. Aldosterone deficiency also results in potassium retention (48). Potassium retention has been demonstrated to inhibit ammonia synthesis by the kidney (85). If ammonia synthesis is decreased, then acid excretion will likewise be decreased. It is also believed that aldosterone has a direct effect on acidification independent of any effect attributable to distal delivery or to potassium retention. Animals with metabolic alkalosis induced by potassium depletion and mineralocorticoid excess are unable to maintain their metabolic alkalosis when aldosterone excess is eliminated without potassium repletion (45). Thus acid excretion diminishes in animals with a constant degree of potassium depletion when mineralocorticoid administration is decreased. This effect of mineralocorticoid excess—enhancement of acid excretion independent of any effect of potassium—is likely attributable to a direct effect of aldosterone on ammonia synthesis.

When the factors favoring acid excretion are present, i.e. a state of sodium avidity and increased levels of mineralocorticoid, the anion accompanying sodium into the collecting duct plays a critical role determining acid excretion (75). As increasing amounts of sodium chloride in this condition reach the collecting duct, the sodium may be reabsorbed as sodium chloride; thus, sodium-for-hydrogen ion exchange will not be enhanced to the same degree as would occur if sodium were delivered to the collecting duct accompanied by a nonreabsorbable anion. The administration of sodium in the form of sodium sulfate or sodium phosphate results in greater acid excretion than that seen following the administration of sodium chloride, all other things being equal (7, 15, 75). In the case of phosphate administration the increase in acid excretion is in the form of titratable acidity while the administration of sulfate results in increased ammonium excretion. Another example of the importance of distal anion delivery is the demonstration that feeding dogs the same amount of hydrogen ion in the form of hydrochloric acid, sulfuric acid, or nitric acid results in different degrees of metabolic acidosis. Hydrochloric acid resulted in a striking decrease in plasma bicarbonate, sulfuric acid resulted in a small decrease in plasma bicarbonate, whereas with nitric acid plasma bicarbonate was unchanged (19). Sulfate and nitrate are poorly reabsorbable anions and thus resulted in decreased distal delivery of sodium with consequent enhancement of acid excretion (19).

It has recently been demonstrated that chronic hypotonic volume expansion is associated with increased distal hydrogen ion secretion (47). This enhancement of acid excretion is apparently due to increased distal sodium delivery and increased levels of aldosterone secondary to the hyponatremia (17).

Urine pH may reach very low levels even in the total absence of aldosterone (21). The ability of the collecting duct to secrete hydrogen ions against a pH gradient is thus not dependent upon the presence of aldosterone. The exact nature of the secretory pump for hydrogen ions and the internal factors which regulate it remain to be elucidated.

METABOLIC ALKALOSIS AND SALT AND WATER REGULATION

Definition

Metabolic alkalosis is a primary pathophysiologic state characterized by a gain of bicarbonate or a loss of nonvolatile acid from extracellular fluid.

Generation

The development of metabolic alkalosis requires either the gain of base or a loss of acid (45, 78, 79). Administration of alkaline solutions provides base while the loss of acid may occur via the gastrointestinal tract or from the kidney. Depletion of hydrochloric acid from the stomach as the consequence of vomiting or nasogastric suction leaves behind large amounts of bicarbonate. The kidney generates metabolic alkalosis by increasing net acid excretion; this results in the addition of excess amounts of bicarbonate to the blood (45, 76, 78, 79).

The excess bicarbonate added to the blood may be excreted by the kidney thus preventing the development of metabolic alkalosis. Sustained metabolic alkalosis develops when all the excess bicarbonate generated or administered is not excreted; the kidney reabsorbs an increased fraction of the filtered bicarbonate and thus maintains metabolic alkalosis. An increase in bicarbonate reabsorption unaccompanied by the gain of bicarbonate or loss of acid cannot generate metabolic alkalosis.

Two mechanisms are then extremely important in metabolic alkalosis: (a) the generation of new bicarbonate, and (b) the maintenance of a high plasma bicarbonate concentration, which is accomplished by increased tubular reabsorption of bicarbonate (78, 79).

Hydrogen Ion Secretion and Generation of Bicarbonate

For each mEq of acid excreted in the urine one mEq of bicarbonate is added to the blood. Normally the amount of bicarbonate added to the blood is equal to the amount of bicarbonate consumed to neutralize endogenous acid production; thereby normal acid-base homeostasis is maintained. If the kidney increases net acid excretion, excess bicarbonate is added to the blood and metabolic alkalosis may develop.

Salt restriction increases the capacity of both proximal and distal tubules to reabsorb sodium and secrete hydrogen ions (78–80). In order for net acid excretion to increase one must have increased amounts of sodium delivered to the distal nephron and a stimulus for sodium-hydrogen exchange (75). Increasing distal delivery of sodium salts by infusion or dietary supplements without a concomitant stimulus to sodium-hydrogen ion exchange will not result in increased net acid excretion. The administered sodium salts will appear in the urine. As has been stated, the increase in net acid excretion is also dependent on the anion delivered to the distal nephron (75).

If a sodium load is given in the form of sodium phosphate, hydrogen excretion increases in the form of titratable acid (8); if sodium is given in the form of sodium sulfate, ammonium excretion will be increased (75). If sodium is given in the form of sodium chloride (chloride being easily reabsorbed), hydrogen secretion does not increase (76).

Decreased sodium delivery to the distal nephron (low salt diet, acute reduction in glomerular filtration rate) enhances the capacity of the distal nephron to secrete hydrogen ions. This increased capacity to secrete hydrogen ions will be evident only when distal sodium delivery is restored by the administration of the sodium salt of a nonreabsorbable anion or a diuretic (78, 79).

Role of Potassium and Aldosterone in Generation

The renal generation of metabolic alkalosis is essentially dependent on an increased capacity of the distal nephron to secrete hydrogen ions at a time when there is adequate sodium delivery. Subjects with excessive aldosterone commonly have metabolic alkalosis (78, 79). Aldosterone excess increases sodium reabsorption in the distal nephron and enhances potassium excretion and hydrogen ion secretion. The sodium retained results in extracellular volume expansion, which in turn depresses proximal reabsorption, thus increasing distal sodium delivery. This type of metabolic alkalosis is almost invariably accompanied by hypokalemia. Kurtzman et al (45) reported data suggesting that both hyperaldosteronism and hypokalemia are required for the kidney to generate metabolic alkalosis. Dogs were depleted of potassium by the administration of potassium-exchange resin and deoxycorticosterone acetate (DOCA) (20 mg day^{-1}). Their diet contained both sodium chloride and sodium bicarbonate. They developed metabolic alkalosis. When DOCA was discontinued, metabolic alkalosis was rapidly corrected, without correction of hypokalemia. If DOCA was then restarted in the same potassium-depleted animals, metabolic alkalosis developed again, but only when the dosage of DOCA was very high. Once metabolic alkalosis redeveloped, the dosage of DOCA was kept constant and sodium bicarbonate was removed from the diet and replaced with equal amounts of potassium bicarbonate. This resulted in correction of potassium depletion and of the metabolic alkalosis even though excessive amounts of DOCA were still being administered. In this animal model of primary aldosteronism, generation and maintenance of metabolic alkalosis were dependent on the simultaneous presence of potassium depletion and aldosterone excess. Either factor alone was unable to generate or maintain metabolic alkalosis.

In subjects with primary mineralocorticoid excess the generation and maintenance of metabolic alkalosis are probably the consequence of the accelerated distal hydrogen ion secretion stimulated by the simultaneous presence of steroid excess and potassium depletion (45, 79).

Maintenance and Correction

The following factors seem to be important in the maintenance of metabolic alkalosis:

EXTRACELLULAR VOLUME CONTRACTION   It is well established that
the severity of metabolic alkalosis generated by potassium depletion and
mineralocorticoid excess in dogs can be significantly altered by variations
in the salt intake (45). Animals receiving a lower salt diet develop a more
severe degree of metabolic alkalosis than animals maintained on a higher
intake of salt. The greater the degree of volume contraction, the higher the
bicarbonate reabsorption, thus explaining the severer metabolic alkalosis in
animals on very low sodium diets (45). Expansion of the extracellular
volume with saline should depress bicarbonate reabsorption and lead to
correction of the metabolic alkalosis. Cohen (16) demonstrated that correction of metabolic alkalosis could be achieved by expansion of the extracellular fluid volume with a solution that contained the same concentration of
sodium chloride and bicarbonate as the plasma of the alkalotic animals.
Expansion of the extracellular fluid with this solution led to the excretion
of bicarbonate and retention of chloride, resulting in correction of the
metabolic alkalosis.

POTASSIUM DEPLETION   Most cases of metabolic alkalosis can be corrected by volume expansion alone, without repletion of potassium deficits
(36, 45). This has cast doubt on the role of potassium in metabolic alkalosis
(36). More recently it has been established definitely that potassium depletion enhances bicarbonate reabsorption and can maintain metabolic alkalosis. There are a few examples of metabolic alkalosis associated with severe
potassium depletion that are not corrected by saline alone ("saline resistant
metabolic alkalosis") (79). In subjects with primary mineralocorticoid excess, metabolic alkalosis is maintained by a distal mechanism. Although
these subjects are potassium-depleted they are also volume-expanded.
Potassium depletion enhances proximal bicarbonate reabsorption, whereas
volume expansion depresses it (41). These two mechanisms tend to counter-
balance each other; therefore, enhanced proximal reabsorption does not
play a major role in the maintenance of this type of metabolic alkalosis. This
explains why saline fails to correct the metabolic alkalosis.

There is no question that potassium depletion alone may maintain metabolic alkalosis regardless of the mechanism responsible for its generation if
the degree of potassium depletion is extreme. Severe potassium depletion
may increase proximal bicarbonate reabsorption to such a marked extent
that volume expansion cannot lower it to the "normal" range. For example,
a subject with severe hypokalemia may be volume-contracted and have a
plasma bicarbonate concentration of 50 mEq l^{-1}. Volume expansion
without replacing the potassium deficit may lower bicarbonate concentration to 40 mEq l^{-1}. Full correction of the alkalosis requires potassium administration.

Causes

It should be pointed out that factors responsible for the generation of metabolic alkalosis need to be present only transiently in order for the metabolic alkalosis to develop (79). In the assessment of the pathophysiology of metabolic alkalosis it is important to recognize the cause responsible for the generation of the alkalosis as well as the mechanism that is maintaining it.

GASTRIC ALKALOSIS   The pathogenesis of metabolic alkalosis resulting from the loss of acid from the stomach has been extensively studied (34–36, 39, 55). This was accomplished experimentally by depleting subjects of hydrochloric acid while replacing electrolytes (other than hydrochloric acid and water). Two phases were defined in this type of metabolic alkalosis (34–36, 55, 79).

Gastric drainage   The continuous depletion of hydrochloric acid leads to a rise in plasma bicarbonate and a decrease in plasma chloride. Bicarbonate is generated at a greater rate than can be reabsorbed by the kidney with consequent increased bicarbonate and sodium excretion in the urine and suppressed acid excretion. Potassium excretion is also enhanced due to enhanced delivery of sodium as well as bicarbonate to the sodium-for-potassium exchange site in the distal nephron in the presence of a high circulating level of aldosterone. While the urinary sodium concentration may be high, urine chloride is vanishingly low. The volume contraction of gastric alkalosis results from the loss of hydrochloric acid from the stomach and of sodium bicarbonate in the urine. This combination is the equivalent of sodium chloride, carbon dioxide and water loss. For metabolic alkalosis to result, gastric hydrochloric acid loss must exceed that of sodium bicarbonate in the urine.

Post-drainage   If gastric drainage is discontinued, plasma bicarbonate falls slightly but still remains elevated. During this period, acid excretion is suppressed in the first several days but in the following days it increases to control levels and the urine pH falls. During the period of gastric drainage (or vomiting) the urinary sodium is high whereas urinary chloride is low. This emphasizes the need for measuring both urinary sodium and chloride when trying to assess the state of effective arterial volume. In the post-drainage period, both sodium and chloride concentration are low. The decreased urinary chloride concentration signals the low state of effective arterial volume that maintains metabolic alkalosis in the post-drainage phase. Since this type of alkalosis is maintained mainly by contracted extracellular volume, saline administration leads to full correction.

KIDNEY AND GENERATION   Two conditions are essential if the kidney is to generate metabolic alkalosis: (*a*) enhanced capacity to secrete hydrogen ions, and (*b*) adequate delivery of sodium salts to the distal nephron. The increased delivery of sodium to the distal nephron may result from the dietary sodium chloride, depressed sodium reabsorption by diuretics, and/ or sodium administration of salts of poorly reabsorbable anions.

Steroids   Mineralocorticoid administration or clinical conditions associated with mineralocorticoid excess activity are almost invariably associated with metabolic alkalosis (45, 78, 79). After administration of these hormones the following events take place: (*a*) Sodium reabsorption in the distal nephron increases, resulting in enhanced potassium excretion. (*b*) Retention of sodium (and chloride) expands extracellular volume and depresses proximal reabsorption; this leads to increased distal delivery of sodium, which is exchanged for potassium and hydrogen ions; acid excretion as well as potassium excretion is therefore increased. (*c*) Metabolic alkalosis ensues because of enhanced acid excretion. If expansion of extracellular volume, following steroid administration, is prevented by a sodium-free diet (80), metabolic alkalosis does not develop. A low salt diet enhances proximal reabsorption, thereby decreasing the amount of sodium delivered to the distal tubule and preventing the increase in acid excretion.

The main factors responsible for the maintenance of steroid-induced metabolic alkalosis are enhanced proximal bicarbonate reabsorption caused by potassium depletion, and increased distal hydrogen ion secretion secondary to excessive amounts of aldosterone. It is likely that this type of metabolic alkalosis is maintained mainly by the distal mechanism (45, 79).

Hypercapnia   Chronic hypercapnia enhances acid and chloride excretion (60, 74, 88). At the same time it stimulates bicarbonate reabsorption, causing an increased plasma bicarbonate concentration (43, 69). Following the return of the CO_2 to normal there usually is retention of chloride and excretion of bicarbonate in the urine (74). If subjects with hypercapnia are on a low salt diet or are treated with diuretics, proximal reabsorption is enhanced (secondary to volume contraction) and bicarbonate reabsorption remains elevated following the return of the pCO_2 to normal; this results in post-hypercapnic metabolic alkalosis (79). This type of metabolic alkalosis can be corrected by salt administration.

"Contraction" alkalosis   Administration of thiazides, ethacrynic acid, and furosemide is commonly associated with metabolic alkalosis. It has been suggested that ethacrynic acid and furosemide, which have their diuretic site of action in the loop of Henle, may induce metabolic alkalosis without

loss of acid (14). This alkalosis has been called "contraction" alkalosis and is thought to be due to enhanced excretion of sodium and chloride without proportional loss of bicarbonate (bicarbonate reabsorption in the loop of Henle is small). It should be pointed out, however, that adrenalectomized dogs treated with maintenance doses of dexamethasone and DOCA and with furosemide fail to develop metabolic alkalosis. When the dogs were volume-contracted at a time when large amounts of DOCA were given, metabolic alkalosis developed (45). The generation of this type of metabolic alkalosis is due to enhanced acid excretion brought on by potassium depletion and secondary hyperaldosteronism. Once generated, diuretic-induced metabolic alkalosis is maintained by volume contraction and potassium depletion (24, 45). Contraction per se seems a simplistic explanation for this type of metabolic alkalosis (24). It seems likely that excess renal acid excretion is essential to its development (24).

Literature Cited

1. Arruda, J. A. L., Carrasquillo, T., Cubria, A., Rademacher, D. R., Kurtzman, N. A. 1976. Bicarbonate reabsorption in chronic renal failure. *Kidney Int.* 9:481–489

2. Arruda, J. A. L., Nascimento, L., Kumar, S., Kurtzman, N. A. 1977. Factors influencing the formation of urinary carbon dioxide tension. *Kidney Int.* 11:307

3. Arruda, J. A. L., Nascimento, L., Westenfelder, C., Kurtzman, N. A. 1977. Effect of parathyroid hormone on urinary acidification. *Am. J. Physiol.* 1: F429

4. Arruda, J. A. L., Kurtzman, N. A. 1977. Metabolic acidosis and alkalosis. *Clin. Nephrol.* 7:201

5. Arruda, J. A. L., Nascimento, L., Mehta, P. K., Rademacher, D. R., Sehy, J. T., Westenfelder, C., Kurtzman, N. 1977. The critical importance of urinary concentrating ability in the generation of urinary carbon dioxide tension. *J. Clin. Invest.* In press

6. Atkins, E. L., Schwartz, W. B. 1962. Factors governing correction of the alkalosis associated with potassium deficiency; the critical role of chloride in the recovery process. *J. Clin. Invest.* 41: 218–29

7. Bank, N., Aynedjian, H. S. 1976. A micropuncture study of the effect of parathyroid hormone on renal bicarbonate reabsorption. *J. Clin. Invest.* 58:336–44

8. Bank, N., Schwartz, W. B. 1960. The influence of anion penetrating ability on urinary acidification and the excretion of titratable acid. *J. Clin. Invest.* 39: 1516–25

9. Bennett, C. M., Springberg, P. D., Falkinburg, N. R. 1974. Glomerulotubular balance for bicarbonate in the dog. *Am. J. Physiol.* 228:98–106

10. Blaedel, W. J., Meloche, V. W. 1963. *Elementary Quantitative Analysis,* pp. 327–35. New York: Harper & Row. 2nd ed.

11. Brodsky, W. A., Carrasquer, G. 1961. Mechanisms of acidification of the urine. *Progr. Cardiovasc. Dis.* 4:105–33

12. Brodsky, W. A., Schilb, T. 1974. *Current Topics in Membranes and Transport,* pp. 161–224. New York: Academic

13. Caflisch, C. R., Carter, N. W. 1974. A micro pCO₂ electrode. *Anal. Biochem.* 60:252–57

14. Cannon, P. J., Heinemann, H. O., Albert, M. S., Laragh, J. H., Winters, R. W. 1965. "Contraction" alkalosis after diuresis in edematous patients with ethacrynic acid. *Ann. Intern. Med.* 62:979

15. Clapp, J. R., Rector, F. C. Jr., Seldin, D. W. 1962. Effects of unreabsorbed anions on proximal and distal transtubular potentials in rats. *Am. J. Physiol.* 202:781–86

16. Cohen, J. J. 1968. Correction of metabolic alkalosis by the kidney after isometric expansion of extracellular fluid. *J. Clin. Invest.* 47:1181–92

17. Cohen, J. J., Hulter, H. N., Smithline, N., Melby, J. C., Schwartz, W. B. 1976. The critical role of the adrenal gland in

the renal regulation of acid-base equilibrium during chronic hypotonic expansion. *J. Clin. Invest.* 58:1201–8
18. Crumb, C. K., Martinez-Maldonado,
M., Eknoyan, G., Suki, W. N. 1974.
Effects of volume expansion, purified
parathyroid extract, and calcium on renal bicarbonate absorption in the dog.
J. Clin. Invest. 54:1287–93
19. De Sousa, R. C., Harrington, J. T.,
Ricanati, E. S., Shelkrot, J. W.,
Schwartz, W. B. 1974. Renal regulation
of acid-base equilibrium during chronic
administration of mineral acid. *J. Clin.
Invest.* 53:465–76
20. Diaz-Buxo, J. A., Ott, C. E., Cuche, J.
L., Marchand, G. R., Wilson, D. M.,
Knox, F. G. 1975. Effects of extracellular volume contraction and expansion
on the bicarbonaturia of parathyroid
hormone. *Kidney Int.* 8:105–9
21. DiTella, P., Sodhi, B., McCreary, J.,
Arruda, J. A. L., Kurtzman, N. A.
1977. Urinary acidification in mineralocorticoid deficient rats. *Clin. Res.* 25:
429A
22. Edsall, J. T., Wyman, J. 1958. *Biophysical Chemistry,* pp. 550–89. New York:
Academic
23. Farrow, S. L., Stinebaugh, B. J., Rouse,
D., Suki, W. N. 1976. Effects of hypocalcemia on renal bicarbonate absorption in the dog. *Proc. 2nd Int. Congr.
PO₄, Heidelberg, 1976.* In press
24. Garella, S., Chang, B. S., Kahn, S. I.
1975. Dilution acidosis and contraction
alkalosis: Review of a concept. *Kidney
Int.* 8:279–83
25. Garrett, E. S., Nahmias, C. 1974. The
effect of glucose on the urinary excretion of sodium and hydrogen ion in
man. *Clin. Sci. Mol. Biol.* 47:589
26. Gold, L. W., Massry, S. G., Arieff, A.
I., Coburn, J. W. 1973. Renal bicarbonate wasting during phosphate depletion.
J. Clin. Invest. 52:2556–62
27. Gross, J. B., Imai, M., Kokko, J. P.
1975. A functional comparison of the
distal convoluted tubule and the cortical collecting tubule. *J. Clin. Invest.*
55:1284–94
28. Gross, J. B., Kokko, J. P. 1977. Effects
of aldosterone and potassium sparing
diuretics on electrical potential difference across the distal nephron. *J. Clin.
Invest.* 59:82–89
29. Gulyassy, P. F., Van Ypersele de Strihou, C., Schwartz, W. B. 1962. On the
mechanism of nitrate-induced alkalosis;
the possible role of selective chloride depletion in acid-base regulation. *J. Clin.
Invest.* 42:1850–62
30. Halperin, M. L., Goldstein, M. B.,
Haig, A., Johnson, M. D., Stinebaugh,
B. J. 1974. Studies on the pathogenesis
of type I (distal) renal tubular acidosis
as revealed by the urinary pCO_2 tensions. *J. Clin. Invest.* 53:669–77
31. Hulter, H. N., Ilnicki, L. P., Harbottle,
J. A., Sebastian, A. 1977. Impaired renal H^+ secretion and NH_3 production
in mineralocorticoid-deficient gluco-
corticoid-replete dogs. *Am. J. Physiol.*
232:F136–46
32. Karlinsky, M. L., Sager, D. S., Kurtzman, N. A., Pillay, V. K. G. 1974.
Effect of parathormone and cyclic
adenosine monophosphate on renal bicarbonate reabsorption. *Am. J. Physiol.*
227:1226–31
33. Karlmark, B., Danielson, B. G. 1974.
Titratable acid, pCO_2, bicarbonate and
ammonium ions along the rat proximal
tubule. *Acta Physiol. Scand.* 91:243–58
34. Kassirer, J. P., Berkman, P. M., Lawr-
enz, D. R., Schwartz, W. B. 1965. The
critical role of chloride in the correction
of hypokalemic alkalosis in man. *Am. J.
Med.* 38:172–89
35. Kassirer, J. P., Schwartz, W. B. 1966.
The response of normal man to selective
depletion of hydrochloric acid: Factors
in the genesis of persistent gastric alkalosis. *Am. J. Med.* 40:10–18
36. Kassirer, J. P., Schwartz, W. B. 1966.
Correction of metabolic alkalosis in
man without repair of potassium deficiency: A re-evaluation of the role of
potassium. *Am. J. Med.* 40:19–26
37. Kennedy, T. J. Jr., Eden, M., Berliner,
R. W. 1957. Interpretation of urine
CO_2 tension. *Fed. Proc.* 16:72 (Abstr.)
38. Kennedy, T. J. Jr., Orloff, J., Berliner,
R. W. 1952. Significance of carbon dioxide in urine. *Am. J. Physiol.* 169:596–
608
39. Kennedy, T. J. Jr., Winkley, J. H., Dun-
ning, M. F. 1949. Gastric alkalosis with
hypokalemia. *Am. J. Med.* 6:790–94
40. Kunau, R. T. Jr., Frick, A., Rector, F.
C. Jr., Seldin, D. W. 1966. Effect of extracellular fluid volume expansion,
potassium deficiency, and pCO_2 on bicarbonate reabsorption in the rat kidney. *Clin. Res.* 14:380A (Abstr.)
41. Kunau, R. T. Jr., Frick, A., Rector, F.
C. Jr., Seldin, D. W. 1968. Micropuncture study of the proximal tubular factors responsible for the maintenance of
alkalosis during potassium deficiency in
the rat. *Clin. Sci.* 34:223–31
42. Kurtzman, N. A. 1970. Regulation of
renal bicarbonate reabsorption by ex-

tracellular volume. *J. Clin. Invest.* 49:586–95

43. Kurtzman, N. A. 1970. Relationship of extracellular volume and CO_2 tension to renal bicarbonate reabsorption. *Am. J. Physiol.* 219:1299

44. Kurtzman, N. A., White, M. G., Rogers, P. W. 1971. Aldosterone deficiency and renal bicarbonate reabsorption. *J. Lab. Clin. Med.* 77:931

45. Kurtzman, N. A., White, M. G., Rogers, P. W. 1973. Pathophysiology of metabolic alkalosis. *Arch. Intern. Med.* 131:702

46. Kurtzman, N. A., White, M. G., Rogers, P. W. 1973. The effect of potassium and extracellular volume on renal bicarbonate reabsorption. *Metabolism* 22:481

47. Lowance, D. C., Garfinkel, H. B., Mattern, W. D., Schwartz, W. B. 1972. The effect of chronic hypotonic volume expansion on the renal regulation of acid-base equilibrium. *J. Clin. Invest.* 51:2928–40

48. Luke, R. G. 1974. Effect of adrenalectomy on the renal response to chloride depletion in the rat. *J. Clin. Invest.* 54:1329–36

49. Malnic, G., Giebisch, G. 1972. Mechanism of renal hydrogen ion secretion. *Kidney Int.* 1:280–96

50. Malnic, G., Steinmetz, P. R. 1976. Transport processes in urinary acidification. *Kidney Int.* 9:172–88

51. Malnic, G., Mello-Aires, M., Cassola, A. C. 1974. Kinetic analysis of renal tubular acidification by antimony microelectrodes. In *Ion Selective Microelectrodes*, ed. H. J. Berman, N. C. Hebert, p. 89. New York: Plenum

52. Maren, T. H. 1967. Carbonic anhydrase: chemistry, physiology and inhibition. *Physiol. Rev.* 47:595–781

53. Maren, T. H. 1974. Chemistry of renal reabsorption of bicarbonate. *Can. J. Physiol. Pharmacol.* 52:1041–50

54. Nascimento, L., Rademacher, D. R., Hamburger, R., Arruda, J. A. L., Kurtzman, N. A. 1977. On the mechanism of lithium-induced renal tubular acidosis. *J. Lab. Clin. Med.* 89:455–62

55. Needle, M. A., Kaloyanides, G. J., Schwartz, W. B. 1964. The effects of selective depletion of hydrochloric acid and acid-base and electrolyte equilibrium. *J. Clin. Invest.* 43:1836–46

56. Ochwadt, B. K., Pitts, R. F. 1956. Effect of intravenous infusion of carbonic anhydrase on carbon dioxide tension of alkaline urine. *Am. J. Physiol.* 185:426–29

57. Peraino, R., Ghaffary, E., Rouse, D., Suki, W. N. 1977. Effects of 25-hydroxyvitamin D_3 in the intact and acutely thyroparathyroidectomized dog. In *Phosphate Metabolism*, ed. S. G. Massry, E. Ritz, pp. 77–84. New York: Plenum

58. Pitts, R. F., Ayer, J. L., Schiess, W. A. 1949. The renal regulation of acid-base balance in man. III: the reabsorption and excretion of bicarbonate. *J. Clin. Invest.* 28:35–44

59. Pitts, R. F., Lotspeich, W. D. 1949. Bicarbonate and the renal regulation of acid-base balance. *Am. J. Physiol.* 147:138–54

60. Polak, A., Haynie, G. D., Hayes, R. M., Schwartz, W. B. 1961. Effects of chronic hypercapnia on electrolyte and acid-base equilibrium. I: Adaptation. *J. Clin. Invest.* 40:1223–37

61. Portwood, R. M., Seldin, D. W., Rector, F. C. Jr., Cade, R. 1959. The relationship of urinary CO_2 tension to bicarbonate excretion. *J. Clin. Invest.* 38:770

62. Purkerson, M. L., Lubowitz, H., White, R. W., Bricker, N. S. 1969. On the influence of extracellular fluid volume expansion on bicarbonate reabsorption in the rat. *J. Clin. Invest.* 48:1754–60

63. Puschett, J. B., Zurbach, P. 1976. Acute effects of parathyroid hormone on proximal bicarbonate transport in the dog. *Kidney Int.* 9:501–10

64. Rademacher, D. R., Arruda, J. A. L., Kurtzman, N. A. 1976. On the quantitation of HCO_3 reabsorption (R). *Clin. Res.* 24:409A (Abstr.)

65. Rector, F. C. Jr. 1973. Acidification of the urine. In *Handbook of Physiology*, ed. J. Orloff & R. W. Berliner, pp. 431–54. Baltimore: Williams & Wilkins

66. Rector, F. C. Jr. 1976. Renal acidification and ammonia production; Chemistry of weak acids and bases; Buffer mechanism. In *The Kidney*, ed. F. C. Rector, B. M. Brenner, pp. 318–42. Philadelphia: Saunders

67. Rector, F. C. Jr., Buttram, H., Seldin, D. W. 1962. An analysis of the mechanism of the inhibitory influence of K^+ on renal H^+ secretion. *J. Clin. Invest.* 41:611–17

68. Rector, F. C. Jr., Carter, N. W., Seldin, D. W. 1965. The mechanism of bicarbonate reabsorption in the proximal and distal tubules of the kidney. *J. Clin. Invest.* 44:278–90

69. Rector, F. C. Jr., Portwood, R. M., Seldin, D. W. 1959. Examination of the mixing hypothesis as an explanation for

elevated urinary CO_2 tensions. *Am. J. Physiol.* 197:861–64

70. Rector, F. C. Jr., Seldin, D. W., Roberts, A. D. Jr., Smith, J. S. 1960. The role of plasma CO_2 tension and carbonic anhydrase activity in the renal reabsorption of bicarbonate. *J. Clin. Invest.* 39:1706–21

71. Reid, E. L., Hills, A. G. 1965. Diffusion of carbon dioxide out of the distal nephron in man during antidiuresis. *Clin. Sci.* 28:15–28

72. Roscoe, J. M., Goldstein, M. B., Halperin, J. L., Wilson, D. R., Stinebaugh, B. J. 1976. Lithium induced impairment of urine acidification. *Kidney Int.* 9:344–50

73. Schmidt, R. W., Bricker, N. S., Gavellas, G. 1976. Bicarbonate reabsorption in dogs with experimental renal disease. *Kidney Int.* 10:287–94

74. Schwartz, W. B., Hays, R. M., Polak, A., Haynie, G. D. 1961. Effects of chronic hypercapnia on electrolyte and acid-base equilibrium. II: Recovery with special reference to the influence of chloride intake. *J. Clin. Invest.* 40:1238–49

75. Schwartz, W. B., Jenson, R. L., Relman, A. S. 1955. Acidification of the urine and increased ammonia excretion without change in acid-base equilibrium: Sodium reabsorption as a stimulus to the acidifying process. *J. Clin. Invest.* 34:673–80

76. Schwartz, W. B., Van Ypersele de Strihou, C., Kassirer, J. P. 1968. Role of anions in metabolic alkalosis and potassium deficiency. *N. Engl. J. Med.* 279:630–39

77. Sebastian, A., McSherry, E., Morris, R. C. Jr. 1974. On the mechanism of the inappropriately low urinary carbon dioxide tension (U-P_{CO_2}) in classic (type 1) renal tubular acidosis (RTA). *Clin. Res.* 22:544A (Abstr.)

78. Seldin, D. W. 1976. Metabolic alkalosis. In *The Kidney* ed. F. C. Rector, B. M. Brenner, pp. 661–702. Philadelphia: Saunders

79. Seldin, D. W., Rector, F. C. Jr. 1972. The generation and maintenance of metabolic alkalosis. *Kidney Int.* 1:306–21

80. Seldin, D. W., Welt, L. G., Cort, J. H. 1956. The role of sodium salts and adrenal steroids in the production of hypokalemic alkalosis. *Yale J. Biol. Med.* 29:229–47

81. Siegfried, D., Kumar, R., Arruda, J. A. L., Kurtzman, N. A. 1976. Influence of vitamin D on bicarbonate reabsorption. See Reference 57, pp. 395–404

82. Slaughter, B. D., Osiecki, H. S., Cross, R. B., Budtz-Olsen, O., Jedrzejczyk, H. 1974. The regulation of bicarbonate reabsorption. The role of arterial pH, pCO_2, and plasma bicarbonate concentration. *Pfluegers Arch.* 349:29–40

83. Stinebaugh, B. J., Schloeder, F. X. 1972. Glucose-induced alkalosis in fasting subjects. *J. Clin. Invest.* 51:1326–36

84. Suki, W. N., Herbert, C. S., Stinebaugh, B. J., Martinez-Maldonado, M., Eknoyan, G. 1974. Effects of glucose on bicarbonate reabsorption in the dog kidney. *J. Clin. Invest.* 54:1–8

85. Tannen, R. L., McGill, J. 1976. The influence of potassium on renal ammonia production. *Am. J. Physiol.* 231:1178–84

86. Thirakomen, K., Kozlov, N., Arruda, J. A. L., Kurtzman, N. A. 1976. Renal hydrogen ion secretion following the release of unilateral ureteral obstruction. *Am. J. Physiol.* 231:1233–39

87. Uhlich, E., Baldamus, C. A., Ullrich, K. J. 1968. Verhalten von CO_2-Druck und Bicarbonat im Gegenstromsystem des Nierenmarks. *Pfluegers Arch.* 303:31–48

88. Van Ypersele de Strihou, C., Gulyassy, P. F., Schwartz, W. B. 1962. Effects of chronic hypercapnia on electrolyte and acid-base equilibrium. III: Characteristics of the adaptive and recovery process as evaluated by provision of alkali. *J. Clin. Invest.* 41:2246–52

89. Vieira, F. L., Malnic, G. 1968. Hydrogen ion secretion by rat renal cortical tubules as studied by an antimony microelectrode. *Am. J. Physiol.* 214:710–18

90. Waring, D. W., Sullivan, L. P., Mayhew, D. A., Tucker, J. M. 1974. A study of factors affecting renal bicarbonate reabsorption. *Am. J. Physiol.* 226:1392–1400

Ann. Rev. Physiol. 1978. 40:67–92
Copyright © 1978 by Annual Reviews Inc. All rights reserved

THE PERIPHERAL CIRCULATION: Local Regulation

❖1186

Harvey V. Sparks, Jr.

Francis L. Belloni

Department of Physiology, University of Michigan, Ann Arbor, Michigan 48109

INTRODUCTION

The roles of the circulation in nutrient supply, metabolite removal, fluid exchange, and the response to tissue injury are greatly influenced by local vascular control mechanisms. The particular orchestration of local controls operating at any one time in any one tissue depends on a variety of factors related to the particular situation and the tissue in question. Given the large number of publications that have appeared on the general topic during the period covered by this review (1974–1976), we could only provide coherent coverage of three organ systems. Even within these areas we have developed only a fraction of the possible themes. Several recent reviews complement and supplement the material presented here (42, 58, 61, 77, 94, 96, 101, 121, 135, 143).

KIDNEY

Over the past three years the availability of chemical tools to examine the role of the proposed local renal hormone systems involving prostaglandins (PG) and the renin-angiotensin system have stimulated a great deal of research on the local control of renal blood flow (RBF).

Reactive Hyperemia

Reactive hyperemia appears to be the result of the accumlation of PG, during or after the ischemic period. Reactive hyperemia is greatly reduced by indomethacin in anesthetized (66, 123) and awake (147) dogs and tran-

67

0066-4278/78/0301-0067$01.00

quilized baboons (147). PGE is released into renal venous blood during ischemia (55, 65, 137).

Basal Renal Vascular Tone

Basal renal vascular tone and cortical flow distribution have also been the subject of a number of studies. Blood flow of isolated kidneys and some in situ kidneys falls following administration of indomethacin or meclofenamate (75, 83, 89, 123, 138, 147). Indomethacin had no effect on renal vascular resistance of awake dogs (147, 157). It is not simply the administration of anesthesia that produces indomethacin-blockable renal vasodilation. Data, Chang & Nies (30) did not observe any effect of indomethacin or meclofenamate on total RBF or distribution of microspheres in anesthetized dogs. Using clearance methods and anesthetized dogs, Anderson et al (5) also observed no significant effect of indomethacin on resting renal vascular resistance, although meclofenamate caused increased vascular resistance. Satoh & Zimmerman (138) have studied the problem most directly. Under control conditions, anesthetized dogs without laparotomy or loss of a large volume of blood exhibited very little release of PGE (radioimmunoassay) by the kidney. In this situation meclofenamate had little effect on renal vascular resistance. Renal PGE release increased and there was a transient decrease in renal vascular resistance after the introduction of a circuit that involved removing blood and running it over bioassay preparations. Thus, it appears that inhibitors of PG synthesis do not influence basal RBF unless a stimulus for PG synthesis is present. The proximate stimuli for renal PG synthesis in this situation remain to be elucidated. The decrease in RBF caused by indomethacin was blocked by a competitive inhibitor of angiotensin II (107). Angiotensin II stimulated PG release (116). This raises the possibility that the renin-angiotensin system initiates the events leading to release of PG (137).

When PG release occurs under "resting" conditions, the local effect appears to be on the inner cortex. The isolated perfused kidney displayed gradually rising inner cortical flow (microsphere distribution) and PGE-like synthesis. Indomethacin and meclofenamate blocked both of these trends (75, 83). Indomethacin and meclofenamate also caused redistribution of RBF in situ (89). Indomethacin lowered inferior vena cava plasma PGE and PGA concentrations together with inner medullary flow measured by the accumulation of labelled albumin (142). Infusion of the prostaglandin precursor sodium arachidonate increased the relative distribution of microspheres to the inner cortex of rabbits (95) and dogs (26). This is in contrast to PGE infusions, which raised both outer and inner cortical blood flow (8, 26). Thus, although PG are capable of causing vasodilation throughout the cortex, the localization of synthesis to the medulla and juxtamedullary cortex confines the physiological effect to this region. Renin substrate infusion selectively reduced inner cortical flow of the isolated dog kidney, as did angiotensin I infusion (74).

Autoregulation

Perhaps closely related to the determinants of basal renal vascular tone are the mechanism(s) of autoregulation of RBF and glomerular filtration rate (GFR). Using awake dogs, the characteristic autoregulation curve was obtained, with very close to perfect autoregulation above an arterial pressure of 80 mm Hg. However, acetylcholine produced vasodilation even when arterial pressure was as low as 20 mm Hg, indicating that even at so low a perfusion pressure, renal autoregulation does not achieve maximum vasodilation (56). RBF autoregulation occurred in puppies and, as is also the case for adult dogs (see below), was not affected by an infusion of an angiotensin II–competitive antagonist (81).

The anesthetic used may affect autoregulation of RBF but not GFR (28); however, contradictory evidence is available (41). Rat RBF was not well autoregulated below an arterial pressure of approximately 100 mm Hg (7, 28).

Renal artery vasodilation associated with either ureteral constriction or high urine flow (caused by saline infusion plus diuretics) can be reversed by elevated arterial pressure (132). If intrarenal pressure was raised 40–50 mm Hg by either ureteral constriction or diuresis, the lower end of the autoregulatory range was raised to 130 mm Hg. This would suggest that transmural pressure is an important variable in autoregulation of RBF. A contrary observation is that equivalent increases in renal interstitial fluid pressure produced by ureteral and venous pressure elevation do not produce equal vasodilation (82).

The initial indication that indomethacin markedly reduces autoregulation of RBF (65) has not been reproduced. Indomethacin and meclofenamate had no effect on autoregulation of the rat (41), of the in situ kidney of anesthetized dogs (5, 123, 153), or of the isolated dog kidney (83).

Autoregulatory escape of RBF from vasoconstrictor influence may be partially mediated by PG release. Vasoconstriction in response to angiotensin II was enhanced by indomethacin in awake dogs (147) and anesthetized rats (41). Methoxamine vasoconstriction was also enhanced by these drugs (147). Vasoconstriction produced by periarterial nerve stimulation of rabbit kidney was reduced by PGE, PGA, and arachidonate infusion and was enhanced by prostaglandin synthetase inhibition. However, the effects were just the reverse for the rat kidney, indicating that the role of PG in modulating nerve effects may be species-dependent, enhancing vasoconstriction in one species and inhibiting it in another (105). Elevated ureteral pressure in anesthetized cats inhibited vasoconstriction produced by central and peripheral nerve stimulation as well as norepinephrine infusion. Indomethacin partially reversed the effect of elevated ureteral pressure (139).

Prostaglandin synthetase inhibitors alter the renal vascular response to hemorrhage. Two recent studies have emphasized that renal vasodilation may accompany hemorrhage in dogs (30, 152). Indomethacin blocked the vasodilation. After prostaglandin synthetase inhibition with aspirin, hemorrhage caused vasoconstriction (30). Both drugs abolished the increase in inner cortical blood flow that accompanied the hemorrhage (30).

The most debated alternative to a myogenic mechanism for autoregulation of renal blood flow is the mechanism championed by Thurau (149): Increased perfusion pressure raises GFR which, in turn, via the macula densa, increases intrarenal formation of angiotensin, which causes afferent arteriolar constriction, lowering both GFR and RBF. The opposite chain of events occurs with lowered arterial pressure. Because a rise in pressure reduces renin release by the kidney [judging from renal venous and lymph renin and angiotensin concentration (see 59)], an intrarenal mechanism that is not discernible from renal venous and lymph measurements is suggested. Several experiments have been performed in an effort to test whether an intact renin-angiotensin system is necessary for autoregulation. If the macula densa is a necessary link in the feedback loop described above, then removing tubular fluid before it reaches the distal tubule (proximal tubular collection) should prevent autoregulation of GFR of that nephron. Two complete studies on the point report different results. In one study, when arterial pressure was lowered within the autoregulatory range, single nephron GFR determined by proximal tubular collection decreased but single nephron GFR measured from distal collections was constant (115). In the other study, interruption of flow to the distal tubule did not alter single nephron GFR (90). The groups exchanged views on the possible differences in their experiments in subsequently published letters (114). Some nonfiltering, denervated kidneys exhibited both renin release and autoregulation of blood flow when perfusion pressure was lowered. Thus, autoregulation of blood flow can apparently occur when no change in distal tubular fluid composition is possible (52).

When kidneys were depleted of renin by DOCA plus a high sodium diet (with care to experimentally verify the depletion of renal renin), autoregulation of RBF and GFR was impaired (19, 20, 84). The relative distribution of flow to the outer cortex was increased with increased perfusion pressure in the poorly autoregulating, renin-depleted kidneys. Because it is the outer cortex that normally contains the greatest concentration of renin, it follows that renin depletion would prevent autoregulation of outer cortical flow. Thus it appears that the renin-angiotensin system may be necessary for normal autoregulation of RBF and GFR, at least of the outer cortex.

A dose of the angiotensin-converting enzyme inhibitor SQ 20881, which blocked the hemodynamic effects of angiotension I infusion, had no effect on autoregulation of RBF or GFR (46). 1–8-substituted analogs of angiotensin II, which act as competitive antagonists, did not effect autoregulation of flow of the isolated (85) or in situ kidney (1, 5). Both groups point out that although this finding does not support the Thurau hypothesis, it is possible that angiotensin receptors inaccessible to arterially delivered blocker are involved in the autoregulatory response.

In the absence of renin substrate, an isolated perfused rat kidney autoregulates RBF poorly in response to slow changes in perfusion pressure, but abrupt changes in perfusion pressure result in a good autoregulatory response (69).

Hall, Guyton & Cowley (59) recently demonstrated that renin depletion leaves the dog kidney still able to autoregulate RBF, but not GFR. They suggest that renin release normally results in efferent arteriolar constriction, which tends to maintain glomerular hydrostatic pressure when perfusion pressure is reduced. Renin depletion then leaves other blood flow autoregulating mechanism(s) (eg. the myogenic response) unopposed, and reduced perfusion pressure can cause efferent, in addition to afferent, arteriolar dilation. This could result in decreased GFR. Another set of calculations suggests that only afferent arteriolar resistance changes with autoregulation (9).

Not even the facts are clear in this very interesting area, but it is probably fruitful to view autoregulation of RBF and GFR as separate entities that may act coincidentally most of the time. Present evidence does not favor the renin-angiotensin system as a necessary link in the autoregulation of RBF. Perhaps it is involved in control of GFR and this sometimes "spills over" into RBF autoregulation.

SKELETAL MUSCLE

Autoregulation

Two recent studies have dealt with the effect of arterial hypoxia on the autoregulation of skeletal muscle blood flow. At normal arterial O_2 saturation, a reduction in perfusion pressure of the hind limb muscles of dogs caused very small changes in vascular resistance but large changes in filtration coefficient (K_f) and extraction of O_2 (54). In the presence of mild arterial hypoxia (which lowered skeletal muscle venous Po_2 from approximately 40 to 30 mm Hg), the same reduction in perfusion pressure resulted in little change in K_f but a large decrease in resistance to flow. These results indicate that precapillary sphincter tone (determining K_f) is more sensitive to changes in tissue oxygenation than resistance vessel tone. Either arterial hypoxia or reduction of perfusion pressure is sufficient to relax precapillary sphincters, but both interventions are necessary to cause relaxation of resistance vessels. This result agrees with a model of the control of the microvasculature proposed by the same group (53). Another group (126) used the transient changes in flow accompanying a step increase in perfusion pressure as a measure of autoregulation. Hypoxia resulted in a reduction of the autoregulatory transients that accompanied the rise in perfusion pressure. Both of these studies suggest that tissue oxygenation has an important effect on the resistance vessel autoregulatory response; hypoxia enhances the dilatory response to reduced arterial pressure and reduces the constrictor response to elevated pressure. This does not help to distinguish between myogenic and metabolic mechanisms because hypoxia could directly influence the myogenic response of blood vessels or could amplify a metabolic mechanism.

Järhult & Mellander (76) have provided evidence that precapillary resistance vessel adjustments tend to hold capillary hydrostatic pressure (P_c) constant over a wide range of arterial pressures. This suggests that P_c is closely related to the sensed variable in the autoregulation feedback loop. An error signal that could provide a relatively constant capillary hydrostatic pressure is stretch of the wall of small precapillary resistance vessels. Stretch of the wall could, in turn, cause a myogenic vasoconstriction, which is then propagated upstream. Auoregulatory responses apparently affect determination of P_c by the isogravimetric method, which involves experimental alterations of transmural pressure (100).

Reactive Hyperemia

Reactive hyperemia probably has both myogenic and metabolic components. Red cell velocity of cat sartorius muscles was measured following arterial occlusions lasting from 5–120 sec. A short occlusion (10–15 sec) produced a peak capillary red cell velocity that is 70% of the maximum obtained with a 120 sec occlusion. The high peak capillary velocity after short occlusion suggests a myogenic mechanism. The gradual increase in excess flow with larger occlusions suggests a metabolic component that becomes more important with greater ischemia (79). Other skeletal muscles, e.g. frog pectoralis, may have a more dominant metabolic mechanism (80). Intrinsic arteriolar neurons apparently do not play a role in autoregulation or reactive hyperemia (72).

When flow of a dog gracilis muscle was held constant at the resting level, the duration of reactive hyperemia was increased as compared to the free flow situation (122). This could be explained by (a) slower washout of accumulated vasodilator metabolites, (b) reduced myogenic tone because of the lack of an abrupt rise in perfusion pressure when the flow is reinstated, or (c) release of other vasodilators because of tissue hypoxia during the recovery phase.

Peak reactive hyperemia of dog forelimb is reduced by a previous period of edema-producing venous congestion (156). If the edema was removed by infusion of Dextran 70, the peak hyperemic response was restored. The authors suggest that compression of the venous end of the capillaries by increased tissue pressure may be responsible for the increased vascular resistance. Another possibility is dilution of metabolic vasodilator substance(s) in the larger interstitial fluid volume.

Significant K release does not occur during a three minute cessation of flow to dog muscle (150). With constant flow perfusion, a three minute period of ischemia produced statistically significant increases in adenosine and/or AMP release during reactive vasodilation (150). With free flow, adenosine and/or AMP release did not increase during reactive hyperemia. The authors believe that they failed to observe an increase in release of adenosine and/or AMP because adenosine is more effectively broken down by vascular smooth muscle during free flow. Another possible interpretation is that constant flow produces slower recovery of tissue oxygenation and that this results in a rise in adenosine and/or AMP.

PG-like substance(s) were released from the dog hind limb during reactive hyperemia in six of ten dogs (63). Indomethacin reduced the hyperemic response to a five minute arterial occlusion of the forearm of man and suppressed the release of PG-like substances (88).

Exercise Hyperemia

Fixler et al (44) used radioactive microspheres to measure the magnitude of exercise hyperemia occurring in respiratory and limb muscles of awake dogs. Muscle blood flow was 15–17 ml min^{-1} 100 g^{-1} with the dog standing quietly on a treadmill. Diaphragm, intercostal muscle, and gastrocnemius muscle blood flow increased to 96, 43, and 55 ml min^{-1} 100 g^{-1} respectively with treadmill running (44).

The passive effect of transmural pressure exerts an important influence on exercise hyperemia. Elevation of the lower leg did not reduce resting anterior tibial muscle blood flow, but reduced flow during exercise (91). The duration of sustained contractions above a certain force is not dependent on muscle blood flow (^{133}Xe clearance) because flow is markedly reduced or stopped by vessel compression. The duration of less forceful contractions, which do not compress the vessels as much, is directly related to muscle blood flow (16).

There appear to be several mediators of exercise hyperemia. The pattern and duration of exercise as well as the conditions under which the exercise is performed are important determinants of the relative significance of the various mediators. The initiation of exercise hyperemia is extremely rapid, which has led some investigators to suggest a mechanical rather than a chemical stimulus at the beginning of exercise (6). This is supported by the finding that the vasodilator response to a 1 sec period of tetanus could be partly accounted for by a 1 sec period of external compression that raised intramuscular pressure an equal amount. This vasodilator response may be a myogenic response to the transient reduction in transmural pressure (109).

Another extremely rapid signal that could mediate the onset of exercise hyperemia is potassium ion [K] release. Potassium release with action potentials even precedes the mechanical activity of the muscle. The calculated time course of interstitial [K] change accompanying one second tetanic stimulation indicates that interstitial [K] changed rapidly enough to precede and therefore partially cause the vascular response to brief tetanus (108). Hnik et al (68) used an ion exchange electrode to measure extracellular [K] changes associated with tetanic and twitch stimulation. Increases in [K] ranged from 1.5 to 4 meq l^{-1} as tetanus duration increased from 1 to 20 sec. It appears that, at least in some cases, venous [K] returned more quickly than did extracellular [K]. If this is the case, the true rate of return of extracellular [K] must have been faster than that recorded. This may be explained by a relatively slow time constant of the tissue electrode.

Potassium release cannot be responsible for the sustained increase in flow associated with longer periods of exercise. Venous [K] returned to control within 60 min of the onset of twitch exercise of dog muscle (112, 131, 145) and dynamic forearm work of man (37), but resistance remained low. K probably loses its vasodilator effect long before 1 hr. Skeletal muscle arterioles of hamsters dilated when superperfused with a solution high in K but the vasodilation was transient, with a return to the control diameter occurring within approximately 3 min (34). The relaxation of isolated strips of rabbit skeletal muscle arteries faded within 5–6 min (47). These results agree with those of organ perfusion studies (17). Duling (34) has used data from several sources to calculate that changes in interstitial [K] occurring with exercise could cause as much as a five- to six-fold transient increase in vascular conductance.

Changes in tissue osmolarity are probably linked closely to changes in tissue metabolism, e.g. breakdown of high energy phosphate compounds and formation of lactic acid, ammonium ions, and other osmotically active particles. If this is so, tissue osmolarity is probably a less rapidly changing signal than either K or extravascular pressure. Isometric contractions of human forearm muscles for 2 min were associated with an increase in deep venous plasma osmolality of 23 mOsm l^{-1} (37). The decrease in osmolality after exercise paralleled the decrease in flow. Dog venous plasma osmolality rarely exceeds 10–15 mOsm l^{-1} above arterial during exercise but the value for cat can be 40 mOsm l^{-1} or higher (see 36, 58). Venous plasma osmolality of both man and dog decreased from its initial peak over a 1–2 hr period

(37, 112, 131, 145). Raised muscle bath osmolarity caused a transient relaxation of isolated artery strips from rabbit skeletal muscle which lasted 15–60 min (47). Superfusion of hamster cremaster muscle with a 312 mOsm l^{-1} solution did not elicit a change in arteriolar diameter. A superfusate osmolarity of 332 mOsm l^{-1} produced a 123% increase in diameter, but the dilation was not apparent until the fifth minute after beginning the hypertonic superfusion. Arterioles in the epithelial portion of the cheek pouch were more responsive to raised osmolarity than were muscle arterioles (36). In summary, the role of osmolarity may be species-dependent or may depend on the mix of white and red muscle fibers. Tissue osmolarity may rise the most in the species with the most white muscle (cat) and the least in the species with the most red muscle (dog). Osmolarity, like [K], appears to be increased only transiently and to produce only a transient relaxation; thus it can participate in the middle phase (perhaps 1–20 min) of exercise hyperemia, but does not appear to be an important steady-state vasodilator.

Gellai & Detar (47) argue that because lowering muscle bath Po_2 around a skeletal muscle strip produced a sustained relaxation whereas increased [K] and osmolarity did not, lowered vessel wall Po_2 is the best candidate as a mediator of sustained vasodilation. There appears to be no doubt that raising tissue Po_2 results in decreased flow to muscle. Raising superfusion fluid Po_2 reduced red cell velocity and the number of open capillaries (27, 129). Mean tissue Po_2 was held constant at approximately 19 mm Hg when superfusion fluid was equilibrated with 0, 5, or 10% oxygen (129). Even when the superfusion fluid was equilibrated with N_2, the lowest Po_2 found was 2.9 mm Hg, well above currently accepted values for critical mitochondrial Po_2 (129). Reduction of the O_2 in inspired gas resulted in vasodilation of terminal arterioles, metarterioles and distribution arterioles of precapillary sphincters, or major arterioles. Vasodilation was not blocked by atropine, propranolol, diphenhydramine, guanethedine, phenoxybenzamine, or phentolamine (73).

Superfusion of the hamster cheek pouch with solutions high in O_2 causes constriction of arterioles. If, instead, a small perivascular area was superfused using a micropipette, even larger changes in perivascular Po_2 resulted in only a small vasoconstriction. Even the small vasoconstriction is probably not the result of increased O_2, because application of a N_2-equilibrated solution had the same effect (33). This result suggests that in situ vascular smooth muscle is sensitive to changes in tissue Po_2 via changes in vasoactive metabolites rather than via a direct vascular effect. Duling recently summarized evidence indicating that tissue hypoxia may actually cause an increase in vessel wall Po_2 because the O_2 delivery via increased blood flow raises arteriolar wall Po_2 (35). In this circumstance the vasodilation associated with tissue hypoxia cannot be the result of a direct effect of tissue P_{O_2} on vascular smooth muscle. During cessation of flow, when both blood and tissue P_{O_2} fall, the direct effects of O_2 on vascular smooth muscle may be quite important.

Stowe et al (145) used a bioassay organ to assess the causal role of changes in P_{O_2} and P_{CO_2} in exercise hyperemia. Exercise of a donor muscle at 6 stimuli per second for 60 min produced increases in venous [K] and osmolality that returned to control between 45 and 60 min. At 60 min, vascular resistance and venous P_{O_2} remained low and P_{CO_2} remained elevated. The recipient bioassay muscle was also dilated at this time. If the P_{O_2} and P_{CO_2} of the donor's venous blood were corrected before it perfused the recipient muscle, recipient muscle vascular resistance increased to pre-control but not to post-control levels. Correction of the P_{O_2} alone had a much greater effect than correction of the P_{CO_2} alone. These results suggest that under the conditions of these experiments, vasoactive metabolites other than blood gases either (a) do not change during the exercise pattern, (b) are destroyed between the donor and recipient muscles, or (c) are not removed from the vicinity of the vascular smooth muscle of the donor muscle in sufficient quantities to cause recipient muscle vasodilation. This study does not appear to provide information about the direct role of P_{O_2} or P_{CO_2} on vascular smooth muscle for the following reason: Arteriolar wall P_{O_2} is primarily influenced by blood P_{O_2}, not tissue P_{O_2} (35). The low P_{O_2} of blood draining the donor exercising muscle reflects low tissue P_{O_2}, which may have relatively little direct effect on resistance vessels of that organ because the arterial P_{O_2} was high. That same blood perfusing the recipient muscle provides a low luminal P_{O_2} and thus probably causes a low arteriolar wall P_{O_2}. Thus it becomes difficult to know how to compare the vasodilations observed in donor and recipient muscle.

Granger and his colleagues have presented a model (53) and experimental results (54) which they interpret to indicate that the resistance and exchange functions of skeletal muscle are differentially affected by tissue oxygenation. When venous P_{O_2} was lowered by mild hypoxemia or catecholamine infusion, K_f increased. When exercise was then initiated, the increase in capillary filtration coefficient was less than had occurred with exercise at a higher venous P_{O_2}. This was apparently because precapillary sphincters were already dilated by tissue hypoxia caused by hypoxemia or catecholamines. The percentage increase in flow, on the other hand, was greater when venous O_2 was low. This may be because of the increased sensitivity provided by the lower tissue O_2 (54), or because the same changes from a lower point give a larger percentage change with no increased sensitivity. This interesting concept deserves further exploration. These experiments do not provide information on the question of whether O_2 acts directly on vascular smooth muscle.

If arteriolar smooth muscle does not respond directly to reduced O_2 during exercise hyperemia, there is probably a vasodilator metabolite whose release is closely linked to tissue oxygenation. One strong candidate for this role is adenosine. Bockman, Berne & Rubio (15) stimulated hind limb muscles of dogs to contract at a frequency of 2–4 twitches per second while holding flow constant at the resting level. Muscle adenosine was not significantly increased at 5 min after initiation of stimulation, but was at 10 and at 25 min. Thirty minutes after cessation of exercise, tissue adenosine was at control levels. Venous plasma adenosine did not change during exercise. Earlier, this group reported release of adenosine into an aqueous perfusate of isolated rat hind limbs (14). The authors commented that the conditions of the experiments in rat were severe and that adenosine should be measured under more physiological conditions. The dog muscle preparation is a significant step in that direction. However, because flow was held constant at the resting level, the question of whether tissue adenosine rises during exercise hyperemia is still open. Another group found adenosine and/or AMP released into venous blood during exercise of dog muscle with constant flow but not with free flow (150). Although other interpretations of this result are possible, one conclusion is that adenosine release only occurs in the presence of tissue hypoxia. If this is the case, exercise hyperemia without tissue hypoxia would necessarily be the result of another vasodilator substance.

Exercise hyperemia of dog muscle was reduced by indomethacin (64). In addition, during exercise, a PG-like substance was found in venous blood. The PG release occurred only after 3–5 min and was sustained for at least 10–20 min after exercise. Indomethacin abolished the release. Indomethacin reduced functional hyperemia of the forearm of man as well as PG-like substance release into deep venous blood (88). PGA_1, A_2, E_1, and E_2 cause vasodilation of resistance and capacitance vessels of skin and muscle (29). PGA_1 did not change small vein resistance (125).

Although tissue P_{CO_2} and $[H^+]$ rise during exercise, there is little reason to believe that they are powerful mediators of exercise hyperemia. Reexamination of the potency of H^+ and CO_2 as vasodilators (38, 39, 145) confirms previous conclusions: They are not potent vasodilators of skeletal muscle resistance vessels.

Honig & Frierson (72) have reported that intrinsic arteriolar neurons may initiate postcontraction vasodilation. After a single twitch of gracilis muscle, vasodilation was observed; but a downstream recipient muscle did not dilate. Contraction at 2 sec^{-1} produced dilation in 1 sec, but vasodilation occurred much more slowly in the downstream recipient muscle. Local anesthetics blocked the vasodilator response to short periods of stimulation at 2 sec^{-1}. Honig & Frierson conclude that intrinsic neurons initiate postcontraction vasodilation, but metabolites account for sustained vasodilation. Other interpretations include the possibility that local anesthetics reduce the release of K from skeletal muscle cells or reduce myogenic vasodilation.

If dog skeletal muscle is exercised for 20 min with restricted flow, a period of prolonged vasodilation, outlasting the period of increased O_2 consumption, follows cessation of contraction (112, 122). The vasodilation does not appear to be the result of a change in tissue osmolality, [K], [lactic acid], or O_2 level (112). Eklund has observed a delayed time course for the return of forearm blood flow following long periods of exercise (37). Patients with occlusive artery disease exhibit lower blood flow during contraction of leg muscles and a longer period of hyperemia following exercise (6). The mechanism of this prolongation of exercise hyperemia is unknown.

In summary, several factors at least partially responsible for exercise hyperemia have been identified. At present insufficient information is available on the time course of changes in these factors and on the conditions under which changes occur. Until this information is available we will not know whether the currently recognized vasodilator systems are suffient to explain the changes in blood flow occurring during and after exercise.

CORONARY

Reactive Hyperemia

Reactive hyperemia of the coronary vasculature has been the subject of a recent review (121). Evidence suggesting a myogenic component in this response is discussed there. More recently, the fall in intravascular pressure associated with coronary artery occlusion was prevented by infusion of saline or plasma distal to the occlusion. Reactive hyperemia was attenuated by 25%, presumably because the fall in intravascular pressure was prevented, eliminating a myogenic response (12). This result could also be explained by flow removal of a vasodilator or failure to trigger reflex vasodilation.

Interest in K as a mediator of coronary vasoregulation has been revived by the observations that hypokalemia, achieved by dialysis, caused a transient vasoconstriction in dog hearts (18) and that K infusion caused a transient vasodilation in isolated, perfused guinea pig hearts (23). Both of these actions were blocked by ouabain. Ouabain had no effect on the reactive hyperemia of the isolated, saline-perfused guinea pig heart following a 10 sec occlusion, but did somewhat attenuate the coronary reactive hyperemia following a 40 sec occlusion (23).

Graded hypercapnic acidosis enhanced, in a dose-dependent fashion, both the hyperemic response to coronary artery occlusion of 15–40 heartbeats' duration and the vasodilator response to adenosine injections in thoractomized dogs (130). This result is consistent with adenosine being the mediator of reactive hyperemia but could also be explained by enhanced nonspecific sensitivity of vascular smooth muscle to vasodilators or increased release of another vasodilator during the occlusion. Acid infusion in isolated guinea pig hearts did increase tissue adenosine levels (31). If this occurred in the experiment above, adenosine may have been raised into a more potent vasodilator range of concentrations.

There are conflicting bits of evidence with regard to a role for PG in mediating the coronary vascular response to ischemia (4, 121, 123). A recent study casts another vote against such a role for PG. Following 30, 60, and 120 sec cessations of coronary perfusion, isolated, saline-perfused rabbit hearts exhibited a period of coronary vasodilation and a release of PG-like material (bioassay) proportional to the duration of the ischemia. Indomethacin eliminated the PG release but had no effect on the vascular response (117).

Wennmalm and co-workers, using isolated rabbit hearts, found that hypoxia but not hypoglycemia or low perfusion pressure was a stimulus for prostaglandin release. They concluded that it was the hypoxic consequences of ischemia that were responsible for the PG release seen after coronary occlusion (155).

Reactive hyperemia in the coronary bed appears, then, to be a complicated response whose mechanism(s) are only incompletely understood. Potassium ion, adenosine, PG, and a myogenic mechanism may be involved in mediating the coronary vascular response to brief periods of ischemia.

Autoregulation

Autoregulation of coronary blood flow has been examined with respect to the causal roles for K and PG. Ouabain failed to alter the autoregulatory behavior of isolated guinea pig hearts perfused with a saline perfusate (23). This result is strong evidence against the involvement of K in the determination of the steady-state coronary autoregulatory response. This finding is consistent with the observation that K infusion causes only a transient coronary vasodilation (23). It remains possible that K plays a role in the initiation of coronary autoregulation.

In contrast to these guinea pig hearts, which autoregulated quite well when perfused with a physiological salt solution, isolated rabbit hearts did not autoregulate (i.e. vascular resistance fell as perfusion pressure was increased) unless small amounts of plasma were added to the perfusate. The addition of plasma also resulted in a coronary vasoconstriction and a four-fold increase in the release of PG-like activity (bioassay) by the hearts. Indomethacin blocked these effects of plasma (111). These results suggest the involvement of PG in the mediation of rabbit coronary autoregulation, although it is also possible that the autoregulatory behavior was dependent simply upon the presence of vascular smooth muscle tone and not any specific involvement of PG.

Basal Coronary Vascular Tone

This work (111) also suggests that PG may determine, in part, the resting coronary artery tone since both coronary tone and PG release were induced by addition of plasma to the perfusate and were blocked by indomethacin. Previous work with isolated rabbit hearts indicated no tonic vasoactive role for PG (13, 117) although this may be due to the use of saline perfusates. Species differences may prove to be significant since isolated, saline-perfused guinea pig hearts vasoconstrict slightly in the presence of indomethacin (140). At least three groups studying intact, anesthetized dogs reported no change in resting coronary blood flow or resistance following indomethacin administration (2, 4, 123). One unexplored possibility in all these cases is that a redundant vasoregulatory mechanism conceals the effects of removal of the PG vasoactive influence. At least one group reports a gradual rise in coronary flow with a subsequent return to baseline during administration of indomethacin to an isolated rat heart preparation (148). This suggests the presence of some compensatory process.

Kalsner measured a basal release of prostaglandin (identified as PGE_1 by chromatographic separation) from strips of bovine coronary artery. PG synthesis inhibitors were added to the muscle bath and resulted in (a) decreased release of PGE_1 and (b) contraction of the arterial strip. PGE_2 and $PGF_{2\alpha}$ led to contraction and PGE_1 to relaxation of the strips (86). The actions of PGE_1 and PGE_2 on bovine coronary artery strips were confirmed by Needleman et al (118). The implication is that a basal production of PGE_1 by the arterial wall itself may be important in determining basal vascular tone. The source of the prostaglandins may be vascular smooth muscle, endothelial cells, or some other element of the arterial wall. Cultured human umbilical-vein smooth-muscle cells (3) and human vascular endothelial cells (49) can produce immunoreactive PGE. This basal production was virtually eliminated by indomethacin.

Hypoxic Coronary Vasodilation

Hypoxic coronary vasodilation has been studied with regard to the possible involvement of adenosine, ATP, K, and PG. Coronary flow and myocardial tissue adenosine concentration were measured in isolated guinea pig hearts perfused with saline equilibrated with gases of different O_2 contents. Parallel increases in flow and adenosine concentration were observed when the equilibration gas contained 15% or less O_2 (134) in one study, or 20% O_2 in another (31). A problem with these studies is that the Po_2 surrounding the arteriolar smooth muscle may be low enough during hypoxia to have a direct vasodilating effect. When, however, the venous effluent of isolated guinea pig hearts perfused with an hypoxic saline solution was oxygenated and then used to perfuse another isolated guinea pig heart, the recipient heart vasodilated (21). This indicated the release of a vasodilator metabolite by the first, hypoxic heart.

The possibility that ATP might participate in mediating hypoxic coronary vasodilation was investigated using isolated guinea pig hearts perfused with saline. Anoxia resulted in coronary vasodilation and a three-fold increase in venous effluent ATP concentration [firefly luciferin-luciferase assay (124)]. This suggests the involvement of ATP in hypoxic coronary vasodilation. It was also noticed, however, that with repetitive hypoxic stimuli, the ATP release was attenuated while the hypoxic vasodilation was unchanged; but this may have been due to increasing ATPase activity (124). More work is needed to fully evaluate this hypothesis.

The coronary vasodilation that accompanied hypoxia of isolated guinea pig hearts was slightly greater (by about 15%) in the presence than in the absence of ouabain. The greater vascular response with ouabain could not be attributed to greater myocardial activity since heart rate and peak ventricular pressure were "similar" with and without ouabain. Ouabain had no noticeable effect on the time course of the hypoxic vasodilation. The authors concluded that K plays no major role in mediating the coronary vascular response to hypoxia (23).

PG appear not to participate in mediating the coronary vasodilation that accompanies anoxia. Perfusion of isolated rabbit hearts with anoxic saline caused coronary vasodilation but no change in the release of PG (bioassay) from the hearts (13, 117). This is not surprising since O_2 is required for PG synthesis. Restoration of perfusion with oxygenated saline caused a return of coronary resistance to control and a transiently increased output of PG (13, 117). The post-anoxia release of PG is not consistent with their playing a role in the anoxic vasodilation.

During perfusion with hypoxic saline (15% O_2), isolated rabbit hearts exhibited a sustained fall in coronary vascular resistance but only a transient release of PG. Furthermore, restoration of well oxygenated perfusate returned control tone and caused another transient release of PG (117). Even a role in initiating the response, although possible, seems unlikely since a transient release of PG was associated with the onset of both vasodilation and vasoconstriction. It is possible that the bursts of PG at the onset of hypoxia and at the restoration of well-oxygenated perfusion represent different types of PG. Finally, Afonso and co-workers (2) found that systemic hypoxemia in anesthetized, closed-chest dogs increased coronary sinus blood flow (thermodilution) by 81%, but only by 63% after indomethacin.

We can summarize hypoxic coronary vasodilation as follows: Adenosine seems to be a likely participant in mediating this response. ATP may be involved, but the evidence collected so far is rather fragmentary. Potassium ion seems not to be involved. Prostaglandins may participate in hypoxic coronary vasodilation but they seem not to be involved in mediating the coronary vascular response to anoxia.

Metabolic Coronary Vasoregulation

The most common coronary vasoregulatory event is that of matching nutrient supply, through the coronary blood flow, to the metabolic requirements of the myocardium. Decreasing myocardial O_2 supply and increasing myocardial O_2 requirements may be two sides of a single coin, but there is no a priori foundation for this assumption. The metabolic processes of the myocardium respond differently to decreased O_2 supply on the one hand [where, for example, anaerobic processes are stimulated (119)] and increased energy use on the other. So might the vasoregulatory mechanisms operate differently in these two situations. Descriptions of metabolic coronary vasoregulation frequently state that it results in a near perfect matching of myocardial O_2 supply and demand as either (a) evidenced by the relative constancy of myocardial tissue and coronary sinus Po_2, or (b) brought about by a high-gain control system in which tissue Po_2 is, at least indirectly, an error signal. Several recent studies, however, have cast doubt upon the validity of these ideas.

Müller-Ruchholtz & Neil (113) were able to dissociate changes in coronary flow and coronary sinus Po_2 using isolated, saline-perfused, working guinea pig hearts. These experiments indicated that (a) coronary sinus Po_2 was not always kept constant; and (b) coronary flow could increase despite an increase in coronary sinus Po_2 as occurred when cardiac work and arterial Po_2 were raised simultaneously. Assuming that coronary sinus Po_2 reflects tissue Po_2, it is apparent that tissue Po_2 is not the sole error signal involved in coronary vasoregulation. However, oxygen may well participate to some extent in metabolic coronary vasoregulation. For example, for a given myocardial O_2 consumption, hearts with a higher arterial Po_2 had a higher coronary sinus Po_2 and a lower coronary flow than hearts with a lower arterial Po_2 (113).

Even though coronary sinus Po_2 stays relatively constant in most circumstances, there are regional and transmural differences in small vein and capillary hemoglobin saturation (57, 110), tissue Po_2 (99, 154), and myocardial blood flow (10, 154). These distributions may merely reflect different offset errors in a control system where P_{O_2} is directly or indirectly the prime error signal; or there may be other feedback signals, with the flow to any particular region dependent upon some integration of several signals. Finally, Bradley (21) perfused two isolated guinea pig hearts in series with physiological saline. Various stimuli (epinephrine, isoproterenol, histamine, and electrical pacing) were applied to the first heart and caused vasodilation. Despite the application of appropriate blocking agents (propranolol or antihistamines) and regassing of the effluent from the first heart, the second heart also vasodilated. Again, the presence of error signals distinct from P_{O_2} per se is implied.

Recent studies have revived interest in CO_2 as a potentially important influence on coronary arteries of open-chest dogs at constant flow. When coronary arterial P_{CO_2} was selectively lowered from 42 to 24 mm Hg, coronary vascular resistance increased by 84% (25). The quantitative relation between myocardial tissue P_{CO_2} and coronary vascular resistance is not known, nor is it clear how much myocardial tissue P_{CO_2} changes with alterations in myocardial metabolic activity or in other vasoregulatory situations. Carbon dioxide may modulate coronary flow in certain pathological situations. Coronary blood flow (^{133}Xe washout) decreased in 12 of 13 patients with ischemic heart disease upon voluntary hyperventilation that lowered arterial P_{CO_2} from 33 to 19 mm Hg (120).

The role of adenosine in coronary metabolic vasoregulation continues to be evaluated. Aminophylline, a competitive inhibitor of adenosine-induced coronary vasodilation, inhibited by 64% the coronary vasodilatory response to increased heart pacing rate in closed-chest, anesthetized dogs (93). Myocardial O_2 consumption was not measured but, judging from the values of circumflex coronary artery flows and arterial and coronary sinus blood gases given (93), it appears that about one third of the aminophylline effect may be explained by a decreased increment in O_2 consumption with pacing. It is tempting to attribute the remainder of aminophylline's effect to its adenosine antagonism. The specificity of the inhibition is open to question, however. The closely related compound, theophylline, has been shown to block the coronary dilating effects of ADP, ATP, dipyridamole, and papaverine, in addition to those of adenosine (22). Another interesting observation is that aminophylline had no effect on the resting coronary flow rate in the experiments described above (93). Adenosine is thought to be produced and to be present in vasodilator concentrations even in the well-oxygenated heart, and aminophylline blockade might have been expected to cause a coronary vasoconstriction at rest. Perhaps a redundancy of steady-state vasoregulatory mechanisms is the explanation for this paradox.

For example, the positive inotropic action of aminophylline might have triggered a metabolic vasodilation that counteracted the effect of adenosine blockade.

Coronary flow and tissue adenosine concentration in isolated, saline-perfused guinea pig hearts in various inotropic states were fairly well correlated (32). This result supports a role for adenosine in metabolic coronary vasoregulation.

Other work, however, suggests that adenosine release by the heart may be more important with ischemia than when O_2 consumption is increased per se. Coronary sinus blood collected from human subjects during pacing or exercise did not contain measurable concentrations of adenosine except in patients who developed anginal pain during the experimental period. In 11 of 13 patients in this latter group, coronary sinus blood adenosine concentration was below detectable levels at rest (45). The sensitivity of measurements of adenosine in coronary sinus blood is impaired somewhat by the rapid uptake and metabolism of adenosine by red blood cells, and so a physiological role for adenosine cannot be ruled out by this study.

As already mentioned, hypokalemia caused a transient vasoconstriction in the dog heart (18) and hyperkalemia caused a transient vasodilation in the isolated guinea pig heart (23). In both cases, the changes in [K] were associated with sustained cardiac inotropic changes that may have acted, through other metabolic vasoregulatory mechanisms, to counteract any direct vascular effects of lowered or raised [K]. On the other hand, the transient relaxation of rabbit coronary arterial vascular smooth muscle with a sustained increment in the [K] of the bathing solution indicates that the vasoaction of K is, indeed, only transient (47).

The possibility that K is a participant in metabolic vasoregulation is suggested, for example, by the recent observation that increasing and decreasing the heart rate of isolated rat heart preparations resulted in transient K loss and uptake, respectively (48). If, indeed, K release is only transient and its vascular effect is only transient, it may be that K acts as an initiator of coronary vascular responses to changing heart rate (or in other situations) and not as a steady-state regulator of coronary blood flow.

The possibility that temperature changes, which might occur with metabolic rate changes, might regulate coronary blood flow was tested. The left coronary arteries of thoracotomized dogs were perfused with blood at temperatures between 32° and 44°C. Intracoronary temperature variation in this range had no effect on coronary blood flow (98).

There is evidence indicating that PG may act to limit the coronary vasodilator response to increased cardiac activity. In isolated cat or rat hearts perfused with physiological saline, injections of norepinephrine, calcium, or isoproterenol resulted in transient increases in left ventricular activity and coronary flow. Aspirin or indomethacin enhanced the flow response but did not affect the other aspects of cardiac hyperactivity (141, 148). Infusion of PGE_2 reduced the flow responses but not the cardiac hyperactivity (141, 146, 148).

In summary, O_2 and adenosine appear to be likely mediators of metabolic vasoregulation in the heart. Other substances, such as K, CO_2 and prostaglandins, may also be involved, although the evidence concerning these substances is fragmentary at present.

OTHER ORGANS

Local regulation of gut blood flow was the subject of a review by Lanciault & Jacobson (94). Advances in our understanding of the myogenic responses (78) and pressure regulation (51) of the gut microvasculature have been summarized recently. Changes in K (128) and osmolality (102) may be partially responsible for the local regulation of salivary gland blood flow, and evidence against a role for the kallikrein system has been presented (40).

The cutaneous circulation has been discussed by Ryan (135). The tendency of external pressure to lower skin blood flow is counteracted by what appears to be autoregulation (71).

The status of our knowledge of the pulmonary vascular response to hypoxia has been summarized (42).

The debates over whether apparent autoregulation (43, 87, 106, 127, 144) and hypercapnic vasodilation (11, 62, 70, 87, 106, 127, 144) in the cerebral vascular bed are locally or reflexively mediated have continued. No consensus has been reached on either question. Most of these studies involved pharmacological or surgical elimination of a single neural effector mechanism. It is possible that compensatory adjustments in other local or neural vasoregulatory mechanisms account for the variability of the results.

Several proposed local cerebral vasoregulatory mechanisms have been investigated. Lowered arterial pressure that would evoke autoregulatory vasodilation caused increases in rat brain adenosine levels (133) but no change in monkey cerebrospinal fluid pH, P_{CO_2}, or P_{O_2} (67). Cerebral blood flow varies with brain activity and metabolism (50, 103, 104, 136, 151). Electrical stimulation of rat cortex caused increased tissue adenosine levels (133). In the cat, local P_{O_2} and flow both rose with electrical cortical stimulation (97). This speaks against O_2 as the mediator of metabolic cerebral vasoregulation. Since central nervous system K levels rose with either electrical stimulation (92) or ischemia (60), and since K is a vasodilator in the rabbit hypothalamus (24), K should be considered as a potential vasoregulatory metabolite in brain.

CONCLUSION

It has become clearer that local regulation of blood flow is accomplished by numerous, somewhat redundant, but nonetheless independent mechanisms. Within the same organ, different mechanisms operate simultaneously to stabilize capillary hydrostatic pressure, provide sufficient nutrient flow, and respond to tissue injury. An observed flow response depends on the particular mix of mechanisms that arises out of the given conditions. Ahead of us is the interesting and challenging job of quantitatively sorting out the relative importance of these regulatory agents in a variety of physiological and pathological circumstances.

Literature Cited

1. Abe, Y., Kishimoto, T., Yamamoto, K. 1976. Effect of angiotensin II antagonist infusion on autoregulation of renal blood flow. *Am. J. Physiol.* 231:1267–71
2. Afonso, S., Bandow, G. T., Rowe, G. G. 1974. Indomethacin and the prostaglandin hypothesis of coronary blood flow regulation. *J. Physiol.* 241:299–308
3. Alexander, R. W., Gimbrone, M. A. Jr. 1976. Stimulation of prostaglandin E synthesis in cultured human umbilical vein smooth muscle cells. *Proc. Natl. Acad. Sci. USA* 73:1617–20
4. Alexander, R. W., Kent, K. M., Pisano, J. J., Keiser, H. R., Cooper, T. 1975. Regulation of postocclusive hyperemia by endogenously synthesized prostaglandins in the dog heart. *J. Clin. Invest.* 55:1174–81
5. Anderson, R. J., Taher, M. S., Cronin, R. E., McDonald, K. M., Schrier, R. W. 1975. Effect of β-adrenergic blockade and inhibitors of angiotensin II and prostaglandins on renal autoregulation. *Am. J. Physiol.* 229:731–36
6. Arai, M., Endoh, H. 1974. Blood flow through human skeletal muscle during and after contraction. *Tohoku J. Exp. Med.* 114:379–84
7. Arendshorst, W. J., Finn, W. F., Gottschalk, C. W. 1975. Autoregulation of blood flow in the rat kidney. *Am. J. Physiol.* 228:127–33
8. Arendshorst, W. J., Johnston, P. A., Selkurt, E. E. 1974. Effect of prostaglandin E_1 on renal hemodynamics in nondiuretic and volume-expanded dogs. *Am. J. Physiol.* 226:218–25
9. Balint, P., Tarjan, E., Juszko, J. 1975. Quantitative aspects of autoregulation in the canine kidney. *Pfluegers Arch.* 353:83–96
10. Ball, R. M., Bache, R. J., Cobb, F. R., Greenfield, J. C. Jr. 1975. Regional myocardial blood flow during graded treadmill exercise in the dog. *J. Clin. Invest.* 55:43–49
11. Bicher, H. I. 1974. Brain oxygen autoregulation: A protective reflex to hypoxia? *Microvasc. Res.* 8:291–313
12. Bittar, N., Pauly, T. J., Koke, J. R. 1975. Changes in ischemic coronary vasodilation produced by blood, plasma, and saline infusion. *Rec. Adv. Stud. Cardiac. Struct. Metab.* 10: 475–82
13. Block, A. J., Feinberg, H., Herbaczynska-Cedro, K., Vane, J. R. 1975. Anoxia-induced release of prostaglandins in rabbit isolated hearts. *Circ. Res.* 36:34–42
14. Bockman, E. L., Berne, R. M., Rubio, R. 1975. Release of adenosine and lack of release of ATP from contracting skeletal muscles. *Pfluegers Arch.* 355: 229–41
15. Bockman, E. L., Berne, R. M., Rubio, R. 1976. Adenosine and active hyperemia in dog skeletal muscle. *Am. J. Physiol.* 230:1531–37
16. Bonde-Petersen, F., Mork, A. L., Nielsen, E. 1975. Local muscle blood flow and sustained contractions of human arm and back muscles. *Europ. J. Appl. Physiol.* 34:43–50
17. Brace, R. A. 1974. Time course and mechanisms of the acute effects of hypokalemia and hyperkalemia on vascular resistance. *Proc. Soc. Exp. Biol. Med.* 145:1389–94
18. Brace, R. A., Anderson, D. K., Chen, W. -T., Scott, J. B., Haddy, F. J. 1974. Local effects of hypokalemia on coronary resistance and myocardial con-

tractile force. *Am. J. Physiol.* 227: 590–97

19. Brech, W. J. 1976. Über die Beziehungen zwischen Autoregulation des renalen Butflüsses, intrarenaler Hämodynamik, und dem Renin-Angiotensin-System. *Klin. Wochenschr.* 54:245-54

20. Brech, W. J., Sigmund, E., Kadatz, R., Weller, R., Adam, W., Franz, H. E., 1974. The influence of renin on the intrarenal distribution of blood flow and autoregulation. *Nephron* 12:44–58

21. Bradley, K. J., 1975. The release of a coronary vasodilator metabolite from the guinea-pig isolated perfused heart stimulated by catecholamines, histamine and electrical pacing and by exposure to anoxia. *Brit. J. Pharmacol.* 58:89–100

22. Bunger, R., Haddy, F. J., Gerlach, E. 1975. Coronary responses to dilating substances and competitive inhibition by theophylline in the isolated perfused guinea pig heart. *Pfluegers Arch.* 358: 213–24

23. Bunger, R., Haddy, F. J., Querengasser, A., Gerlach, E. 1976. Studies on potassium induced coronary dilation in the isolated guinea pig heart. *Pfluegers Arch.* 363:27–31

24. Cameron, I. R., Caronna, J. 1976. The effect of local changes in potassium and bicarbonate concentration on hypothalamic blood flow in the rabbit. *J. Physiol. London* 262:415–30

25. Case, R. B., Greenberg, H. 1976. The response of canine coronary vascular resistance to local alterations in coronary arterial Pco_2. *Circ. Res.* 39:558–66

26. Chang, L. C. T., Splawinski, J. A., Oates, J. A., Nies, A. S. 1975. Enhanced renal prostaglandin production in the dog. II. Effects on intrarenal hemodynamics. *Circ. Res.* 36:204–7

27. Childs, C. M., Arfors, K. E., Tuma, R., McKenzie, F. N. 1975. Continuous capillary red cell velocity measurements in the tenuissimus muscle under changing local oxygen tensions. *Bibl. Anat.* 13:153–54

28. Conger, J. D., Burke, T. J. 1976. Effects of anesthetic agents on autoregulation of renal hemodynamics in the rat and dog. *Am. J. Physiol.* 230:652–57

29. Conway, J., Hatton, R. 1975. Effects of prostaglandins E_1, E_2, A_1, and A_2 on the resistance and capacitance vessels in the hind limb of the dog. *Cardiovasc. Res.* 9:229–35

30. Data, J. L., Chang, L. C. T., Nies, A. S. 1976. Alteration of canine renal vascular response to hemorrhage by inhibitors of prostaglandin synthesis. *Am. J. Physiol.* 230:940–45

31. Degenring, F. H., 1976. The effects of acidosis and alkalosis on coronary flow and cardiac nucleotide metabolism. *Basic Res. Cardiol.* 71:287–90

32. Degenring, F. H. 1976. Cardiac nucleotides and coronary flow during changes of cardiac inotropy. *Basic Res. Cardiol.* 71:291–96

33. Duling, B. R. 1974. Oxygen sensitivity of vascular smooth muscle. II. In vivo studies. *Am. J. Physiol.* 227:42–49

34. Duling, B. R. 1975. Effects of potassium ion on the micro-circulation of the hamster. *Circ. Res.* 37:325–30

35. Duling, B. R., Pittman, R. N. 1975. Oxygen tension: dependent or independent variable in local control of blood flow? *Fed. Proc.* 34:2020–24

36. Duling, B. R., Staples, E. 1976. Microvascular effects of hypertonic solutions in the hamster. *Microvasc. Res.* 11:51–56

37. Eklund, B. 1974. Influence of work duration on the regulation of muscle blood flow. *Acta Physiol. Scand. Suppl.* 411: 2–64

38. Emerson, T. E. Jr. 1974. Local vascular effects of alkalosis in the dog gracilis muscle. *Proc. Soc. Exp. Biol. Med.* 146:50–55

39. Emerson, T. E. Jr., Parker, J. L., Jelks, G. W. 1974. Effects of local acidosis on vascular resistance in dog skeletal muscle. *Proc. Soc. Exp. Biol. Med.* 145: 273–76

40. Ferreira, S. H., Smaje, L. H. 1976. Bradykinin and functional vasodilation in the salivary gland. *Brit. J. Pharmacol.* 58:201–9

41. Finn, W. F., Arendshorst, W. J. 1976. Effect of prostaglandin synthetase inhibitors on renal blood flow in the rat. *Am. J. Physiol.* 231:1541–45

42. Fishman, A. P. 1976. Hypoxia in the pulmonary circulation. *Circ. Res.* 38: 221–31

43. Fitch, W., MacKenzie, E. T., Harper, A. M. 1975. Effects of decreasing arterial blood pressure on cerebral blood flow in the baboon. *Circ. Res.* 37: 550–57

44. Fixler, D. E., Atkins, J. M., Mitchell, J. H., Horwitz, L. D. 1976. Blood flow to respiratory, cardiac and limb muscles in dogs during graded exercise. *Am. J. Physiol.* 231:1515–19

45. Fox, A. C., Reed, G. E., Glassman, E., Kaltman, A. J., Silk, B. B. 1974. Release of adenosine from human hearts

during angina induced by rapid atrial pacing. *J. Clin. Invest.* 53:1447–57

46. Gagnon, J. A., Rice, M. K., Flamenbaum, W. 1974. Effect of angiotensin converting enzyme inhibitor on renal autoregulation. *Proc. Soc. Exp. Biol. Med.* 146:414–18

47. Gellai, M., Detar, R. 1974. Evidence in support of hypoxia but against high potassium and hyperosmolarity as possible mediators of sustained vasodilation in rabbit cardiac and skeletal muscle. *Circ. Res.* 35:681–91

48. Gilmore, J. P., Gerlings, E. D., Bregman, R. 1974. Potassium balance and potentiation phenomena in the rat heart. *Am. J. Physiol.* 226:45–49

49. Gimbrone, M. A., Alexander, R. W. 1975. Angiotensin II stimulation of prostaglandin production in cultured human vascular endothelium. *Science* 189:219–20

50. Gjedde, A., Hindfelt, B. 1975. Wholebrain blood flow and oxygen metabolism in the rat after halothane anesthesia. *Acta Anaesthesiol. Scand.* 19:310–15

51. Gore, R. W., Bohlen, H. G. 1975. Pressure regulation in the microcirculation. *Fed. Proc. Fed. Am. Soc. Exp. Biol.* 34:2031–37

52. Gotshall, R. W., Davis, J. O., Blaine, E. H., Musacchia, X. J., Braverman, B., Freeman, R., Johnson, J. A. 1974. Increased renin release during renal artery dilation in dogs. *Am. J. Physiol.* 227:251–55

53. Granger, H. J., Goodman, A. H., Cook, B. J. 1975. Metabolic models of microcirculatory regulation. *Fed. Proc. Fed. Am. Soc. Exp. Biol.* 34:2025–30

54. Granger, H. J., Goodman, A. H., Granger, D. N. 1976. Role of resistance and exchange vessels in local microvascular control of skeletal muscle oxygenation in the dog. *Circ. Res.* 38:379–85

55. Gross, D. M., Mujovic, V. M., Jubiz, W., Fisher, J. W. 1976. Enhanced erythropoietin and prostaglandin E production in the dog following renal artery constriction. *Proc. Soc. Exp. Biol. Med.* 151:498–501

56. Gross, R., Kirchheim, H., Brandstetter, K., 1976. Basal vascular tone in the kidney. *Circ. Res.* 38:525–31

57. Grunewald, W. A., Lübbers, D. W. 1975. Die Bestimmung der intracapillären HbO_2-Sättigung mit einer kryomikrofotometrischen Methode angewandt am Myokard des Kaninchens. *Pfluegers Arch.* 353:255–73

58. Haddy, F. J., Scott, J. B. 1975. Metabolic factors in peripheral circulatory regulation. *Fed. Proc. Fed. Am. Soc. Exp. Biol.* 34:2006–12

59. Hall, J. E., Guyton, A. C., Cowley, A. W. Jr. 1977. Dissociation of renal blood flow and filtration rate autoregulation by renin depletion. *Am. J. Physiol.* 232:215–21

60. Hansen, A. K. 1976. The potassium concentration in cerebrospinal fluid in young and adult rats following complete brain ischemia. Effects of pretreatment with hypoxia. *Acta Physiol. Scand.* 97:519–22

61. Heistad, D. D., Abboud, F. M. 1974. Factors that influence blood flow in skeletal muscle and skin. *Anesthesiology* 41:139–56

62. Heistad, D. D., Marcus, M. L., Ehrhardt, J. C., Abboud, F. M. 1976. Effect of stimulation of carotid chemoreceptors on total and regional cerebral blood flow. *Circ. Res.* 38:20–25

63. Herbaczynska-Cedro, K., Staszewska-Barczok, J., Janczewska, H. 1974. The release of prostaglandin-like substance during reactive and functional hyperemia in the hind leg of the dog. *Pol. J. Pharmacol. Pharm.* 26:167–70

64. Herbaczynska-Cedro, K., Staszewska-Barczok, J., Janczewska, H. 1976. Muscular work and the release of prostaglandin-like substances. *Cardiovasc. Res.* 10:413–20

65. Herbaczynska-Cedro, K., Vane, J. R. 1973. Contribution of intrarenal generation of prostaglandin to autoregulation of renal blood flow. *Circ. Res.* 33:428–36

66. Herbaczynska-Cedro, K., Vane, J. R. 1974. Prostaglandins as mediators of reactive hyperaemia in kidney. *Nature* 247:492

67. Hernandez-Perez, M. J., Anderson, D. K. 1976. Autoregulation of cerebral blood flow and its relation to cerebrospinal fluid pH. *Am. J. Physiol.* 231:929–35

68. Hník, P., Holas, M., Krekule, I., Kříž, N., Mejsnar, J., Smieško, V., Ujec, E., Vyskocil, F. 1976. Work-induced potassium changes in skeletal muscle and effluent venous blood assessed by liquid ion-exhanger microelectrodes. *Pfluegers Arch.* 362:85–94

69. Hofbauer, K. G., Zschiedrich, H., Hackenthal, E., Gross, F. 1974. Function of the renin-angiotensin system in the isolated perfused rat kidney. *Circ. Res.* 35:I-193–201

70. Hoff, J. T., MacKenzie, E. T., Harper, A. M. 1977. Responses of the cerebral circulation to hypercapnia and hypoxia after seventh cranial nerve transection in baboons. *Circ. Res.* 40:258–62

71. Holloway, G. A. Jr., Daly, C. H., Kennedy, D., Chimoskey, J. 1976. Effects of external pressure loading on human skin blood flow measured by ^{133}Xe clearance. *J. Appl. Physiol.* 40:597–600

72. Honig, C. R., Frierson, J. L. 1976. Neurons intrinsic to arterioles initiate postcontraction vasodilation. *Am. J. Physiol.* 230:493–507

73. Hutchins, P. M., Bond, R. F., Green, H. D. 1974. Participation of oxygen in the local control of skeletal muscle microvasculature. *Circ. Res.* 40:85–93

74. Itskovitz, H. D., McGiff, J. C. 1974. Hormonal regulation of the renal circulation. *Circ. Res.* 35:I-65–73

75. Itskovitz, H. D., Terragno, N. A., McGiff, J. C. 1974. Effect of a renal prostaglandin on distribution of blood flow in the isolated canine kidney. *Circ. Res.* 34:770–76

76. Jarhult, J., Mellander, S. 1974. Autoregulation of capillary hydrostatic pressure in skeletal muscle during regional arterial hypo- and hypertension. *Acta Physiol. Scand.* 91:32–41

77. Jarrett, A. 1973. *The Physiology and Pathophysiology of the Skin, Vol. 2.* New York: Academic

78. Johnson, P. C., 1977. The myogenic response and the microcirculation. *Microvasc. Res.* 13:1–18

79. Johnson, P. C., Burton, K. S., Henrich, H., Henrich, U. 1976. Effect of occlusion duration on reactive hyperemia in sartorius muscle capillaries. *Am. J. Physiol.* 230:715–19

80. Johnson, P. C., Henrich, H. A. 1975. Metabolic and myogenic factors in local regulation of the microcirculation. *Fed. Proc. Fed. Am. Soc. Exp. Biol.* 34:2020–24

81. Jose, P. A., Slotkoff, L. M., Montgomery, S., Calcagno, P. L., Eisner, G. 1975. Autoregulation of renal blood flow in the puppy. *Am. J. Physiol.* 229:983–88

82. Kallskog, O., Wolgast, M. 1975. Effect of elevated intersitial pressure on the renal cortical hemodynamics. *Acta Physiol. Scand.* 95:364–72

83. Kaloyanides, G. J., Ahrens, R. E., Shepherd, J. A., DiBona, G. F. 1976. Inhibition of prostaglandin E$_2$ secretion. Failure to abolish autoregulation in the isolated dog kidney. *Circ. Res.* 38:67–73

84. Kaloyanides, G. J., Bastron, R. D., DiBona, G. F. 1974. Impaired autoregulation of blood flow and glomerular filtration rate in the isolated dog kidney depleted of renin. *Circ. Res.* 35:400–12

85. Kaloyanides, G. J., DiBona, G. F. 1976. Effect of angiotensin II antagonist on autoregulation in the isolated dog kidney. *Am. J. Physiol.* 230:1078–83

86. Kalsner, S., 1975. Endogenous prostaglandin release contributes directly to coronary artery tone. *Can. J. Physiol. Pharmacol.* 53:560–65

87. Kawamura, Y., Meyer, J. S., Hiromoto, H., Asyagi, M., Hushi, K. 1974. Neurogenic control of cerebral blood flow in the baboon. Effects of alpha-adrenergic blockade with phenoxybenamine on cerebral autoregulation and vasomotor reactivity to changes in PaCo$_2$. *Stroke* 5:747–58

88. Kilbom, A., Wennmalm, A. 1976. Endogenous prostaglandins as local regulators of blood flow in man: effect of indomethacin on reactive and functional hyperemia. *J. Physiol. London* 257:109–21

89. Kirschenbaum, M. A., White, N., Stein, J., Ferris, T. F. 1974. Redistribution of renal cortical blood flow during inhibition of prostaglandin synthesis. *Am. J. Physiol.* 227:801–5

90. Knox, F. G., Ott, C., Cuche, J. L., Gasser, J., Haas, J. 1974. Autoregulation of single nephron filtration rate in the presence and the absence of flow to the macula densa. *Circ. Res.* 34:836–42

91. Krehan, L., Kober, G., Kaltenbach, M. 1974. Einfluss von Perfusionsdruck und Arbeitsform auf die Muskeldurchblutung. *Z. Kardiol.* 63:950–59

92. Kriz, N., Sykova, E., Ujec, E., Vyklicky, L. 1974. Changes of extracellular potassium concentration induced by neuronal activity in the spinal cord of the cat. *J. Physiol.* 238:1–15

93. Lammerant, J., Becsei, I. 1975. Inhibition of pacing-induced coronary dilation by aminophylline. *Cardiovasc. Res.* 9:532–37

94. Lanciault, G., Jacobson, E. D. 1976. The gastrointestinal circulation. *Gastroenterology* 71:851–73

95. Larsson, C., Anggard, E. 1974. Increased juxtamedullary blood flow on stimulation of intrarenal prostaglandin biosynthesis. *Eur. J. Pharmacol.* 25:326–34

96. Lassen, N. A. 1974. Control of cerebral circulation in health and disease. *Circ. Res.* 34:749–60

97. Leniger-Follert, E., Lübbers, D. W. 1976. Behavior of microflow and local Po_2 of the brain cortex during and after direct electrical stimulation. A contribution to the problem of metabolic regulation of microcirculation in the brain. *Pfluegers Arch.* 366:39–44

98. Liedtke, A. J., Hughes, H. C. 1974. Effects of intracoronary temperature variation on the coronary circulation. *Cardiovasc. Res.* 8:787–95

99. Losse, B., Schuchhardt, S., Neiderle, N. 1975. The oxygen pressure histogram in the left ventricular myocardium of the dog. *Pfluegers Arch.* 356:121–32

100. Lund, M. G., Rovick, A. A., Dobrin, P. B. 1974. Influence of vascular smooth muscle tone upon isogravimetric capillary pressure. *Microvasc. Res.* 7:250–67

101. Lundgren, O. 1974. The circulation of the small bowel mucosa. *Gut* 15:1005–13

102. Lundvall, J., Holmberg, J. 1974. Role of tissue hyperosmolality in functional vasodilation in the submandibular gland. *Acta Physiol. Scand.* 92:165–74

103. MacKenzie, E. T., McCulloch, J., O'Keane, M., Pickard, J. D., Harper, A. M. 1976. Cerebral circulation and norepinephrine relevance of the blood-brain barrier. *Am. J. Physiol.* 231:483–88

104. MacKenzie, E. T., McCulloch, J., Harper, A. M. 1976. Influence of endogenous norepinephrine on cerebral blood flow and metabolism. *Am. J. Physiol.* 231:489–94

105. Malik, K. U., McGiff, J. C. 1975. Modulation by prostaglandins of adrenergic transmission in the isolated perfused rabbit and rat kidney. *Circ. Res.* 36:599–609

106. Meyer, J. S., Okamota, S., Sari, A., Koto, A., Itoh, Y., Ericsson, A. D. 1974. Effects of beta-adrenergic blockade on cerebral autoregulation and chemical vasomotor control in patients with stroke. *Stroke* 5:167–79

107. Mimran, A., Casellas, D., Dupont, M., Barjon, P. 1975. Effect of a competitive angiotensin antagonist on the renal haemodynamic changes induced by inhibition of prostaglandin synthesis in rats. *Clin. Sci. Mol. Med.* 48:299s–302s

108. Mohrman, D. E., Sparks, H. V. 1974. Role of potassium ions in the vascular response to a brief tetanus. *Circ. Res.* 35:384–90

109. Mohrman, D. E., Sparks, H. V. 1974. Myogenic hyperemia following brief tetanus of canine skeletal muscle. *Am. J. Physiol.* 227:531–35

110. Monroe, R. G., Gamble, W. J., La-Farge, C. G., Benoualid, H., Weisul, J. 1975. Transmural coronary venous O_2 saturations in normal and isolated hearts. *Am. J. Physiol.* 228:318–24

111. Moretti, R. L., Abraham, S., Ecker, R. R. 1976. The stimulation of cardiac prostaglandin production by blood plasma and its relationship to the regulation of coronary flow in isolated isovolumic rabbit hearts. *Circ. Res.* 39:231–38

112. Morganroth, M. L., Mohrman, D. E., Sparks, H. V. 1975. Prolonged vasodilation following fatiguing exercise of dog skeletal muscle. *Am. J. Physiol.* 229:38–43

113. Muller-Ruchholtz, E. R., Neill, W. A. 1976. The mechanism of coronary hyperemia induced by increased cardiac work. *Pfluegers Arch.* 361:197–99

114. Navar, L. G. 1975. Renal autoregulation. Letter to editor. *Circ. Res.* 36:358

115. Navar, L. G., Burke, T. J., Robinson, R. R., Clapp, J. R. 1974. Distal tubular feedback in the autoregulation of single nephron glomerular filtration rate. *J. Clin. Invest.* 53:516–25

116. Needleman, P., Kauffman, A. H., Douglas, J. R., Johnson, E. M., Marshall, G. R. 1973. Specific stimulation and inhibition of renal prostaglandin release by angiotensin analogs. *Am. J. Physiol.* 224:1415–19

117. Needleman, P., Key, S. L., Isakson, P. C., Kulkarni, P. S. 1975. Relationship between oxygen tension, coronary vasodilation and prostaglandin biosynthesis in the isolated rabbit heart. *Prostaglandins* 9: 123–34

118. Needleman, P., Kulkarni, P. S., Raz, A. 1977. Coronary tone modulation: formation and action of prostaglandins, endoperoxides, and thromboxanes. *Science* 195:409–12

119. Neely, J. R., Whitmer, J. T., Rovetto, M. J. 1975. Effect of coronary blood flow on glycolytic flux and intracellular pH in isolated rat hearts. *Circ. Res.* 37:733–41

120. Neill, W. A., Hattenhauer, M. 1975. Impairment of myocardial O_2 supply due to hyperventilation. *Circulation* 52:854–58

121. Olsson, R. A., 1975. Brief reviews: myocardial reactive hyperemia. *Circ. Res.* 37:263–70

122. Owen, T. L., Ehrhart, I. C., Scott, J. B., Haddy, F. J. 1975. A comparison of recovery time from exercise and ischemic dilations at constant pressure and flow. *Proc. Soc. Exp. Biol. Med.* 149:1040–43

123. Owen, T. L., Ehrhart, I. C., Weidner, W. J., Scott, J. B., Haddy, F. J. 1975. Effects of indomethacin on local blood flow regulation in canine heart and kidney. *Proc. Soc. Exp. Biol. Med.* 149: 871–76

124. Paddle, B. M., Burnstock, G. 1974. Release of ATP from perfused heart during coronary vasodilation. *Blood Vessels Lymphatics* 11:110–19

125. Parker, J. L., Daugherty, R. M. Jr., Emerson, T. E. Jr. 1974. Vascular responses of skin and skeletal muscle to prostaglandin A$_1$ infusion. *Am. J. Physiol.* 227:1109–15

126. Pohost, G. M., Newell, J. B., Hamlin, N. P., Powell, W. J. Jr. 1976. Observations on autoregulation in skeletal muscle: the effects of arterial hypoxia. *Cardiovasc. Res.* 10:405–12

127. Ponte, J., Purves, M. J. 1974. The role of the carotid body chemoreceptors and carotid sinus baroreceptors in the control of cerebral blood vessels. *J. Physiol. London* 237:315–40

128. Poulsen, J. H. 1975. Two phases of chord-lingual induced vasodilatation in the cat's submandibular gland during prolonged perfusion with Locke solution. *J. Physiol. London* 253:79–94

129. Prewitt, R. L., Johnson, P. C. 1976. The effect of oxygen on arteriolar red cell velocity and capillary density in the rat cremaster muscle. *Microvasc. Res.* 12: 59–70

130. Raberger, G., Schutz, W., Kraupp, O. 1975. Coronary reactive hyperemia and coronary dilator action of adenosine during normal respiration and hypercapnic acidosis in the dog. *Clin. Exp. Pharmacol. Physiol.* 2:373–82

131. Radawski, D. P., Hoppe, W., Haddy, F. J. 1975. Role of vasoactive substances in active hyperemia in skeletal muscle. *Proc. Soc. Exp. Biol. Med.* 148:270–76

132. Raeder, M., Omvik, P. Jr., Kiil, F. 1975. Renal autoregulation: evidence for the transmural pressure hypothesis. *Am. J. Physiol.* 228:1840–46

133. Rubio, R., Berne, R. M., Bockman, E. L., Curnish, R. R. 1975. Relationship between adenosine concentration and oxygen supply in rat brain. *Am. J. Physiol.* 228:1896–1902

134. Rubio, R., Wiedmeier, V. T., Berne, R. M. 1974. Relationship between coronary flow and adenosine production and release. *J. Mol. Cell. Cardiol.* 6:561–66

135. Ryan, T. J. 1976. The blood vessels of the skin. *J. Invest. Dermatol.* 67:110–18

136. Sandor, P., Demchenko, I. T., Kovach, A. G. B., Moskalenko, Y. E. 1976.

137. Satoh, S., Zimmerman, B. G. 1975. Influence of the renin-angiotensin system on the effect of prostaglandin synthesis inhibitors in the renal vasculature. *Circ. Res.* 36:I-89–96

138. Satoh, S., Zimmerman, B. G. 1976. Renal effect of meclofenamate in presence and absence of superfusion bioassay. *Am. J. Physiol.* 230:711–14

139. Schramm, L. P., Carlson, D. E. 1975. Inhibition of renal vasoconstriction by elevated ureteral pressure. *Am. J. Physiol.* 228:1126–33

140. Schror, K., Krebs, R., Nookhwun, C. 1976. Increase in the coronary vascular resistance by indomethacin in the isolated guinea pig heart preparation in the absence of changes in mechanical performance and oxygen consumption. *Eur. J. Pharmacol.* 39:161–69

141. Sen, A. K., Sunahara, F. A., Talesnik, J. 1976. Prostaglandin E$_2$ and cyclic AMP in the coronary vasodilation due to cardiac hyperactivity. *Can. J. Physiol. Pharmacol.* 54:128–39

142. Solez, K., Fox, J. A., Miller, M., Heptinstall, R. H. 1974. Effects of indomethacin on renal inner medullary plasma flow. *Prostaglandins* 7:91–98

143. Stazewska-Barczak, J., Vane, J. R. 1975. The role of prostaglandins on the local control of circulation. *Clin. Exp. Pharm. Physiol.* Suppl. 2:71–78

144. Stone, H. L., Raichle, M. E., Hernandez, M. 1974. The effect of sympathetic denervation on cerebral CO$_2$ sensitivity. *Stroke* 5:13–18

145. Stowe, D. F., Owen, T. L., Anderson, D. K., Haddy, F. J., Scott, J. B. 1975. Interaction of O$_2$ and CO$_2$ in sustained exercise hyperemia of canine skeletal muscle. *Am. J. Physiol.* 229:28–33

146. Sunahara, F. A., Talesnik, J. 1974. Prostaglandin inhibition of metabolically induced coronary vasodilation. *J. Pharmacol. Exp. Ther.* 188:135–47

147. Swain, J. A., Heyndrickx, G. R., Boettcher, D. H., Vatner, S. F. 1975. Prostaglandin control of renal circulation in the unanesthetized dog and baboon. *Am. J. Physiol.* 229:826–30

148. Talesnik, J., Sunahara, F. A. 1973. Enhancement of metabolic coronary dilatation by aspirin-like substances by suppression of prostaglandin feedback control? *Nature* 244:351–53

149. Thurau, D., Mason, J. 1974. The intrarenal function of the juxtaglomerular apparatus. In: *MTP Internation Review*

of Science. Physiology. Kidney and Urinary Tract Physiology, ed. K. Thurau, Ser. I, Vol. 6, pp. 357–90. Baltimore: Univ. Park Press

150. Tominaga, S., Watanabe, K., Nakamura, T. 1975. Role of adenosine or AMP as a probable mediator of blood flow regulation in canine hind limb muscles. Tohoku J. Exp. Med. 115: 185–95

151. Townsend, R. E., Prinz, P. N., Obrist, W. D. 1973. Human cerebral blood flow during sleep and waking. J. Appl. Physiol. 35:620–25

152. Vatner, S. F. 1974. Effects of hemorrhage on regional blood flow distribution in dogs and primates. J. Clin. Invest. 54:225–35

153. Venuto, R. C., O'Dorisio, T., Ferris, T.

F., Stein, J. H. 1975. Prostaglandins and renal function. II.The effect of prostaglandin inhibition on autoregulation of blood flow in the intact kidney of the dog. Prostaglandins 9:817–28

154. Weiss, H. R. 1974. Control of myocardial oxygenation-effect of atrial pacing. Microvasc. Res. 8:362–76

155. Wennmalm, A., Chanh, P. H., Junstad, M. 1974. Hypoxia causes prostaglandin release from perfused rabbit hearts. Acta Physiol. Scand. 91:133–35

156. Zelis, R., Lee, G., Mason, D. T. 1974. Influence of experimental edema on metabolically determined blood flow. Circ. Res. 34:482–90

157. Zins, G. R., 1975. Renal prostaglandins. Am. J. Med. 581:14–24

Ann. Rev. Physiol. 1978. 40:93–131
Copyright © 1978 by Annual Reviews Inc. All rights reserved

SKELETAL MUSCLE ENERGETICS AND METABOLISM[1]

❖1187

Earl Homsher and Charles J. Kean

Department of Physiology, School of Medicine, University of California, Los Angeles, California 90024

INTRODUCTION

When muscles contract, chemical energy is converted into mechanical energy and heat, physical quantities necessary for locomotion, circulation, digestion, respiration, reproduction, and thermal regulation. The task of the muscle energeticist is to learn how much chemical energy is used [and/or heat and work (enthalpy) produced], how chemical energy utilization varies and is regulated, what the mechanism of chemomechanical transduction is, and how substrates used during contraction are restored. To answer these questions, the extent of chemical change (and/or enthalpy production) must be measured. To this end, a variety of techniques have been developed, including measurement of: (a) the muscle's enthalpy production (myothermometry); (b) chemical change by quantitative analysis of frozen muscle extracts; (c) chemical change by ^{31}P nuclear magnetic resonance studies of the whole living tissue; (d) oxygen consumption; (e) lactic acid production; (f) the intracellular concentration of NADH; and (g) cellular pH changes. No single technique alone is wholly satisfactory as the general tool for the study of energetics. In some cases a technique lacks the requisite time resolution and/or sensitivity. Other methods require assumptions about the

[1]The following abbreviations will be used: ATP, ADP, AMP, adenosine tri-, di-, and monophosphate; IMP, inosine monophosphate; PC, phosphoryl-creatine; F-6-P, fructose-6-phosphate; G-1-P, glucose-1-phosphate; 1,6 FDP, fructose 1,6 diphosphate; FDNB, fluorodinitrobenzene; IAA, iodoacetate; NADH, reduced nicotinamide adeninedinucleotide; P_o, the isometric tetanus tension at maximum thick and thin filament overlap; l_o, the muscle length corresponding to maximum thick and thin filament overlap; V_{max}, the maximal shortening velocity.

93

0066-4278/78/0301-0093$01.00

specific pathway or coupling factors involved in the resynthesis of the ATP hydrolysis associated with contractile activity. Still others involve assumptions about the physical state of the system, or knowledge of the reactions that are occurring. Much wasted effort and distraction has been caused by the measurement of an energetic parameter using one of these techniques followed by the unwarranted extrapolation of those results to the results from other techniques.

One of the more significant developments in the period covered by this review (1971–1977) has been an increasing attention to the realization that to make meaningful conclusions about the relationship between chemical change and energy production in contraction, two or more of the parameters mentioned above must be measured on muscles contracting under identical conditions. The results of one technique then serve as a check on the assumptions of the other, and the unavoidable variation among batches and species of animals is cancelled. Perhaps the most influential combination in this approach has been the direct comparison of enthalpy production with quantitative chemical analysis of extracts from frozen muscle—the energy balance technique. Myothermometry is capable of resolving nondestructively the time course of energy liberation during and after contraction. A temporal correlation between enthalpy production and the extent of various known reactions provides a test of our understanding of the reactions occurring. Further, because myothermometry is nonspecific (i.e. it measures the sum of the enthalpy changes for all reactions occurring) it establishes, at the very least, limits to which any hypothesis of contraction must conform. For these reasons a large portion of this review is devoted to this topic.

Energetics is of fundamental significance for the understanding of muscle contraction. Conversely, energetics is dependent on advances along other lines of muscle research for its interpretation and experimental design. The development of the sliding filament model, and advances in our understanding of excitation-contraction coupling and muscle protein biochemistry [see (1–4) for reviews of these areas], have lead muscle energeticists to reexamine and extend some of the older ideas about the factors responsible for the energy output of contracting muscle. As a result of these developments the following trends have emerged over the last six years:

1. It was once axiomatic that muscle energy liberation could be temporally divided into two phases: (a) an *initial* phase, in which ATP and/or PC ($\sim$P) were consumed in reactions associated with contraction and relaxation; and (b) a *recovery* phase, in which substrates used during the initial phase were resynthesized via glycolysis and oxidative phosphorylation. Recent evidence, however, indicates that $\sim$P splitting probably continues well after the muscle has relaxed.

2. The amount of energy associated with activating a resting muscle and maintaining activation has never been unambiguously examined. Recent work, although not completely unambiguous, indicates that 30–50% of the energy liberated by contracting-muscle is associated with Ca^{2+} release into the myoplasm and reaccumulation by the sarcoplasmic reticulum.

3. The premise of A. V. Hill's challenges to biochemists (5, 6) was that the time course of initial enthalpy production was accounted for by ATP hydrolysis. Theories of muscle contraction have simulated the enthalpy production based on this idea (7–9). However, recent data show that there is no simple proportionality between enthalpy production and the extent of $\sim$P hydrolysis.

In this review, we do not survey all the published contributions to the field of muscle energetics and metabolism, but instead attempt to appraise critically the evidence that applies to the topics indicated above. Consequently, the literature has been selected on the basis of the extent to which it is pertinent to the authors' personal view of the field. To fill in particular gaps the reader is urged to consult a variety of excellent reviews and texts available on this subject. A good elementary introduction is furnished by the text of Carlson & Wilkie (10). For comprehensive coverage and historical perspective, the reviews by Mommaerts (11), Abbott & Howarth (12), and Woledge (13), the last showing uncommon insight, should be consulted. Additional coverage of metabolic aspects of contraction can be found in reviews by Maréchal (14), Curtin & Davies (15), and Kushmerick (16). For a review of cardiac muscle energetics the article by Gibbs (17) should be consulted.

METHODOLOGY

Since the application of classical thermodynamics to the study of muscle contraction has been clearly described by Wilkie and others (10, 13, 16, 18–20), it is necessary to discuss basic aspects of this topic here only as they apply to the design and interpretation of experiments in muscle energetics. As currently practiced, muscle energetics primarily uses the first law of thermodynamics,

$$h + w = \sum_{1}^{i} \xi_i \, \Delta H_i, \qquad\qquad 1.$$

which states that the enthalpy change (heat h plus work w) evolved by a closed reaction system is equal to the sum of the individual enthalpy changes occurring, where ξ_i is the extent (in moles) and ΔH_i, the molar enthalpy change (in $kJ \cdot mole^{-1}$), of the ith reaction (ΔH_i is negative for any reaction liberating enthalpy). Using the energy balance technique, one measures, under specified conditions, the amount of heat + work produced (the observed enthalpy change) and, in separate experiments under identical conditions, the extent of the reactions thought to be occurring. (In unpoisoned and IAA-poisoned muscles the number of net reactions occurring is thought to be small for tetani lasting less than 10 sec at 0°C, these being dephosphorylation of ATP and/or PC.) Using the measured extents of reactions (ξ_i and ΔH_i), the right-hand side of equation 1, the explained enthalpy, is calculated. If the measured reactions are the only energetically significant reactions occurring, the observed and explained enthalpy changes will be equal. (This does not mean that all the reactions are accounted for; some may occur with $\Delta H = 0$ kJ·mole^{-1}.) If ($h + w$) and ($\sum \xi_i \Delta H_i$) are different, and the measurements of ($h + w$), ξ_i, and ΔH_i are accurate, an energetically significant and unknown reaction(s) must be identified.

Thus the principle of the energy balance technique is simple and should not be obscured by discussions of free energy and entropy changes. Reliable measurements of ΔH_i, ($h + w$), and ξ_i are essential in this approach, and a major advance in recent years has been the accurate determination of relevant molar enthalpy changes (13, 21). This is not a simple matter because a net chemical change, such as PC splitting, involves several associated reactions, among which are reactions of substrate and products with intracellular buffers and H$^+$ and Mg^{2+} ions. Though determination of the enthalpy changes of these additional reactions is straightforward for in vitro systems, account must be taken for possible ill-defined intracellular conditions. Woledge (13, 21) has dealt with this problem and shown that ΔH_{PC} and ΔH_{ATP} do not vary substantially under the conditions that might prevail in the cell. In nonideal systems, it is also possible that ΔH may vary with the concentration of the reactants. However, (R. C. Woledge, personal communication) it has been found that within the physiological range, ΔH_{PC} is independent of PC concentration. From these studies (13, 21) the net enthalpy change for the following reactions can be given:

$$\text{ATP} \rightarrow \text{ADP} + \text{P}_i, \qquad -48 \text{ kJ} \cdot \text{mole}^{-1}$$
$$\text{PC} + \text{ADP} \rightarrow \text{ATP} + \text{C}, \qquad +14 \text{ kJ} \cdot \text{mole}^{-1}$$
$$\text{PC} \rightarrow \text{P}_i + \text{C}, \qquad -34 \text{ kJ} \cdot \text{mole}^{-1}$$
$$2\text{ADP} \rightarrow \text{ATP} + \text{AMP}, \qquad -6 \text{ kJ} \cdot \text{mole}^{-1}$$
$$\text{AMP} \rightarrow \text{IMP} + \text{NH}_3, \qquad -12 \text{ kJ} \cdot \text{mole}^{-1}$$
$$(\text{C}_6\text{H}_{10}\text{O}_5)_n + \text{P}_i \rightarrow (\text{C}_6\text{H}_{10}\text{O}_5)_{n-1} + \text{G-1-P}, \qquad -12 \text{ kJ} \cdot \text{mole}^{-1}$$

Measurements of the observed enthalpy ($h + w$) are now reliable to within several percent. This has been made possible by introduction of techniques in which the muscle-thermopile system is calibrated by liberating known amounts of energy into the systems (22–25). One possible source of error remains since, for technical reasons, $(h + w)$ measurements are not made on the muscles used for the chemical analysis. With the development of rapid fabrication of thermopiles (26) it may be possible to measure $(h + w)$ and ξ_i on the same muscles and thus eliminate a potential source of error.

Recent ^{31}P nuclear magnetic resonance measurement on living contracting muscles have provided an independent confirmation of the validity of the conventional chemical analysis of frozen muscle extracts (27). It is usual to calculate ξ_i from the difference in the relative amounts of i between the experimental and control muscle, on the assumption that prior to the experiment the relative amount of i was the same in both muscles. Albeit statistically valid, this procedure requires the analysis of many muscle pairs for a single mean value. A significant technical advance would be achieved if one were able to determine, in a nondestructive manner, how closely muscle pairs were matched prior to the experiment. Alternatively, it may be possible, given technical developments, to use ^{31}P NMR techniques to monitor the time course of chemical changes on a given muscle. The muscle would then be used to determine $(h + w)$.

To illustrate the arguments that follow, it is useful to consider the time course of the enthalpy change that could occur in a system similar to muscle. Suppose there is a system in which $A \rightarrow B$ (reaction a), having a molar enthalpy change of ΔH_A, and that reaction a occurs rapidly upon a given pulsatile stimulus. Assume further the existence of a reaction $X \rightarrow Y$, with a molar enthalpy change ΔH_X, which can be coupled to reverse reaction a slowly via reaction b as shown below.

(a) 2.

Let the initial contents of the system be $A = A_o$ and $X = X_o$. If the amounts in the system at a time, t, after the stimulation, are defined as A_t and X_t, the extent of reaction a at time t, ξ_A, will be $(A_o - A_t)$ and that of reaction b, ξ_X, is $(X_o - X_t)$. From the first law of thermodynamics the enthalpy change of the system will be

$$h + w = \xi_A \cdot \Delta H_A + \xi_X \cdot \Delta H_X.$$ 3.

At a time when reaction a is complete but before reaction b has proceeded significantly, $(h + w)$ will equal $\xi_A \cdot \Delta H_A$. After a long period of time, when A has been completely resynthesized, $(h + w)$ will equal $\xi_X \cdot \Delta H_X$. The enthalpy change, $(h + w)$, at intermediate times is given by equation 3. A concrete example of a similar system in muscle is the hydrolysis of ATP to ADP and P_i, and the very rapid rephosphorylation of ADP coupled to PC splitting (the Lohmann reaction). Although significant amounts of ATP are split during contraction, the occurrence of the Lohmann reaction prevents any net change in ATP content. Thus the enthalpy change in the muscle would be given by $\xi_{PC} \cdot \Delta H_{PC}$ if no other reactions were occurring.

THE ENERGETICS OF ISOMETRIC CONTRACTIONS

Enthalpy Production Near l_o.

When a frog sartorius is tetanically stimulated at a sarcomere spacing of 2.0–2.2 μm at 0°C, force increases rapidly and within 0.5 sec reaches a maximum value which, with continued stimulation, very gradually declines

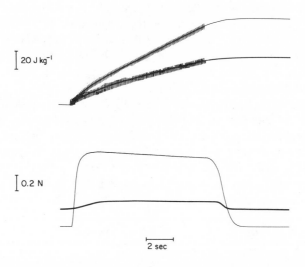

Figure 1 The heat production in a 10 sec isometric tetanus. A pair of *R. pipiens* semitendinosus muscles (dorsal heads) was tetanized for 10 sec at either l_o (2.0–2.2 μm sarcomere spacing) or at a stretched length ($\sim$3.5 μm spacing) and the heat and tension production measured. In the upper panel are the heat recordings and in the lower, the tension recordings. In both panels the upper record is from the muscles contracting at l_o while the lower (and thicker-lined) recording is from the stretched muscle. The vertical marks on the thermal records are stimulus artifacts. Note that at both lengths the heat is produced initially at a rapid rate that gradually declines to a constant rate at $\sim$ 5 sec after beginning stimulation. In this experiment the l_o was 23 mm and muscle weight was 70 mg. The stimulus heat was 2.3 J · kg^{-1} at l_o and 4.9 J · kg^{-1} at the stretched length. (Data from C. J. Kean, unpublished observations.)

[at $<$ 1% sec^{-1} (28); also see Figure 1]. Simultaneous measurement of the heat production reveals that the rate of heat production is initially rapid and thereafter it declines until at $\sim$ 5 sec it becomes relatively constant (see Figure 1). Upon cessation of stimulation, both tension and heat production continue at a constant rate for about 0.5 sec and thereafter both decline during relaxation to their pre-stimulation levels. Because only small amounts of internal work are produced ($\sim$ 2 mJ $\cdot$ g^{-1}, which is dissipated as heat during relaxation), the heat production is virtually the same as the enthalpy change of the reactions associated with contraction and relaxation.

The traditional view (11) held that this heat production, the initial heat, could be accounted for by the splitting of ATP and/or PC. One observes that following a period of 20–30 sec after relaxation, the rate of heat production again exceeds the pre-contraction level and gradually, over a time course of 40–50 min, returns to the basal rate (29). The post-contractile suprabasal heat production, the recovery heat, is about equal in amount to the initial heat production, although the ratio of recovery heat to initial heat can vary with temperature or other conditions (29–31). Because the recovery heat parallels the consumption of oxygen (32) and the changes in intracellular NADH levels (30, 33), and can be strongly suppressed by the removal of oxygen, it has been linked to the reactions of oxidative phosphorylation and glycolysis that resynthesize substrates consumed during contraction. Because the initial heat production is not affected by the presence or absence of oxygen, and because initial and recovery heat production are temporally separate, it has generally been thought that in the amphibian muscle one can temporally separate the reactions consuming $\sim$ P from those processes restoring it. [Such a separation does not apply to contractions in mammalian cardiac and skeletal muscle (17, 31, 34), in which a part of the recovery may occur during the contraction itself.]

Returning to the time course of initial heat production we must now inquire into the processes associated with its production. It has been shown (13, 35) that during a tetanus, up to a time t, the heat produced by the muscle, h_t, can be described by

$$\frac{h_t}{P_o l_o} = \frac{\dot{h}_\alpha/\alpha}{P_o l_o}(1 - e^{-\alpha t}) + \frac{\dot{h}_a/a}{P_o l_o}(1 - e^{-at}) + \frac{\dot{h}_B t}{P_o l_o} \qquad 4.$$

in which P_o is the isometric tension; l_o is the muscle length; $\dot{h}_a/a$ is the total labile heat (LMH) evolved in an exponential fashion with the rate constant a; $\dot{h}_B$ is the stable maintenance heat rate (SMH); and $\dot{h}_\alpha/\alpha$ is a very rapid and relatively small burst of heat (amounting to 2–4 mJ $\cdot$ g^{-1}) occurring in an exponential fashion (with a rate constant α, 20–30 sec^{-1}) during the first 100–200 msec following the first stimulus. Table 1 contains values for the

Table 1 Heat production and mechanical properties of various muscles

Species, muscle and temperature	Maximum tetanus tension $P_o \cdot l_o^{-1} \cdot M^{-1}$ (mN·mm^{-2})	Labile maintenance heat $h_a \cdot a^{-1} \cdot P_o^{-1} \cdot l_o^{-1}$ (dimensionless)	Stable maintenance heat, $\dot{h}_B$ (mJ·g^{-1}·sec^{-1})	Normalized $\dot{h}_B$ $\dot{h}_B \cdot P_o^{-1} \cdot l_o^{-1}$ (sec^{-1})	Tetanic activation heat (% $\dot{h}_B$)	Twitch activation heat (% twitch heat)	$\dfrac{a \cdot b}{P_o l_o}$ (sec^{-1})
R. pipiens Sart							
0°C (36)[e]	200	0.13[c]	10.9[c]	0.054[c]	~30	33	0.064[c]
20°C (36)	290	NM	169.0[c]	0.56[c]	NM	NM	NM
R. pipiens Semi							
0°C (36, 37)	160[a]	0.12[a,c]	8.0[c]	0.055[a,c]	40	30	0.129[a,c]
R. temporaria Sart							
0°C (35, 38–41)	200	0.11–0.15	15.1	0.074–0.083	NM	NM	0.083
17°C (35, 38–41)	260	0.11–0.15[b]	144.0	0.56–0.64	NM	NM	0.22
Rat EDL 27°C (34)	290	N	136.0	0.60	35	NM	0.38 (48)
Sol 27°C (42)	240	N	21.3	0.10	41	NM	0.05 (48)
Chicken PLD 20°C (43–45)	50–100	N	14.7–58.6	0.4–0.8	42	18	0.08
ALD 20°C (43–45)	50–100	SN	2.1–8.8	0.055–0.095	49	26	0.17
Rabbit RCC 27°C (46)	160	SN	3.3–5.0	0.023–0.032	NM	NM	0.02
Tortoise RF 0°C (47)	190	N	0.02	0.002	NM	NM	0.0012

[a] The l_o of the muscle fibers were assumed to be 55% of the muscle length.
[b] Data from (35).
[c] Includes data from C. J. Kean and E. Homsher, unpublished.
[d] Abbreviations: Sart = sartorius; Semi = semitendinosus; EDL = extensor digitorum longus; Sol = soleus; PLD = posterior latissimus dorsi; ALD = anterior latissimus dorsi; RCC = rectococcygeus; RF = rectus femoris; NM = not measured or reported; N = none; SN = small or none.
[e] Numbers in parentheses are reference numbers.

labile and stable maintenance heat rates and other pertinent data as they have been measured in various muscles (34–48). It has been found that LMH and SMH vary under different circumstances; in certain cases the variations do not occur in parallel, which has led to the idea that they may derive from different processes occurring in the muscle (13). The evidence for this idea is as follows: (a) Above fusion frequency, h_B is constant as the frequency is increased—as is h_a/a, although a increases (35). (b) In any two successive tetani, the value of h_B/P_ol_o remains constant. However, if the interval between two tetani is reduced to less than 20 min at 0°C, h_a/a declines; when the interval is less than 3 sec, h_a/a is reduced to about 35% of its initial value (49, 50). It would be interesting to know whether LMH can be further suppressed with additional tetani. (c) As temperature is increased, h_B/P_ol_o increases with a Q_{10} of 3.1, while the Q_{10} of $\dot{h}_a/a/P_ol_o$ is ~ 1.0, even though a has a Q_{10} of 2.8 (35, 39; C. J. Kean and E. Homsher, unpublished observations). (d) If the Cl^- in frog Ringers solution is replaced by I^- [a twitch potentiator (51)], h_a and a are increased but h_B is not (52). (e) Upon stretching a muscle beyond 2.2 μm, h_B declines linearly with the decline in myofilament overlap, while $\dot{h}_a/a$ remains relatively constant (35, 36, 41).

These results suggest that LMH and SMH may be manifestations of two or more different processes occurring in the muscle. With advances in our understanding of the mechanisms underlying excitation-contraction coupling, and with the development of the sliding filament model, it has been increasingly clear that there are two major ATP-consuming processes occurring in the contracting muscle. The first is an ATP utilization associated with the interaction of the thick and thin filaments; the second is an ATP splitting associated with the Ca^{2+} pump of the sarcoplasmic reticulum. To understand the mechanisms involved in the energy liberation in contraction, the energy utilization by each process must be measured. Some headway has been made in this direction and the energetics associated with calcium release and sequestration, the activation heat, are discussed below.

Activation Heat

Activation heat has been variously defined. A. V. Hill (53) introduced the concept to designate the thermal accompaniment of a "... triggered reaction setting the muscle in a state in which it can shorten and do work." Today this definition seems to refer to those reactions accompanying the release and sequestration of Ca^{2+}. Indeed, the fact that A. V. Hill, using various techniques, designated as activation heat that heat remaining after eliminating tension, shortening, and work production (53–55) seems to support this point of view.

On the other hand, Abbott & Howarth (12) and Carlson & Wilkie (10) have suggested that activation heat (AH) be defined by the time course of the heat production; i.e. AH is taken as the rapid initial burst of heat following stimulation, and is synonymous with the term $\dot{h}_\alpha/\alpha(1 - e^{-\alpha t})$ in equation 4. We feel that this definition is too restrictive and should be abandoned for several reasons: (a) It poses the difficult mathematical problem of showing that this heat can be isolated from other heat production that may be occurring concurrently. (b) Such an activation heat only occurs in muscles of frog and toad, yet it seems unlikely that the muscles of other species, such as the rat, chicken, and tortoise are not activated by a similar sort of calcium release mechanism. (c) As it stands, this "activation heat" would only signal the release of calcium, not its sequestration. (d) The definition implies that Ca^{2+} is released only on the first stimulus. Studies using calcium sensitive dyes and aequorin (56, 57) indicate that each stimulus in a tetanus is associated with some calcium release. We therefore favor the broader interpretation described above. We designate the energy liberation associated with the calcium release and sequestration in the twitch the *twitch activation heat,* and that in a tetanus, the *tetanic activation heat.*

The strategy used to estimate AH has been to measure the heat production under conditions in which mechanical manifestation of thick and thin filament interaction is inhibited. The essentials for a successful measurement of AH would be that (a) interaction between the thick and thin filaments should be prevented so that no tension could develop, no shortening occur, no work be performed, and (b) the processes involved in Ca^{2+} release and reaccumulation should be left intact. No technique has yet been devised that fully meets these criteria. Pre-shortening of the muscles, so that no external force is developed, fails because myofibrillar interaction may still occur (58, 59) along with some shortening (53), and because Ca^{2+} release is probably inhibited (59, 60) at short sarcomere lengths. Estimation of the twitch AH from isotonic recordings at different loads (53) is based on a circular argument and leads to results that vary by almost two-fold on the same muscle [see Figure 4 of (53)]. Use of the double twitch technique (61) is model-dependent and assumes that the E-C coupling mechanism is rapidly reprimed. Hypertonic treatment of the muscle to block mechanical activity (55, 62) still permits thick and thin filament interaction (63) [although reducing it substantially (64, 65)], and at tonicities ranging from 2–4 times greater than normal, Ca^{2+} release is inhibited between 20% and 100%, respectively (41, 64, 65).

The best estimates of AH are those obtained by stretching a muscle to a length at which the thick and thin filament overlap becomes vanishingly small. This can be done using sartorius muscles, even though the muscles are often damaged. However, Smith (41) and Homsher et al (36) have taken advantage of the fact that the dorsal head of the semitendinosus muscle can be reversibly stretched to sarcomere spacings of 3.6 μm or more without the danger of fiber damage. It was shown that as the muscle was stretched beyond maximum overlap, both the isometric twitch tension and the heat decline linearly with muscle length; and at a length at which twitch tension was zero, the twitch heat was $\sim$ 25–30% of the isometric twitch heat at 2.2 μm (2.6–4.2 mJ $\cdot$ g^{-1}). Similar behavior has been observed in both fast and slow muscles of the chicken (44), in which the twitch activation heat ranged between 18% and 26% of the heat produced in the isometric twitch at l_o. It was assumed in these papers that lengthening the muscle does not materially inhibit the processes of E-C coupling. The evidence for this assumption is as follows: (*a*) Neither the resting potential nor the action potential is affected by stretching the muscle (41, 66, 67). (*b*) When twitch heat is plotted as a function of the isometric force as the muscle is stretched beyond 2.2 μm, a straight line relation with a typical correlation coefficient of 0.998 is obtained (36, 41, 44). If Ca^{2+} release were inhibited by the stretch, an inflection in the heat vs tension relationship would be seen. This has not been seen in any of the muscles from the three species so far examined (34, 36, 41, 44). (*c*) The twitch : tetanus ratio is constant at lengths beyond l_o (41, 44). Since the decline in tetanic force with increases in muscle length is caused by a decline in myofilament overlap and not by an insufficiency of Ca^{2+} (68), this result indicates that upon stimulation, enough calcium is released to saturate the Ca^{2+} binding sites. If calcium release were inhibited by stretch, a decrease in the twitch : tetanus ratio would be observed. (*d*) The relationship between membrane potential and the fraction of maximum force development in potassium contractures is, if anything, potentiated (37) at longer muscle lengths. This result is inconsistent with a stretch-induced inhibition of Ca^{2+} release.

There is some evidence, however, for a length-dependent inhibition of calcium release. Taylor et al (69) have shown that at 3.6 μm, the aequorin signal is depressed to about 35% of that seen at 2.0 μm. Similarly, Frank & Winegrad (70) have shown that the increased Ca^{2+} efflux from tetanized skeletal muscle was inhibited at a sarcomere spacing of $\sim$ 3.9 μm by 50–70%, which could mean that during the tetanus the myoplasmic calcium concentration was less than that at 2.2 μm. While these data seem to suggest a very potent stretch inhibition of Ca^{2+} release, they may in fact indicate only a marginal inhibition of Ca^{2+} release. Available data from skinned and glycerinated muscle fibers indicate that the free myoplasmic Ca^{2+} concentration in resting fibers is $\sim$ 1 $\times$ 10^{-7} M and that of fully active muscle fibers is between 1 $\times$ 10^{-6} and 2 $\times$ 10^{-5} M (71–73). Studies on Ca^{2+} binding by myofibrils (74–76) show they are fully activated at a

[Ca^{2+}] of $\sim 2 \times 10^{-5}$ M and the amount of Ca^{2+} bound in increasing the [Ca^{2+}] from 1×10^{-7} M to 2×10^{-5} M is ~ 2 nmoles $\cdot$ mg^{-1} myofibrils. Thus in one gram of muscle about 0.22 μmoles of Ca^{2+} must be released (0.2 μmoles bound to the myofibrils and 0.02 μmoles to bring the free [Ca^{2+}] to 2×10^{-5} M) to fully activate the muscle. According to the aequorin calibration study of Allen et al (77), at 2×10^{-5} M Ca^{2+}, aequorin would emit 0.165 of its maximum light. If stretch inhibition caused the calcium concentration to reach only 1×10^{-5} M Ca^{2+}, the light emitted by the aequorin would decline to 0.056; i.e. the aequorin light signal recorded from the muscle would be reduced to 33% of that seen at full activation. Additionally, the Ca^{2+} efflux from such fibers would be reduced to about 50%, since the driving force for calcium efflux would be halved. However, the total amount of Ca^{2+} released by the SR to reach 1×10^{-5} M Ca^{2+} would be 0.21 μmoles (0.198 μmoles bound to the myofibrils and 0.01 μmoles to bring the free myoplasmic calcium to 1×10^{-5} M), a reduction in the total calcium release and activation heat of less than 5%. Thus there may be striking changes in the free myoplasmic calcium concentration (changes of 50–70%) with only slight alterations of the total calcium released. This conclusion is supported by the fact that in tetani near l_o, as the stimulus frequency is increased beyond that for mechanical fusion, the aequorin light emission increases (R. Rüdel, S. R. Taylor, and J. R. Blinks, personal communication) but the heat production does not (35). Further experimentation is required, however, to prove that Ca^{2+} release is not materially affected by stretches beyond 2.2 μm sarcomere spacings.

Studies of the AH production in stretched muscle have shown the following: (a) The amount of twitch activation heat produced depends on the species and ranges from 18–33% of the isometric heat production at l_o (see Table 1). (b) In frog skeletal muscle at 0°C, twitch activation heat is produced in two phases: a rapid phase, amounting to 60% of the total, produced with a rate constant of ~ 22 sec^{-1}; and a slower phase produced with a rate constant of ~ 3 sec^{-1} (36, 41). The rapid phase probably corresponds to $\dot{h}_\alpha/\alpha$ of equation 4. At 20°C, there is but one discernible phase with a time constant of 25 sec^{-1}. (c) With repetitive stimulation, the activation heat produced per stimulus decreases as the interval between stimuli is reduced. This behavior (Figure 2) suggests that a temperature-dependent repriming time is required for the full production of AH by successive stimuli. (d) Treatment of muscles with NO_3^- and Zn^{2+}, twitch potentiators, increases the amount of AH (41). (e) In a tetanus $\sim 40\%$ of the SMH is tetanic activation heat (see Figure 1 and Table 1). This value is somewhat greater than that given by Homsher et al (36), first because their estimation was based on a regression of the heat rate vs *peak* tetanic tension (i.e. they did not correct for the "creep" in tension that occurs in

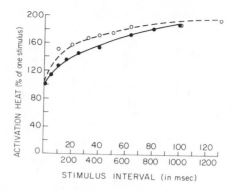

Figure 2 The variation of activation heat production with stimulus interval. In the experiment shown in this figure a pair of *R. pipiens* semitendinosus muscles was stretched to such a length that the twitch tension was reduced to $\sim$ 1–2% of that at l_o, and the twitch activation heat recorded and assigned the value of 100%. The muscles were then given two stimuli and the interval between the two varied. The experiment was performed at 0°C (filled circles) and at 23°C (open circles). The amount of activation heat produced by the two stimuli (ordinate) was plotted as a function of the stimulus interval (abscissa). The numbers below the abscissa are the stimulus intervals at 0°C, and those above, the stimulus interval at 23°C. The data show that the muscle's ability to produce twitch activation heat increases as the interval between successive stimuli is increased (E. Homsher, unpublished observations).

stretched muscles [78]), and second because the tetanic activation heat rate is rather variable, ranging from 33–45% of the stable maintenance heat rate.

Chemical Change Associated With Activation Heat

The simplest hypothesis is that activation heat is derived from the splitting of ATP and/or PC. The results of attempts to test this idea (36, 79–82) are listed in Table 2. In most experiments, the enthalpy production by muscles contracting under the same conditions was not measured; thus the extent to which chemical changes account for the heat production cannot be assessed, save to say that ATP is or is not hydrolyzed. Two of the techniques used to isolate the energetics associated with Ca^{2+} release and reaccumulation (hypertonic treatment and pre-shortening of the muscle) do not achieve the desired objective. Consequently one does not know how much of the ATP splitting comes from the activation mechanism and how much comes from thick and thin filament interaction. In fact the results of lines A and B of Table 2 suggest that the hypertonic solutions rendered the muscles inexcitable. In stretched muscles, a significant amount of PC is hydrolyzed over a series of activation cycles; but the extent to which the observed

Table 2 The energetics of activation

Muscle	AH[c] isolation	Experimental conditions			Δ~P[a, c] (nmole·g⁻¹)	Explained[a] enthalpy (mJ·g⁻¹)	Observed[a] enthalpy (mJ·g⁻¹)
		Stim. freq. (sec⁻¹)	Stim. duration (sec)	Inhibition used			
A Sart[c] (79)[d]	3 × R[c]	5, 10 & 20	1	FDNB[c]	40 ± 80	1.9 ± 3.8	—
B Sart[b]	3 × R	10	1	FDNB	80 ± 100	3.8 ± 4.8	—
C Sart (80)	PS[c]	15	1.5	FDNB	390 ± 150	18.7 ± 7.2	—
D Sart (79)	PS	1	10	FDNB	510 ± 17	24.5 ± 8.2	—
E Sart (79)	PS	10	1	FDNB	250 ± 200	12.0 ± 9.6	—
F Sart (81)	PS	1	1	FDNB	72 ± 8	3.5 ± 0.4	4.2
G Sart (80)	S[c]	15	1.5	FDNB	370 ± 190	17.8 ± 9.1	—
H Sart (66)	S	10	20	IAA[c]	1400 ± 720	47.6 ± 24.5	—
I Semi (36)	S	0.3	90	IAA	2000 ± 500	68 ± 17	84.8 ± 21
J Semi (36)	S	1	10	FDNB	550 ± 70	26.4 ± 3.4	23.1 ± 0.8
K Semi (82)	S	15	5	None	305 ± 48	10.4 ± 1.6	20.1 ± 0.7

[a] Values given as mean ± SEM.
[b] Data from E. Homsher and A. Wallner, unpublished.
[c] Abbreviations: Sart = sartorius of *R. pipiens*, except in line F where sartorius of *R. temporaria* were used; Semi = semitendinosus of *R. pipiens*; AH = technique used to isolate activation heat; 3 × R = treatment with Ringers solution of 3 times normal tonicity; PS = pre-shortening the muscle; S = stretching the muscle to sarcomere spacings of ~3.6 μm; FDNB = muscles treated with fluorodinitrobenzene; IAA = treatment with iodoacetate; Δ~P designates the amount of ATP hydrolyzed in the presence of FDNB, or of PC split in the presence of IAA.
[d] Numbers in parentheses are reference numbers.

enthalpy production is accounted for by ~P splitting is obscured by the large standard errors (line I, Table 2). The results in Table 2 (line J) seem to indicate that there is a good accounting for the AH production over several stimulus cycles in FDNB. However, this result does not indicate that a similar balance would be seen in unpoisoned muscles; FDNB reduces the AH production (E. Homsher, unpublished observations) and is known to reduce significantly the amount of unexplained enthalpy production (83). In recent measurements of the chemical changes in unpoisoned muscles that have been tetanized for 5 sec at sarcomere spacings of ~ 3.6 μm (82), the amount of PC splitting can account for only 50% of the observed enthalpy production (see line K, Table 2). This result indicates that at the time of its production, the activation heat cannot be fully accounted for by ~P splitting.

Factors Potentially Influencing the Time Course of Activation Heat Production

Currently available data (2) indicate that calcium is stored in a bound fashion in the terminal cisterns (perhaps to calsequestrin) in the resting muscle. Upon stimulation, the potential across the SR membrane changes (84), and Ca^{2+} diffuses into the myoplasm where it binds to troponin, thus relieving the inhibition of thick and thin filament interaction. As the myoplasmic $[Ca^{2+}]$ increases, calcium is bound by the longitudinal elements of the SR interior, and from there returns to the terminal cisterns by diffusion or by some energy-requiring mechanism (85). Within this framework there are a number of processes that could account for AH production. Among these are (a) enthalpy changes accompanying the generation of the action potential; (b) a discharge of the membrane capacitance of the SR membrane upon depolarization; (c) release of Ca^{2+} from sites in the terminal cisterns; (d) Ca^{2+} binding to troponin; (e) conformational changes in the troponin-tropomyosin complex; (f) Ca^{2+} binding to the longitudinal elements of the SR; (g) Ca^{2+} binding to parvalbumin; (h) activation-dependent crossbridge motion; and (i) Ca^{2+}-dependent phosphorylation of myosin and/or troponin subunits. Of these, a, b, d, e, and h are the type that would occur during activation of the muscle but would be reversed by the time the muscle relaxed or shortly thereafter and would thus produce no net initial heat.

These hypotheses could be tested with energy balance studies in stretched muscles before and after relaxation. Process a is improbable, since muscles whose calcium release mechanism has been blocked by the disruption of the transverse tubules (86) produce less than 0.2 mJ $\cdot$ g^{-1} per stimulus (87). It has been calculated (36) that process b is unlikely to account for more than 5% of the observed AH. The enthalpy change for Ca^{2+} binding to troponin has been measured and was found to be -32 to -39 kJ $\cdot$ mole^{-1} for the high affinity Ca^{2+} binding sites and -32 to -74 kJ $\cdot$ mole^{-1} for the low affinity Ca^{2+} binding sites (88, 89). Given that 0.15–0.2 μmoles of Ca^{2+} bind per gram of muscle, Ca^{2+} binding to troponin could contribute 5–11 mJ $\cdot$ g^{-1}, which is 1–2 times the amount needed to account for the activation heat. Thus Ca^{2+} binding (as in processes c–g) is certainly an important factor. Similar calorimetric measurements on regulated thin filaments (the actin-troponin-tropomyosin complex) would be of use, as would be those on cal-sequestrin, a Ca^{2+} binding protein that exists in substantial amounts in the SR.

Parvalbumin, which exists in considerable quantities in frog muscle ($\sim$ 0.4 μmoles Ca^{2+} binding sites per gram of muscle [90]), is a protein whose function and location are as yet unknown. However, Gerday & Gillis (91) have shown that parvalbumin's Ca^{2+} affinity is so great as to remove calcium bound to frog myofibrils. This result argues against its being free in the myoplasm. Baron et al (92) have shown that parvalbumin is present in significant amounts in those tissues that have an extensive sarcoplasmic reticulum. One might speculate that parvalbumin acts as a storage protein in the longitudinal tubules of the SR. This idea is made all the more interesting by R. C. Woledge's finding (personal communication) that the enthalpy change for Ca^{2+} binding to parvalbumin is about -28 kJ $\cdot$ mole^{-1} Ca^{2+} bound. Clearly, additional work directed at learning parvalbumin's location, the kinetics of calcium binding, and its role in contraction is needed.

Haselgrove (93) has shown, in muscles stretched beyond sarcomere spacings of 3.6 μm, that upon stimulation, the X-ray diffraction pattern is consistent with a radial movement of the crossbridges away from the backbone of the thick filament. This raises the possibility of a Ca^{2+} control mechanism residing in vertebrate myosin. Such a mechanism would be thermally neutral over a complete activation-relaxation cycle, unless a phosphorylation step mediated by ATP splitting were involved. Further speculation is, however, unwarranted until a regulatory mechanism is in fact discovered and elucidated.

Fraser & Carlson (94, 95) and Mulieri et al (26) have performed experiments that bear directly on the mechanism of production of activation heat. They find, in muscles contracting at l_o and 15°C, that a second stimulus, given within 50 msec of the first, causes the rate of energy liberation to increase to only 50% of that seen immediately after the first stimulus. These authors correctly conclude that if the amount of calcium released by the second stimulus is about the same as in the first, then their results are incompatible with the idea that much of the AH production is derived from reactions associated with calcium release and/or Ca^{2+} binding to troponin. The activation heat–producing reactions would thus be narrowed to those involving calcium binding to the SR. This argument, however, hinges on how much and how fast Ca^{2+} is released with the second stimulus. As shown in Figure 2, a second stimulus administered within 50 msec of the first at 23°C will produce less than half the twitch activation heat given by the first stimulus, which suggests that less than half as much Ca^{2+} is released by the second pulse. The results from calcium transient studies with aequorin yield no insight because they do not indicate how much Ca^{2+} is released. It would be useful to repeat the double-stimulus experiments at a sarcomere spacing of ~ 3.6 μm, so that the total amount of AH could be used as an index of the amount of calcium released. The AH rate changes could then be compared as the stimulus interval is varied. One might well reach the same conclusion as others (26, 94, 95) but be on somewhat more stable ground.

The Stable and Labile Maintenance Heat

From the foregoing it is clear that a substantial fraction of the stable maintenance heat is derived from processes associated with Ca^{2+} release and reaccumulation. Stable maintenance heat data are now available from a variety of different muscles (see Table 1). One striking feature is that, whether the muscle produces heat at a fast or slow rate, over a sixty-fold variation in absolute value the contribution to the stable maintenance heat rate by the tetanic activation heat remains a relatively constant proportion, from 30–50%. This observation implies that, while there may have been evolutionary pressures to increase the speed of a muscle, presumably by increasing the actomyosin ATPase rate, the rate of processes associated with calcium removal kept pace with these changes. A. V. Hill observed (38) that the SMH rate ($\dot{h}_B/P_ol_o$) was the same as the product of the mechanical constants a/P_o and b/l_o derived from force-velocity curve measurements. Table 1 shows that the identity of $\dot{h}_B/P_ol_o$ and $a \cdot b/P_ol_o$ does not hold true in most muscles examined; this result suggests that Hill's observation was coincidental.

Both Woledge (13) and Abbott & Howarth (12) have argued that the LMH may be produced by Ca^{2+} cycling between a releaser site (the terminal cisterns) and a calcium sequestration site (the longitudinal tubules and fenestrated collar) in a manner similar to that described by Winegrad (55). In this hypothesis, upon stimulation, Ca^{2+} is released from its releaser site, the myoplasmic [Ca^{2+}] increases, the longitudinal tubules rapidly sequester the Ca^{2+}, and from there Ca^{2+} is returned to the releaser site. The labile maintenance heat is thought of as the heat production associated with the approach of this Ca^{2+} cycling to a steady state; i.e. the Ca^{2+} content of each site becomes constant. Support for this idea comes from Abbott's observation that as the duration of the tetanus is increased, the rate of relaxation slows (96), as might be expected were Ca^{2+} accumulating in the longitudinal tubules. On completion of LMH production, no further slowing of the rate of relaxation is observed. In addition, Curtin (97) has shown that this slowing of relaxation is the same at sarcomere lengths of 2.2 and 3.6 μm. This result indicates that the phenomenon is directly associated with processes occurring upon Ca^{2+} release and reaccumulation. Finally, Woledge (47) found that tortoise muscles, which produce no LMH, exhibit no slowing of relaxation with increasing tetanus duration. It is natural to suppose that, all else being equal, animals having a well-developed sarcoplasmic reticulum should exhibit similar behavior. As shown in Table 1, however, no sign of the LMH is seen in tetani of muscles of the rat, tortoise, or chicken, even though they all possess a well-developed sarcoplasmic reticulum (98–100). Thus while there is good evidence indicating that LMH may be associated with Ca^{2+} release and reaccumulation, additional work must be done to determine precisely what processes it corresponds. An interesting fact in this regard is that while frog muscles contain substantial amounts of parvalbumin, higher vertebrate muscles contain much smaller amounts (101); it may be that such differences are related to the presence or absence of the LMH.

Chemical Changes in Isometric Contractions

It is obviously possible that tetanic heat production is derived from the enthalpy changes accompanying $\sim$P hydrolysis. Prior to 1971, most efforts were aimed at showing that either ATP or PC was hydrolyzed over a complete contraction-relaxation cycle; the view emerged that, for the most part, the energy liberation in isometric contractions could be accounted for by the splitting of $\sim$P [see (11) for a summary of this point of view]. The evidence for this conclusion was weak for several reasons. In few of these experiments was the muscle's energy liberation measured. The chemical results, obtained from IAA- or FDNB-treated muscles were instead compared to existing literature values for the energy liberation in unpoisoned *R. temporaria* muscles. This procedure is imprecise, not only because the energy liberation can vary in different batches of frogs, but also because there are species differences (see Table 1) and unknown effects of the metabolic inhibitors. Additionally, many chemical experiments were performed at temperatures 1°–2°C greater than those of the heat measurements, and since the isometric heat rate has a large Q_{10}, an error of 15–25% was introduced. In those cases in which the energy liberation was measured [e.g. Wilkie (22)], the freezing of the muscles could not be accomplished until times > 40 sec after the cessation of stimulation; consequently there may have been post-contractile PC splitting while the muscles were readied for freezing. Finally, earlier estimates of ΔH_{PC} were 30% too great, causing an overestimate of the explained enthalpy.

At this point, a line of investigation was initiated in Wilkie's laboratory that was to question some of the existing views of the energetics of isometric contractions (83, 102–104). In these experiments (*a*) the enthalpy production by contracting muscles was compared to chemical changes in muscles contracting under identical conditions at 0°C; (*b*) the muscles were unpoisoned; (*c*) the muscles used for the chemical experiments were frozen by a technique that reduced the freezing time from $\sim$300 msec to 80 msec; and (*d*) the *time course* of enthalpy production and $\sim$P hydrolysis were measured. Using this technique (102) they concluded that during both contraction and relaxation, the ratio of enthalpy production ($h + w$) to PC split was substantially greater than $-46 \, \text{kJ} \cdot \text{mole}^{-1}$. Measurements of ATP levels during contraction showed, if anything, a slight ATP synthesis. The amount of PC split was a linear function of time during the tetanus. At times greater than 5 sec, ($h + w$) evolution became linear, and the ratio ($h + w$)/(PC split) was not different from $-46 \, \text{kJ} \cdot \text{mole}^{-1}$. If one accepted $-34 \, \text{kJ} \cdot \text{mole}^{-1}$ as ΔH_{PC}, these results suggestd that there were two unknown exothermic reactions occurring in an isometric tetanus: one that produced heat early in the tetanus, and a second that occurred in an amount proportional to the duration of the tetanus. Subsequent work in various laboratories (24, 50, 83, 103–105) using a similar protocol resulted in the modification and refinement of some of these conclusions. A picture has emerged indicating that of the ($h + w$) produced during an isometric tetanus, a substantial amount is not accounted for by ATP or PC splitting. A summary of these data is shown in Figure 3A, B, and C, and will serve to focus our discussion.

In Figure 3A, the energy liberated by tetanized *R. temporaria* muscles is plotted as a function of time. On the same graph, the explained enthalpy liberation is also plotted. In Figure 3B, the difference between the observed and explained enthalpy, the unexplained enthalpy, is plotted as a function of tetanus duration. In Figure 3C, the observed, explained, and unexplained enthalpy productions in *R. pipiens* muscles are plotted. Several features should be noted: (*a*) From the spread of thermal and biochemical data, one can better appreciate the need to perform both heat and chemical measurements in a similar fashion on muscles from the same batch of frogs. (*b*) In each instance the amount of explained enthalpy is insufficient to account for the observed enthalpy; in *R. temporaria* the explained enthalpy is about 50% of the observed, while in *R. pipiens,* it is about 70%. In absolute terms, the amount of unexplained enthalpy in a 5 sec isometric tetanus is about 40 mJ $\cdot$ g^{-1} in *R. temporaria,* and 25 mJ $\cdot$ g^{-1} in *R. pipiens.* (*c*) The explained enthalpy (or alternatively, the chemical change) does not appear to be a linear function of time, but PC splitting begins at an initially high rate and appears to decline to a constant rate. (*d*) The amount of unexplained enthalpy (Figure 3B, C) seems to be produced at a rapid rate early in the contraction. The available data do not allow one to decide whether the unexplained enthalpy is produced early and then ceases to be produced (indicated by the dashed line, Figure 3B) or continues to be produced at later times (indicated by the solid line, Figure 3B).

While it may be argued that the unexplained enthalpy is accounted for by ATP and/or PC splitting during relaxation, Curtin & Woledge (103) have directly tested and rejected this hypothesis. Measurements of the ATP levels in tetanized muscles (24, 83, 103, 106) have shown no significant changes; this indicates that PC rephosphorylates ADP as rapidly as the latter is produced. Energy balance studies on FDNB-poisoned muscles (83) show that while the unexplained enthalpy is considerably reduced in a 2 sec tetanus, there is still a significant amount of energy liberated that cannot be accounted for by ATP splitting. Finally, energy balance studies on tortoise muscles (107), rat soleus muscles (25, 108), and chicken PLD muscles (45) all indicate that about 30% of the energy liberated cannot be accounted for by known chemical reactions.

The fact that ($h + w$) is greater than ($\Delta H_{PC} \cdot \xi_{PC}$) invites several types of explanation.

1. (h + w) *has been overestimated.* This case might occur if there were an inaccuracy in the techniques used to measure the energy produced by

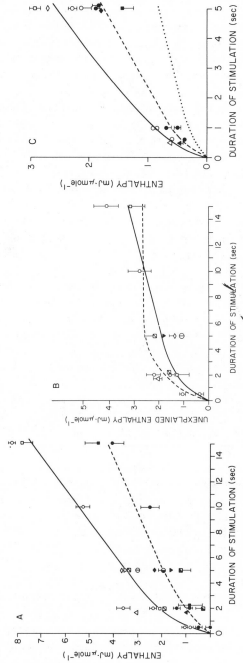

Figure 3   The results of energy balance studies on isometric tetani of *R. temporaria* (A and B) and *R. pipiens* (C) sartorius muscles at 0°C. In panels A, B, and C, the observed enthalpy $(h + w)$ is given by the open symbols and solid drawn lines; the explained enthalpy $(\xi_i \Delta H_i)$, by the filled symbols and dashed lines. The symbol size or brackets represent the standard error of the mean of the observation. The unexplained enthalpy for the data from *R. temporaria* is plotted in panel B, where the solid and dashed lines represent possible time courses of the unexplained enthalpy that might fit the data. The approximate time course of the unexplained enthalpy production in *R. pipiens* is given by the dotted line in panel C. The results in A and B were calculated from data from the following references: $\bigcirc, \bullet$, (102); $\square, \blacksquare$, (103); $\triangle, \blacktriangle$, (104); $\boxtimes, \blacksquare$, (83); $\triangledown, \blacktriangledown$, (24); $\diamondsuit, \blacklozenge$, (50); $\oplus, \bullet$, C. Kean and E. Homsher, manuscript in preparation. The data in C were calculated from data in: $\bigcirc, \bullet$, (24); $\square, \blacksquare$, (105); $\triangle, \blacktriangle$, (147); $\diamondsuit, \blacklozenge$, C. Kean and M. Mahler, unpublished.

the contracting muscle. This possibility has been discussed in the section above on methodology and found to be unlikely. It is more likely that the estimate of $(h + w)$ is accurate and reflects the presence during contraction of unidentified exothermic reactions that are reversed subsequent to relaxation by ATP and/or PC splitting.

2. ΔH_{PC} *has been underestimated.* There may be systematic errors in the calorimetric estimation of ΔH_{PC}. If ΔH_{PC} has been carefully measured, as discussed above, a second possible source of error remains: the assumed enthalpy change for intracellular buffering of H^+ ions. This value has been measured in the past (109), and although there was a calibration error in those measurements (39), it does not seem of sufficient magnitude to account for the present discrepancy, although this point should be checked. Additionally, the results from FDNB-poisoned muscles (83) argue against this possibility: During ATP hydrolysis, H^+ ion buffering occurs in a direction opposite to that during PC splitting. It is unlikely that an error in the value of ΔH_{PC} can account for the data.

3. ξ_{PC} *has been underestimated.* The freezing and extraction of the muscles may somehow reduce the chemical difference between muscle pairs. This possibility, as discussed above and elsewhere (25, 27, 102), is unlikely. A second possibility is that some PC may be synthesized by glycolysis or oxidative phosphorylation during the tetanus. However, while resynthesis can certainly occur during contractions in muscles tetanized for longer times at higher temperatures (25, 110, 111), this does not seem the case in the rather shorter contractions considered here because (a) the increased O_2 consumption is delayed until well after relaxation (111–113); (b) there is no significant accumulation of glycolytic intermediates or lactate (83, 102, 106); and (c) an energy imbalance is observed in IAA-poisoned muscles (102). The only other possibility is that some PC splitting occurs during recovery.

The energy imbalance shown in Figure 3 is thus likely to be derived from an unknown exothermic reaction(s) occurring during the tetanus, which would presumably be reversed by PC splitting during "recovery." Work in Kushmerick's laboratory along a completely different line of experimentation leads to a similar conclusion (106, 111, 112). In these experiments, the amount of PC split during a tetanus was compared to the amount of O_2 consumed during recovery. On the basis of the known metabolic pathways in frog muscle, one would predict that for each mole of O_2 consumed, 6.3 moles of PC should be synthesized; i.e. the ratio of PC split during the tetanus to suprabasal O_2 consumed during the recovery period ($\Delta \sim P / \Delta O_2$) should be 6.3. Measurements on *R. pipiens* showed that the $\Delta \sim P / \Delta O_2$ ratio in tetani of 5, 10 and 20 sec duration at 0°C was ~ 4.5, which indicates that either there was additional PC splitting after the tetanus or that the mitochondria were uncoupled. The latter explanation is rendered unlikely, though it cannot be excluded, by the fact that the ratio of moles of ADP phosphorylated to moles of O_2 consumed by isolated frog skeletal muscle mitochondria is 6.2 (106, 114). A $\Delta{\sim}P/\Delta O_2$ ratio of 4.5 agrees with energy balance studies on *R. pipiens* (24), as is illustrated by a modification of a calculation suggested by Woledge (13). If a muscle contracts and hydrolyzes 1 mole of PC, the initial heat produced will be $(\Delta H_{PC} + \Delta X)$ where ΔX is the enthalpy derived from the unknown reaction, which is assumed to parallel PC splitting and ΔH_{PC} is -34 kJ $\cdot$ mole^{-1}. From Kushmerick & Paul's data (106), 1/4.5 (or 0.22) moles of O_2 are used in oxidative phosphorylation for each mole of PC split during the tetanus. In the frog, about -460 kJ of enthalpy is produced for each mole of O_2 consumed (13). During recovery the initial PC splitting and the unknown reaction will be reversed, and consequently the net heat produced during recovery will be $[-460$ kJ $\cdot$ mole^{-1} (0.22 mole) $- (\Delta H_{PC} + \Delta X)]$. Therefore the ratio of recovery heat to initial heat, R, will be given by

$$R = \frac{-102 \text{ kJ} - (\Delta H_{PC} + \Delta X)}{(\Delta H_{PC} + \Delta X)}. \qquad 5.$$

Since R is $\sim$1.0 at 0°C (29), equation 5, when solved, shows ΔX to be -17 kJ $\cdot$ mole^{-1} of PC split. Thus the initial heat will equal $[-34 + (-17)]$ or -51 kJ $\cdot$ mole^{-1} PC, which is very close to the value of -46 kJ $\cdot$ mole^{-1} reported for *R. pipiens* (24). In fact a value for $\Delta{\sim}P/\Delta O_2$ of 5.0, which has been obtained (M. Mahler and C. Kean, personal communication) for *R. pipiens* at 0°C, lowers the value of ΔX to -12 kJ $\cdot$ mole^{-1} and thus exactly matches the energy balance studies. To account for the results in *R. temporaria* the $\Delta{\sim}P/\Delta O_2$ ratio would need to be 3.5, and such experiments ought to be done using *R. temporaria*. One additional feature of the work of Kushmerick & Paul (106) deserves comment. The $\Delta{\sim}P/\Delta O_2$ ratios in their 5, 10, and 20 sec tetani were the same. From this they conclude that the extent of the unknown reaction parallels the extent of PC splitting. But because there was an indication that the $\Delta{\sim}P/\Delta O_2$ ratio tended to increase with tetanus duration in one of their experiments (111), and because the error in their ratios was relatively large and was not normally distributed, one cannot rule out the possibility that the extent of the unknown reaction does not parallel PC splitting.

Additional results indicating a post-contractile PC splitting come from experiments in which the amounts of PC split during a tetanus and the lactic acid produced during anaerobic recovery were compared (115). Based on knowledge of the glycolytic pathways, and given evidence that (*a*) oxidative phosphorylation is completely inhibited, (*b*) there is no significant ATP synthesis during the tetanus, (c) upon recovery the precontractile levels of ATP, PC, P_i and Cr are restored, and (d) lactate is the only end product of glycolysis, one would predict that if all the ATP and/or PC splitting occurred during a tetanus the $\Delta{\sim}P/\Delta$lactate ratio should be 1.5. While $\Delta{\sim}P/\Delta$lactate ratios ranging from 1.3–2.0 have previously been measured (116–118), the criteria listed above have not been met. DeFuria & Kushmerick (115) have performed the appropriate control experiments and found that in isometric tetani at 20°C the $\Delta{\sim}P/\Delta$lactate ratio was 1.1–1.2, which suggests a post-contractile splitting of ATP amounting to 20–25% of the total. It is tempting to conclude that these results further confirm the conclusion derived from energy balance and $\Delta{\sim}P/\Delta O_2$ studies, and that some process is being reversed by this post-contractile ATP splitting. This would, however, be premature for several reasons. First, as the authors point out, a similar result could be obtained as a result of futile substrate cycling (e.g. F-6-P → 1,6 FDP → F-6-P, which would act as an ATPase). Such cycling might be occasioned as a result of the experimental conditions (anaerobiosis, 20°C) and be different from the situation occurring in oxygen at 0°C. Second, in experiments in *R. pipiens* in O_2 at 20°C, Mahler (113) has found a $\Delta{\sim}P/\Delta O_2$ ratio of 6.3, which suggests there may not be post-contractile PC splitting at higher temperatures. Finally, energy balance studies on *R. pipiens* at 20°C have yet to be performed for comparison with those at 0°C.

Although the above data certainly suggest the presence of a post-contractile PC splitting, direct evidence on this point is contradictory. While there have been reports of measured PC splitting during recovery (102, 116, 119), there have also been reports in which post-contractile splitting (28, 106, 120) was not observed. Because PC should be synthesized at the same time the hypothetical PC splitting is occurring, the latter effect would be obscured.

Clearly, during an isometric tetanus at 0°C additional exothermic reaction(s) besides ATP and/or PC splitting are occurring. In addition, we can infer that ATP continues to be hydrolyzed during recovery [presumably to reverse the unknown reaction(s)], which is contrary to the idea that muscle metabolism can be separated into initial and recovery phases. We must next inquire into possible mechanisms for such behavior, of which three are readily apparent.

The first is that there may be an unidentified high energy phosphate compound that can power crossbridge cycling and/or calcium pumping and whose enthalpy change is negative. NMR studies (27, 121) indicate there is about 1 μmole · g^{-1} of glycerophosphorylcholine in frog muscle along with similar amounts of several other unidentified phosphorylated compounds. However, although the data are not unambiguous, the NMR measurements (27) suggest that the amounts of these compounds do not change significantly during and after contraction. Furthermore, most studies of PC splitting during contraction indicate that the decline of PC matches the increase in Cr and P_i. It thus seems unlikely that the hydrolysis of an unidentified high energy phosphate compound could account for the data.

Woledge (122) has suggested a clever hypothesis that is attractive in light of recent advances in our understanding of the mechanism of myosin and actomyosin ATPase. Figure 4 shows a simplified scheme for the mechanisms of myosin and actomyosin ATPase (123). At rest, as actin and myosin interaction is inhibited, myosin will exist as M, MATP, $M \cdot ADP \cdot P_i$, and $M \cdot ADP$, and the relative amount of each intermediate will be governed by the rate constants of reactions 1 through 4. Work on frog myosin kinetics (M. A. Ferenczi, E. Homsher, D. R. Trentham, and R. M. Simmons, unpublished observations) indicates that in the resting muscle the ratio $M : M \cdot ATP : M \cdot ADP \cdot P_i : M \cdot ADP$ will be about $1 : 4 : 93 : 2$. It is important to recognize that the enthalpy content of the system will depend on the amounts of these myosin intermediates. If, as a result of muscle contraction, there were a redistribution of the myosin intermediates on reaching the steady state, so that the relative amounts of myosin were $M = 1$, MATP $= 1$, $M \cdot ADP \cdot P_i = 60$, $AM \cdot ADP \cdot P_i = 30$, $AM \cdot ADP = 5$, and MADP $= 3$ (using hypothetical values), one would expect to observe an enthalpy change in the system (in a fashion exactly the same as when the enthalpy content of an ATP system decreases upon ATP hydrolysis). Whether the enthalpy change is large or small would depend on the enthalpy change

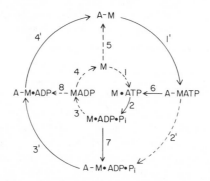

Figure 4 A simplified reaction mechanism for myosin and actomyosin. The inner circle, designated by reactions 1–4 indicates the mechanism of ATP hydrolysis by myosin, M. The outer circle, designated by reactions 1'–4' indicates a mechanism of ATP hydrolysis by a system containing actin, A, and myosin. The probable reaction pathway for an actomyosin system given by the Lymn-Taylor mechanism (123) is indicated by the solid arrows.

associated with the reactions 1, 1', 2, 2', etc, and the difference in amounts of myosin intermediate in resting and in contracting muscle. Work is now underway to measure the enthalpy change associated with each of the reactions (124–126). The results so far are encouraging. The enthalpy change associated with reaction 4 is +70 kJ · mole^{-1}; with reactions (1 + 2), $\sim$ 0 kJ · mole^{-1}; with reaction 3, –140 kJ · mole^{-1}; and with reaction 5, $\sim$ +20 kJ · mole^{-1}. If such a scheme is responsible for the unexplained enthalpy production, one would be forced to conclude that in an isometric tetanus, the muscle requires a rather long time ($\sim$ 5 sec) to reach a steady state, if in fact it does; and that upon relaxation, a protracted time ($>$ 180 sec) is required for myosin species to become redistributed to their precontractile level. While these times seem too long to fit with the known values for the in vitro myosin and actomyosin rate constants, there are data (127) to indicate that some sort of structural changes may be occurring in the sarcomere well after muscle has mechanically relaxed.

A third hypothesis for the unexplained enthalpy is that it is associated with the calcium release and the reaccumulation mechanism, and there are several observations that render this hypothesis attractive. (*a*) Curtin et al (104) stimulated muscles that were either maximally working or contracting isometrically. The duration of stimulation (1.7 sec for isometric muscles and 1.1 sec for working muscles) was arranged so that both muscles produced the same amount of energy. Their results showed that the amount of unexplained enthalpy was dependent on the duration of stimulation (as in Figure 3B) and independent of the type of contraction. Because the behavior of the crossbridges should be very different in the two types of contraction, this result tends to argue against myofibrillar involvement in the production of the unexplained enthalpy. (*b*) Labile maintenance heat has been implicated (though not unequivocally so) in the calcium release and sequestering mechanism. Curtin & Woledge (50) have shown, in two consecutive 5 sec tetani spaced 3 sec apart, that while the first tetanus produces 37 ± 1.2 mJ · g^{-1} of LMH, the second tetanus produces only 12.7 ± 0.8 mJ · g^{-1}. From chemical measurements, they found the unexplained enthalpy in the first tetanus to be 38.3 ± 7.2 mJ · g^{-1} and in the second, 14.8 ± 7.7 mJ · g^{-1}. These results suggest that the unexplained enthalpy is associated with the LMH production and, by inference, with the activation mechanism. This hypothesis could be tested by performing energy balance experiments in which ($h + w$) and ξ_i are measured in muscle pairs stimulated for 5 or 10 sec. If the hypothesis is true, there will be an energy balance in the 5–10 sec interval. (*c*) In experiments in which *R. pipiens* semitendinosus muscles were tetanized for 5 sec at sarcomere spacings of 2.2 μm or 3.6 μm, Kean et al (128) found that the unexplained enthalpy at 2.2 μm was 9.5 mJ · g^{-1}, and was 9.7 mJ · g^{-1} at 3.6 μm. This result indicates that the unexplained enthalpy is the same whether or not there is thick and thin filament interaction, and again implicates the activation mechanism in the generation of the unexplained enthalpy. (*d*) Finally, although it may be coincidental, the amount of tetanic activation heat produced is just about enough to account for the energy imbalance in all species so far examined.

THE ENERGETICS OF CONTRACTIONS IN WHICH MUSCLE LENGTH CHANGES

Shortening Muscles

The amount of external work performed by a muscle shortening against a load is determined by the force-velocity curve and the duration of shortening (38). A. V. Hill (38, 129) showed that if a tetanized muscle contracting isometrically near l_o shortened, the rate of heat production during shortening exceeded the isometric rate; after shortening, the rate of heat production returned to an isometric value commensurate with the muscle's new length. The excess heat production above the isometric baseline was called the shortening heat. (This definition of shortening heat does *not* imply that during shortening, one set of processes produce maintenance heat and another produce shortening heat; rather the isometric maintenance heat is taken only as a convenient reference.) Furthermore, the rate of shortening heat production is proportional to the velocity of shortening, and the amount of shortening heat produced per centimeter of shortening, α, is linearly dependent on load ($\alpha = 0.16 P_o + 0.18\ P$) and independent of the time at which shortening occurs (at least within the first 2 sec of stimulation) (37, 38). Thus *during* shortening in tetani near l_o, the rate of energy liberation, $(\dot{h} + \dot{w})$, is given by

$$\dot{h} + \dot{w} = (0.16\ P_o + 0.18\ P)v + Pv + \dot{M}, \qquad\qquad 6.$$

where P is the afterload; P_o, the isometric tetanus tension; v, the shortening velocity; and M, the isometric maintenance heat rate.

As Woledge (47) has pointed out, equation 6 indicates that as the load against which the muscle shortens is decreased, the rate of energy liberation increases to a maximum of ~ 4 times the isometric rate at a load 0.15 P_o. At loads $< 0.15\ P_o$, the rate of energy liberation decreases, so that at zero load the rate of energy liberation is 3.6 times the isometric rate (47). Upon the *completion* of shortening, the amount of energy produced from the beginning of shortening is thus

$$h + w = (0.16\ P_o + 0.18\ P)x + Px + \dot{M}\Delta t, \qquad\qquad 7.$$

where x is the distance shortened and Δt is the duration of shortening. Equation 7 is simply a statement of observed facts. Subsequent to shortening, with continued stimulation, the difference between the heat produced by the shortening and isometric muscles remains constant (130, 131). However, after mechanical relaxation, the net thermal effect of shortening, which we shall call the "net shortening heat" is $\sim 85\%$ of that produced at the end of shortening (130, 131). This is because the amount of heat produced from the cessation of stimulation to complete mechanical relaxation, the relaxation heat, is slightly less in the muscle that had shortened (130, 131). Equation 7 still applies, but with a slightly smaller shortening heat term. A net shortening heat production negates an earlier hypothesis that shortening was related to an entropy production associated with coiling in the tertiary structure of the crossbridges (132).

Whether or not shortening heat is produced in isotonic twitches is a complicated question. During shortening from near l_o, the heat produced in an isotonic twitch exceeds that produced in an isometric twitch near l_o (37, 53, 131, 133); but by the end of relaxation, the heat produced (provided the work stored in the lifted load is not dissipated as heat) is about the same in both contractions (37, 131, 133, 134). The total energy ($h + w$) in variously afterloaded twitches is given by

$$h + w = I + w, \qquad\qquad 8.$$

in which I is the isometric heat produced near l_o; this is the Fenn effect (134). Equation 8 seems to contradict equation 7 and implies there is no net shortening heat in the isotonic twitch. Furthermore, at temperatures greater than $0°C$, ($h + w$) is maximal in the isometric twitch and declines as the afterload is reduced (135–137). A. V. Hill argued that the difference between equations 7 and 8 was explained by the presence of "feedback heat", an additional heat production associated with the presence of tension during relaxation of the isometric twitch (138). However, recent measurements (37) failed to find any feedback heat production. Others have argued that the isometric muscle produces heat associated with the development and maintenance of tension, which occur to a lesser extent in the isotonic twitch (37, 139).

While a phenomenological treatment can be obtained (136) which reconciles equations 7 and 8, the plain fact of the matter is that shortening heat production in twitches has not been measured in exactly the same way as in tetani. Consequently, direct comparison of the results from the twitch and the tetanus is not possible, for several reasons: (a) During shortening in a tetanus, the isometric reference is the heat rate of an isometric contraction at the average length of the muscle during shortening. Use of the isometric twitch heat at l_o as a reference, as is implied in equation 8, is inappropriate because the isometric heat production decreases at lengths less than l_o (54, 61). (*b*) Tetanic shortening heat is usually measured after the muscle has reached a constant force with maintained stimulation. This is not possible in a twitch and raises two problems: First, in a twitch (unlike a tetanus) the isometric control will not be fully isometric but will be shortening against the series elastic element while the muscle develops force. Second, while a tetanized muscle should be fully activated both during and after shortening by the maintained stimulation, there is good evidence that in the twitch shortening per se partially inactivates the muscle (140–142). This is likely to reduce the heat production both during and after shortening. Additional information on this point is needed and might be obtained from studies of the effect of shortening on Ca^{2+} transients. (*c*) *After* shortening in a tetanus, the isometric baseline is taken as the isometric heat production at the length to which the muscle has shortened. In the twitch, such an isometric control will have produced more tension than the shortening muscle and consequently will produce more thermoelastic heat and degraded internal work during the relaxation than the isotonic muscle. Until comparable protocols have been used in both the twitch and the tetanus, the question of existence of a net shortening heat in a twitch will not be resolved.

Additional information is now available regarding tetanic shortening heat production. Dickinson & Woledge (143) have found that when frog muscle shortens between two set lengths in successive tetani spaced 5 sec apart, the amount of shortening heat produced in each successive tetanus is reduced. By the third tetanus α is depressed by 15–30%, even though P_o and the force-velocity curve are not materially affected. Control experiments showed that this effect was related to active shortening per se. Finally, when the interval between tetani was increased to 40 sec there was no significant depression of α. These results show that at least a fraction of shortening heat production is not necessary for shortening and the performance of work, and raise the question of whether shortening heat production can be completely suppressed. It may also be that muscles of other species produce no shortening heat at all. Comparative studies are therefore needed.

J. LeBacq and E. Homsher (unpublished observations) have attempted to discover whether shortening heat production is related to the interaction of the thick and thin filaments by studying the variation in the amount of shortening heat production as the amount of thick and thin filament overlap was varied. Frog semitendinosus muscles were set at various sarcomere lengths beyond 2.0 μm and the isometric heat rate and tension development measured. The muscles were then stretched to 3.6 μm, tetanized, and allowed to shorten at velocities near V_{max} for 0.4 μm per sarcomere; the net shortening heat production above isometric controls at the same length was then measured. This process was repeated in contractions shortening in successive 0.4 μm per sarcomere steps down to 2.0 μm in both ascending and descending order. Plots of the shortening heat produced per centimeter of shortening, α, against mean sarcomere length during shortening, declined with decreasing thick and thin filament overlap just as did isometric force development. The plots indicate that shortening heat is probably produced by thick and thin filament interaction. This conclusion gains further support from experiments by Gilbert & Matsumoto (144), who found that in very small quick releases, unless shortening is greater than ~ 10 nm per half sarcomere, no shortening heat is produced. This result suggests that crossbridges must detach to allow net shortening heat production.

Chemical Change and Shortening

The obvious explanation for the increased rate of enthalpy production during shortening is that crossbridges cycle more rapidly with a concomitant increase in the rate of ATP splitting. It has been shown that when muscle shortens against loads less than P_o, the rate of ~P splitting does in fact increase substantially (145, 146). Over one or more contraction-relaxation cycles in which shortening occurs against small or moderate loads, the ratio of enthalpy production to PC split is the same as is seen in isometric contractions (22, 133, 146), implying that the different amounts of enthalpy produced have the same metabolic cost. During contractions against moderate loads, Curtin et al (104) found that the amount of unexplained enthalpy was the same as or less than that in a comparable isometric contraction. In muscles performing large amounts of external work, enough ~P is hydrolyzed both during (104, 145, 146) and after (22, 133) contraction to account for the work done if (as seems likely) ΔG for ATP splitting is more negative than -28 kJ $\cdot$ mole^{-1} (104, 145). These observations support the notion that upon shortening, crossbridges cycle more rapidly, and that work is derived from the hydrolysis of ATP.

A major problem arises, however, when the time course of enthalpy production is compared to the time course of PC splitting in rapidly shortening muscles that produced negligible amounts of work. During rapid shortening (near V_{max}) less than 25% of the observed enthalpy can be explained by PC splitting (102, 147). This result suggests that when a muscle shortens and produces a large amount of shortening heat, less of the enthalpy can be accounted for than in isometrically contracting muscle. It introduces the possibility that rapid shortening results in a type of energy imbalance fundamentally different from that seen in the isometric contraction. Rall et al (147) tested this idea in experiments in which one of a muscle pair contracted isometrically while the other shortened against a very small afterload. The duration of stimulation (300 msec) and the time at which the reactions were arrested (500 msec) were so arranged that the total enthalpy production, $(h + w)$, by the two muscles was the same. If shortening resulted in less ATP splitting for a given observed enthalpy, the isotonic muscle would hydrolyze significantly less ATP and/or PC; this was indeed the result. A corollary to this result is that one cannot regard shortening heat production as a process occurring above a given isometric baseline, for if this were the case the two muscles would have split the same amount of ATP. Kushmerick et al (145) have obtained similar results; they did not measure enthalpy production. After relaxation (3 sec) the explained enthalpy increases to $\sim 70\%$ of the observed enthalpy. This result suggests that subsequent to shortening there is an ATP splitting with little or no heat production; it implies the presence of a reaction that is reversed by a thermoneutral ATP splitting. This idea must be tested directly.

The results above allow calculation of the number of crossbridges attached to the thin filaments during shortening. Assuming a crossbridge throw of 12 nm (148), a shortening of $\sim 30\%$ of the muscle length (or 330 nm per half-sarcomere) requires 28 crossbridge throws [(330 nm per half-sarcomere)/(12 nm per crossbridge throw)]. Since 0.12 μmole ATP $\cdot$ g^{-1} was hydrolyzed during shortening, a maximum of 4.3 nmoles of crossbridges [(0.12 μmole $\cdot$ g^{-1})/(28)] were attached during any one throw. Assuming there are 140 nmoles myosin $\cdot$ g^{-1} (149), maximally 3.0% of the crossbridges were attached to actin at any one time. If the PC split subsequent to shortening is included, from 7–10% of the crossbridges were attached. A similar calculation using the data (104) from maximally working muscles shortening about the same distance but 40% as fast as contractions near V_{max}, indicates that $\sim 20\%$ of the crossbridges were attached at any one time.

From the foregoing, several conclusions about the energetics of rapidly shortening muscle can be drawn: (a) Shortening heat production is derived from the interaction of the thick and thin filaments; (b) over a complete contraction-relaxation cycle there is a net shortening heat production; (c) shortening heat production is reduced as the time between successive shortening contractions is reduced; (d) at the time shortening heat is produced, insufficient ATP or PC is split to account for it; and (e) by the end of relaxation or shortly thereafter, shortening heat has the same metabolic cost as is seen in the isometric case. These observations seem well established, and imply that upon rapid shortening, processes occur in the myofibrils that liberate heat; subsequent to shortening, these processes are reversed by ATP splitting; i.e. shortening induces a temporal separation between the processes that liberate enthalpy and those that hydrolyze ATP. If a similar process occurs in isometric contractions, its extent is very much limited.

What, then, are the processes producing heat during shortening, and how are they later reversed by ATP splitting? One possibility is that an intrinsic temporal separation exists between enthalpy production and ATP hydrolysis in the actomyosin ATPase mechanism itself and that rapid shortening accentuates this separation. It has been found that myosin binds and cleaves ATP with essentially no enthalpy change (see Figure 4, reactions 1 and 2), while product dissociation (Figure 4, reactions 3 and 4) is accompanied by a large enthalpy change (122, 124). Assuming that the Lymn-Taylor mechanism (123) applies to rapidly shortening muscle, that the enthalpy changes by the actomyosin ATPase mechanism are similar to those of myosin, and that the myosin species that attaches to the thin filament is $M \cdot ADP \cdot P_i$ (150), several conclusions can be reached. Since thick and thin filaments slide past each other at 1200 nm $\cdot$ sec^{-1} in a rapidly shortening frog muscle at 0°C, and since the crossbridge throw is 12 nm, the crossbridge can remain attached for $\sim$ 10 msec. Thus reactions 7,3',4',1', and 6 must occur within 10 msec, and it is presumably during this interval that heat is liberated by a crossbridge. The rate at which $M \cdot ATP$ is converted to $M \cdot ADP \cdot P_i$ would then determine the time course of ATP splitting. Unfortunately a value for this rate constant at physiological ATP concentrations has not been measured. However, to account for the temporal dissociation of shortening heat production and ATP splitting this would need to be of the order of 1 sec^{-1}.

Alternatively, rapid shortening may involve reactions or branch points not seen in Figure 4. It is not yet known to what extent mechanical or structural constraints alter the reaction mechanism and/or rate constants because they have been deduced from in vitro measurements on unorganized systems. For example, it may be that during rapid shortening some thin filament–crosssbridge linkages are broken prior to ADP release, thus forming $M \cdot ADP$. Net formation of $M \cdot ADP$ from $M \cdot ADP \cdot P_i$ will result in a heat production since the ΔH for reaction 3 (see Figure 4) is large [–140 kJ (mole ADP)$^{-1}$]. The formation of 0.05–0.10 μmoles of $M \cdot ADP$ per gram of muscle in this fashion could account for the unexplained enthalpy in rapidly shortening muscles. In vitro, the rate constant for ADP dissociation from frog myosin (reaction 4, Figure 4) at 0°C is 0.5 sec^{-1} (M. Ferenczi, E. Homsher, D. Trentham, R. Simmons, unpublished observations), which would cause ATP hydrolysis to lag behind shortening as a consequence of the relatively slow ADP release. From these hypotheses, one sees that to retain the essentials of the Lymn-Taylor mechanism (23) one must postulate that the amounts of various myosin intermediates vary with time during rapid shortening. Finally, it may be that during shortening, processes are occurring that are not directly related to the ATPase mechanism and are as yet unknown.

The understanding of the energetics of rapidly shortening muscles is thus still at a rudimentary stage. Further studies characterizing the enthalpy production by shortening muscles and the shortening-induced energy imbalance must be performed. Information is needed concerning the mechanism, rate constants, and associated enthalpy changes of frog actomyosin ATPase in both unorganized and, more importantly, organized protein systems such as myofibrils and skinned muscle fibers. Perhaps when such information is available, models that account for the energy liberation by shortening muscles can be designed and tested.

Stretches of Actively Contracting Muscles

If an actively contracting muscle is forcibly lengthened at slow or moderate speeds, the enthalpy produced by the muscle is substantially reduced (151, 152) or altogether suppressed (153). During the stretch, work is done on the muscle and will appear as heat. The heat produced during the stretch, h_s, will equal the enthalpy produced by the muscle, h_m, plus the work done on it. The results described above indicate that h_m may approach zero. [How uniformly the temperature change is distributed over the length of the muscle, however, is subject to question. Work in our laboratory indicates that h_m is never reduced to less than 30–40% of the isometric value if temperature is sampled from almost the whole of the muscle (E. Homsher, unpublished results).] Does the imposed stretch only suppress ATP splitting, or does it result in an ATP synthesis? To answer this question, the amount of ATP or PC split during a contraction in which the muscle was lengthened was compared to the amount of ATP and/or PC split in an isometric contraction (154–156). In general ATP and/or PC splitting was suppressed during forcible lengthening; the extent of suppression depended on the velocity at which the muscle was stretched. At low velocities, $\sim 0.2\ l_o \cdot sec^{-1}$, a maximum reduction of the ATP hydrolysis to 25% of that measured in the isometric contraction was seen (156). At higher velocities, the ATP hydrolysis was not suppressed as much. This line of investigation provides no evidence for stretch-induced ATP synthesis. (If complete suppression could be achieved, this would constitute reasonable evidence for ATP synthesis, since during the stretch the sarcoplasmic reticulum ought to pump Ca^{2+} and split ATP). Likewise, attempts to demonstrate ATP synthesis by measuring ^{18}O and $^{32}PO_4$ incorporation into ATP during stretch have, for a variety of technical reasons, been inconclusive (157, 158). The best that can be said is it now appears that forcible lengthening of muscles primarily depresses ATP utilization.

Following the forcible lengthening of stimulated muscles, the force exerted by the muscle under continuing stimulation very substiantially exceeds (by $\sim 70\%$) that which the muscle could develop isometrically at the same length (152, 159). This "extra" tension can be maintained for about ten seconds. Associated with the maintained elevated force is a maintenance heat rate the same as or less than that of a muscle contracting isometrically at the same length (152; C. Kean and E. Homsher, unpublished observations). These results are not consistent with the hypothesis that the muscle is more fully activated and that an increased number of crossbridges are attached and cycling, since such activation would imply an increased maintenance heat rate. Instead they seem to indicate that in addition to the usual number and cycling rate of crossbridges, there are some crossbridges that, as a result of the stretch, are "locked" onto the thin filament and detach relatively slowly (158). This would imply that the product release, ATP binding, or actomyosin dissociation rate constants may be sensitive to the crossbridge position, and would constitute evidence for the presence of mechanical constraints on the ATPase mechanism of the thick and thin filaments.

CONCLUSION

The work described above indicates that the energy liberation during muscle contraction cannot be accounted for solely by ATP and/or PC splitting. Additional reactions, whose identity and role in contraction are not yet known, must therefore occur. Furthermore, the results suggest that such reactions may be associated with events occurring in both the myofibrils and the sarcoplasmic reticulum. Finally, available data suggest that ATP hydrolysis continues during recovery, presumably coupled to the reversal of the reactions that occurred during contraction and relaxation. In order to identify these unknown processes, and to learn the role they play in contraction, future work in muscle energetics will probably focus on (a) further characterization of the energy liberation and biochemical changes occurring during and after contractions (Of particular urgency is the need to determine accurately the time course of *unexplained* enthalpy production in isometric and isotonic contractions, the role of the sarcoplasmic reticulum and the myofibrils in the unexplained enthalpy production, and the time course of $\sim$P splitting and resynthesis during recovery); (b) energetic studies (i.e. measurement of enthalpy and biochemical changes) of simplified systems such as skeletal muscle proteins (myosin, actomyosin, and the actin-tropomyosin-troponin complex) and isolated membrane systems (e.g. sarcoplasmic reticulum). Work has already begun in the latter area and promises to yield valuable information. However, results from these studies may require modification once it is learned to what extent the structural and mechanical constraints existing in the intact muscle affect the interpretation of results from in vitro systems.

ACKNOWLEDGMENTS

Preparation of this review and some of the cited experimental work were supported by USPHS grant HL 11351 and American Heart Association grant LA 525. Dr. Homsher is supported by Research Career Development Grant AM 70792.

Literature Cited

1. Huxley, A. F. 1974. Review lecture: Muscle contraction. *J. Physiol. London* 243:1–43
2. Endo, M. 1977. Calcium release from the sarcoplasmic reticulum. *Physiol. Rev.* 57:71–108
3. Weber, A., Murray, J. M. 1973. Molecular control mechanisms in muscle contraction. *Physiol. Rev.* 53:612–73
4. Trentham, D. R., Eccleston, J. F., Bagshaw, C. R. 1976. Kinetic analysis of ATPase mechanisms. *Quart. Rev. Biophys.* 9:217–81
5. Hill, A. V. 1950. A challenge to biochemists. *Biochim. Biophys. Acta* 4: 4–11
6. Hill, A. V. 1966. A further challenge to biochemists. *Biochem. Z.* 345:1–8
7. Huxley, A. F. 1957. Muscle structure and theories of contraction. *Prog. Biophys. Biophys. Chem.* 7:255–318
8. Deshcherevskii, V. I. 1968. Two models of muscular contraction. *Biophysics* 13:1093–1101
9. Chaplain, R. A., Frommelt, B. 1971. A mechanochemical model for muscular contraction. I. The rate of energy liberation and steady state velocities of shortening and lengthening. *J. Mechanochem. Cell Motility* 1:41–56
10. Carlson, F. D., Wilkie, D. R. 1974. *Muscle Physiology.* Englewood Cliffs, N. J.: Prentice-Hall. 170 pp.
11. Mommaerts, W. F. H. M. 1969. Energetics of muscular contraction. *Physiol. Rev.* 49:427–508
12. Abbott, B. C., Howarth, J. V. 1973. Heat studies in excitable tissues. *Physiol. Rev.* 53:120–58
13. Woledge, R. C. 1971. Heat production and chemical change in muscle. *Prog. Biophys. Mol. Biol.* 22:39–74
14. Maréchal, G. 1972. Les sources d'énergie immediate de la contraction musculaire. *J. Physiol. Paris* 65:5–50A
15. Curtin, N. A., Davies, R. E. 1973. ATP breakdown following activation of muscle. In *The Structure and Function of Muscle,* ed. G. H. Bourne, Vol III, pp. 471–515 New York: Academic
16. Kushmerick, M. J. 1977. Energy balance in muscle contraction: A Biochemical approach. *Curr. Top. Bioenerg.* 6:1–37
17. Gibbs, C. 1974. In *The Mammalian Myocardium,* ed. G. A. Langer, A. J. Brady, pp. 105–34. New York: Wiley
18. Wilkie, D. R. 1961. Thermodynamics and the interpretation of biological heat measurements. *Prog. Biophys. Biophys. Chem.* 10:260–98
19. Wilkie, D. R. 1970. Thermodynamics and Biology. *Chem. Brit.* 6:472–76
20. Wilkie, D. R. 1974. The efficiency of muscular contraction. *J. Mechanochem. Cell Motility* 2:257–67
21. Woledge, R. C. 1972. *In vitro* calorimetric studies relating to the interpretation of muscle heat experiments. *Cold Spring Harbor Symp. Quant. Biol.* 37:629–34
22. Wilkie, D. R. 1968. Heat, work and phosphorylcreatine breakdown in muscle. *J. Physiol. London* 195:157–83
23. Kretzschmar, K. M., Wilkie, D. R. 1972. A new method for absolute heat measurement utilizing the Peltier effect. *J. Physiol. London* 202:66–67
24. Homsher, E., Rall, J. A., Wallner, A., Ricchiuti, N. V., 1975. Energy liberation and chemical change in frog skeletal muscle during single isometric tetanic contractions. *J. Gen. Physiol.* 65:1–21
25. Gower, D., Kretzschmar, K. M. 1976. Heat production and chemical change during isometric contraction of rat soleus muscle. *J. Physiol. London* 258: 659–71
26. Mulieri, L. A., Luhr, G., Trefry, J., Alpert, N. R. 1977. Metal-film thermopiles for use with rabbit right ventricular papillary muscles. *Am. J. Physiol.* In press
27. Dawson, J. M., Gadian, D. G., Wilkie, D. R. 1977. Contraction and recovery of living muscles studies by ^{31}P nuclear magnetic resonance. *J. Physiol. London.* 267:703–35
28. Maréchal, G., Mommaerts, W.F.H. M. 1963. The metabolism of phosphoryl-

creatine during an isometric tetanus in frog sartorius muscle. *Biochim. Biophys. Acta* 70:53–67

29. Hill, A. V. 1965. *Trails and Trials in Physiology.* Baltimore: Williams & Wilkins. 374 pp.

30. Godfraind-de Becker, A. 1972. Heat production and fluorescence changes of toad sartorius muscle during aerobic recovery after a short tetanus. *J. Physiol. London* 223:719–34

31. Chapman, J. B., Gibbs, C. L., Vogelsanger, H. 1975. Simultaneous recording of heat and fluorescence following contraction of isolated cardiac muscle. *Experientia* 31:445–47

32. Hill, D. K. 1940. The time course of the oxidative recovery heat of frog's muscles. *J. Physiol. London* 98:207–27

33. Jöbsis, F. F., Duffield, J. C. 1967. Force, shortening, and work in muscular contraction: relative contributions to overall energy utilization. *Science* 156:1388–92

34. Wendt, I. R., Gibbs, C. L. 1973. Energy production of rat extensor digitorum longus muscle. *Am. J. Physiol.* 224:1081–86

35. Aubert, X. 1956. *Le Couplage Énergétique de la Contraction Musculaire.* Brussels: Editions Arscia. 320 pp.

36. Homsher, E., Mommaerts, W.F.H.M., Ricchiuti, N. V., Wallner, A. 1972. Activation heat, activation metabolism and tension-related heat in frog semitendinosus muscles. *J. Physiol. London* 220:601–25

37. Homsher, E., Rall, J. A. 1973. Energetics of shortening muscles in twitches and tetanic contractions. I. A reinvestigation of Hill's concept of the shortening heat. *J. Gen. Physiol.* 62:663–76

38. Hill, A. V. 1938. The heat of shortening and the dynamic constants of muscle. *Proc. R. Soc. London Ser. B* 126:136–95

39. Hill, A. V., Woledge, R. C. 1962. An examination of absolute values in myothermic measurements. *J. Physiol. London* 162:311–33

40. Hill, A. V. 1970. *First and Last Experiments in Muscle Mechanics.* London: Cambridge. 141 pp.

41. Smith, I. C. H. 1972. Energetics of activation in frog and toad muscle. *J. Physiol London* 220:583–99

42. Gibbs, C. L., Gibson, W. R. 1972. Energy production of rat soleus muscle. *Am. J. Physiol.* 223:864–71

43. Canfield, S. P. 1971. The mechanical properties and heat production of chicken latissimus dorsi muscles during tetanic contractions. *J. Physiol London* 219:281–302

44. Rall, J. A., Schottelius, B. A. 1973. Energetics of contraction in phasic and tonic skeletal muscles of the chicken. *J. Gen. Physiol.* 62:303–23

45. Bridge, J. H. B. 1976. *A thermochemical investigation of chicken latissimus dorsi muscle.* PhD thesis, Univ. Calif., Los Angeles, California. 139 pp.

46. Davey, D. F., Gibbs, C. L., McKirdy, H. C. 1975. Structural, mechanical and myothermic properties of rabbit rectococcygeus muscle. *J. Physiol. London* 248:207–30

47. Woledge, R. C. 1968. The energetics of tortoise muscle. *J. Physiol. London* 197:685–707

48. Wells, J. B. 1965. Comparison of mechanical properties between slow and fast mammalian muscles. *J. Physiol. London* 178:252–69

49. Aubert, X. 1968. In *Symposia Biologica Hungarica 8,* ed. E. Ernst, F. B. Straub, pp. 187–89. Budapest: Akadémiae Kiádó.

50. Curtin, N. A., Woledge, R. C. 1977. A comparison of the energy balance in two successive isometric tetani of frog muscle. *J. Physiol. London.* In press

51. Sandow, A. 1965. Excitation-contraction coupling in skeletal muscle. *Pharmacol. Rev.* 17:265–320

52. Godfraind-de Becker, A. 1965. Effet de l'iodure, potentiateur de la secousse musculaire, sur la thermogénèse du tétanos. *Arch. Int. Physiol. Biochem.* 73:162–63

53. Hill, A. V. 1949. The heat of activation and the heat of shortening in a muscle twitch. *Proc. R. Soc. London Ser. B.* 136:195–211

54. Hill, A. V. 1950. A note on the heat of activation in a muscle twitch. *Proc. R. Soc. London Ser. B.* 139:330–31

55. Hill, A. V. 1958. The priority of heat production in a muscle twitch. *Proc. R. Soc. London Ser. B.* 148:397–402

56. Jöbsis, F. F., O'Connor, M. J. 1966. Calcium release and reabsorption in the sartorius muscle of the toad. *Biochem. Biophys. Res. Commun.* 25:246–52

57. Blinks, J. R. 1973. Calcium transients in striated muscle cells. *Eur. J. Cardiol.* 1:135–42

58. Gordon, A. M., Huxley, A. F., Julian, F. J. 1966. The variation in isometric tension with sarcomere length in vertebrate muscle fibres. *J. Physiol. London* 184:170–92

59. Schoenberg, M., Podolsky, R. J. 1972. Length-force relation of calcium ac-

tivated muscle fibers. *Science* 176:52–55

60. Taylor, S. R., Rudel, R. 1970. Striated muscle fibers: Inactivation of contraction induced by shortening. *Science* 167:882–84

61. Gibbs, C. L., Ricchiuti, N. V., Mommaerts, W. F. H. M. 1966. Activation heat in frog sartorius muscle. *J. Gen. Physiol.* 49:517–35

62. Hodgkin, A. L., Horowicz, P. 1957. The differential action of hypertonic solutions on the twitch and action potential of a muscle fibre. *J. Physiol. London* 136:17P

63. Howarth, J. V. 1958. The behavior of frog muscle in hypertonic solutions. *J. Physiol. London* 144:167–75

64. Gordon, A. M., Godt, R. E., Donaldson, S. K. B., Harris, C. E. 1973. Tension in skinned frog muscle fibers in solutions of varying ionic strength and neutral salt compositon. *J. Gen. Physiol.* 62:550–74

65. Homsher, E., Briggs, F. N., Wise, R. M. 1973. Effects of hypertonicity on resting and contracting frog skeletal muscles. *Am. J. Physiol.* 226:855–63

66. Sandberg, J. A., Carlson, F. D. 1966. The dependence of phosphorylcreatine hydrolysis during an isometric tetanus. *Biochem. Z.* 345:212–31

67. Edman, K. A. P. 1968. In Ref. 49, pp. 171–75

68. Podolsky, R. J. 1964. The maximum sarcomere length for contraction of isolated myofibrils. *J. Physiol. London* 170:110–23

69. Taylor, S. R., Rudel, R., Blinks, J. R. 1975. Calcium transients in amphibian muscle. *Fed. Proc.* 34:1379–81

70. Frank, J. S., Winegrad, S. 1976. Effect of muscle length on ^{45}Ca efflux in resting and contracting skeletal muscle. *Am. J. Physiol.* 231:555–59

71. Julian, F. J. 1971. The effect of calcium on the force velocity relation of briefly glycerinated frog muscle fibres. *J. Physiol. London* 218:117–46

72. Moss, R. L., Sollins, M. R., Julian, F. J. 1976. Calcium activation produces a characteristic response to stretch in both skeletal and cardiac muscle. *Nature* 260:619–21

73. Podolsky, R. J., Teichholz, L. E. 1970. The relation between calcium and contraction kinetics in skinned fibres. *J. Physiol. London* 211:19–35

74. Weber, A., Herz, R., Reiss, I. 1964. The regulation of myofibrillar activity by calcium. *Proc. R. Soc. London Ser. B.* 160:489–501

75. Fuchs, F., Briggs, F. N. 1968. The site of calcium binding in relation to the activation of myofibrillar contraction. *J. Gen. Physiol.* 51:655–76

76. Bremel, R. D., Weber, A. M. 1972. Cooperation within actin filament in vertebrate skeletal muscle. *Nature New Biol.* 238:97–101

77. Allen, D. G., Blinks, J. R., Prendergast, F. E. 1977. Aequorin luminescence: relation of light emission to calcium concentration—a calcium independent component. *Science* 195:996–98

78. Gordon, A. M., Huxley, A. F., Julian, F. J. 1966. Tension development in highly stretched vertebrate muscle fibres. *J. Physiol. London* 184:143–69

79. Kushmerick, M. J., Larson, R. E., Davies, R. E. 1969. The chemical energetics of muscle contraction. I. Activation, heat of shortening, and ATP utilization for activation-relaxation processes. *Proc. R. Soc. London Ser. B* 174:293–313

80. Infante, A. A., Klaupiks, D., Davies, R. E. 1964. Length, tension, and metabolism during short isometric contractions of frog sartorius muscle. *Biochim. Biophys. Acta* 88:215–17

81. Chaplain, R. A., Pfister, E. 1970. The relationship between activation heat and calcium transients in frog sartorius mucle. *Experientia* 26:505–6

82. Kean, C., Homsher, E., Sarian-Garibian, V., Zemplenyi, J. 1976. Phosphocreatine (PC) splitting by stretched frog muscle. *Physiologist* 19:250

83. Curtin, N. A., Woledge, R. C. 1975. Energy balance in DNFB-treated and untreated frog muscle. *J. Physiol. London* 246:737–52

84. Bezanilla, F., Horowitz, P. 1975. Fluorescence intensity changes associated with contractile activation in frog muscle stained with nile blue A. *J. Physiol. London* 246:709–35

85. Winegrad, S. 1970. Intracellular calcium localization in muscle. *J. Gen. Physiol.* 55:77–88

86. Howell, J. N. 1969. A lesion of the transverse tubules of skeletal muscle. *J. Physiol. London* 201:515–33

87. Homsher, E., Mommaerts, W. F. H. M., Ricchiuti, N. V., Wallner, A. 1970. The magnitude, time course and source of activation heat production in frog semitendinosus muscles at 0°C. *Fed. Proc.* 29: 655 (Abstr.)

88. Yamada, K., Mashima, H., Ebashi, S. 1976. The enthalpy change accompanying the binding of calcium to troponin relating to the activation heat pro-

duction of muscle. *Proc. Jpn. Acad.* 52:252–55

89. Potter, J. D., Hsu, F., Pownall, H. J. 1977. The thermodynamics of Ca^{2+} binding to troponin-C. *J. Biol. Chem.* 252:2452–54

90. Pechère, J. F., Demaille, J., Capony, J. P. 1971. Muscular parvalbumins: preparative and analytical methods of general applicability. *Biochim. Biophys. Acta* 236:391–408

91. Gerday, C., Gillis, J. M. 1976. The possible role of parvalbumins in the control of contraction. *J. Physiol. London* 258:96–97

92. Baron, G., Demaille, J., Dutruge, E. 1975. The distribution of parvalbumins in muscle and in other tissues. *FEBS Lett.* 56:156–60

93. Haselgrove, J. C. 1975. X-ray evidence for conformational changes in myosin filaments of vertebrate striated muscle. *J. Mol. Biol.* 92:113–43

94. Fraser, A. 1972. Comments on activation heat and its relation to activation. *Cold Spring Harbor Symp. Quant. Biol.* 37:627–28

95. Fraser, A., Carlson, F. D. 1973. Initial heat production in isometric frog muscle at 15°C. *J. Gen. Physiol.* 62:271–85

96. Abbott, B. C. 1951. The heat production associated with the maintenance of a prolonged contraction and the extra heat produced during large shortening. *J. Physiol. London* 112:438–45

97. Curtin, N. A. 1976. The prolongation of relaxation after an isometric tetanus. *J. Physiol. London* 258:80–81P

98. Schiaffino, S., Hanzlíková, V., Pierobon, S. 1970. Relations between structure and function in rat skeletal muscle fibers. *J. Cell. Biol.* 47:107–19

99. Page, S. G. 1969. Structure and some contractile properties of fast and slow muscles of the chicken. *J. Physiol. London* 205:131–45

100. Page, S. G. 1968. Fine structure of tortoise skeletal muscle. *J. Physiol. London* 197:709–15

101. Lehky, P., Blum, H. E., Stein, E. A., Fischer, E. H. 1974. Isolation and characterization of parvalbumins from the skeletal muscles of higher vertebrates. *J. Biol. Chem.* 249:4332–34

102. Gilbert, C., Kretzschmar, K. M., Wilkie, D. R., Woledge, R. C. 1971. Chemical change and energy output during muscular contraction. *J. Physiol. London* 218:163–93

103. Curtin, N. A., Woledge, R. C. 1974. Energetics of relaxation in frog muscle. *J. Physiol. London* 238:437–46

104. Curtin, N. A., Gilbert, C., Kretzschmar, K. M., Wilkie, D. R. 1974. The effect of the performance of work on total energy output and metabolism during muscular contraction. *J. Physiol. London* 238:455–72

105. Dawson, J., Gower, D., Kretzschmar, K. M., Wilkie, D. R. 1975. Heat production and chemical change in frog sartorius; a comparison of *Rana pipiens* with *Rana temporaria*. *J. Physiol. London* 254:41–42P

106. Kushmerick, M. J., Paul, R. J. 1976. Relationship between initial chemical reactions and oxidative recovery metabolism for single isometric contractions of frog sartorius at 0°C. *J. Physiol. London* 254:711–27

107. Walsh, T. H., Woledge, R. C. 1970. Heat production and chemical change in tortoise muscle. *J. Physiol. London* 206:457–69

108. Kretzschmar, K. M. 1975. Heat production and metabolism during the contraction of mammalian skeletal muscle. *J. Supramol. Struct.* 3:175–80

109. Stella, G. 1928. The combination of carbon dioxide in muscle, its heat of neutralization and its dissociation curve. *J. Physiol. London* 68:49–66

110. Canfield, P., Lebacq, J., Maréchal, G. 1973. Energy balance in frog sartorius muscle during an isometric tetanus at 20°C. *J. Physiol. London* 232:467–83

111. Paul, R. J., Kushmerick, M. J. 1974. Apparent P/O ratio and chemical energy balance in frog sartorius muscle *in vitro*. *Biochim Biophys. Acta* 347:483–90

112. Kushmerick, M. J., Paul, R. J. 1976. Aerobic recovery metabolism following a single isometric tetanus in frog sartorius muscle at 0°C. *J. Physiol. London* 254:693–709

113. Mahler, M. 1977. Relationship between initial creatine phosphate (CP) breakdown and recovery oxygen consumption for single isometric tetani of the frog sartorius at 20°C. *Biophys. J.* 17:203a

114. Skoog, C. M., Stephens, N. L. 1973. Oxidative phosphorylation in frog skeletal muscle mitochondria. *Proc. Can. Fed. Biol. Soc.* 16:34

115. DeFuria, R., Kushmerick, M. J. 1977. ATP utilization associated with recovery metabolism in anaerobic frog muscle. *Am. J. Physiol.* 1:C30–C36

116. Lundsgaard, E. 1931. Über die Energetik der anaeroben Muskelkontraktion. *Biochem. Z.* 223:322–43

117. Ambrosoli, G., Cerretelli, P. 1973. The anaerobic recovery of frog muscle. *Pfluegers Arch.* 345:131–43

118. Cerretelli, P., Di Prampero, P. E., Ambrosoli, G. 1972. High-energy phosphate resynthesis from anaerobic glycolysis in frog gastrocnemius muscle. *Am. J. Physiol.* 222:1021–26

119. Spronck, A. C. 1965. Évolution temporelle de l'hydrolyse de la phosphocréatine et de la synthèse d'hexosediphosphate après cinq secousses simples. *Arch. Int. Physiol.* 73:241–59

120. Mommaerts, W. F. H. M., Wallner, A. 1967. The breakdown of adenosine triphosphate in the contraction cycle of the frog sartorius muscle. *J. Physiol. London* 170:343–57

121. Burt, C. T., Glonek, T., Bárány, M. 1977. ^{31}P nuclear magnetic resonance detection of unexpected phosphodiesters in muscle. *Biochemistry.* In press

122. Woledge, R. C. 1977. Calorimetric studies of muscle and muscle proteins. In *Applications of Calorimetry in Life Sciences,* ed. I. Lamprecht, B. Schaurschmidt. Berlin: de Gruyter. In press

123. Taylor, E. W. 1973. In *Current Topics in Bioenergetics.* ed. P. R. Sanadi, L. Pacher, 5:210–31. New York: Academic

124. Yamada, T., Shimizu, H., Suga, H. 1973. A kinetic study of the energy storing enzyme-product complex in the hydrolysis of ATP by heavy meromyosin. *Biochim. Biophys. Acta* 305:642–53

125. Kodama, T., Woledge, R. C. 1976. Calorimetric studies of the interaction of myosin with ADP. *J. Biol. Chem.* 251:7499–7503

126. Kodama, T., Watson, I. D., Woledge, R. C. 1977. Calorimetric studies of the ADP binding to myosin filament, heavy meromyosin, and subfragment-1. *J. Biol. Chem.* In press

127. Bonner, R. F., Carlson, F. D. 1975. Structural dynamics of frog muscle during isometric contraction. *J. Gen. Physiol.* 65:555–81

128. Kean, C., Homsher, E., Sarian-Garibian, V. 1977. The energy balance of crossbridge cycling in frog skeletal muscle. *Biophys. J.* 17:202a

129. Hill, A. V. 1964. The effect of load on the heat of shortening of muscle. *Proc. R. Soc. London Ser. B* 150:297–318

130. Aubert, X., Lebacq, J. 1971. The heat of shortening during the plateau of tetanic contraction and at the end of relaxation. *J. Physiol. London* 216:181–200

131. Dickinson, V. A., Woledge, R. C. 1973. The thermal effects of shortening in tetanic contractions of frog muscle. *J. Physiol. London* 233:659–71

132. Davies, R. E. 1963. A molecular theory of muscle contraction: Calcium-dependent contractions with hydrogen bond formation plus ATP dependent extensions of part of the myosin-actin crossbridges. *Nature* 199:1068–74

133. Carlson, F. D., Hardy, D. J., Wilkie, D. R. 1963. Total energy production and phosphorylcreatine hydrolysis in the isotonic twitch. *J. Gen. Physiol.* 46:851–82

134. Fenn, W. O. 1923. A quantitative comparison between the energy liberated and the work performed by isolated sartorius of the frog. *J. Physiol. London* 58:175–203

135. Hill, A. V. 1930. The heat production in isometric and isotonic twitches. *Proc. R. Soc. London Ser B.* 107:115–31

136. Homsher, E., Mommaerts, W. F. H. M., Ricchiuti, N. V. 1973. Energetics of shortening muscles in twitches and tetanic contractions. II. Force-determined shortening heat. *J. Gen. Physiol.* 62:677–92

137. Gibbs, C. L., Chapman, J. B. 1974. Effects of stimulus conditions, temperature, and length on energy output of frog and toad sartorius. *Am. J. Physiol.* 227:964–71

138. Hill, A. V. 1964. The effect of tension in prolonging the active state in a twitch. *Proc. Roy. Soc. London Ser. B.* 159:589–95

139. Mommaerts, W. F. H. M. 1970. What is the Fenn effect? *Naturwissenschaften* 57:326–30

140. Briden, K. L., Alpert, N. R. 1972. The effect of shortening on the time course of active state decay. *J. Gen. Physiol.* 60:202–20

141. Edman, K. A. P. 1975. Mechanical deactivation induced by active shortening in isolated muscle fibers of the frog. *J. Physiol. London* 246:255–75

142. Edman, K. A. P. 1976. Depression of mechanical activity induced by active shortening in frog skeletal muscle fibers. *Acta Physiol. Scand.* 98:384–86

143. Dickinson, V. A., Woledge, R. C. 1974. Reduction of shortening heat during a series of tetanic contractions in frog sartorius muscle. *J. Physiol. London* 242:98–99

144. Gilbert, S. H., Matsumoto, Y. 1976. A reexamination of the thermoelastic effect in active striated muscle. *J. Gen. Physiol.* 68:81–94

145. Kushmerick, M. J., Davies, R. E. 1969. The chemical energetics of muscle con-

traction. II. The chemistry, efficiency, and power of maximally working sartorius muscle. *Proc. R. Soc. London Ser. B.* 174:315–50

146. Chaplain, R. A., Frommelt, B. 1972. The energetics of contraction I. Total energy output and phosphorylcreatine splitting in isotonic tetani of frog sartorius. *Pfluegers Arch.* 334:167–80

147. Rall, J. A., Homsher, E., Wallner, A., Mommaerts, W. F. H. M. 1976. A temporal dissociation of energy liberation and high energy phosphate splitting during shortening in frog skeletal muscles. *J. Gen. Physiol.* 68:13–27

148. Huxley, A. F., Simmons, R. M. 1971. Proposed mechanism of force generation in striated muscle. *Nature* 233:533–38

149. Ebashi, S., Endo, M., Ohtsuki, I. 1969. Control of muscle contraction. *Quart. Rev. Biophys.* 2:351–84

150. Marsten, S. 1973. The nucleotide complexes of myosin in glycerol-extracted muscle fibres. *Biochim. Biophys. Acta* 305:397–412

151. Abbott, B. C., Aubert, X. 1951. Changes of energy during very slow stretches. *Proc. R. Soc. London Ser. B.* 139:104–17

152. Abbott, B. C., Aubert, X. 1952. The force exerted by active striated muscle during and after change of length. *J. Physiol. London* 117:77–86

153. Hill, A. V., Howarth, J. V. 1959. The reversal of chemical reactions in contracting muscle during an applied stretch. *Proc. R. Soc. London Ser. B.* 151:169–93

154. Maréchal, G. 1964. *Le Métabolisme de la Phosphorylcreatine et de l'Adénosine Triphosphate durant la Contraction Musculaire.* Brussels: Editions Arscia. 184 pp.

155. Infante, A. A., Klaupiks, D., Davies, R. E. 1964. Adenosine triphosphate: changes in muscles doing negative work. *Science* 144:1577–78

156. Curtin, N. A., Davies, R. E. 1975. Very high tension with very little ATP breakdown by active skeletal muscle. *J. Mechanochem. Cell Motility* 3:147–54

157. Maréchal, G., Mommaerts, W. F. H. M., Seraydarian, K. 1974. The exchange of O^{18} between water and phosphate compounds in isolated frog sartorius muscle under conditions of negative work. *J. Mechanochem. Cell Motility* 3:39–54

158. Gillis, J. M., Maréchal, G. 1974. The incorporation of radioactive phosphate into ATP in glycerinated fibres stretched or released during contraction. *J. Mechanochem. Cell Motility* 3:55–68

159. Sugi, H. 1972. Tension changes during and after stretch in frog muscle fibers. *J. Physiol. London* 225:237–53

Ann. Rev. Physiol. 1978. 40:133–56
Copyright © 1978 by Annual Reviews Inc. All rights reserved

RESPIRATORY ADAPTATIONS IN SLEEP

❖1188

Eliot A. Phillipson

Department of Medicine, University of Toronto, Toronto, Ontario, Canada

INTRODUCTION

The current era of research into the physiology of sleep began in 1953 when Aserinsky and Kleitman (2) first described REM[1] sleep and its association with a characteristic EEG pattern, dreaming, and changes in autonomic nervous system activity including respiration. This important discovery demonstrated conclusively that the traditional view of sleep as a homogeneous state was incorrect, and indicated that preexisting observations or theories regarding sleep had to be reexamined or reinterpreted taking the stage of sleep into consideration. Accordingly much of the research in sleep physiology during the past twenty years has been directed towards a definition of the physiological differences between REM and NREM sleep and towards elucidation of the specific mechanisms and purposes that underlie the different sleep stages. In recent years these same goals have been applied increasingly to the study of respiration during sleep. To the extent that the fundamental purposes and mechanisms of sleep itself remain uncertain, so too are the purposes and mechanisms of the respiratory adaptations to sleep. Nevertheless the changes in respiration that occur in the different stages of sleep have now been studied extensively, at least in purely descriptive terms. In addition, attempts have been made, although fewer in num-

---

[1]Abbreviations used: EEG = electroencephalogram; W = wakefulness; NREM = non-rapid-eye-movement; REM = rapid-eye-movement; SWS = slow-wave sleep; $\dot{V}$ = volume of ventilation per unit time; $\dot{V}_A$ = volume of alveolar ventilation per unit time; $\dot{V}_{O_2},\dot{V}_{CO_2}$ = volume of O_2 consumption or CO_2 production per unit time; V_T = tidal volume; f = respiratory frequency; $P_{A_{CO_2}},P_{A_{O_2}}$ = alveolar CO_2 or O_2 pressure; Pa_{CO_2},Pa_{O_2} = arterial CO_2 or O_2 pressure; Sa_{O_2} = arterial O_2 saturation.

133

0066-4278/78/0301-0133$01.00

ber, to examine systematically the respiratory control system and the mechanics of breathing during NREM and REM sleep. This review summarizes these recent advances and analyzes them on the basis of current concepts of both sleep-wakefulness on the one hand, and respiratory control on the other.

Because of space limitations this review does not cover disorders of breathing during sleep, except where these further our understanding of the normal situation. However, it should be recognized that much of the recent work on respiration during sleep has been stimulated by the growing realization that disordered breathing during sleep may underlie a variety of clinical problems ranging from the sudden-infant-death syndrome (110) to a number of hypersomniac (57) and insomniac (41) disorders of adults. Indeed such disorders have made urgent the need to understand normal respiratory adaptations to sleep, for it is from such knowledge that the mechanisms underlying the clinical problems will likely emerge.

This review does not cover studies of respiration during anesthesia. Anesthesia and sleep obviously share one important feature: abolition of conscious activity. However, even in this regard there is an important difference: the ability to arouse almost instantly from sleep and the inability to do so from anesthesia. More importantly the abolition of REM sleep by many anesthetics, and the widespread pharmacological effects of anesthesia apart from abolition of consciousness make the physiological similarity between sleep and anesthesia highly questionable and one that still remains to be fully determined.

Throughout this review reference to sleep stages is based on the classification of Rechtschaffen & Kales (86). Other classifications and terminology were used in many of the studies covered in the review, but the sleep stages from these studies are referred to by the corresponding Rechtschaffen & Kales sleep stage.

VENTILATION DURING SLEEP

In his classical monograph on respiration in sleeping man, which was published in 1944, Magnussen (59) demonstrated that $\dot{V}$ was decreased in (behavioral) sleep compared to W. A similar observation had been made earlier in children by de Bruin (23). These findings were confirmed subsequently in a number of studies (68, 88, 96) that demonstrated reductions of $\dot{V}$ of up to 27% during sleep compared to quiet W. Although these investigations either antedated the discovery of REM sleep or were done without EEG monitoring, the studies were likely confined to NREM sleep. This assumption derives from the fact that measurements were made either when breathing was regular (10, 59), a condition more likely to occur in

NREM than in REM sleep, or within the first hour of sleep (88, 96), which would generally exclude even the first REM sleep period. Subsequent studies (10, 16) in which sleep was defined by EEG confirmed the reduction of $\dot{V}$ during NREM sleep. The most comprehensive study is that of Bulow (15), who found that in 70 normal subjects $\dot{V}$ decreased 0.9 l min^{-1} m^{-2} in NREM sleep (stages 2 and 3) compared to quiet W. This critical finding was challenged recently by Duron (25, 26), who found no significant change in $\dot{V}$ during SWS compared to quiet W. He stressed the importance and difficulty of obtaining an accurate resting $\dot{V}$ in awake man. This contention is supported by a recent study demonstrating that a mouthpiece and nose-clip induce ventilatory changes in awake man (35). Nevertheless Bulow (15) had found a reduction in $\dot{V}$ even between drowsiness or light sleep and SWS. In addition, measurements of Pa_{CO_2} in young adults unperturbed by a mouthpiece or a face mask also suggested a reduction of $\dot{V}$ during sleep (9). Finally, recent studies in animals (67, 77) also confirm a small but significant reduction of $\dot{V}$ between quiet W and NREM sleep.

Thus the weight of present evidence demonstrates a small decrease in $\dot{V}$ during SWS, the magnitude of which varies from one individual or animal to another. The decrease can be attributed to two other changes: (*a*) reductions in $\dot{V}o_2$ and $\dot{V}co_2$ of 10%–20% (13, 15, 23, 59, 61, 77, 96), although there are also contrary reports (25, 109); and (*b*) decreases in effective $\dot{V}_A$ based on measurements of Pa_{CO_2} (see the section on blood gases.)

$\dot{V}$ has been measured in REM sleep only recently. A major problem in such analyses is selection of data. Breathing during REM sleep is characteristically rapid and often highly irregular. Therefore it may be difficult to define a steady state in which to make measurements. This difficulty likely accounts for the discrepant results reported by various investigators, although the majority have found an increase in $\dot{V}$ during REM sleep. In adult man, Bulow (15) reported $\dot{V}$ in REM sleep to be about the same as during drowsiness, which implies an increase of 13% over that present in SWS. The only other quantitative measurements of $\dot{V}$ in REM sleep are in infants and animals. In infants increases of 14% to 23% have been found over NREM values (11, 29, 32, 44, 83). In dogs breathing through a tracheostomy tube $\dot{V}$ was almost doubled in REM sleep in which there were frequent phasic muscular movements (77). On the other hand no consistent increases in $\dot{V}$ could be demonstrated in tracheostomized cats during less physically active REM sleep (67). These differences suggest that the degree of muscular activity during REM sleep may correlate better with the level of $\dot{V}$ than does the mere presence of REM sleep per se.

Some increase in $\dot{V}$ in REM sleep is to be expected in view of an increase in metabolic rate (13). However, measurements of Pa_{CO_2} (see the section on blood gases) indicate that alveolar hyperventilation also occurs.

In summary, $\dot{V}$ is decreased in SWS compared to quiet W and increased in REM sleep compared to SWS. These differences reflect alterations in metabolic rate and important changes in $\dot{V}A$.

ALVEOLAR VENTILATION AND BLOOD GASES

In 1923 Endres (28) reported that PA_{CO_2} increased 3 to 7 mm Hg in sleeping man. Similar changes during probable NREM sleep were reported by Ostergaard (68) and by Magnussen (59) in 1944. By careful simultaneous measurements of alveolar (end-tidal) CO_2 concentration, $\dot{V}$, and $\dot{V}CO_2$, Magnussen calculated a 15% reduction in $\dot{V}A$ during sleep. Using a similar approach Robin et al (96) found a reduction in $\dot{V}A$ of over 30% in sleep, coincident with which PA_{CO_2} increased by an average of 3.2 mm Hg. Subsequent studies in man (15, 16) and animals (77, 112) in which sleep state was monitored by EEG, confirmed that PA_{CO_2} increases a small but significant amount during NREM sleep (range of mean increases, 1.3–3.8 mm Hg). However, no concomitant change in PA_{CO_2} has been reported (25, 94). Direct measurements of Pa_{CO_2} in man (9, 10) and animals (40) show mean increases of 4.1 to 6.5 mm Hg in NREM sleep. These increases, despite reductions in $\dot{V}CO_2$, indicate that effective $\dot{V}A$ has decreased. This important change was attributed by Magnussen (59), Bulow (15), and most subsequent investigators to decreased ventilatory drive. However recent studies in awake man have clearly shown that $\dot{V}A$ can be impaired by increased mechanical impedance to breathing, despite normal or even augmented respiratory drive (73). Robin and co-workers (96) considered this possibility in regard to sleep, and measured pulmonary compliance and airway resistance using an esophageal balloon technique. The absence of mechanical changes in sleep supported the concept of decreased ventilatory drive.

Coincident with decreased $\dot{V}A$ during NREM sleep are small but statistically significant decreases in PA_{O_2} and Pa_{O_2} ranging from 3.5 to 9.4 mm Hg (40, 96), and decreases in arterial pH ranging from 0.03 to 0.05 units (9, 10, 40). At sea level the decrease in Pa_{O_2} results in only neglible changes in Sa_{O_2} of 2.0% or less (10, 60, 89, 96), because of the relationship between Pa_{O_2} and hemoglobin saturation at high O_2 pressures. However similar changes in Pa_{O_2} have also been found in sleep at altitudes of 14,000 feet (Pa_{O_2}, 50–55 mm Hg), resulting in decreases in Sa_{O_2} averaging 5.7% (89). This observation has obvious clinical implications with regard to sleep in hypoxemic patients. Although these changes in blood oxygenation in NREM sleep are attributable to decreased $\dot{V}A$, it should be noted that measurements of ventilation-perfusion ($\dot{V}/Q$) distributions have not been made. There is reason to suspect that $\dot{V}/Q$ changes might occur in sleep, related to alterations in functional residual capacity and pattern of breathing.

Measurement of representative $\dot{V}A$ and blood gases during REM sleep may be difficult because of the absence of steady-state ventilation. In addition, as a result of the rapid and irregular pattern of breathing and the frequent absence of an end-tidal plateau on the CO_2 record, it is often impossible accurately to measure PA_{CO_2}. Furthermore when muscular twitchings are prominent in REM sleep, $\dot{V}A$ may be higher than during other segments of REM sleep (112). Thus it is not surprising that different conclusions have been reached by different investigators. However, one finding seems to be clear: $\dot{V}A$ during REM sleep is as high and often higher than in NREM sleep. Bulow (15) reported that PA_{CO_2} in REM sleep was the same as in stage 1 NREM sleep (i.e. lower than in SWS). In cats Wurtz & O'Flaherty (112) found PA_{CO_2} to average 4 mm Hg less in REM sleep than in SWS, but Guazzi & Freis (40) found a difference of only 1.0 mm Hg in Pa_{CO_2}, and Remmers and associates (94) found no difference in PA_{CO_2}. A recent report in human newborns also found no difference in PA_{CO_2} between NREM and REM sleep (29). The largest reported decrease in PA_{CO_2} in REM sleep is in dogs where the mean change from SWS was 5.2 mm Hg (77). These latter measurements were made in REM sleep during which there were numerous muscular contractions.

Alveolar hyperventilation during REM sleep could result either from an increased sensitivity to chemical stimuli or from a nonchemical drive to breathing. Available evidence favors the latter explanation, as is discussed below.

There have been only a few reports of blood oxygenation during REM sleep. During apneic periods that often occur in REM sleep, Sa_{O_2} has been found to drop by up to 5% in healthy men (1). However in general, Pa_{O_2} is unchanged or slightly increased over the course of a REM sleep cycle (40). Of note are the lack of measurements of arterial oxygenation during REM sleep in healthy human infants, who spend the majority of their time in REM sleep (81).

In summary $\dot{V}A$, as reflected by alveolar or arterial P_{CO_2}, is decreased in NREM (particularly slow-wave) sleep and may be increased a variable amount in REM sleep compared to SWS. These changes reflect important alterations in respiratory drive.

PATTERN OF BREATHING

NREM Sleep

In 1926 Reed & Kleitman (87) studying adult man concluded that there was no relationship between the state of wakefulness or sleep and the rate or pattern of breathing. This conclusion strongly influenced subsequent thinking by many investigators, but later evidence has shown it to be incorrect.

In 1936 de Bruin (23) reported that children aged 1–9 years characteristically breathed periodically when drowsy, but regularly when asleep. This conclusion was also reached by Magnussen (59) in his study of behavioral sleep in adults. The first extensive studies of breathing pattern in which sleep stage was defined by EEG criteria were those of Bulow & Ingvar in adult man (15, 16). They demonstrated clearly that in SWS, variations of EEG pattern, $\dot{V}$, f, V_T, and $P_{A_{CO_2}}$ were small. In contrast, during drowsiness and light sleep periodic breathing was common and was synchronized with fluctuations in the level of wakefulness. As the subject fell asleep there was a gradual waning of ventilation, interrupted by periods of W in which there was alpha activity on the EEG and a waxing of $\dot{V}$. Eventually after a number of such cycles sleep became established and both EEG and breathing assumed a stable pattern with $\dot{V}$ at a new level (below that of W). Bulow (15) further noted that individuals with a greater fall in $\dot{V}$ and increase in $P_{A_{CO_2}}$ during sleep had greater degrees of periodic breathing at the onset of sleep. Thus he linked oscillations in respiration with both oscillations in the state of wakefulness and with the magnitude of decrease in $\dot{V}_A$ during sleep.

The association of periodic breathing in adults with drowsiness and stages 1 and 2 NREM sleep, and of regular respiration with stages 3 and 4 NREM sleep has been confirmed repeatedly (25, 36, 58, 102, 108). Webb (108) found that 9 of 11 men over the age of 45 years breathed periodically particularly during stage 2 sleep. In many of the subjects the waning of $\dot{V}$ led to periods of outright apnea of 10 sec or more (classical Cheyne-Stokes respiration). None of these subjects breathed periodically in stage 3 or 4 sleep. Using a Jerkin plethysmograph to record the pattern of breathing, Gillam (36) found undulating respiration in normal man even during quiet W. Application of a face mask increased $\dot{V}$ and abolished the periodicity. In a study of 2000 subjects, Specht & Fruhmann (102) found an incidence of periodic breathing of 1.5% during drowsy W. Reite and coworkers (91) demonstrated in young adults that ascent to an altitude of 14,000 feet induced periodic breathing during sleep in 5 of 6 subjects, none of whom showed this pattern of respiration at sea level. Associated with this change at altitude was a marked decrease in stages 3 and 4 sleep, an increase in stage 1 sleep, and an increased number of arousals. In fact the periods of increasing ventilation were characteristically associated with EEG evidence of arousal. These observations again highlight the important association of respiratory oscillations in sleep with oscillations in the state of sleep-wakefulness. The same study also demonstrated that administration of supplemental O_2 abolished periodic breathing at altitude. Similar observations were made in preterm infants by Rigatto & Brady (95) and by Fenner et al (31), both of whom found that periodic breathing could be induced by hypoxia or abolished by supplemental O_2 (although sleep stage was not mentioned in the studies). These observations contrast with those of Bulow (15), who showed that periodic breathing in adults during NREM sleep under normoxic conditions was unresponsive to changes in inspired O_2. The different findings have led to the conclusion that the etiology of periodic breathing in NREM sleep is different under different circumstances. However, in all these conditions periodic breathing can be attributed to the same fundamental mechanisms (Figure 1): a decrease in $\dot{V}A$ as sleep develops, followed by arousal (due to the changing blood-gas pressures or other stimuli); with arousal, an augmentation of $\dot{V}$, the magnitude of which depends on the awake ventilatory sensitivity to hypercapnia and hypoxia and the degree of hypercapnia or hypoxia that developed when $\dot{V}A$ decreased; a gradual return of blood gases and $\dot{V}$ to the normal awake values; decrease in level of wakefulness, waning of $\dot{V}$, and repetition of the cycle. (For further explanations, see Figure 1.)

Periodic breathing is common in newborn infants (31, 95), but its relationship to NREM sleep is less certain. More characteristically, infants show irregular (nonperiodic) patterns of breathing related to REM sleep, which accounts for the majority of their sleep time. These distinctions in pattern are important since the mechanisms underlying irregular breathing in REM sleep and periodic breathing in NREM sleep are likely quite different in both adults and infants (see below).

In summary, the pattern of breathing is highly regular in SWS, and often periodic in stages 1 and 2 sleep. The periodicity relates to fluctuations in the level of wakefulness and magnitude of associated change in blood-gas pressures.

REM Sleep

In their original description of REM sleep Aserinsky and Kleitman (2) demonstrated that during bursts of eye movements respiration became faster and more irregular. The association of rapid and irregular breathing with REM sleep has been confirmed subsequently by numerous investigators in adult man (15, 25, 38, 48, 100, 101, 103), infants (3, 11, 32, 44, 81), a number of animal species (21, 30, 67, 77, 94, 100), and fetal lambs (22). The magnitude of change in respiratory variables from NREM to REM sleep has not been measured systematically in all of these studies. When measured, considerable variation is noted from one report to another: f has increased from 10%–150% (mean, 47%), $\dot{V}T$ has decreased 0%–44% (mean, 19%); and indexes of variability have increased 55%–410% (mean, 219%) over those found in NREM sleep. The change to a more rapid and shallow pattern of breathing is associated with increased $\dot{V}$ but with smaller changes in $\dot{V}A$, indicating that much of the ventilation is wasted (dead-space

---→

Figure 1   Semi-quantitative description of mechanisms underlying periodic breathing in NREM sleep. Line ab shows changes in Pa_{CO_2} resulting from changes in $\dot{V}A$ (at a fixed $\dot{V}_{CO_2}$), calculated according to the equation $Pa_{CO_2} = K \cdot \dot{V}_{CO_2}/\dot{V}A$. Line cd shows corresponding changes in Pa_{O_2} (at sea level), calculated with the alveolar air equation and assuming no alveolar-arterial Po_2 difference. Line ef shows changes in $\dot{V}A$ during wakefulness resulting from induced changes in Pa_{CO_2} (i.e. ventilatory response to CO_2). Line gh shows changes in $\dot{V}A$ during wakefulness resulting from induced changes in Pa_{O_2} (i.e. ventilatory response to hypoxia).

Points A and C represent prevailing values during wakefulness. As sleep ensues, $\dot{V}A$ decreases (15) along lines ab and cd, leading to slight increases in Pa_{CO_2} (point B) and slight decreases in Pa_{O_2} (point D). These changes in blood gases, or other stimuli, result in arousal. At this instant $\dot{V}A$ increases from the value at point B to the value at point F (the latter being the $\dot{V}A$ "demanded" by that Pa_{CO_2} during wakefulness). With increased $\dot{V}A$, Pa_{CO_2} decreases, and $\dot{V}A$ and Pa_{CO_2} return along line ef from point F to the normal awake value at point A. As the level of wakefulness again declines, the cycle repeats itself. Thus $\dot{V}A$ oscillates from point A to B to F and back to A, and the magnitude of oscillation is represented by the vertical height BF. The Pa_{O_2} that was present in sleep at point D would stimulate only a minimal increase in $\dot{V}A$ to point G when arousal occurs. Therefore under normoxic conditions, periodic breathing is not induced by the small changes in Pa_{O_2} that occur with sleep; hence administration of O_2 does not abolish periodic breathing.

In contrast, with ascent to high altitude, the isometabolic line cd moves to lower Pa_{O_2} values, represented by line ij (at 14,000 ft). In response to hypoxia, $\dot{V}A$ increases along line gh from point C to point I (89, 91). This increase in $\dot{V}A$ induces a decrease in Pa_{CO_2} from point A to point K. Line kl now represents the $\dot{V}A$ response to CO_2. With the onset of sleep a small decrease in $\dot{V}A$ still ensues (88), and Pa_{CO_2} increases a small amount to point M, and Pa_{O_2} decreases a small amount to point J. With arousal, the $\dot{V}A$ "demanded" by the Pa_{O_2} of point J drives $\dot{V}A$ to point H, whereas the $\dot{V}A$ that would be "demanded" by the Pa_{CO_2} of point M is that at point L. Since JH is of greater magnitude than DG (or ML), periodic breathing at altitude is due to hypoxic ventilatory drive and is therefore abolished by administration of O_2.

Note that at sea level a very small decrease in $\dot{V}A$ at sleep onset would lead to only small changes in Pa_{CO_2} and therefore to little or no periodic breathing. However at altitude the same small decrease in $\dot{V}A$ would lead to sufficient drop in Pa_{O_2} to induce periodic breathing (because of the almost vertical shape of the $\dot{V}A/Pa_{O_2}$ response curve at low values of Pa_{O_2}.) Therefore, periodic breathing may occur at altitude in individuals who do not breathe periodically at sea level (91). The same mechanism would apply to hypoxemic patients at sea level.

With sleep onset there is a slight decrease in $\dot{V}_{CO_2}$ that moves line ab slightly downward. However, for purposes of clarity the sleeping point B is shown on the same isometabolic line as the waking point A. Small errors due to this simplification, and to other minor assumptions in calculating the various values, produce only small changes in the position of the lines and points and do not alter the basic relationships and concepts.

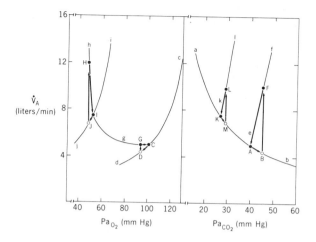

ventilation). The differences in f and V_T during REM sleep found by various investigators likely relate to the unsteady state of ventilation and indeed the inhomogeneity of REM sleep per se. For example, Aserinsky (1) noted that the pattern of breathing was more rapid and shallow during bursts of eye movements than in REM sleep without eye movements. In a review of the autonomic nervous system manifestations of REM sleep, Snyder (100) stressed this same finding, as have others (38). In cats ponto-geniculate-occipital spikes, a striking and characteristic feature of REM sleep, were associated with phasic changes in f and heart rate (5). Spreng and associates (103) noted in man that as the length of an eye movement burst increased, f increased and amplitude of breathing decreased progressively.

The mechanisms underlying the respiratory pattern changes of REM sleep have been the subject of considerable interest and controversy. The irregularities of breathing clearly differ from the cyclical pattern of periodic breathing in NREM sleep, and are not associated with EEG evidence of arousal. Furthermore, recent studies indicate that the irregularities of REM sleep persist after vagotomy (22, 77, 94), section of the spinal cord at T1 or T2 (82, 104; A. Netick, unpublished data), afferent denervation of the entire mid-thoracic chest wall (74), denervation of the carotid and aortic chemo- and baroreceptors (40; C. E. Sullivan and E. A. Phillipson, unpublished data), and during hypercapnia (76) or hypoxia (78). These results demonstrate that peripheral respiratory inputs are not essential for breathing irregularities in REM sleep. Indeed, the results suggest (74, 78) that respiratory control during REM sleep essentially bypasses the automatic control system. However, what is responsible for the changes is less certain. Aserinsky and Kleitman (2) originally suggested that the eye movements and autonomic activity of REM sleep were related temporally and causally to cortical activity associated with dreaming. Later Aserinsky (1) concluded that although there was a temporal relationship, the respiratory changes were not part of an emotional reaction to the dream content, but rather due to more basic neurophysiological changes. There is considerable evidence favoring this viewpoint, including the occurrence of REM-related respiratory changes in fetal lambs, newborn humans, a wide variety of animal species, and decorticate cats (50). However these findings do not exclude a modification of respiratory pattern in REM sleep by cortical processes. In support of this possibility is the demonstration by Hobson et al (48) that respiratory frequency and variability in REM sleep were greater when the emotional content of dreams was great and when the dreams involved physical activity that has a relationship to breathing such as phonation, laughter, crying, or choking. More recently Goodenough and associates (38) found that the viewing of stressful movies before sleep, which significantly increased dream anxiety, also increased REM-related respiratory irregularity in those subjects who, in the waking state, showed irregular breathing in response to the films.

Current concepts suggest that a basic process arising in the pontine reticular formation (47, 50) underlies REM sleep and its associated physiological changes including, probably, the respiratory manifestations. However as Snyder has pointed out (100), this conclusion "does not obviate the possibility that these same variations may be integrated in some fashion with the higher nervous system processes which dreams are made of . . ." In the same vein, Spreng and co-workers (103) suggested that tonic changes in the respiratory pattern (increased f, decreased amplitude) have a fundamental neurophysiological basis, whereas the phasic changes in pattern (breath-to-breath variability) may somehow reflect dream content.

In summary, the pattern of breathing in REM sleep is usually rapid and often highly irregular. These changes do not appear to result from activity in the automatic respiratory control system, but their specific origin is unknown.

RESPIRATORY CONTROL

Central Neural Mechanisms

In contrast to the relatively large number of studies relating to ventilation and to respiratory chemosensitivity during sleep, there have been extremely few studies of central respiratory mechanisms. In a recent series of interesting studies, Orem and colleagues (64, 65) used microelectrodes to record discharges from respiratory-related neurons in the medulla of intact cats during W, NREM, and REM sleep. Some of the cells discharged rhythmically with respiration during W, reduced their discharge during NREM sleep, and became silent in REM sleep. Some were active only in W, and others lost their respiratory synchronization during sleep. Although firm conclusions regarding central respiratory control cannot be drawn from these observations, they do begin to offer insight into the neuronal events that may underlie the respiratory adaptations to sleep.

Respiratory Chemosensitivity

RESPONSE TO CO_2 In their studies of sleeping man, Magnussen (59) and Ostergaard (68) both had two subjects breathe mixtures of 2.5%–6% CO_2 in air while awake and again during sleep. The resulting lines relating V to Pa_{CO_2} were either shifted to higher CO_2 pressures, or had a decrease in slope of up to 50% during sleep. They concluded that the respiratory centers were less sensitive to CO_2, thus accounting for the spontaneous increase of Pa_{CO_2} characteristic of sleep. Subsequent investigators (10, 96) using similar steady-state techniques arrived at the same conclusion. However, since supplemental O_2 was not provided in any of these studies, the results cannot distinguish decreased central responses from decreased peripheral chemoreceptor drive. Accordingly, the critical studies were those of Reed & Kellogg (88) and of Bellville et al (6) who found that when CO_2 was breathed in high O_2 mixtures, there was little decrease in slope of the response line during NREM sleep, but rather a shift to higher CO_2 pressures of up to 7–9 mm Hg. Smaller shifts were noted during drowsiness. These results and later studies of peripheral chemoreceptor activity (see the section on hypoxic responses) indicated that sleep was associated with diminished central rather than peripheral respiratory drive. However, the magnitude of this change may have been overestimated in these steady-state studies of CO_2 responsiveness. Specifically, many of the subjects awoke as a result of hypercapnia before a steady state of ventilation was achieved. Thus subjects with low arousal thresholds to hypercapnia would have been systematically excluded from the analyses. If these individuals also had higher ventilatory sensitivities to CO_2, they might have demonstrated smaller shifts in position or decrease in slope of the CO_2 response lines had they remained asleep. In support of this notion is the observation by Birchfield et al (10) that subjects who remained asleep while breathing 5% CO_2 had a mean Pa_{CO_2} while awake (breathing room air) of 49 mm Hg, whereas those who awoke on 5% CO_2 had a Pa_{CO_2} during W of 44 mm Hg. This latter group was of course excluded from the analysis of ventilatory sensitivity during sleep.

For these reasons a rebreathing method (with supplemental O_2), in which many levels of CO_2 can be obtained before arousal, is preferable to a steady-state technique for examination of ventilatory responses during sleep. Such a method was used by Bulow (15) in whose extensive study some

3000 $\dot{V}/P_{A_{CO_2}}$ data points were obtained in various stages of sleep. He found that the mean slope of the $\dot{V}/P_{A_{CO_2}}$ response line decreased progressively from 1.25 l min^{-1} m^{-2} (mm Hg)$^{-1}$ in W, to 0.5 l min^{-1} m^{-2} (mm Hg)$^{-1}$ in stages 3 and 4 NREM sleep.

In contrast to numerous studies of ventilatory responsiveness to CO_2 in NREM sleep is the paucity of studies in REM sleep. Bulow (15) reported one CO_2 response test in one subject during REM sleep. The slope of the $\dot{V}/P_{A_{CO_2}}$ line was similar to that in stage 1 NREM sleep. Recently Phillipson et al (76) reported both waking and ventilatory responses to hyperoxic progressive hypercapnia in sleeping dogs using the rebreathing method of Read (84). This method, in which cerebral P_{CO_2} is independent of ventilation, is highly preferable to a steady-state technique in REM sleep because of the irregular pattern of breathing. [For further explanation, see (84).] These workers found that the $P_{A_{CO_2}}$ associated with arousal was significantly higher in REM sleep than in SWS, a finding that is in keeping with elevated arousal thresholds to other stimuli during REM sleep (7, 24, 50). The responses of $\dot{V}$, $\dot{V}_T$ and f to CO_2 were markedly decreased in REM sleep (regression coefficients, 14%–33% of those in SWS). In addition the highly irregular pattern of breathing characteristic of REM sleep persisted during hypercapnia, suggesting that the respiratory control system was being little influenced by the CO_2 stimulus.

Two other studies in REM sleep, both in normal infants, also appeared recently. Fagenholz et al (29) found a $\dot{V}$ response to 5% CO_2 in air of 54 ml kg^{-1} min^{-1} (mm Hg)$^{-1}$ compared to 73 in NREM sleep, but the difference was not statistically significant. However, in view of the intact response to hypoxia in REM sleep (see below), the failure to provide supplemental O_2 may have masked a greater decrease in the response to CO_2. In contrast Bryan et al (14) using 4% CO_2 in air found a significant decrease in the response of both $\dot{V}$ and $\dot{V}_T$ to CO_2.

A decreased ventilatory response to CO_2 during REM sleep is compatible with the suspension of other homeostatic control functions during this sleep stage. For example a recent series of interesting studies (37, 69–72) demonstrated that REM sleep is associated with a change from homeothermic to poikilothermic temperature regulation. This change is due to fundamental alterations of hypothalamic function rather than to simple changes in threshold of the central thermoreceptors. By analogy it is reasonable to suggest that the diminished $\dot{V}$ response to CO_2 in REM sleep may be due to changes in integrative function of central respiratory neurons rather than to changes in activity of the central chemoreceptors. However there are no data on this question. In fact the interpretation of the mechanism underlying the decreased $\dot{V}$ response to CO_2 is open to question. On the basis of assessment of abdominal and thoracic displacement with pairs of magnetometers, Bryan et al (14) suggested that in infants the decrease in $\dot{V}$ was not due to impaired central diaphragmatic drive. Rather it was attributed to distortion of the rib cage that diminished the effective $\dot{V}T$ generated by diaphragmatic contraction. Thus the question is whether the impaired $\dot{V}$ response to CO_2 is due to decreased central drive to the diaphragm or to the intercostal muscles. Others (78) have argued that since the $\dot{V}$ response to hypoxia is intact in REM sleep, despite rib cage distortion, the decreased response to CO_2 must represent an overall decrease in respiratory drive in response to this particular stimulus. The issue will likely remain unresolved until more precise indexes of respiratory drive are measured, such as electrical activity of the phrenic nerve and respiratory muscles. Unfortunately, a popular new method of assessing respiratory drive, airway occlusion pressure (111), cannot be used to settle the issue since the pressure generated does not separate diaphragmatic and intercostal muscle contributions.

Regardless of the underlying mechanism, the finding of a decreased $\dot{V}$ response to CO_2 in REM sleep leads to one important conclusion: The spontaneous increase in $\dot{V}A$ during REM sleep cannot be attributed to increased ventilatory sensitivity to CO_2. Since hypoxic sensitivity is also not increased (see below), alveolar hyperventilation must be due to a nonchemical respiratory drive.

In summary, the response of $\dot{V}$ to CO_2 is moderately reduced in SWS compared to W, and markedly decreased and irregular in REM sleep compared to SWS. These changes likely result from fundamental alterations in central respiratory control during each of the sleep stages.

HYPOXIC RESPONSES   Reed & Kellogg (89) demonstrated in man that the ventilatory response to hypoxia was the same during sleep as in W. Although sleep stage was not defined by EEG, the measurements were likely made during NREM sleep. The response to hypoxia was measured in two ways: firstly, by a steady-state method in which subjects breathed graded mixtures of O_2 and N_2; and secondly, by measuring the transient respiratory depression produced by abruptly interrupting hypoxia with 100% inspired O_2. Subsequently they demonstrated (90) that the effect of hypoxia in shifting the position and slope of the $\dot{V}/P_{A_{CO_2}}$ response curve (CO_2–O_2 interaction) was also unaffected during sleep. A contrary report is that of Honda & Natsui (49), who claimed that sleep virtually abolished O_2–CO_2 interaction on ventilation. However, in their subjects sleep was induced pharmacologically and it "was so deep during the experiment that the subjects were rarely awaked [sic] by the strong stimulus from hypoxia combined with hypercapnia," a most unphysiological situation.

The only comparison of hypoxic responses in sleep and W in which sleep stage was defined by EEG is in a recent report by Phillipson and co-workers

(78). In this study eucapnic progressive hypoxia was induced in dogs by a rebreathing technique (85), and the magnitude of hypoxemia was assessed by use of a recently developed, accurate, stable ear-oximeter (98). The response of $\dot{V}$ to hypoxia during SWS [mean, 1.24 l min^{-1} ($\%Sa_{O_2}$)$^{-1}$] was the same as in W[1.15 l min^{-1} ($\%Sa_{O_2}$)$^{-1}$].

The demonstration of intact hypoxic responses during NREM sleep indicates that the decreased $\dot{V}A$ (and increased Pa_{CO_2}) characteristic of this sleep stage cannot be attributed to decreased peripheral chemoreceptor activity. The possibility that such a mechanism could have accounted for the alveolar hypoventilation is based on three observations: (a) that SWS may be associated with an overall decrease in sympathetic nervous tone (100); (b) that interruption of sympathetic tone to the peripheral chemoreceptors markedly reduces their response to stimulation (62); and (c) that peripheral chemoreceptor denervation in man and animals decreases $\dot{V}A$ (even under normoxic conditions) and increases Pa_{CO_2} by 5–6 mm Hg (8, 12, 107), the same magnitude of increase noted during SWS. Direct evidence that the peripheral chemoreceptors are not involved in the decrease of $\dot{V}A$ during NREM sleep comes from the demonstration that denervation of the carotid and aortic chemoreceptors in cats did not prevent an increase of Pa_{CO_2} during NREM sleep (40).

Responses to hypoxia during REM sleep were examined in three recent studies. In dogs (78), the $\dot{V}$ response [1.11 l min^{-1} ($\%Sa_{O_2}$)$^{-1}$] was not significantly different than in SWS or W, unlike the $\dot{V}$ response to hypercapnia (76). In contrast to the $\dot{V}$ response, the arousal threshold to hypoxia was greatly elevated in REM sleep (mean waking Sa_{O_2}, 70.5% in REM sleep; 87.5% in SWS). The $\dot{V}$ response indicates that peripheral chemoreceptor activity remains intact during REM sleep and may therefore be of importance in terminating apneic spells that are common in this stage of sleep and during which significant hypoxemia can develop (1). In this regard the report of Guazzi & Freis (40) is of particular interest. They found that the range of fluctuation of Pa_{O_2} during REM sleep was doubled (to 22 mm Hg) in cats following denervation of the peripheral chemoreceptors, whereas the fluctuation during NREM sleep (8 mm Hg) was unaffected by the procedure.

The only data in man on hypoxic responses during REM sleep are from newborn infants. Bolton & Herman (11) found that 100% inspired O_2 transiently depressed $\dot{V}$ by 13% in both NREM and REM sleep. They therefore concluded that hypoxic drive was the same in the two sleep stages. Using a similar approach Fagenholz et al (29) came to the same conclusion despite a 31% decrease in $\dot{V}$ during NREM sleep and no decrease in REM sleep. It should be noted that this method of assessing hypoxic sensitivity, while of obvious practical advantage in man, could lead to erroneous interpretations. If, as suggested earlier, ventilation in REM sleep is driven by nonchemical stimuli, resulting in alveolar hyperventilation, 100% O_2 would not be expected to decrease $\dot{V}$. The lack of a change might give the impression of an absence of hypoxic sensitivity, whereas hypoxia could, and probably would, augment the drive and increase $\dot{V}$ in a normal manner.

In summary, although only a few reports are available, the response of $\dot{V}$ to hypoxia appears to be the same in W, NREM, and REM sleep.

Respiratory Reflexes

Both NREM and REM sleep are associated with marked and often opposite changes in the strength of a number of spinal and brainstem somatic reflexes. [For detailed reviews see (17, 54, 79, 80).] Furthermore these changes may be age-dependent (17). Sleep-state dependency of respiratory reflexes has been examined only recently.

VAGAL REFLEXES   Farber & Marlow (30) investigated pulmonary inflation and deflation reflexes in the opossum and found them to be equally active in NREM and REM sleep, although more variable in the latter. In contrast, in the dog the inflation reflex was stronger in SWS than in W, but was virtually abolished in REM sleep (77). Using the prolongation of inspiration during an occluded breath at functional residual capacity as an index of vagal activity (39), Finer and associates (32) concluded that the inflation reflex was present in healthy infants in NREM sleep but abolished in REM sleep. However, many of the infants showed marked shortening of inspiration during airway occlusion in REM sleep, suggestive of the action of another reflex such as the intercostal-phrenic reflex described by Knill & Bryan (53).

There have been no studies of vagal irritant or J-reflexes, or of vagal efferent (bronchopulmonary) reflexes during sleep.

Although vagal reflexes could theoretically play a role in causing apnea and other respiratory irregularities during REM sleep, there is no direct evidence that this is of major significance. For example, analyses of the relationship between V_T and inspiratory duration in human infants (44) and in cats (67, 94) show a positive correlation between the two variables during REM sleep (also during W and NREM sleep) that is opposite to what would be predicted on the basis of a current model of vagal respiratory control (18). Furthermore this relationship persisted following vagotomy (94) as did the respiratory irregularities of REM sleep (77, 94). In contrast, in animals the vagal influence on breathing during SWS is profound, as indicated by the observation that blockade of the cervical vagus nerves in dogs caused marked slowing of respiratory frequency to as low as 3 breaths per minute (74). This frequency was considerably slower than either during SWS with the vagi intact or during W with the vagi blocked.

CHEST WALL REFLEXES   In anesthetized animals intercostal reflexes, likely arising in intercostal muscle spindles, can profoundly influence respiratory rhythm (93). Such reflexes have not been directly examined in unanesthetized animals or in man. However, by inference Knill & Bryan (53) have demonstrated that such reflexes may be active in newborn infants, particularly during REM sleep. They suggest that the reflex is stimulated by distortion of the rib cage, a common finding in REM sleep (see the section on mechanics), and serves to shorten inspiratory time. The combination of distortion and shortened inspiratory duration can markedly reduce the effective V_T. More recently Hagen et al (43) demonstrated in newborns that stabilization of the chest wall so as to prevent distortion significantly prolonged inspiratory duration. The authors suggest that an intercostal-phrenic reflex contributes to the respiratory pattern irregularities of REM sleep, although it does not appear to be essential (see the section on pattern of breathing).

Respiratory Integrative Mechanisms

An excellent summary of respiratory integrative mechanisms and pathways is provided in a recent review (63). Current concepts indicate that breathing is controlled by two systems, one voluntary and the other automatic, that arise from separate neural structures and project via anatomically distinct descending pathways to the spinal cord where functional integration occurs. The voluntary (or behavioral) system arises in the cortex and descends by corticobulbar and corticospinal tracts to the reticular formation and spinal cord. The automatic (or metabolic) system arises in neurons in the pons and medulla and descends to the spinal motoneurons in the ventral and lateral columns of the cord.

The control of sleep and wakefulness appears to involve groups of neurons located in the reticular formation of the brainstem and midbrain. From these centers impulses ascend to the cortex and descend to the spinal cord. [For a detailed review, see (47, 50).] The pathways by which the sleep-wakefulness system exerts an influence on respiratory control are not clear, but the current evidence does suggest some reasonable possibilities. That wakefulness stimulates respiration is implicit in the observation that $\dot{V}_A$ is diminished during NREM sleep. Although this stimulation may modify breathing by altering inputs from chemoreceptors or peripheral respiratory reflexes, evidence indicates that it can operate independently of these systems. For example Fink (33) demonstrated in normal subjects that following a period of alveolar hyperventilation (i.e. "removal" of the CO_2 respiratory drive), rhythmic breathing continued if the subjects remained awake, but apnea developed during sleep. An analogous "experiment of nature" occurs in patients with the central hypoventilation syndrome, a characteristic feature of which is reduction or abolition of

CO_2 sensitivity (63). Despite the loss of this important respiratory drive such patients breathe rhythmically when awake but hypoventilate and may become apneic during sleep. Finally, recent studies in dogs (74, 77) demonstrated that abolition of vagal respiratory control resulted in only moderate slowing of respiration during wakefulness but profound slowing during SWS. A corollary of these "lesion" observations is that in the absence of the wakefulness stimulus, such as during NREM sleep, the automatic control system is of critical importance in maintaining respiration. Further support for this conclusion comes from the numerous experiments (reviewed above) in which the automatic system was stimulated during NREM sleep (by CO_2, hypoxia, or lung inflation), resulting in reproducible ventilatory responses that mimic those of anesthetized or decerebrate preparations in which only the automatic control system is presumed to be operating.

In contrast, during REM sleep breathing behaves as if it were virtually independent of the automatic system. Alveolar hyperventilation is often present and cannot be attributed to increased ventilatory sensitivity to CO_2; indeed the available evidence indicates decreased responses to CO_2. Furthermore the irregular breathing pattern of REM sleep is essentially unaffected by hypercapnia, hypoxia, vagal, and other automatic system inputs. Additional evidence that respiratory control during REM sleep bypasses the automatic system is derived from a recent report (99) of two infants with central hypoventilation syndrome and marked insensitivity to CO_2. During NREM sleep the infants stopped breathing entirely. In REM sleep they had normal ventilation. Despite these considerations, the normal response of $\dot{V}$ to hypoxia in REM sleep indicates that under appropriate circumstances the automatic system is able to stimulate breathing in this sleep stage. It has been pointed out (74) that certain features of respiratory control during REM sleep resemble those found in awake man when the nonautomatic, voluntary system is operative, such as during speaking. Although direct evidence linking this system to respiration during REM sleep is lacking, the possibility is a reasonable one. Activation of voluntary system pathways in REM sleep could occur at the cortical level or in the pontine reticular formation where REM sleep per se is thought to originate (47, 50).

RESPIRATORY MECHANICS

Airway Resistance and Pulmonary Compliance

Decreased tone of submental and cervical muscles is a characteristic feature of REM sleep (56). Recently Sauerland & Harper (97) demonstrated in healthy subjects that during W and NREM sleep the genioglossus muscle, which protrudes the tongue, has a tonic level of electromyographic (EMG) activity that is augmented phasically during inspiration. This important function prevents relapse of the tongue and obstruction of the oropharynx, particularly in the supine position. In REM sleep the tonic activity disappeared and the phasic bursts were reduced or abolished intermittently. Orem, Netick & Dement (66) recently measured upper airway (principally laryngeal) resistance in cats during W and sleep. They found that in REM sleep the mean resistance was 29% higher than in NREM sleep; cyclical decreases of resistance during inspiration, which were prominent in NREM sleep, diminished significantly or were abolished intermittently in REM sleep. Both of these studies have interesting clinical implications regarding the pathogenesis of upper airway obstructive disorders during sleep.

In an earlier study Robin and associates (96), using the esophageal balloon technique, found a small decrease in total airway resistance during probable NREM sleep, compared to W. Pulmonary compliance was unchanged. No such measurements have been made during REM sleep. In view of the marked autonomic activity of REM sleep (100) there may well be changes in vagal bronchomotor tone, a phenomenon that conceivably could be involved in the triggering of nocturnal asthma.

Respiratory Muscles

Recent studies in adults (25, 27, 106), infants (42), and animals (46, 72), have demonstrated that during REM sleep there is a reduction in both tonic and phasic (i.e. inspiratory-related) EMG activity of the intercostal muscles. This electrical change is associated mechanically with decreased expansion or even outright paradoxical motion of the rib cage (42, 46, 52, 106). As a consequence, effective V_T may be reduced, and intercostal-phrenic reflexes may be elicited that shorten inspiratory duration (53). Electrical activity in the diaphragm is highly variable from breath to breath in REM sleep. However, in general the amount of activity is normal or even increased, particularly when related to the V_T generated (42, 72, 106).

The mechanism underlying depression of intercostal muscle activity in REM sleep is probably similar to that in other skeletal muscles. These mechanisms, which have been summarized by Pompeiano (79, 80), include tonic supraspinal inhibition of segmental gamma (and to some extent alpha) motoneurons, and phasic presynaptic inhibition of 1a primary afferent terminals from muscle spindles. Thus the normal facilitatory influence of the muscle spindle loop on alpha motoneurons is depressed in REM sleep. The diaphragm, which is driven primarily by alpha motoneurons (20), apparently escapes these REM-related events.

Respiratory Load Compensation

During NREM sleep application of a mechanical load to the respiratory system (either airway occlusion or inspiration from a rigid container) results in a progressive increase in V_T or inspiratory effort that closely resembles the response during W (75). In contrast, studies in healthy newborn humans (34, 52, 83) and lambs (46) have shown that the ventilatory response to loading is irregular and diminished in REM sleep. The mechanisms involved in respiratory load compensation have been reviewed in a recent symposium (73), and include proprioceptive reflexes acting segmentally on the intercostal muscles, and chemoreceptor (primarily hypoxic) reflexes acting on central respiratory drive. Since central drive is irregular and intercostal muscle activity is diminished in REM sleep, defective responses to loading are predictable. Furthermore in view of the potential for upper airway obstruction during REM sleep (see the section on airway resistance) the observation of impaired load-compensating responses is of obvious clinical importance, particularly in individuals whose hypoxic sensitivity is low.

NONRESPIRATORY ADAPTATIONS

Sleep, particularly REM sleep, is characterized by a number of physiological changes that, under other circumstances, exert direct or indirect effects on respiration. These include fluctuations in heart rate, systemic blood pressure, and cardiac output (19, 51, 101); alterations in cerebral blood flow (92, 105); and changes in temperature regulation (4, 37, 45, 69–72). To what extent if any these changes are responsible for the respiratory adaptations to sleep is uncertain, although it is known, for example, that the respiratory frequency response to hyperthermia is virtually suspended in REM sleep (37, 69).

CONCLUSION

In this century there have been three phases of research into the respiratory adaptations in sleep. The first phase, exemplified by Magnussen's classical study published in 1944, largely predated the early EEG classifications of sleep (55). Sleep was therefore defined by behavioral criteria. In the second phase, culminating with Bulow's massive study in 1963, the respiratory changes of NREM sleep were defined. Although certain additions to this knowledge have been made subsequently, the basic observations of this phase have been confirmed. We are now in the third phase, studying the respiratory adaptations of REM sleep. Much has been learned, particularly during the past few years, and some attempts have been made to integrate this knowledge into basic concepts. While this phase still continues, another one has dawned—the realization that disorders of breathing during sleep may underlie a wide variety of clinical problems. Our understanding of these problems is largely at a descriptive stage, but as basic knowledge of the first three phases is expanded, solutions to the problems of the fourth phase will hopefully emerge.

ACKNOWLEDGMENTS

The author wishes to thank Mrs. D. Barbour and Mrs. M. Dorward for their assistance in preparation of the review and Dr. C. E. Sullivan for critical reading of the manuscript.

Literature Cited

1. Aserinsky, E. 1965. Periodic respiratory pattern occurring in conjunction with eye movements during sleep. *Science* 150:763–66
2. Aserinsky, E., Kleitman, N. 1953. Regularly occurring periods of eye motility, and concomitant phenomena, during sleep. *Science* 118:273–74
3. Ashton, R., Connolly, K. 1971. The relation of respiration rate and heart rate to sleep states in the human newborn. *Dev. Med. Child Neurol.* 13:180–87
4. Baker, M. A. 1972. Influence of the carotid rete on brain temperature in cats exposed to hot environments. *J. Physiol. London* 220:711–28
5. Baust, W., Holzbach, E., Zechlin, O. 1972. Phasic changes in heart rate and respiration correlated with PGO-spike activity during REM sleep. *Pfluegers Arch. Gesamte Physiol. Menschen Tiere.* 331:113–23
6. Bellville, J. W., Howland, W. S., Seed, J. C., Houde, R. W. 1959. The effect of sleep on the respiratory response to carbon dioxide. *Anesthesiology* 20:628–34
7. Benoit, O., Bloch, V. 1960. Seuil d'excitabilité reticulaire et sommeil profond chez le chat. *J. Physiol. Paris* 52:17–18
8. Berger, A. J., Krasney, J. A., Dutton, R. E. 1973. Respiratory recovery from CO₂ breathing in intact and chemodenervated awake dogs. *J. Appl. Physiol.* 35:35–41
9. Birchfield, R. I., Sieker, H. O., Heyman, A. 1958. Alterations in blood gases during natural sleep and narcolepsy. *Neurology* 8:107–12
10. Birchfield, R. I., Sieker, H. O., Heyman, A. 1959. Alterations in respiratory function during natural sleep. *J. Lab. Clin. Med.* 54:216–22
11. Bolton, D. P. G., Herman, S. 1974. Ventilation and sleep state in the newborn. *J. Physiol. London* 240:67–77
12. Bouverot, P., Candas, V., Libert, J. P. 1973. Role of the arterial chemoreceptors in ventilatory adaptation to hypoxia of awake dogs and rabbits. *Respir. Physiol.* 17:209–19
13. Brebbia, D. R., Altshuler, K. Z. 1965. Oxygen consumption rate and electroencephalographic stage of sleep. *Science* 150:1621–23
14. Bryan, H. M., Hagan, R., Gulston, G., Bryan, A. C. 1976. CO₂ response and sleep state in infants. *Clin. Res.* 24:A689 (Abstr.)
15. Bulow, K. 1963. Respiration and wakefulness in man. *Acta Physiol. Scand.* 59(Suppl.):209
16. Bulow, K., Ingvar, D. H. 1961. Respiration and state of wakefulness in normals, studied by spirography, capnography and EEG. *Acta Physiol. Scand.* 51:230–38
17. Chase, M. H. 1974. Central neural control of brainstem somatic reflexes during sleeping and waking. In *Advances in Sleep Research,* ed. E. D. Weitzman, 1:251–304. New York: Spectrum
18. Clark, F. J., von Euler, C. 1972. On the regulation of depth and rate of breathing. *J. Physiol. London* 222:267–95
19. Coccagna, G., Mantovani, M., Brignani, F., Manzini, A., Lugaresi, E. 1971. Arterial pressure changes during spontaneous sleep in man. *Electroencephalogr. Clin. Neurophysiol.* 31:277–81
20. Corda, M., von Euler, C. Lennerstrand, G. 1965. Proprioceptive innervation of the diaphragm. *J. Physiol. London* 178:161–77
21. David, J., Grewal, R. S., Wagle, G. P. 1972. EEG patterns in relation to respiratory rate and body movement in Macaca Mulatta. *Physiol. Behav.* 9:337–42
22. Dawes, G. S., Fox, H. E., Leduc, B. M., Liggins, G. C., Richards, R. T. 1972. Respiratory movements and rapid eye movement sleep in the foetal lamb. *J. Physiol. London* 220:119–43

23. de Bruin, M. 1936. Respiration and basal metabolism in childhood during sleep. *Acta Pediatr. Stockholm* 18: 279–86

24. Dement, W. 1958. The occurrence of low voltage, fast, electroencephalogram patterns during behavioral sleep in the cat. *Electroencephalogr. Clin. Neurophysiol.* 10:291–96

25. Duron, B. 1972. La fonction respiratoire pendant le sommeil physiologique. *Bull. Physio-pathol. Resp.* 8:1031–57

26. Duron, B., Andrac, C., Laval, P. 1968. Ventilation pulmonaire globale, CO_2 alveolaire et consommation d'oxygène, au cours du sommeil chez l'homme normal. *Soc. Biol.* 162:139–45

27. Duron, B., Tassinari, C. A., Gastaut, H. 1966. Analyse spirographique et electromyographique de la respiration au cours du sommeil controlé par l'E. E. G. chez l'homme normal. *Rev. Neurol.* 115:562–74

28. Endres, G. 1923. Atmungsregulation und Blutreaktion im Schlaf. *Biochem. Z.* 141–142:53–67

29. Fagenholz, S. A., O'Connell, K., Shannon, D. C. 1976. Chemoreceptor function and sleep state in apnea. *Pediatrics* 58:31–36

30. Farber, J. P., Marlow, T. A. 1976. Pulmonary reflexes and breathing pattern during sleep in the opossum. *Respir. Physiol.* 27:73–86

31. Fenner, A., Schalk, U., Hoenicke, H., Wendenburg, A., Roehling, T. 1973. Periodic breathing in premature and neonatal babies: incidence, breathing pattern, respiratory gas tensions, response to changes in the composition of ambient air. *Pediatr. Res.* 7:174–83

32. Finer, N. N., Abroms, I. F., Taeusch, H. W. Jr. 1976. Ventilation and sleep state in new born infants. *J. Pediatr.* 89:100–108

33. Fink, B. R. 1961. Influence of cerebral activity in wakefulness on regulation of breathing. *J. Appl. Physiol.* 16:15–20

34. Frantz, I. D. III, Adler, S. M., Abroms, I. F., Thach, B. T. 1976. Respiratory response to airway occlusion in infants: sleep state and maturation. *J. Appl. Physiol.* 41:634–38

35. Gilbert, R., Auchincloss, J. H. Jr., Brodsky, J., Boden, W. 1972. Changes in tidal volume, frequency, and ventilation induced by their measurement. *J. Appl. Physiol.* 33:252–54

36. Gillam, P. M. S. 1972. Patterns of respiration in human beings at rest and during sleep. *Bull. Physio-pathol. Resp.* 8:1059–70

37. Glotzbach, S. F., Heller, H. C. 1976. Central nervous regulation of body temperature during sleep. *Science* 194: 537–39

38. Goodenough, D. R., Witkin, H. A., Koulack, D., Cohen, H. 1975. The effects of stress films on dream affect and on respiration and eye-movement activity during rapid-eye-movement sleep. *Psychophysiology* 12:313–20

39. Grunstein, M. M., Younes, M., Milic-Emili, J. 1973. Control of tidal volume and respiratory frequency in anesthetized cats. *J. Appl. Physiol.* 35:463–76

40. Guazzi, M., Freis, E. D. 1969. Sinoaortic reflexes and arterial pH, PO_2, and PCO_2 in wakefulness and sleep. *Am. J. Physiol.* 217:1623–27

41. Guilleminault, C., Eldridge, F. L., Dement, W. C. 1973. Insomnia with sleep apnea: a new syndrome. *Science* 181: 856–58

42. Hagan, R., Bryan, A. C., Bryan, H. M., Gulston, G. 1976. The effect of sleep state on intercostal muscle activity and ribcage motion. *Physiologist* 19:214 (Abstr.)

43. Hagan, R., Bryan, A. C., Bryan, H. M., Gulston, G. 1977. Neonatal chest wall afferents and regulation of respiration. *J. Appl. Physiol. Respir. Environ. Exercise Physiol.* 42:362–67

44. Hathorn, M. K. S. 1974. The rate and depth of breathing in new-born infants in different sleep states. *J. Physiol. London* 243:101–13

45. Henane, R., Buguet, A., Roussel, B., Bittel, J. 1977. Variations in evaporation and body temperature during sleep in man. *J. Appl. Physiol. Respir. Environ. Exercise Physiol.* 42:50–55

46. Henderson-Smart, D. J., Read, D. J. C. 1976. Depression of respiratory muscles and defective responses to nasal obstruction during active sleep in the newborn. *Aust. Paediatr. J.* 12:261–66

47. Hobson, J. A. 1974. The cellular basis of sleep cycle control. See Ref. 17, pp. 217–50

48. Hobson, J. A. Goldfrank, F., Snyder, F. 1965. Respiration and mental activity in sleep. *J. Psychiatr. Res.* 3:79–90

49. Honda, Y., Natsui, T. 1967. Effect of sleep on ventilatory response to CO_2 in severe hypoxia. *Respir. Physiol.* 3:220–28

50. Jouvet, M. 1965. Paradoxical sleep—a study of its nature and mechanisms. In *Progress in Brain Research Sleep Mechanisms,* ed. K. Akert, C. Bally, J. P.

Schadé, 18:20–62. Amsterdam:Elsevier
51. Khatri, I. M., Freis, E. D. 1967. Hemodynamic changes during sleep. *J. Appl. Physiol.* 22:867–73
52. Knill, R., Andrews, W., Bryan, A. C., Bryan, M. H. 1976. Respiratory load compensation in infants. *J. Appl. Physiol.* 40:357–61
53. Knill, R., Bryan, A. C. 1976. An intercostal-phrenic inhibitory reflex in human newborn infants. *J. Appl. Physiol.* 40:352–56
54. Lenard, H. G., von Bernuth, H., Prechtl, H. F. R. 1968. Reflexes and their relationship to behavioral state in the newborn. *Acta Paediatr. Scand.* 57:177–85
55. Loomis, A. L., Harvey, E. N., Hobart, G. 1935. Further observations on the potential rhythms of the cerebral cortex during sleep. *Science* 82:198–200
56. Lugaresi, E. 1972. Polygraphic aspects of sleep in man. *Bull. Physio-pathol. Resp.* 8:1071–74
57. Lugaresi, E., Coccagna, G., Mantovani, M., Cirignotta, F. 1976. Hypersomnia with periodic apnea. In *Narcolepsy,* ed. C. Guilleminault, W. C. Dement, P. Passouant, p. 351. New York:Spectrum
58. Lugaresi, E., Coccagna, G., Mantovani, M., Lebrun, R. 1972. Some periodic phenomena arising during drowsiness and sleep in man. *Electroencephalogr. Clin. Neurophysiol.* 32:701–5
59. Magnussen, G. 1944. *Studies on the Respiration During Sleep.* London: H. K. Lewis. 276 pp.
60. Mangold, R., Sokoloff, L., Conner, E., Kleinerman, J., Therman, P. O. G., Kety, S. S. 1955. The effects of sleep on the cerebral circulation and metabolism of normal young men. *J. Clin. Invest.* 34:1092–1100
61. Mayevsky, A., Samuel, D. 1975. The use of $^{18}O_2$ in studying oxygen metabolism in various behavioral situations. *J. Neurosci. Res.* 1:495–99
62. Mills, E., Sampson, S. R. 1969. Respiratory responses to electrical stimulation of the cervical sympathetic nerves in decerebrate unanaesthetized cats. *J. Physiol. London* 202:271–82
63. Mitchell, R. A., Berger, A. J. 1975. Neural regulation of respiration. *Am. Rev. Respir. Dis.* 111:206–24
64. Orem, J., Dement, W. C. 1976. Neurophysiological substrates of the changes in respiration during sleep. See Ref. 17, 2:1–42
65. Orem, J., Montplaisir, J., Dement, W. C. 1974. Changes in the activity of respiratory neurons during sleep. *Brain Res.* 82:309–15
66. Orem, J., Netick, A., Dement, W. C. 1977. Increased upper airway resistance to breathing during sleep in the cat. *Electroencephalogr. Clin. Neurophysiol.* 43:14–22
67. Orem, J., Netick, A., Dement, W. C. 1977. Breathing during sleep and wakefulness in the cat. *Respiration Physiol.* 30:265–89
68. Ostergaard, T. 1944. The excitability of the respiratory centre during sleep and during Evipan anesthesia. *Acta Physiol. Scand.* 8:1–15
69. Parmeggiani, P. L., Franzini, C., Lenzi, P. 1976. Respiratory frequency as a function of preoptic temperature during sleep. *Brain Res.* 111:253–60
70. Parmeggiani, P. L., Franzini, C., Lenzi, P., Cianci, T. 1971. Inguinal subcutaneous temperature changes in cats sleeping at different environmental temperatures. *Brain Res.* 33:397–404
71. Parmeggiani, P. L., Franzini, C., Lenzi, P., Zamboni, G. 1973. Threshold of respiratory responses to preoptic heating during sleep in freely moving cats. *Brain Res.* 52:189–201
72. Parmeggiani, P., Sabattini, L. 1972. Electromyographic aspects of postural, respiratory and thermoregulatory mechanisms in sleeping cats. *Electroencephalogr. Clin. Neurophysiol.* 23:1–13
73. Pengelly, L. D., Rebuck, A. S., Campbell, E. J. M. 1974. *Loaded Breathing,* Don Mills, Ont.:Longman
74. Phillipson, E. A. 1977. Regulation of breathing during sleep. *Am. Rev. Respir. Dis.* 115(Suppl.): 217–24
75. Phillipson, E. A., Kozar, L. F., Murphy, E. 1976. Respiratory load compensation in awake and sleeping dogs. *J. Appl. Physiol.* 40:895–902
76. Phillipson, E. A., Kozar, L. F., Rebuck, A. S., Murphy, E. 1977. Ventilatory and waking responses to CO_2 in sleeping dogs. *Am. Rev. Respir. Dis.* 115:251–59
77. Phillipson, E. A., Murphy, E., Kozar, L. F. 1976. Regulation of respiration in sleeping dogs. *J. Appl. Physiol.* 40: 688–93
78. Phillipson, E. A., Sullivan, C. E., Read, D. J. C., Murphy, E., Kozar, L. F. 1978. Ventilatory and waking responses to hypoxia in sleeping dogs. *J. Appl. Physiol.* In press
79. Pompeiano, O. 1967. The neurophysiological mechanisms of the postural and motor events during desynchronized sleep. In *Sleep and Altered States of Consciousness,* ed. S. S. Kety, E. V.

Evarts, H. L. Williams, p. 351. Baltimore, Md.:Williams & Wilkins

80. Pompeiano, O. 1976. Mechanisms responsible for spinal inhibition during desynchronized sleep:experimental study. See Ref. 57, p. 411

81. Prechtl, H. F. R. 1974. The behavioral states of the newborn infant (a review). *Brain Res.* 76:185–212

82. Puizillout, J. J., Ternaux, J. P., Foutz, A. S., Fernandez, G. 1974. Les stades de sommeil chez la preparation encephale isolé. 1. Declenchement des pointes ponto-geniculo-occipitales et du sommeil phasique à ondes lentes. Rôle des noyaux du raphe. *Electroencephalogr. Clin. Neurophysiol.* 37:561–76

83. Purcell, M. 1976. Response in the newborn to raised upper airway resistance. *Arch. Dis. Child.* 51:602–7

84. Read, D. J. C. 1967. A clinical method for assessing the ventilatory response to carbon dioxide. *Australas. Ann. Med.* 16:20–32

85. Rebuck, A. S., Campbell, E. J. M. 1974. A clinical method for assessing the ventilatory response to hypoxia. *Am. Rev. Respir. Dis.* 109:345–50

86. Rechtschaffen, A., Kales, A. 1968. *A Manual of Standardized Terminology, Techniques and Scoring System for Sleep States of Human Subjects.* Natl. Inst. Health Publ. 204. Washington DC: GPO

87. Reed, C. I., Kleitman, N. 1926. Studies on the physiology of sleep. IV. The effect of sleep on respiration. *Am. J. Physiol.* 75:600–8

88. Reed, D. J., Kellogg, R. H. 1958. Changes in respiratory response to CO_2 during natural sleep at sea level and at altitude. *J. Appl. Physiol.* 13:325–30

89. Reed, D. J., Kellogg, R. H. 1960. Effect of sleep on hypoxic stimulation of breathing at sea level and altitude. *J. Appl. Physiol.* 15:1130–34

90. Reed, D. J., Kellogg, R. H. 1960. Effect of sleep on CO_2 stimulation of breathing in acute and chronic hypoxia. *J. Appl. Physiol.* 15:1135–38

91. Reite, M., Jackson, D., Cahoon, R. L., Weil, J. V. 1975. Sleep physiology at high altitude. *Electroencephalogr. Clin. Neurophysiol.* 38:463–71

92. Reivich, M., Isaacs, G., Evarts, E., Kety, S. 1968. The effect of slow wave sleep and REM sleep on regional cerebral blood flow in cats. *J. Neurochem.* 15:301–6

93. Remmers, J. E. 1970. Inhibition of inspiratory activity by intercostal muscle afferents. *Respir. Physiol.* 10:358–83

94. Remmers, J. E., Bartlett, D. Jr., Putnam, M. D. 1976. Changes in the respiratory cycle associated with sleep. *Respir. Physiol.* 28:227–38

95. Rigatto, H., Brady, J. P. 1972. Periodic breathing and apnea in preterm infants. II. Hypoxia as a primary event. *Pediatrics* 50:219–28

96. Robin, E. D., Whaley, R. D., Crump, C. H., Travis, D. M. 1958. Alveolar gas tensions, pulmonary ventilation and blood pH during physiologic sleep in normal subjects. *J. Clin. Invest.* 37: 981–89

97. Sauerland, E. K., Harper, R. M. 1976. The human tongue during sleep:electromyographic activity of the genioglossus muscle. *Exp. Neurol.* 51:160–70

98. Saunders, N. A., Powles, A. C. P., Rebuck, A. S. 1976. Ear oximetry: accuracy and practicability in the assessment of arterial oxygenation. *Am. Rev. Respir. Dis.* 113:745–49

99. Shannon, D. C., Marsland, D. W., Gould, J. B., Callahan, B., Todres, I. D., Dennis, J. 1976. Central hypoventilation during quiet sleep in two infants. *Pediatrics* 57:342–46

100. Snyder, F. 1967. Autonomic nervous system manifestations during sleep and dreaming. See Ref. 79, p. 469

101. Snyder, F., Hobson, J. A., Morrison, D. F., Goldfrank, F. 1964. Changes in respiration, heart rate, and systolic blood pressure in human sleep. *J. Appl. Physiol.* 19:417–22

102. Specht, H., Fruhmann, G. 1972. Incidence of periodic breathing in 2000 subjects without pulmonary or neurological disease. *Bull. Physio-pathol. Respir.* 8:1075–83

103. Spreng, L. F., Johnson, L. C., Lubin, A. 1968. Autonomic correlates of eye movement bursts during stage REM sleep. *Psychophysiology* 4:311–23

104. Thach, B. T., Abroms, I. F., Frantz, I. D. III, Sotrel, A., Bruce, E. N., Goldman, M. D. 1977. REM sleep breathing pattern without intercostal muscle influence. *Fed. Proc.* 36:445 (Abstr.)

105. Townsend, R. E., Prinz, P. N., Obrist, W. D. 1973. Human cerebral blood flow during sleep and waking. *J. Appl. Physiol.* 35:620–25

106. Tusiewicz, K., Moldofsky, H., Bryan, A. C. 1977. Mechanics of the rib cage and diaphragm during sleep. *J. Appl. Physiol.* In press

107. Wade, J. G., Larson, C. P. Jr., Hickey, R. F., Ehrenfeld, W. K., Severinghaus,

J. W. 1970. Effect of carotid endarterectomy on carotid chemoreceptor and baroreceptor function in man. *N. Engl. J. Med.* 282:823–29

108. Webb, P. 1974. Periodic breathing during sleep. *J. Appl. Physiol.* 37:899–903

109. Webb, P., Hiestand, M. 1975. Sleep metabolism and age. *J. Appl. Physiol.* 38:257–62

110. Weitzman, E. D., Graziani, L. 1974. Sleep and the sudden infant death syndrome: a new hypothesis. See Ref. 17, pp. 327–44

111. Whitelaw, W. A., Derenne, J. P., Milic-Emili, J. 1975. Occlusion pressure as a measure of respiratory center output in conscious man. *Respir. Physiol.* 23:181–99

112. Wurtz, R. H., O'Flaherty, J. J. 1967. Physiological correlates of steady potential shifts during sleep and wakefulness. 1. Sensitivity of the steady potential to alterations in carbon dioxide. *Electroencephalogr. Clin. Neurophysiol.* 22:30–42

Ann. Rev. Physiol. 1978. 40:157–84
Copyright © 1978 by Annual Reviews Inc. All rights reserved

RESPIRATORY MECHANICS ❖1189

Peter T. Macklem

Meakins-Christie Laboratories, Department of Medicine,
Royal Victoria Hospital, McGill University, Montreal, Canada

INTRODUCTION

In selecting certain topics in respiratory mechanics for review, I have ignored important and interesting areas in which substantial advances have been made. Such areas include the pressure flow relationships within the airways, mechanisms limiting maximal expiratory flow rates, and growth and development of the lung.

My review of those areas that are covered is also selective. For example, in dealing with contractile tissue within the lung, I ignore a large body of literature dealing with bronchial and alveolar duct smooth muscle and focus on a small (but, I think, very original and exciting) aspect of airway smooth muscle control.

While preparing this review I was fortunate and privileged to be given a preprint of a chapter on the mechanical properties of the lung by Hoppin & Hildebrandt (51). This chapter is a superb, comprehensive, and critical review of the field. Naturally, it covers many of the same topics reviewed here; it has proven very useful to me in clarifying the ideas expressed in this review, and I am most grateful to Drs. Hoppin and Hildebrandt.

This review is limited almost exclusively to manuscripts published in 1974–1975. I have cited articles published before 1974 to provide background knowledge essential for placing the more recent articles in perspective.

CONTRACTILE TISSUE IN THE LUNG

One of the most interesting developments in the physiology of the airways in recent years has been the demonstration that tracheobronchial smooth

157

0066-4278/78/0301-0157$01.00

muscle is controlled by nonadrenergic inhibitory neurons. Such neurons have been known to play an important role in initiating the relaxation phase of peristalsis in the gastrointestinal tract. The neuronal pathways in the gut are in the myenteric plexus. Ischemic destruction of these neurons results in spasm of those segments of the bowel where the neurons are destroyed, and Hirschsprung's disease is thought to result from a lack of these neurons. The neurotransmitter substance is unknown. Burnstock postulated that it was ATP and suggested the term *purinergic nerves* to describe the system (13).

Coburn & Tomita (14), the first to describe such a system in guinea pig trachea smooth muscle, were followed closely by Bando et al (9) and Coleman & Levy (15). They showed that electrical stimulation of the isolated guinea pig trachea resulted in a biphasic response characterized initially by contraction followed by relaxation. Propranolol, practalol, and guanethidine reduced but did not abolish the relaxation phase. The contraction was abolished by atropine or hyoscine but the relaxation persisted. Relaxation was blocked by tetrodotoxin, which indicated that the relaxation was mediated via nerve pathways. Subsequently, Richardson demonstrated that the nonadrenergic inhibiting system was potent in causing relaxation of trachea smooth muscle previously constricted either by an antigen–antibody reaction or by histamine (77). He also demonstrated that the system was present in human lungs in the trachea, bronchi, and bronchioles (76), and suggested that a lack of this system in the airways would lead to the hyperreactivity characteristic of asthma. It is still too early to assess the importance of this system.

Another fascinating observation has been made by Kapanci and associates, who found by electron microscopy that about 50% of alveolar interstitial cells of rat, human, lamb, and monkey lungs, which otherwise resembled fibroblasts, contain fibrils measuring 30–80 Å in diameter (55). The authors postulated that these are contractile and, in support of this hypothesis, they demonstrated that many lung interstitial cells bind sera containing anti-actin antibodies. In addition, they found that lung parenchymal strips contracted with hypoxia and epinephrine, whereas bronchial strips relaxed with both. Arterial strips did not respond to hypoxia. Serotonin had little effect on parenchymal strips, whereas it contracted both bronchial and arterial strips. Kapanci et al (55) stated that "since serotonin triggers violent contraction of arterial and/or bronchial musculature, we conclude that in epinephrine-induced as well as hypoxia-induced contractions, tissues other than arterial and bronchial musculature are implicated." They felt that the contractile cells were not smooth muscle in alveolar ducts because these are seldom observed in normal alveolar septa in man and monkey, and (the authors asserted) "they do not exist in the rat lung." Thus they postulated that the alveoli contain a contractile system in addition to smooth muscle which may play a role in the regulation of ventilation : perfusion ratios.

Although the authors did not present incontrovertible evidence that these cells are contractile, the idea is certainly intriguing. Most physiologists have regarded the elastic properties of lungs as more or less fixed. However, the observation that lung elastic recoil can decrease astonishingly rapidly in some asthmatics upon the initiation of an asthmatic attack and can just as rapidly revert to normal in response to bronchodilator therapy (34, 70) is forcing a revision of these views. Perhaps contractile interstitial cells relax during the asthmatic attack as bronchial smooth muscle contracts. Certainly the limited evidence presented by Kapanci et al suggests that the pharmacologic control of the interstitial cells is quite different from that of arterial and bronchial smooth muscle.

Contractile cells might also play a role in controlling collateral flow resistance. This resistance is increased by hypoxia (which contracted parenchymal strips) but decreased by hypercapnia (6, 87). These effects do not appear to be under parasympathetic or α-adrenergic control (10). Although we do not know exactly which channels transmit collateral ventilation, they are almost certainly at the alveolar level. Recently Raskin & Herman described interacinar pathways in human lungs. These were of the size of alveolar ducts, and were continuous with both respiratory bronchioles and alveolar ducts (73). Hansen et al found a similar structure in a polyurethane foam reconstruction of a human acinus extending from a respiratory bronchiole to an alveolar duct (47). Control of the caliber of these structures as well as of pores of Kohn and canals of Lambert would seem to require contractile cells in alveolar walls.

HOW DO LUNGS INFLATE AND DEFLATE?

It is ironic that despite intriguing new possibilities such as a nonadrenergic inhibitory system in bronchial smooth muscle, and the existence of contractile interstitial cells in alveolar septa, we still do not know how the lung inflates and deflates.

There is no agreement about whether the lung inflates by recruiting new alveoli, or by expanding alveoli which are already open. Until 1970, the bulk of evidence favored the latter possibility. For example, Anthonisen found that lung volume and lung volume history had virtually no effect on shunt flow. This suggested that areas of atelectasis did not result from lung deflation (4). Further, Dunnill found that alveolar surface area A varied with lung volume V to a power close to 0.67, which is to be expected if there is no recruitment and if alveolar shape remains constant (30). Storey &

Staub (82) and Klingele & Staub (58) provided evidence that alveolar shape is constant at different lung volumes—at least at lung volumes greater than 40% VC. However, Forrest reexamined the relationship between alveolar volume and surface area and found that A varied directly with V, and that a similar linear fit described Dunnill's data well (32). Subsequently, Gil & Weibel also found a linear relationship between A and V (39). A direct relationship is expected if the lung expands by recruitment. Gil & Weibel published transmission electron photomicrographs indicating substantial folding of alveolar walls with deep clefts between the folds and suggested that unfolding was the morphological basis of recruitment. That the folds involved minute areas of the lung in which alveolar gas was never far from the folded tissue could account for Anthonisen's observations that lung volume had no effect on shunt flow (4); it would still permit the possibility of recruitment on inflation and derecruitment on deflation.

The issue is far from settled, however. Using morphometric techniques D'Angelo found that $A \propto V^{0.66}$ (18). Tsunoda et al reasoned that lung tissue volume should remain constant. Therefore, surface area should vary inversely with alveolar thickness. They measured alveolar thickness at different lung volumes and found that thickness varied as volume to the power of -0.44. Therefore, $A \propto V^{0.44}$ (88). Flicker & Lee used a third method to calculate the relationship between surface area and volume (31). Using reflected light microscopy they observed immediately subpleural alveoli and measured the average perimeter $\overline{L}$ of the alveolar mouth and the average area $\overline{A}$ on the pleural surface. They derived the expression $Ps = \gamma \overline{L}/\overline{A}$, where Ps is the difference between air- and saline-filled transpulmonary pressure, and γ is the surface tension. Because Ps is thought to be the contribution of surface forces to transpulmonary pressure, the work performed on the surface (in contrast to the tissues) is given by $\int Ps \times dV$. But the work performed on the surface is also given by $\int \gamma \times dA$. Equating these two expressions and rearranging yields:

$$Ps = \gamma \, dA/dV.$$

It follows that $dA/dV = \overline{L}/\overline{A}$. They found that $\overline{L}/\overline{A}$ varied as $V^{-1/3}$ at large lung volumes and deviated at most from this fit by 20%. They therefore concluded that $A \propto V^{2/3}$

The reasons for the discrepant results are far from clear. One of the problems with morphometric techniques is sensitivity. Both Forrest's and Dunnill's data seem equally well-fitted by equations of the form $A \propto V^{2/3}$ and $A \propto V$. Flicker & Lee's data were restricted to immediately subpleural alveoli. Although their method is attractive because it avoids artifacts due to fixation, there is no guarantee that the relationship between A and V is the same for alveoli further from the pleural surface. This problem is basic to the solution of a number of other problems in lung mechanics. For example, the explanation of static pressure-volume hysteresis depends upon the pattern of alveolar recruitment and derecruitment on inflation and deflation. Determination of the relationships between area and surface tension in the alveolar lining layer in situ from pressure/volume curves also depends upon knowledge of how A varies with V.

Hills (48) suggested that pressure-volume hysteresis was due to geometric irreversibility, and he demonstrated this using human lungs frozen after autopsy and then thawed. (The distance between two or more markers on the pleural surface was different on inflation and deflation at the same lung volume.) His results were challenged by Ardila et al who found no geometric irreversibility in freshly excised rabbit lungs, either saline-filled or air-filled (5). Dimensional changes between orthogonally placed pleural markers were nearly equal on inflation and deflation and had a slope of 1, falling along the identity line when plotted against $V^{1/3}$. Ardila et al concluded that geometric irreversibility did not account for pressure-volume hysteresis, and suggested that Hills's findings were due to his use of lungs that had deteriorated by the time he studied them. They showed that because $\int Ps \times dV = \int \gamma \times dA$, the work done on the surface in one cycle represents an energy loss in the surface lining. They concluded that geometric irreversibility

> per se cannot be shown to dissipate energy. Rather, irreversibility can exist only because energy dissipation occurs within the lung.... Whatever degree of macroscopic geometrical irreversibility that is present is probably due mainly to hysteretic processes occurring in the surface lining and to a lesser extent in the tissue.

Using a technique identical to that of Ardila et al, D'Angelo (19), too, found no geometric irreversibility. On the other hand, Gil & Weibel, who found a marked surface-to-pressure hysteresis, thought that their data supported Hills's conclusions (39). This suggestion can be challenged. Gil & Weibel found a linear relationship between A and V, except at low volumes on inflation. The data points obtained on inflation fell on the same line as those on deflation. This suggests that at the same lung volume the degree of derecruitment on deflation was identical to the degree of recruitment on inflation. If so, pressure-volume hysteresis cannot be accounted for on the basis of recruitment. This would only be the case if the number of open airspaces were greater on deflation compared to inflation at the same lung volume.

Subsequently Hills showed (49) that dipalmitoyl lecithin, the major constituent of surfactant, does not change the interfacial tension at water–mercury interfaces. Thus the marked pressure-volume hysteresis observed by Pierce et al (71) in mercury-filled lungs must have been due to geometric irreversibility rather than surface irreversibility. This seems incontrovertible, but it applies only to mercury-filled lungs. Hills clearly realized that geometric irreversibility is a function of γ, because saline-filled lungs exhibit little hysteresis. The very high values for γ at the alveolar surface, which must have been present with mercury filling, may have conferred a degree of geometric irreversibility that was far greater than any observed in air-filled lungs. Furthermore, the pressures required to inflate the lungs with mercury were very large and may well have led to geometric irreversibility caused by tissue disruption.

Based upon the equality $dA/dV = Ps/\gamma$, and assuming that $A \propto V^{2/3}$, Hills calculated alveolar surface areas. This calculation, too, can be criticized. If γ confers geometric irreversibility, then the relationship between A and V will be different for air-filled and mercury-filled lungs, and Hills's results apply only to the special case where the lungs contain mercury. Furthermore, his assumption that $A \propto V^{2/3}$ appears to violate his basic premise that there is geometric irreversibility.

Daly et al presented evidence of geometric irreversibility at the alveolar level (17). They used videomicroscopy to study ventilation of subpleural alveoli in rats and measured dimensions from frames taken at 0.033 sec intervals. Plotting one dimension against another showed geometric irreversibility. The plots were irregular, crossing in figure eight loops. Their consistency is not mentioned; one wonders whether the loops are random errors that would be eliminated by taking mean curves, or whether they are real. The former possibility is suggested when the authors write that "another aspect of dynamic irreversibility is the nonrepetitive wall movement observed in the time dimensional curves from breath to breath." The findings may have been distorted by the fact that pipe cleaners were glued to the lobe margins every 0.5 cm in order to attach the lobe to a coverslip. This procedure may have accounted for the finding of geometric irreversibility. Daly et al claimed that because hysteresis is dynamic their system was an improvement over static measurements. Of course the hysteresis that concerns physiologists is static; and static measurements provide sharper pictures with better definition and more reliable results.

Those who wish to explain pressure-volume hysteresis in the normal air-filled lung on the basis of geometric irreversibility conferred upon the tissues by surface forces that are themselves reversible, will have to explain Radford's air pressure-volume curves. These were obtained in lungs that had been rinsed with Tween 20 (72). In these lungs, γ was presumably the same on inflation and deflation, and much greater than any interfacial tension that may have been present during saline-filling. These curves exhibited very little hysteresis.

Thus the bulk of evidence still favors the concept that pressure-volume hysteresis is due to hysteresis in surface tension–area relationships. Recruitment may play a role in determining the relationship between A and V and the distending pressure at a given lung volume, but Gil & Weibel's data indicate that it does not account for hysteresis.

EFFECTS OF SURFACE TENSION IN SITU

Attempts continue to be made to estimate the surface tension of the alveolar lining layer in situ. Bachofen et al used the equations $PsdV = \gamma dA$ and $A = kV^{2/3}$ to solve for the unknowns, γ and A (6). They evaluated k by assuming a maximum value of γ. They compared γ-A loops obtained in situ to those obtained from surface balance measurements and found a number of differences. The initial rate of fall of γ with a decrease in area was much greater in situ, whereas on reinflation the initial increase in γ was considerably less. As total lung capacity (TLC) was approached, γ increased rapidly rather than approaching a maximum value asymptotically. This last discrepancy is particularly troubling. As Hoppin & Hildebrandt pointed out (72), the surface concentration of a surfactant diminishes as its surface area is stretched. As this occurs, the surface tension at the interface is increasingly determined by the surface tension of the subphase. Thus as area increases, γ should approach its maximum value asymptotically (see below).

An approach similar to that used by Bachofen et al was employed by Horie et al, who compared rates of stress relaxation and equilibrium values of transpulmonary pressure to rate of stress adaptation of γ and equilibrium values of γ (53). They found a variety of values for equilibrium in situ, γ being higher on inflation than on deflation. They reported values of γ between 2 and 16 dynes cm^{-1} below 70% TLC. Tierney & Johnson (86), in contrast, reported that γ equilibrium was the same at all areas, and ranged from 24 to 30 dynes cm^{-1}. Furthermore, heating influenced rates of stress adaptation in situ much less than it did rates of stress adaptation in surface balance studies.

Tsunoda et al (88) and Flicker & Lee (31) attempted to measure surface tension in situ without making the assumption that $A \propto V^{2/3}$. Tsunoda et al used their own measured value of $V^{0.44}$ (88). Flicker & Lee (discussed above) used their measured values of L/A in subpleural alveoli to calculate dA/dV and γ in situ. Both Tsunoda et al and Flicker & Lee developed γ-A curves quite similar to those of Bachofen et al (6), yet because their techniques did not require assumptions of the relationship between A and V, the discrepancies between in situ and in vitro surface behavior cannot be attributed to these assumptions.

To what, then, can the discrepancies be attributed? It certainly seems possible that γ-A behavior in situ is different from that of lung extracts in vitro. If so, much of our thinking about the role of surfactant in lung mechanics will have to be reevaluated. The rapid rise in γ near TLC from the in situ curves is particularly disturbing. Common to all the measurements of γ in situ in which this rise was observed is the assumption that the difference in lung recoil pressure between air- and saline-filled lungs is the pressure due to surface forces. This assumes that tissue recoil pressure is independent of surface forces, which is almost certainly incorrect. In saline-filled lungs, when there are no surface forces, the lung tissues assume the configuration associated with minimum energy. In the presence of surface forces this configuration of the lung should be altered. When surface forces are small, radii of curvature should be smaller than when surface forces are large. Thus by altering the configuration, surface tension should cause an increased tissue pressure. This would lead to an overestimate of Ps. This in turn would lead to an overestimate of γ. The sudden rise in calculated γ at maximal area in the in situ curves is due to the flattening and reduced compliance of the air pressure–volume curves as TLC is approached. Saline pressure–volume curves do not demonstrate this. Thus the difference in pressure between the two curves, Ps, rapidly increases as TLC is approached. If lung tissues approach their limit of distensibility as total lung capacity is approached, then the change in alveolar configuration induced by surface forces might tense the tissue elements. The flattening of the pressure–volume curve near TLC may be caused by such tensed tissues. On subsequent deflation, the lowering of surface tension would allow the tissues to relax toward their minimum-energy configuration, which in turn would lead to hysteresis. Thus hysteresis may be due both to differences in tissue recoil on inflation and deflation and to differences in γ. The differences in γ would be responsible for the differences in elastic recoil, because a high γ would cause relatively large distortions away from the minimum-energy configuration, while a low γ would cause only small distortions.

An alternate explanation for the discrepancy between in situ and in vitro γ-A curves was recently put forward by Bienkowski & Skolnick. They suggested that there were two important interfaces in the lung—one at the air–liquid boundary, and the other at the liquid–tissue boundary where surfactant molecules may adsorb and exert an area-dependent interfacial tension (12). They conjectured that saline would abolish both interfaces, whereas an immiscible liquid like mineral oil would eliminate only the air–liquid interface. If so, the difference between inflating pressure during saline-filling and that during oil-filling would give a better estimate of Ps. Bachofen et al (6) had published the necessary pressure–volume data for lungs filled with mineral oil. Bienkowski & Skolnick (12) therefore recalculated in situ γ-A curves from Bachofen's data and found them to be intermediate between surface balance and in situ saline curves. Their curves showed a more rapid rise with expansion, and there was a tendency to approach a limiting value as maximum area was approached.

Before leaving the subject of surface behavior in situ, consider the role of surfactant in maintaining airspace stability and preventing excess liquid from entering the airspaces. The usual description of the influence of surface tension on the mechanical properties of the alveoli assumes that the alveoli are spherical. Therefore the Laplace equation can be used to describe the pressure due to surface forces. The classic thinking is that the surface pressure–volume curves of alveoli have negative slopes and are unstable unless stability is conferred by the tissues or unless γ increases as V increases. Surface tension must be low; otherwise liquid would accumulate in the alveoli.

This classical model has recently been challenged by Fung (38) and by Reifenrath (75). Fung pointed out that because pressure differences across alveolar walls are essentially zero, the net curvature of the wall (neglecting tissue tension) must also be zero, and the surface is therefore minimal. If the edges of alveolar walls are fixed in space, then the wall is inherently stable (38). Using surface balance measurements of γ-A relationships and tissue stress–strain curves, Fung derived a stress–strain curve for surface and tissue combined. With this relationship he formulated general equations of lung mechanics and examined the equilibrium conditions (37). He concluded that atelectasis resulting from inherent instability of alveolar edges could not occur in the inflated lung, although planar (platelike) atelectasis would result if layers of alveoli were forced to collapse toward a plane by some external agent. Atelectasis was not due to instability among parallel communicating bubbles, because alveoli "in an open lung have no inherent instability. The crux of the matter is a proper account of the topology of the alveolar structure" (38).

Assuming polyhedral rather than spherical alveoli, Reifenrath (75) showed that even if γ were constant, the recoil pressures due to surface forces would increase, not decrease, as volume increased, and would lend stability to the airspaces (75). This would be so if the perimeters of the free edges of the alveoli increase with lung volume and the radii of curvature in the corners decrease. The author pointed out that because the alveoli are interconnected, for alveoli deep within the lung there are a large number of possibilities for stability even though tissue tension is zero. "... Surface tension need be neither variable nor different in different alveoli.... The situation ... permits the coexistence of alveoli of different sizes under conditions of constant surface tension." Even for alveoli at the pleural surface (which, according to Reifenrath, are not polyhedra) unstable behavior does not necessarily result.

Reifenrath assumed a negligible recoil of tissues, and a γ that does not change with A. As both these assumptions are probably invalid, an increase in elastic recoil pressure with inspiration does not necessarily result from surface forces with a constant γ in polyhedral alveoli, as he concluded. Nevertheless, as he points out, it is at least possible for polyhedral alveoli, in the absence of tissue forces and with constant γ, to be stable even though they are of different size.

As usual, the validity of the theoretical development depends upon the validity of the geometry. We are uncertain of the geometry of the alveoli, but Fung's and Reifenrath's models are as good as any, and are much more realistic than those visualizing bubbles on the end of tubes. The geometry is critical to stability. "Let us assume," wrote Reifenrath, "that the basically polyhedral structure of the alveoli is a prerequisite for mechanical stability of the lung; then this stability must be lost once the dense polyhedral packing is transformed into a system of communicating vesicles." Therefore by increasing alveolar liquid alone, without changing γ, the lungs can become unstable if the polyhedra are converted to segments of spheres. "Polyhedral alveoli have the advantage that such low surface tensions are unnecessary, even for fluid balance. At the plane surfaces of septa, surface tension is not involved as a force leading to edema, so that at these surfaces the edema-inhibiting pressure is predominant. . . . Only in corners . . . can there be flow of fluid into the lumen of the alveolus." The author suggested that the following mechanism regulates extracellular alveolar liquid: "Too little fluid leads to small radii of curvature at the corners; this generates high excess pressures and in turn an influx of fluid into the alveolus. With increasing accumulation of fluid in the corners, the radius of curvature becomes larger and the excess pressure falls." Thus equilibrium is reached. However, "should so much fluid enter the alveolus that it encloses a sphere of air, and the radius decreases below the value of the corner radius producing equilibrium . . . the consequence would be a steady rise in excess pressure accompanied by an obligatory influx of fluid into the alveoli. . . . One may also infer that an increase in the average surface tension can lead to an increase in the alveolar fluid volume." Reifenrath's model is appealing not only in the context of alveolar stability, but also in establishing a mechanism whereby the amount of liquid would be autoregulated within limits. The model predicts that once the limit upon excess liquid is exceeded by an alteration in capillary permeability, hydrostatic pressures, or γ, an unstable situation develops, leading to the rapid development of pulmonary edema.

TRANSMISSION OF FORCES THROUGH THE LUNG PARENCHYMA

Before 1972, airspace stability was viewed almost exclusively as if each alveolus were free to expand and contract independently of its neighbors; the mechanisms promoting stability were viewed in light of surface forces and the Laplace relationship. In 1972, Mead, Takashima & Leith (65) published a long overdue analysis of how forces were transmitted through the lung parenchyma.

They pointed out that decreasing the volume of such a structure while keeping lung volume constant would reduce the surface area of that structure and tense the elastic elements attached to its outer surface. This would lower the effective pressure surrounding the area to a value more negative than pleural pressure. They showed that this interdependence between interconnected elements in the lung was a potent mechanism promoting stability. Woolcock & Macklem (92) proposed an equation describing the magnitude of this effect in terms of an interdependence parameter K:

$$K = (Px - P_{PL})/[(Pr - Px) - (P_{ALV} - P_{PL})],$$

where Px is the pressure surrounding a nonhomogeneous region, P_{PL} is pleural pressure, Pr is the pressure within the region, and P_{ALV} is alveolar pressure in the rest of the lung. The difference, $Px - P_{PL}$, can be regarded as the effect of the nonhomogeneity, whereas the difference between the elastic recoil pressure of the region ($Pr - Px$) and the elastic recoil pressure of the lung ($P_{ALV} - P_{PL}$) can be regarded as the magnitude of the nonhomogeneity. Estimates of K have been made recently for the interaction between the lung and other airspaces, airways, and blood vessels.

Hughes et al (54) passed 20 retrograde catheters into lungs. Air was flowed through the catheters, allowing lung volume to remain constant while intrabronchial pressure was lowered. Using tantalum bronchography, they compared bronchial dimensions while air was flowing through the retrograde catheters with dimensions obtained under static conditions with no airflow. By comparing pressure–diameter curves during flow with those obtained under static conditions, they calculated values for K which ranged from approximately 1.35 to 2.25. For small deviations from homogeneous behavior, the calculated peribronchial pressures were similar to those predicted on the basis of a change in the surface area of the outer wall of the airway alone; i.e. it appeared that there was a negligible change in tension in the elastic elements attached to the outer surface. For larger deviations, it appeared that the elastic elements were tensed. Hughes et al suggested that this would allow for moderate variations in smooth muscle tone without establishing an uneven distribution of stresses within the lung.

Takishima, Sasaki & Sasaki (85) also examined interdependence between lung parenchyma and airways. They occluded all but one bronchus in excised lobes. The unoccluded bronchus was cannulated and the parenchyma distant to all bronchi was inflated to any desired distending pressure via collateral channels. Bronchial pressure–volume curves were then generated and compared to pressure–volume curves obtained after the bronchi had been dissected free of surrounding parenchyma. Even when there was no distending pressure in the lungs, bronchial compliance was only 55–95% of that in the dissected bronchi. At higher distending pressures this fell to 25–40%. A comparison of the transmural pressure of the dissected bronchi with the difference between bronchial and pleural pressure in situ, at a given volume, would theoretically allow calculation of peribronchial pressure, and therefore K. Unfortunately, the investigators were not sufficiently confident of the absolute volumes to make this measure. However, it can be shown that the ratio of the compliance with the parenchyma intact to that after it had been dissected equals $K + 1$ (61). On this basis, with the lung distending pressure equal to zero, K ranged from 0.05 to 0.82, whereas at a distending pressure of 26–28 cm H_2O, K ranged from 1.5 to 3. These values agree closely with those of Hughes et al (54).

Quite different results were obtained by Benjamin et al (11) for interdependence between parenchyma and blood vessels. At low transpulmonary pressures, K decreased as the pressure in the vessel decreased. When the pressure in the vessel was 30 cm H_2O, K was 3.3; whereas when the pressure in the vessel was 5 cm H_2O, K fell to 0.7. At higher transpulmonary pressures (10–30 cm H_2O), K was much smaller (0.2 – 0.3). The finding of an increasing value for K as vascular pressure increased and a decreasing value as transpulmonary pressure increased is most curious. A likely explanation is that when interdependence tends to make a nonhomogeneously large unit smaller, its effect is greater at smaller lung volumes, due to distended, circumferentially arranged alveolar walls. This should result in a rapidly increasing Px as vascular volume increased when PL was close to zero or when the lung was atelectactic. With an increase in lung volume, however, there would be fewer circumferentially arranged alveoli in apposition to the vessel wall, so that this effect might diminish rapidly with lung inflation.

Sylvester, Menkes & Stitik measured airspace-parenchymal interdependence in the pig (84). They pointed out that the equation for K contains the hidden assumption that (Pr – Px) is uniquely related to the volume of the region. If nonhomogeneity results in some change in (Pr – Px) or (PALV – PPL) not related to a change in volume, then (Pr – Px) – (PALV – PPL) "does not exclusively express the amount of nonhomogeneity and K is not a pure index of interdependence." Their results suggested that nonhomogeneity simultaneously generates regional distortion, increasing (Pr – Px) at a given volume. This in turn "limits, and could theoretically reverse" the tendency for interdependence to restore homogeneity. This accounted for their observations that when lung volume was large relative to the nonhomogeneous region or when both volumes were large, interdependence was small; but when the region's volume was large relative to the lung volume, interdependence increased.

A different approach was taken by Hoppin & Morgan [quoted in (51)] and by Holland (50), who used elasticity theory to predict the magnitude of K for small spherical deformations. They found that K was a simple function of Poisson's ratio, μ:

$$K = 2(1 - 2\mu)/(1 + \mu).$$

In a study that must have required infinite patience, Hoppin, Lee & Dawson (52) excised cubes of lung parenchyma, attached threads to all six surfaces, and studied the effects of symmetrical and asymmetrical loading. During symmetrical loading they obtained not unreasonable pressure–volume curves. During asymmetrical loading the relationship between load and extension-ratio in the axis along which force was changed (major axis) was curvilinear and indicated more compliance but less hysteresis than during symmetrical loading. The unloaded axis changed length in the opposite sign. Predictions based on elasticity theory were in good agreement with their results and Hoppin et al concluded that "The relationship between behavior in symmetrical and asymmetrical loading, then, is consistent with elastic theory, giving limited support to the applicability of elastic analysis to the behavior of lung parenchyma." These investigators also calculated bulk modulus, Young's modulus, and Poisson's ratio. The first two increased with stress, and values in saline were lower than in air. Poisson's ratio was essentially independent of lung volume or stress, and was about 0.3 in air. It was lower but it increased with stress in saline-filled specimens.

D'Angelo (19) studied stress-strain relationships during uniform and non-uniform expansion of rabbit and cat lungs and found values of Poisson's ratio similar to those obtained by Hoppin et al. However, elastic theory did not fit his results except for relatively small parenchymal distortions. On the other hand Lai-Fook et al (59) calculated Poisson's ratio to be 0.43.

When a value for Poisson's ratio of 0.3 is used, $K \approx 0.6$ and is even lower for a Poisson's ratio of 0.43. These K values are lower than most experimental estimates. Experimental distortions may have exceeded the limits within which elastic theory is applicable. Fung (36) presented a theory of lung elasticity not based on an elastic continuum (which he considers invalid). This may be useful in predicting behavior for larger distortions. To model large deformations, Lee & Frankus (60) formulated a strain-energy function using data obtained by Hoppin et al (52) during symmetrical and asymmetrical loading of cubes of lung parenchyma. In a different approach, Frankus & Lee (33) predicted uniaxial stress-strain properties of alveolar walls from lung pressure–volume curves. Using a finite element analysis, with the alveolus modeled as a dodecahedron, they predicted the mechanical properties of lung parenchyma under distortion. At a "macro" level, the properties in distortion were computed from pressure–volume data and were in good agreement with experimental results. Clearly, much work remains to be done, particularly in the reconciliation of the empirical and theoretical approaches.

SHAPE VERSUS WEIGHT

Controversy continues over the reasons for the regional differences in pleural surface pressure, PPL. D'Angelo & Agostoni (22) stated that "Transpulmonary pressure distribution in liquid-filled lungs of dogs supports the conclusion that this distribution in air-filled lungs is essentially dependent on the effects of gravity upon the chest wall." Their basic idea is that gravity alters the shape of the chest wall and that the lung must change its shape and therefore the distribution of PPL in order to fit the shape of the chest wall. In another paper (20) they stated that "The results of our measurements, in line with our previous data obtained with a different technique . . . show . . . that the shape plays an important role on the distribution of transpulmonary pressure even at mid-lung volume." On the other hand, Vawter, Matthews & West (89) stated "These results are consistent with our finding that shape is a relatively minor factor in the generation of regional differences in pleural pressure compared with the weight of the lung."

Vawter et al reached this conclusion after analyzing a theoretical model of the lung. By use of finite element analysis of a homogeneous isotropic lung, they studied the distribution of stresses, volume, and PPL (a) while the chest wall changed shape during expansion; (b) for a variety of different lung shapes; and (c) for a variety of lung sizes. In the first condition the model lung was inflated either by lowering the diaphragm while keeping rib cage dimensions constant, or by expanding the rib cage while keeping the distance between apex and base constant. They found that except at the apex, regional expansion was similar for both conditions and that despite "gross differences in shape the stress distributions were generally similar." The different types of expansion had little effect on distribution of PPL. The authors concluded that "these results indicate that the effects of shape change are secondary to gravitational effects and rather unimportant except at high states of expansion."

In studying the inherent shape of lungs and chest wall, they concluded that the distribution of volume strains, stresses, and PPL appeared rather insensitive to geometry. When the effects of lung size were examined Vawter et al found that the PPL difference between apex and base was directly proportional to lung height. Grassino et al (45) observed that in human subjects regional lung volumes were independent of the shape of the chest wall both erect and supine (see below).

In apparent conflict with the predictions of Vawter et al (89) were the findings of Minh and colleagues (67), who measured the PPL gradient during electrophrenic stimulation in dogs. With such stimulation there was a marked descent of the diaphragm with a rather small decrease in the rib cage dimensions, thus mimicking the diaphragmatic inspiration studied by Vawter et al (89). In contrast to the latter findings (89), Minh et al reported that the PPL gradient reversed with diaphragmatic contraction. Experimental data also fail to support some other theoretical predictions made by Vawter et al. For example, in studying the inherent shape of lung and chest wall Vawter et al (89) examined the cylindrical shape. In their model, the lung was supported at the pleural surface, not by the hilum. The cylinder therefore received its support only at the apex and/or the base but not along its vertical sides. Under these conditions the investigators found a gradient in regional volumes, stresses, and PPL between apex and base. Yet excised lungs supported solely by the base or by the apex show no such gradient, and there is a difference in alveolar size only at sites very close to the point where the lungs are supported (56). In direct contradiction to the prediction that PPL differences between apex and base are directly proportional to lung height are the findings of Agostoni & D'Angelo (2), who reported that the difference in PPL between apex and base was very little greater in rams than in cats.

Thus a number of predictions arising from the theoretical analysis of Vawter et al are not supported by the somewhat limited experimental evidence. In most instances (as they pointed out themselves) direct comparison with the results of their paper was not feasible because of differences in experimental conditions, shapes, elastic properties, etc. Indeed, finite element analysis appears to be a tool of great potential power in the study of lung elasticity. Nevertheless, the possibility remains that the discrepancies between theoretical predictions and empirical evidence may have resulted from assigning inaccurate values to the parameters describing the elastic behavior of lung tissue.

Agostoni, D'Angelo, and their colleagues have marshalled impressive evidence that matching of lung shape to chest-wall shape is the most important cause of the distribution of PPL. By infusing histamine intravenously into experimental animals they altered the elastic properties of the lungs without changing lung weight (21). Because the lungs became stiffer, they grew more resistant to distortion. Thus the matching of lung and chest-wall shape required greater pressure. As a result, the gradient in PPL increased both in upright and supine animals. This supported their own predictions but contradicted the prediction of West & Matthews (90), who claimed that if the gradient is due to the weight of the lung, it should decrease as the lung becomes stiffer.

D'Angelo & Agostoni also studied the distribution of transpulmonary pressure when the respiratory system was passively expanded in dogs whose abdomens had been widely opened (20). The compliance of the diaphragmatic surface of the chest wall was virtually infinite under these circumstances. On the costal surface, compliance was finite; it approached zero in experiments where the caudal part of the rib cage was restrained so that its diameter was equal to that in the upright dog at FRC. The experiments were performed to determine how these differences in regional compliance of the chest wall influenced the distribution of transpulmonary pressures, PL, over these regions. They found that the changes in PL on the costal surface of the lung were less after opening the abdomen than they had been before. However, with the ribs unrestrained, the differences in PL on the diaphragmatic and costal surfaces only became large at large lung volumes, suggesting a large parenchymal interaction between the two surfaces. When the lower rib cage was restrained from expanding, the difference in PL between the diaphragmatic and costal surface became large. Thus the shape changes produced were accompanied by substantial alterations in PPL distribution.

When D'Angelo & Agostoni studied the distribution of PPL and PL in liquid-filled lungs they again found evidence that the distribution of PL in air-filled lungs is primarily dependent upon the effects of gravity on the chest wall (22). They stated:

> In the horizontal posture at FRC the upper parts of the air-filled lungs are more expanded than lower ones because of deformation of the diaphragm brought forth by the hydrostatic pressure gradient of the abdomen. . . . Hence, when the lungs too are filled with saline the vertical gradient of transpulmonary pressure should disappear . . . and when the lungs are filled with a liquid having a specific gravity higher than that of the abdominal contents this gradient should reverse. . . . Moreover, it is because of the hydrostatic pressure gradient of the abdomen that in the horizontal postures at FRC with air-filled lungs regional chest wall compliance is larger in the dependent than in the upper parts . . . and hence the vertical gradient of transpulmonary pressure decreases upon passive inflation of the respiratory system. . . . Hence, when the lungs are filled with saline transdiaphragmatic pressure should become uniform, differences of regional chest wall compliance should disappear and passive inflation of the respiratory system should not modify the distribution of transpulmonary pres-

sure. . . . Similarly, in the head-up posture, it is because of the effects of gravity upon the chest wall that regional rib cage compliance is larger in the dependent than in the upper parts and that relative expansion of the rib cage of air-filled lungs at FRC is larger in the upper than in the lower part. . . . Hence, when the air-filled lungs and chest wall are passively inflated the vertical gradient of transpulmonary pressure decreases.

All of their predictions were fulfilled in their experiments. Here is impressive evidence that the distribution of PPL depends much upon matching of lung and chest-wall shape and little upon lung weight.

Be that as it may, it is becoming increasingly obvious that these concepts of the influence of gravity on the respiratory system cannot be applied directly to human lungs. Froese & Bryan (35) observed that passive inflation of the respiratory system in anesthetized paralyzed humans in the supine position resulted in greater diaphragmatic motion over superior regions of the diaphragm than over inferior regions, presumably resulting in an increase in the PPL gradient along the diaphragmatic surface. In spontaneously breathing humans, diaphragmatic motion was greater over dependent regions. This directly contradicts the predictions of D'Angelo & Agostoni (22). Douglas et al (29) found that lung compliance was less in anesthetized paralyzed dogs during positive pressure ventilation applied at the airway opening than it was in those breathing spontaneously or in those ventilated by negative pressures applied to the body surface. This difference in compliance could be due to the different motions of superior and inferior regions of the diaphragm reported by Froese & Bryan (35). Rehder et al (74) found that the esophageal pressure gradient in upright man was uninfluenced by positive airway pressure as high as 21 cm H_2O. They concluded "It would appear that, in contrast to experiments in animals, under conditions of this study the distortion of thoracic configuration was not sufficient to abolish the pleural pressure gradient" (74). Abboud et al (1) pointed out that if positive airway pressure were to abolish the PPL gradient, both the slope of the alveolar plateau and the closing capacity should be reduced, but in fact these changes did not occur.

Grassino et al (45) and Bake et al (7) showed that voluntary shape changes of the chest wall produced by varying the distribution of chest-wall volume between rib cage and abdomen resulted in no change in the distribution of regional lung volumes in erect man. Regional differences in lung volume were only produced when the respiratory system was distorted beyond the physiological range by lateral compression of the lower rib cage (43). Also in contrast to the findings of Agostoni & D'Angelo in animals (3), it was found (43) that application of negative pressure to the abdomen in supine humans (or the voluntary achievement of a similar thoracoabdominal configuration) resulted in no change in regional differences in lung volume compared to those measured during relaxation at the same overall lung volume. Greene and co-workers (46) similarly found that immersion of humans in water to the xiphoid failed to alter the gradient in regional volumes or computed PPL. They concluded that in man the weight of the abdomen is unimportant in altering chest-wall shape and therefore the distribution of PPL (46). Grassino et al attributed the differences between their results and those of Agostoni & D'Angelo to differences in rib cage compliance between humans and experimental animals. They suggested that because the human rib cage is less compliant, it moves with a single degree of freedom. Indeed they measured the changes in rib cage dimensions and found them uniform (45). D'Angelo et al (23), found that in their experimental animals the lower rib cage was more compliant than the upper; motion was greater over the lower compared to the upper parts of the rib cage. This appears to be a reasonable explanation of the difference between humans and experimental animals in this regard.

One of the most significant experiments serving to distinguish between the importance of weight and that of shape in determining PPL distribution and regional lung volume in man is that of Grassino & Anthonisen (44), who reported the measurement of thoracoabdominal configuration and regional lung volumes at FRC during increasing cephalocaudal gravitational forces. This increased gravitational force produced minor changes in rib cage and abdominal configuration with small decreases in A-P diameter and concomitant increases in the lateral diameter of rib cage and abdomen. However, there was a large increase in the regional gradient of lung volume between apex and base and presumably a proportional increase in PPL gradient. During "Müller-like" maneuvers they found similar changes in chest-wall shape but opposite effects on the regional gradient of lung volume. Changes in shape alone, produced by the Müller-like maneuvers, caused a reduction in the regional volume and PPL gradient, while increase in lung weight accompanying essentially the same shape changes caused a diametrically opposite effect on regional volumes and PPL gradient. These intriguing experiments clearly demonstrate the importance of gravity on the lung, rather than on the chest wall, in determining the distribution of PPL, regional volumes, and regional ventilation distribution in humans. This conclusion, also reached by West et al (90), is more strongly supported by experimental evidence than is the view held by the school of Agostini & D'Angelo, that gravity exerts its influence on PPL in humans primarily through its action on chest-wall shape.

This does not mean, however, that shape is unimportant. Agostoni and D'Angelo emphasized the importance of shape changes produced by any means (not just gravity) in determining the distribution of PPL. There is growing evidence in humans and other animals that contraction of different respiratory muscles alters ventilation distribution and presumably the distribution of PPL. It seems likely that this effect is mediated by a change in the shape of the chest wall produced by contraction of different muscle groups.

Differences in ventilation distribution caused by contraction of various groups of respiratory muscles have been demonstrated by analyzing the washout of inhaled boluses of inert gases or the slope of the alveolar nitrogen plateau. Variations have been revealed by these methods under conditions when measurements of regional volumes or ventilation with radioisotopes failed to detect differences. This is surprising, since one would expect alveolar gas concentrations appearing at the mouth to be a less sensitive test of regional ventilation distribution than direct measurement of regional lung function measured by radioisotopes. However, most isotope studies examine events at the costal surface only and not those at the diaphragmatic and other surfaces. Washouts of N_2 or other inert gases, on the other hand, are capable of measuring alterations in ventilation distribution occurring anywhere within the lung. This may explain why alterations in ventilation distribution produced by changes in the geometry of the chest wall can be detected by single-breath washout tests whereas they have not generally been detected by radioisotope measurements of regional lung function. (Alternatively, the geometric changes during the isotope studies may not have been as marked as those during inert gas distribution measurements.)

The first indication that diaphragmatic contraction altered the distribution of PPL and therefore of ventilation distribution came from studies in experimental animals. D'Angelo, Sant'Ambrogio & Agostoni (26) showed that phrenic nerve stimulation in dogs caused a change in PPL greater in the lower intercostal spaces than in the upper. The greatest change occurred over the diaphragmatic surface. After phrenicectomy the PPL changes were greatest in the upper intercostal spaces, smaller in the lower intercostal spaces and smallest over the diaphragm. They concluded that "the greater changes in pressure are localized where the respiratory muscles act." These observations accorded with D'Angelo & Sant'Ambrogio's observations on the action of the contracting diaphragm on the rib cage in rabbits and dogs (25). They found that tetanic phrenic stimulation did not influence the relationship between PPL and upper rib cage dimensions in supine animals. They concluded that the upper rib cage dimensions are determined by the difference between PPL and atmospheric pressure. The lower rib cage was drawn inwards by diaphragmatic contraction in rabbits but driven outwards in dogs at volumes below 70% TLC. Results from eviscerated animals were little different: The effects were independent of changes in abdominal pressure. Mechanical anchoring of the dome of the diaphragm in eviscerated animals, however, caused the diaphragm to inflate the lower rib cage in both dogs and rabbits. With pneumothorax the action of the diaphragm was expiratory in both species. D'Angelo & Sant'Ambrogio suggested that whether or not the diaphragm has an inspiratory or an expiratory action on the lower rib cage may depend upon the position of the dome relative to the costal insertions. When the dome is high the diaphragm may have an inspiratory effect, but when it is low its effect may be expiratory. These data suggest some independence between upper and lower parts of the rib cage, in which respect humans may be different from dogs and rabbits. The distribution of P_{PL} changes with diaphragmatic contraction may thus be different between species. The evidence presented below indicates that this is the case.

Independently, Minh and colleagues (67) measured P_{PL} differences between apex and base during bilateral phrenic stimulation. In the upright position phrenic stimulation reversed the P_{PL} gradient. Threshold stimulation altered the gradient to half what it became during maximal stimulation. Changes in the length and diameter of basal airways were greater than those of apical airways. These differences diminished when at the same lung volume the trachea was occluded and stimulation ceased. Marked changes in lung shape were recorded. With phrenic stimulation the apex-to-base lung dimensions increased, whereas the lateral diameters decreased. With relaxation at the same lung volume the apex–base dimension decreased and lateral diameters increased. Ipsilateral phrenic stimulation caused considerably greater P_{PL} changes over basal lobes than apical lobes in the supine position (66). One concludes that even minimal diaphragmatic contractions can alter the P_{PL} gradient and therefore the ventilation distribution. If so, the P_{PL} gradient changes continuously with breathing according to the degree of diaphragmatic tone. As the diaphragm contracts, the gradient diminishes, and the pressure changes are greater over the basal regions than over the apical. This in turn produces greater ventilation in dependent regions. Similarly the measurements of D'Angelo, Sant'Ambrogio & Agostoni (26) indicate that intercostal contraction causes greater pressure swings over apical zones, resulting in an increased gradient and a greater ventilation of apical regions. This dependence of ventilation distribution on the pattern of muscular contraction appears to apply to humans as well as other animals.

Froese & Bryan (35) observed that in the supine posture diaphragmatic displacement with spontaneous ventilation was different from what it was with artificial ventilation in anesthetized paralyzed subjects. In the former instance, diaphragmatic motion was greater over dependent regions, indicating that most of the inspired air was entering dependent zones. In the latter instance, diaphragmatic motion was greater over superior regions, indicating that upper zones were better ventilated than lower ones. These observations indicate that in supine human subjects the P_{PL} gradient also depends upon the degree of diaphragmatic tone; the rhythmic contraction and relaxation of the diaphragm during breathing results in a smaller gradient during inspiration and a larger one during expiration, causing larger swings in P_L and therefore greater ventilation in lower zones than would otherwise be the case (78).

The influence of voluntary diaphragmatic contraction on the washout of helium boluses inhaled at RV in both the lateral and the supine position in human subjects is compatible with this concept (27, 78). With diaphragmatic contraction during expiration in supine and lateral postures, both the slope of phase III and the closing capacity are decreased. The patterns of distribution of inspired gas during inspiration and emptying are dependent on diaphragmatic tension in both vertical and horizontal postures in man (57, 79). Indeed the vertical gradient in esophageal pressures in seated humans decreases with diaphragmatic contraction and increases with contraction of the intercostal/accessory muscles (28). Thus the distribution of inhaled boluses of inert gases and the pattern of lung emptying in human subjects can be voluntarily altered by the pattern of muscular contraction. Contraction of intercostal/accessory muscles leads to preferential ventilation of the apex, while contraction of the diaphragm favors ventilation of the base. This may explain an apparent paradox. Increasing inspiratory flow rate causes a redistribution of ventilation to the apex in upright man (8, 16, 42). This redistribution has been explained in part by the likelihood that apical time constants are smaller than basal ones. Not only are the alveoli more expanded at the apex, but the airways are wider (91). However, Sybrecht et al (83) observed that in supine man, in whom the time constants of apex and base are similar (91), the flow-dependent redistribution of an inhaled bolus is even greater than in the upright posture. As this cannot be explained on the basis of regional time constant differences, the data suggest greater P_{PL} changes at the apex than at the base, as inspiratory flows increase. Sharp et al have observed that as flow rates increase, motion of the rib cage increases progressively over that of the abdomen, which suggests that the intercostals are recruited progressively as inspiratory flow increases (81). This would produce greater changes in P_{PL} over the apical zones than over the basal; and if this effect were more pronounced in the supine posture than in the upright, it would account for the redistribution of the bolus.

The P_{PL} changes in the various regions are produced by active contraction of various muscle groups. However, regional differences in P_{PL} swings can also be produced passively by a mechanism analogous to lung parenchymal interdependence. An area of the lung that lags behind its neighbors will produce a deformation of the overlying chest wall provided that the lungs resist deformation sufficiently (62, 63, 93). It appears that the lungs do resist deformation; in dogs they may be less deformable than the chest wall (68). The deformation of the wall, however, will produce a change in pleural surface pressure which will tend to minimize the non-homogeneity. Thus if a lobe is smaller than its neighbors, the resulting inward displacement of the rib cage will make PPL more negative over that lobe, producing an inflating force that tends to restore the volume of the lobe.

Interdependence between lung and chest wall was originally proposed by Zidulka et al (93) who found that with lobar occlusion there was an amplification of translobar pressure swings tending to inflate the occluded lobe. In artificially ventilated dogs, the inflating pressures over occluded lobes were 30% greater than they had been before occlusion, while in spontaneously breathing animals this amplification of inflating pressure increased to 120%. Presumably the rib cage is much less deformable when the inspiratory muscles are contracted. D'Angelo et al (24) also studied the effects of lobar occlusion and found that it produced regional differences in PPL. However, they did not attribute these differences to chest-wall deformation.

Thus local differences in pleural pressure swings can be produced by two different mechanisms. Contraction of different muscle groups will result in alterations of ventilation distribution different from what they would be if PPL swings were everywhere equal. On the other hand, passive amplification of PPL swings by chest-wall deformation tends to restore homogeneous behavior. These changes in PPL swings can be thought of as homeostatic mechanisms that preserve uniformity of ventilation distribution.

INTERACTION BETWEEN DIAPHRAGM AND RIB CAGE

To further quantify the dependence of PPL and ventilation distribution on the pattern of muscular contraction, a method is required for distinguishing between those respiratory pressure swings attributable to diaphragmatic contraction and those attributable to contraction of the intercostal/accessory muscles of inspiration. Goldman & Mead's hypothesis that abdominal pressure drives the relaxed rib cage (41) makes such a distinction possible. Thus, when the diaphragm is the only muscle contracting, the rib cage moves along its relaxation pressure–volume curve. Departures from this characteristic denote recruitment of either intercostal/accessory muscles of inspiration or the abdominal muscles. Goldman used this concept to partition the work of breathing into that accomplished by the diaphragm and that accomplished by the inspiratory intercostal/accessory muscles (40).

Goldman & Mead (40, 41) suggested that pressures developed by these two muscle groups across the rib cage are additive. Thus the total pressure required to inflate the lungs and displace the chest wall is transdiaphragmatic pressure, PDI, plus the pressure developed by the intercostal/accessory muscles of inspiration, PIC. Inspiration accomplished when PDI remains zero must be performed by intercostal/accessory muscles. When abdominal pressure increases and drives the rib cage along its relaxation curve, the diaphragm is the only muscle contracting, and it performs all the inspiratory work. When abdominal pressure does not change during inspiration, the intercostal/accessory muscles have displaced the chest wall and the diaphragm has inflated the lung. The respiratory pressure swings can be partitioned accordingly. Goldman (40) suggested that the contribution of the intercostal/accessory muscles at any instant during inspiration can be taken as the difference between abdominal pressure at that instant and the abdominal pressure required to inflate the relaxed rib cage to the same volume. The diaphragmatic contribution is, of course, given by PDI.

Although this analysis is intuitively appealing, there may be a flaw in the argument. Certainly when PDI remains zero all the inspiratory work is being done by the intercostal/accessory muscles. Under these circumstances, however, the abdominal pressure falls and the diaphragm is passively stretched. If one imagines just a slight increase in PDI (implying some diaphragmatic contraction) during such a breath, it is apparent that as the diaphragm contracts it is also being lengthened with the result that it produces negative work. At the other extreme, when diaphragmatic contraction results in an increase in abdominal pressure so that the rib cage moves along its relaxation curve, the diaphragm shortens and produces positive work. If at one extreme the diaphragm produces positive work, whereas at the other it produces negative work, it must be possible to inspire in such a way that the diaphragm produces no work, i.e. it contracts isometrically. Under these circumstances all the work must be performed by the intercostal and other inspiratory muscles and these must be responsible for the change in PPL as well as for the pressure required to displace the chest wall. Yet during such an inspiration PDI will clearly increase, and the diaphragm is also responsible for at least some, and possibly all, of the changes in PPL. Because the diaphragm performs no work, it must therefore be acting as a fixator preventing the transmission of PPL to the abdomen (64). However, Goldman & Mead's assumption that when the abdominal muscles remain relaxed the pressures developed across the lungs and rib cage are the sum of P_{DI} and P_{IC} is violated. Both sets of muscles have produced the change in P_{PL}. In other words, the sum of P_{DI} and P_{IC} may be greater than the pressures developed across the lungs and rib cage. Thus it may be that when the diaphragm contracts isometrically and produces no work, it is acting as a fixator, in parallel with other inspiratory muscles, not in series.

Perhaps a more correct approach to partitioning of the respiratory pressure swings would be to start from the premise that an inspiratory muscle cannot produce a net displacement of the chest wall without simultaneously inflating the lung. If this is so, and if the abdominal muscles remain relaxed, then for any finite value of abdominal compliance the diaphragm only performs positive external work to the extent that abdominal pressure increases. When abdominal pressure decreases, the diaphragm produces negative work; when abdominal pressure remains constant, the diaphragm acts as a fixator and the agonists are the intercostal/accessory muscles.

I do not believe that Goldman & Mead are correct in their method of determining the work done by the diaphragm and intercostal/accessory muscles. Nevertheless, their hypothesis that abdominal pressure drives the relaxed rib cage contributes much to our understanding of the mechanics of the respiratory muscles. It will allow important advances in understanding how the inspiratory muscles interact in producing various respiratory maneuvers. However, before accepting their hypothesis it is necessary to reconcile it with D'Angelo & Sant'Ambrogio's observation (25), described above, on the action of the diaphragm on the rib cage in rabbits and dogs. First Goldman & Mead specifically restrict the hypothesis to the upright posture. Apparently the link between diaphragm and rib cage is different in the horizontal postures from that in the upright. Secondly, the hypothesis applies only to humans. As Grassino et al (45) pointed out, there appears to be a marked difference in compliance and therefore distortability between the rib cage of humans and those of other animals (45). In contrast to that of other animals, the human rib cage behaves with a single degree of freedom. Thus in humans the fall in P_{PL} with lung inflation produced solely by the diaphragm does not appear to cause the upper rib cage to move inwards when the lower rib cage is displaced outward by an increase in abdominal pressure. Because the upright human rib cage moves with a single degree of freedom, the Goldman-Mead hypothesis provides a working premise with which to unlock the mysteries of the coupling between diaphragm and rib cage. The proposed coupling may be clinically as well as physiologicially important in view of the recent report of supine respiratory failure in patients with bilateral diaphragmatic paralysis (69), and the possibility that fatigue of the respiratory muscles may play a role in the pathogenesis of respiratory failure (80).

CONCLUSIONS

The concept that forces are transmitted through the lung parenchyma has resulted in application of elastic theory and finite element analysis to the lung. Both promise to be powerful tools which may assist in the study of the nonhomogeneous behavior that occurs in diseases of the lung and may help resolve whether shape or weight is more important in determining the distribution of pleural surface pressure and regional lung expansion.

One result of the shape-weight controversy has been the observation that the distribution of pleural pressure changes is influenced by the pattern of muscle contraction. Thus the distribution of ventilation can be voluntarily controlled. When the contributions of various muscle groups to respiratory pressure swings have been quantified we will have a much clearer knowledge of how to control ventilation distribution voluntarily.

Older questions, such as how the lungs inflate and deflate and what the surface tension is in situ, have remained surprisingly difficult to answer. The notion that there may be two interfacial tensions in situ may help to answer the latter question. The assumption that tissue tension is not influenced by surface tension creates problems, the solution of which requires an approach other than comparing saline pressure–volume curves to curves obtained with other inflating fluids.

Other issues in respiratory mechanics, such as the role of the nonadrenergic inhibitory system in controlling bronchial smooth muscle, and of contractile interstitial cells in controlling lung elasticity, have recently appeared on the horizon. They will probably keep us occupied for some time to come.

Literature Cited

1. Abboud, N., Rehder, K., Rodarte, J. R., Hyatt, R. E. 1975. Lung volumes and closing capacity with continuous positive airway pressure. *Anesthesiology* 42:138–42
2. Agostoni, E., D'Angelo, E. 1970. Comparative features of the transpulmonary pressure. *Respir. Physiol.* 11:76–83
3. Agostoni, E., D'Angelo, E. 1971. Topography of pleural surface pressure during simulation of gravity effect on abdomen. *Respir. Physiol.* 12:102–9
4. Anthonisen, N. R. 1964. Effect of volume and volume history of the lungs on pulmonary shunt flow. *Am. J. Physiol.* 207:235–38
5. Ardila, R., Horie, T., Hildebrandt, J. 1974. Macroscopic isotropy of lung expansion. *Respir. Physiol.* 20:105–15
6. Bachofen, H., Hildebrandt, J., Bachofen, M. 1970. Pressure-volume curves of air- and liquid-filled excised lungs: Surface tension in situ. *J. Appl. Physiol.* 29:422–31
7. Bake, B., Fugl-Meyer, A. R., Grimby, G. 1972. Breathing patterns and regional ventilation distribution in tetraplegic patients and in normal subjects. *Clin. Sci.* 42:117–28
8. Bake, B., Wood, L., Murphy, B., Macklem, P. T., Milic-Emili, J. 1974. Effect of inspiratory flow rate on regional distribution of inspired gas. *J. Appl. Physiol.* 37:8–17
9. Bando, T., Shindo, N., Shimo, Y. 1973. Non-adrenergic inhibitory nerves in tracheal smooth muscle of guinea pig. *Proc. J. Physiol. Soc. Jpn.* 508–9
10. Batra, G., Traystman, R., Rudnick, H., Menkes, H. 1975. *Fed. Proc.* 34(3): 949(Abstr.)
11. Benjamin, J. J., Murtagh, P. S., Proctor, D. F., Menkes, H. A., Permutt, S. 1974. Pulmonary vascular interdependence in

excised dog lobes. *J. Appl. Physiol.* 37:887–94

12. Bienkowski, R., Skolnick, M. 1974. On the calculation of surface tension in lungs from pressure-volume data. *J. Coll. Interface Sci.* 48:350–51

13. Burnstock, G. 1972. Purinergic nerves. *Pharmacol. Rev.* 24:509–81

14. Coburn, R. F., Tomita, T. 1973. Evidence for non-adrenergic inhibitory nerves in the guinea pig trachealis muscles. *Am. J. Physiol.* 224:1072–80

15. Coleman, R. A., Levy, G. P. 1974. Nonadrenergic inhibitory nervous pathway in guinea pig trachea. *Br. J. Pharmacol.* 52:167–74

16. Connolly, T., Bake, B., Wood, L., Milic-Emili, J. 1975. Regional distribution of a ^{133}Xe labelled gas volumes inspired at constant flow rates. *Scand. J. Respir. Dis.* 56:150–59

17. Daly, B. D. J., Parks, G. E., Edmonds, C. H., Hibbs, C. W., Norman, J. C. 1975. Dynamic alveolar mechanics as studied by videomicroscopy. *Respir. Physiol.* 24:217–32

18. D'Angelo, E. 1972. Local alveolar size and transpulmonary pressure in situ and in isolated lungs. *Respir. Physiol.* 14:251–66

19. D'Angelo, E. 1975. Stress-strain relationships during uniform and nonuniform expansion of isolated lungs. *Respir. Physiol.* 23:87–107

20. D'Angelo, E., Agostoni, E. 1974. Distribution of transpulmonary pressure and chest wall shape. *Respir. Physiol.* 22:335–44

21. D'Angelo, E., Agostoni, E. 1974. Effect of histamine on the vertical gradient of transpulmonary pressure. *Respir. Physiol.* 20:331–35

22. D'Angelo, E., Agostoni, E. 1975. Vertical gradient of pleural and transpulmonary pressure with liquid-filled lungs. *Respir. Physiol.* 23:159–73

23. D'Angelo, E., Michelini, S., Miserocchi, G. 1973. Local motion of the chest wall during passive and active expansion. *Respir. Physiol.* 19:47–59

24. D'Angelo, E., Miserocchi, G., Michelini, S., Agostoni, E. 1973. Local transpulmonary pressure after lobar occlusion. *Respir. Physiol.* 18:328–37

25. D'Angelo, E., Sant'Ambrogio, G. 1974. Direct action of contracting diaphragm in the rib cage in rabbits and dogs. *J. Appl. Physiol.* 36:715–19

26. D'Angelo, E., Sant'Ambrogio, G., Agostoni, E. 1974. Effect of diaphragm activity or paralysis on distribution of pleural pressure. *J. Appl. Physiol.* 37:311–15

27. Don, H. F., Ingram, R. H. Jr., Green, M. 1975. Relationship of phase IV to closing volume in lateral body positions. *J. Appl. Physiol.* 39:390–94

28. Dosman, J., Grassino, A., Macklem, P. T., Engel, L. A. 1975. *Physiologist* 18(3):194(Abstr.)

29. Douglas, F. G., Chong, P. Y., Finlayson, D. C. 1974. Effect of artificial ventilation on lung mechanics in dogs. *J. Appl. Physiol.* 36:324–28

30. Dunnill, M. S. 1967. Effect of lung inflation on alveolar surface area in the dog. *Nature* 214:1013–14

31. Flicker, E., Lee, J. S. 1974. Equilibrium of force of subpleural alveoli: Implications of lung mechanics. *J. Appl. Physiol.* 36:366–74

32. Forrest, J. B. 1970. The effect of changes in lung volume on the size and shape of alveoli. *J. Physiol.* 210:533–47

33. Frankus, A., Lee, G. C. 1974. A theory for distortion studies of lung parenchyma based on alveolar membrane properties. *J. Biomech.* 7:101–7

34. Freedman, S., Tattersfield, A. E., Pride, N. B. 1975. Changes in lung mechanics during asthma induced by exercise. *J. Appl. Physiol.* 38:974–82

35. Froese, A. B., Bryan, A. C. 1974. Effects of anesthesia and paralysis in diaphragmatic mechanics in man. *Anesthesiology* 41:242–55

36. Fung, Y. C. 1974. A theory of elasticity of the lung. *J. Appl. Mech.* 41E:8–14

37. Fung, Y. C. 1975. Does the surface tension make the lung inherently unstable? *Circ. Res.* 37:497–502

38. Fung, Y. C. 1975. Stress deformation and atelectasis of the lung. *Circ. Res.* 37:481–96

39. Gil, J., Weibel, E. R. 1972. Morphological study of pressure-volume hysteresis in rat lungs fixed by vascular perfusion. *Respir. Physiol.* 15:190–213

40. Goldman, M. 1974. Mechanical coupling of the diaphragm and rib cage. In *Loaded Breathing,* ed. L. D. Pengelly, A. S. Rebuch, E. J. M. Campbell, pp. 50–63. Don Mills, Ontario: Longman

41. Goldman, M. D., Mead, J. 1973. Mechanical interaction between the diaphragm and rib cage. *J. Appl. Physiol.* 35:197–204

42. Grant, B. J. B., Jones, H. A., Hughes, J. M. B. 1974. Sequence of regional filling during a tidal breath in man. *J. Appl. Physiol.* 37:158–65

43. Grassino, A. E., Anthonisen, N. R. 1975. Chest wall distortion and regional

lung volume distribution in erect humans. *J. Appl. Physiol.* 39:1004–7

44. Grassino, A. E., Anthonisen, N. R. 1975. *Fed. Proc.* 34(2):402(Abstr.)

45. Grassino, A. E., Bake, B., Martin, R. R., Anthonisen, N. R. 1975. Voluntary changes of thoracoabdominal shape and regional lung volumes in humans. *J. Appl. Physiol.* 39:997–1003

46. Greene, R., Hughes, J. M. B., Sudlow, W. F., Milic-Emili, J. 1974. Regional lung volumes during water immersion to the xiphoid in seated man. *J. Appl. Physiol.* 36:734–36

47. Hansen, J. E., Ampaya, E. P., Bryant, G. H., Navin, J. J. 1975. Branching pattern of airways and airspaces of a single human terminal bronchiole. *J. Appl. Physiol.* 38:983–89

48. Hills, B. A. 1971. Geometric irreversibility and compliance hysteresis in the lungs. *Respir. Physiol.* 13:50–61

49. Hills, B. A. 1974. Effects of DPL at mercury/water interfaces and estimates of lung surface area. *J. Appl. Physiol.* 36:41–44

50. Holland, C. S. 1972. *A linear dynamic model of the lung, including the effect of tissue interdependence.* MSc thesis. McGill Univ., Montreal, Canada

51. Hoppin, F., Hildebrandt, J. 1976. Mechanical properties of the lung. In *Bioengineering Aspects of Lung Biology,* ed. J. West. New York: Dekker

52. Hoppin, F. G. Jr., Lee, G. C., Dawson, S. V. 1975. Properties of lung parenchyma in distortion. *J. Appl. Physiol.* 39:742–51

53. Horie, T., Ardila, R., Hildebrandt, J. 1974. Static and dynamic properties of excised cat lung in relation to temperature. *J. Appl. Physiol.* 36:317–22

54. Hughes, J. M. B., Jones, H. A., Wilson, A. G., Grant, B. J. B., Pride, N. B. 1974. Stability of intrapulmonary bronchial dimensions during expiratory flow in excised lungs. *J. Appl. Physiol.* 37:684–94

55. Kapanci, Y., Assimacopoulos, A., Irle, C., Zwahlen, A., Gabbiani, G. 1974. Contractile interstitial cells in pulmonary alveolar septa: A possible regulator of ventilation–perfusion ratio. *J. Cell. Biol.* 60:375–92

56. Katsura, T., Rozencwajg, R., Sutherland, P. W., Hogg, J., Milic-Emili, J. 1970. Effect of external support on regional alveolar expansion in excised dog lungs. *J. Appl. Physiol.* 28:133–37

57. Kelly, S., Roussos, Ch. S., Engel, L. A. 1975. *Clin. Res.* 23(5):645A(Abstr.)

58. Klingele, T. G., Staub, N. C. 1970. Alveolar shape changes with volume in isolated, air-filled lobes of cat lung. *J. Appl. Physiol.* 28:411–14

59. Lai-Fook, S. J., Hyatt, R. E., Rodarte, J. R., Wilson, T. A. 1976. *Fed. Proc.* 35(1):231(Abstr.)

60. Lee, G. C., Frankus, A. 1975. Elasticity properties of lung parenchyma derived from experimental distortion data. *J. Biophys.* 15:481–93

61. Macklem, P. T. 1971. Airway obstruction and collateral ventilation. *Physiol. Rev.* 51:368–436

62. Macklem, P. T. 1973. Relationship between lung mechanics and ventilation distribution. *Physiologist* 16:580–88

63. Macklem, P. T., Murphy, G. 1974. The forces applied to the lung in health and disease. *Am. J. Med.* 57:371–77

64. Macklem, P. T., Roussos, Ch. S., Gross, D. 1976. *Fed. Proc.* 35(2):396(Abstr.)

65. Mead, J., Takashima, T., Leith, D. 1972. Stress distribution in the lungs: a model of pulmonary elasticity. *J. Appl. Physiol.* 28:596–608

66. Minh, V. D., Friedman, P. J., Kurihara, N., Moser, K. M. 1974. Ipsilateral transpulmonary pressures during unilateral electrophrenic respiration. *J. Appl. Physiol.* 37:505–9

67. Minh, V. D., Kurihara, N., Friedman, P. J., Moser, K. M. 1974. Reversal of pleural pressure gradient during electrophrenic stimulation. *J. Appl. Physiol.* 37:496–504

68. Murphy, B. G., Zidulka, A., Nadler, S., Macklem, P. T. 1974. *Fed. Proc.* 33(3):667(Abstr.)

69. Newsom, D. J., Goldman, M., Loh, L., Casson, M. 1976. Diaphragm function and alveolar hypoventilation. *Q. J. Med.* 45:87–100

70. Peress, L., Sybrecht, G., Macklem, P. T. 1976. *Am. J. Med.* 61:165–69

71. Pierce, J. A., Hocott, J. B., Hefley, B. F. 1961. Elastic properties and the geometry of the lungs. *J. Clin. Invest.* 40:1515–24

72. Radford, E. P. Jr. 1962. Influence of physicochemical properties of the pulmonary surface on stability of alveolar air spaces and on static hysteresis of the lungs. *XXII Int. Cong. Physiol. Sci. Leiden, Symp. Spec. Lect.* 1:275–80

73. Raskin, S. R., Nerman, P. G. 1975. Interacinar pathways in the human lung. *Am. Rev. Respir. Dis.* 111:489–95

74. Rehder, K., Abboud, N., Rodarte, J. R., Hyatt, R. E. 1975. Positive airway pressure and vertical transpulmonary

pressure gradient in man. *J. Appl. Physiol.* 38:896–99

75. Reifenrath, R. 1975. The significance of alveolar geometry and surface tension in the respiratory mechanics of the lung. *Respir. Physiol.* 24:115–37

76. Richardson, J., Béland, J. 1976. Non-adrenergic inhibitory nerves in human airways. *J. Appl. Physiol.* 41:764–71

77. Richardson, J., Bouchard, R. 1975. Demonstration of a non-adrenergic inhibitory nervous system in the trachea of the guinea pig. *J. Allergy Clin. Immunol.* 56:473–80

78. Roussos, Ch. S., Fukuchi, Y., Macklem, P. T., Engel, L. A. 1976. Influence of diaphragmatic contraction on ventilation distribution in horizontal man. *J. Appl. Physiol.* 40:417–24

79. Roussos, Ch. S., Genest, J., Cosio, M. G., Engel, L. A. 1975. *Clin. Res.* 23(5):648A(Abstr.)

80. Roussos, Ch. S., Macklem, P. T. 1975. Diaphragmatic fatigue in man. *Physiologist* 18(3):372

81. Sharp, J. T., Goldberg, N. B., Druz, W. S., Danan, J. 1975. Relative contribution of rib cage and abdomen to breathing in normal subjects. *J. Appl. Physiol.* 39:608–18

82. Storey, W. T., Staub, N. C. 1962. Ventilation of terminal air units. *J. Appl. Physiol.* 17:391–97

83. Sybrecht, G., Landau, L., Murphy, B. G., Engel, L. A., Martin, R. R., Macklem, P. T. 1976. Influence of posture on flow dependence of distribution of inhaled ^{133}Xe boli. *J. Appl. Physiol.* 41:489–496

84. Sylvester, J. T., Menkes, H. A., Stitik, F. 1975. Lung volume and interdependence in the pig. *J. Appl. Physiol.* 38:395–401

85. Takishima, T., Sasaki, H., Sasaki, T. 1975. Influence of lung parenchyma on collapsibility of dog bronchi. *J. Appl. Physiol.* 38:875–81

86. Tierney, D. F., Johnson, R. P. 1965. Altered surface tension of lung extracts and lung mechanics. *J. Appl. Physiol.* 20:1253–60

87. Traystman, R. J., Batra, G., Menkes, H. 1975. Local control of collateral ventilation by carbon-dioxide and oxygen. *Am. Rev. Respir. Dis.* 111(6):896(Abstr.)

88. Tsunoda, S., Fukaya, H., Sugihara, T., Martin, C. J., Hildebrandt, J. 1974. Lung volume, thickness of alveolar walls, and microscopic anistropy of expansion. *Respir. Physiol.* 22:285–96

89. Vawter, D. L., Matthews, F. L., West, J. B. 1975. Effect of shape and size of lung and chest wall in stresses in the lung. *J. Appl. Physiol.* 39:9–17

90. West, J., Matthews, F. L. 1972. Stresses, strains and surface pressures in the lung caused by its weight. *J. Appl. Physiol.* 32:332–45

91. Wilson, A. G., Jones, H. A., Hughes, J. M. B. 1974. Effect of posture on airway length and diameter in the dog. *Respir. Physiol.* 22:381–97

92. Woolcock, A. J., Macklem, P. T. 1971. Mechanical factors influencing collateral ventilation in human, dog and pig lungs. *J. Appl. Physiol.* 39:99–115

93. Zidulka, A., Demedts, M., Nadler, S., Anthonisen, N. R. 1976. Pleural pressure with lobar obstruction in dogs. *Respir. Physiol.* 26:239–48

Ann. Rev. Physiol. 1978. 40:185–216
Copyright © 1978 by Annual Reviews Inc. All rights reserved

PHYSIOLOGY OF THE HIPPOCAMPUS AND RELATED STRUCTURES

❖1190

F. H. Lopes da Silva and D. E. A. T. Arnolds

Brain Research Department, Institute of Medical Physics, Organization for Health Research TNO, Utrecht, The Netherlands

INTRODUCTION

Despite the large number of studies on all aspects of the hippocampus, the function of this structure is still an enigma. In our view multidisciplinary studies of input-output relations integrated with behavioral analytical investigations hold the greatest promise for a solution to this problem. Therefore, this review is dedicated to the basic physiology of the hippocampus seen as a group of input-output subsystems.

The first several sections deal with the functional anatomy and electrophysiology. This subject receives more intensive treatment in those sections where recent anatomical data obtained with tracer techniques have provided significant advances. In the second half of the review, hippocampal-behavior correlates are dealt with. The insight of the authors into these aspects is here given precedence over a detailed review of the extensive literature. The treatment of transmitters and pharmacological aspects is omitted here in view of the recent comprehensive review of Storm-Mathisen (194). Several reviews of the physiology of the hippocampus have been published. A classic is that of Brodal (39). The last physiological review is that of Green (86). Since then there have appeared reviews on the pharmacology of the electrical activity of the hippocampus (196); on the physiology of cellular processes (189); and on behavioral correlates of hippocampal function (4, 63, 113, 141). The comprehensive book of Isaacson (103) gives a survey of the limbic system. A collection of papers on several aspects of hippocampal structure and physiology, its relation to behavior, its development and neuroendocrinology has been edited recently by Isaacson & Pribram (104). A book covering the Russian literature on the hippocampus has also appeared (76).

185

0066-4278/78/0301-0185$01.00

BRIEF SYNOPSIS ON STRUCTURE AND NOMENCLATURE

The hippocampal region is the part of the cerebral cortex that forms a relatively long, horn-shaped body along the curvature of the lateral ventricles. This region can be subdivided into the hippocampus proper, or Ammon's horn; the fascia dentata (dentate gyrus); and the subicular complex [prosubiculum, subiculum, presubiculum, and parasubiculum (135, 197)] which is contiguous to the entorhinal cortex, as schematically seen in Figure 1. Lorente de Nó (126) has subdivided the hippocampus proper (Cornus Ammonis, or CA) into 4 fields: CA1, CA2, CA3, CA4. The CA2 and CA3 fields are the region of giant pyramids. The boundary between CA1 and

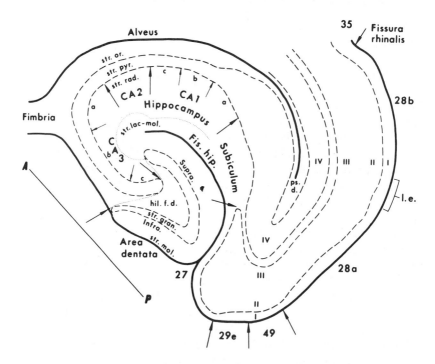

Figure 1   Diagram of a horizontal section of the hippocampal region of a 33-day-old mouse. Different fields and subfields are indicated by arrows. The following hippocampal layers are shown: alveus; stratum oriens; str. pyramidale (pyramidal cell bodies); str. radiatum; str. lacunosum-moleculare; in dentate area: str. moleculare, str. granulosum (granular cell bodies), and the hilus of the fascia dentata. The following related structures are indicated: subiculum; area 27: presubiculum; 29e; area retrosplenialis, part of parasubiculum; 49: parasubiculum; 28a and b: area entorhinalis; 35: area perirhinalis; l.e.: transition zone between subareas 28a and 28b; ps.d.: psalterium dorsale. [From (17a) by permission of author and publisher]

CA2 corresponds to the limit between regio superior and regio inferior as defined by Ramón y Cajal (163). The pyramidal cell layer of CA3 enters the hilus of the fascia dentata (CA4). According to Blackstad (29) these pyramidal cells form a deeper cortical layer of what he preferred to call "dentate area." Considering the existing anatomical evidence, it appears preferable to follow Blackstad (30) in the subdivision of hippocampal fields and to distinguish as main fields the CA1 (regio superior), the CA3 (regio inferior), and the dentate area where the hilus occupies a special place.

As regards the nature of neurotransmitters and their anatomical distribution in the hippocampus, no details can be given here except to say that acetylcholine, serotonin, dopamine, glutamic acid, gamma-aminobutyric acid (GABA), and histamine have been implicated as probable transmitters. The review of Storm-Mathisen (194) should be consulted in this respect, and also with respect of the distribution of heavy metals.

INTRINSIC CIRCUITRY

In this section we examine those properties of the hippocampus and directly related structures that have been discovered in the course of electrophysiological investigations coupled to anatomical studies. We consider here in succession the lamellar organization of the hippocampal formation, the physiology/anatomy of the excitatory inputs to the main areas of the hippocampal formation (dentate area, CA3, CA1), the local inhibitory mechanisms, and the plasticity shown by hippocampus and dentate-area synapses.

Lamellar Organization

Lømo (121) and Andersen et al (10, 12) on physiological grounds in the rabbit, and Blackstad et al (31) and Hjorth-Simonsen & Jeune (98) on anatomical grounds in the rat, have found that the hippocampus is organized in segments or lamellas. This lamellar organization should not be confused with the now obsolete parcellation of the hippocampus proposed by Lorente de Nó; the exact orientation of the lamellas may show species differences (31). Stimulation of the entorhinal inputs leads to sequential excitation of granule cells, CA3, and CA1 pyramidal cells along a four-membered pathway. This pathway is shown in Figure 2 to include: the perforant path [labeled 1], the mossy fibres [2], and the Schaffer collaterals [3] of CA3 axons and CA1 axons in the alveus [4]. CA1 axons project also to the septum via the fimbria (135, 197); this is not shown in Figure 2. The hippocampus is basically organized in parallel lamellas, with inhibition occurring on both sides of the excited beam (121). This functional organization could explain why it has been difficult to find inhibition in thin hippocampal slices (66, 168). It has been shown anatomically that the perforant

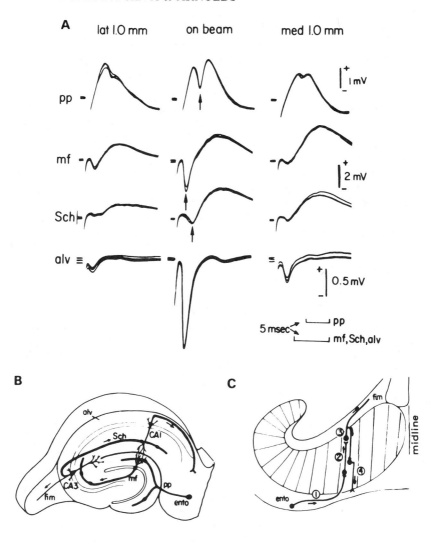

Figure 2 Hippocampal lamellas. (*A*) Records taken on beam (*middle column*) along a hippocampal lamella, and 1 mm lateral and medial to it, in response to stimulation of the perforant path (*upper row*), the mossy fibres (*second row*), the Schaffer collaterals (*third row*), and the alveus (*lower row*). (*B*) Diagram of a lamella with the four-membered neuronal loop heavily outlined. (*C*) Diagram of the hippocampal formation seen from above. The transverse thin lines indicate the orientation of the various lamellae. The encircled numbers give the members of the neuronal loop as they would appear from above. [From (8) with permission of author and publisher]

path fibers corresponding to each lamella have their origin in a separate area in the entorhinal cortex (71, 98, 209). The question arises whether the hippocampus-entorhinal pathway described by Hjorth-Simonsen (96) is aligned with the hippocampal lamellas. If this were the case one would have the possibility of a topographically organized long feedback circuit. However, there appears to be no such circuit; the organization of the hippocampo-entorhinal fibers is not "in register" with the other fiber systems. The lamellas should not be viewed as independent units, although they may have specific functional properties; the fact is that they must interact, in view of the overlap of excitatory and inhibitory processes and the existence of association fibers.

Inputs to the Dentate Area, CA3 (regio superior), and CA1 (regio inferior)

The main input to the hippocampus reaches the dentate area by way of the perforant path (97, 178, 209), which perforates the subiculum and presubiculum and terminates in the dentate area and CA3 field. Electrical stimulation of the perforant path with brief electrical pulses evokes a typical response in the hippocampus characterized by monosynaptic EPSPs (10, 121, 122) and a compound spike potential (population spike); the population spike has an onset latency of about 3.5–4 msec (122).

Following the population spike an extracellular positive wave at the level of the cell bodies can be recorded, which has a maximal duration between 70 and 135 msec (121); it is generally thought that this wave corresponds to an intracellular IPSP (15). The crossed perforant pathway (81, 231) excites also granule cells (222), but this contralateral input is much less effective than the ipsilateral one. An interesting finding is that a lesion of the ipsilateral entorhinal cortex leads to an increase in the efficiency of the contralateral perforant path (193). This enhanced capability of the crossed perforant path has an anatomical basis: the growth of contralateral synapses following ipsilateral entorhinal lesions (192).

The axons of the granule cells (the mossy fibers) project on the CA3 pyramidal cells. As they proceed from the dentate area, the mossy fibers taper and end at the limit between the regio inferior (CA3) and regio superior (CA1) (77). Stimulation of the mossy fibers evokes in CA3 pyramidal cells an EPSP and also a population spike (10). Following the cell discharges, inhibition usually takes place (15); an analysis of the corresponding field potentials has been recently given (146). Data on entorhinal inputs to CA3 pyramidal cells by way of the perforant path should also be referred to (142, 98). These fibers terminate in the depth of the stratum lacunosum-moleculare of CA3 and are also excitatory (79). The CA1 pyramidal cells receive the Schaffer collaterals, which are collaterals of the axons of CA3 pyramidal cells and are also excitatory [(10) in rabbit and (190) in guinea-pig]. The excitation is usually followed by IPSPs. Whether CA1 pyramidal cells also receive a perforant path input has been a subject of controversy. A monosynaptic excitatory effect has been recorded in CA1 and interpreted as caused by volleys in the perforant path (17). However, no firing of CA1 cells was encountered related to the evoked potential. This is probably due to the fact that perforant path inputs to CA1 are scarce. Only a few have been found in one anatomical study (142) and none at all in another (98); but recently entorhinal projections to CA1 have been described (191) in the rat. Segal (170) has investigated specifically this question in unanaesthetized rats. He suggests that stimulation of the direct perforant path may evoke a 4–5 msec latency unit response of CA1 pyramidal cells. It has also been indicated that CA1 pyramidal cells may excite neighboring cells of the same type (8), forming excitatory feed-forward circuits. Other inputs to CA1 via the cingulum have been anatomically described (3) but they have not been explored electrophysiologically. In this brief description we have not considered the activity of two other afferents to the hippocampal pyramidal cells: the commissural fibers arising from contralateral hippocampus, and the septal inputs (also important in the dentate area). The commissural inputs are all excitatory (8). The septal inputs are dealt with in a separate section.

In conclusion it should be noted that all of these hippocampal inputs are excitatory. The relative capacity of these inputs in firing hippocampal cells appears to depend mainly on the location of the corresponding synapses along the soma-dendritic membrane. For details on basic cellular physiological properties of hippocampal cells, including the question of dendritic spikes, the review of Spencer & Kandel (189) (in vivo) and the study of Schwartzkroin (168) (in vitro) are recommended.

Local Circuit Neurons: Inhibitory and Excitatory Actions

In the hippocampus we have as local circuit neurons (LCNs) the basket cells, which are generally assumed to be inhibitory, and possibly also excitatory interneurons about which much less information is available. Andersen, Eccles & Loyning (14,15) showed that the IPSPs encountered in hippocampal cells result from a feedback loop consisting of the following parts: a collateral of the axon of the pyramidal cell, the basket cell, and the arborizations of the axon of the latter, which make synaptic contacts mainly with the cell bodies of the pyramidal cells. Spencer & Kandel (189) suggest, however, that additional recurrent inhibitory pathways (feedback) may exist that terminate on distal parts of the dendritic tree of the pyramidal cells. The possibility that feed-forward inhibition exists has been advanced

(16). This means that afferent fibers may excite the basket cells directly. However, this question has not yet been settled.

The possibility of excitatory feedback on the pyramidal cells has been suggested by the studies of Dichter & Spencer (59, 60, 120). This feedback is also monosynaptic and appears to be weaker than the inhibitory feedback. The same type of inhibitory feedback circuit as described above for the pyramidal cell was also found to exist in the dentate area. In studies of granule cells in slices of rat hippocampus, a lesser degree of inhibition has been encountered (66, 168), that may be due to the lamellar organization of the hippocampus. Indeed the slices have been cut along the lamellar orientation so that excitatory pathways should be preserved (dominant within the lamella) and inhibitory feedback pathways could be decreased (dominant outside the lamella). The dynamics of these local circuits are discussed in the section on quantitative aspects.

Frequency Dependence of Synaptic Transmission and Plasticity Phenomena

The first studies of synaptic transmission in the hippocampus established the fact that frequency dependent responses are observable in this structure (7, 80, 123, 214). Frequency potentiation (FP) has been described in all 3 synapses in a lamella: perforant path–granule cell; mossy fiber–CA3 pyramidal cell; Schaffer collateral–CA1 pyramidal cell (8). This phenomenon has been confirmed in hippocampal slices in vitro and further analyzed in detail (2, 169). As regards the perforant path–granule cell synapse, the investigations using hippocampal slices in vitro have led to results that only partly confirm (66) those obtained in vivo. Teyler & Alger (199), in vitro, did not find evidence for FP of granule cells at the moderate stimulus intensities they used. On the contrary, they showed depression of both EPSP and spike at all frequencies tested; nevertheless they admit that FP could be produced with stronger stimuli. An interesting finding is that of heterosynaptic potentiation of the granule cell response (population spike) to perforant path stimulation by way of conditioning stimulation of the nucleus of the diagonal band of Broca (medial septum) (5). Pairing the septal stimulation with the perforant path stimulation at various intervals showed brief changes of excitability followed by a period of prolonged facilitation.

The phenomenon of post-tetanic potentiation (PTP) was studied in detail in anaesthetized rabbits by Bliss & Lomo (36) and in unanaesthetized rabbits by Bliss & Gardner-Medwin (35). In the unanaesthetized animals PTP was observed to follow a conditioning stimulus (15 sec^{-1} for a 15–20 sec period); PTP lasted from 1 hr to 3 days, and was characterized by at least one of the following phenomena: amplitude increases of synaptic potential and population spike, a decrease in latency of the latter and reduction in its variability. Douglas & Goddard (65) found that tetanic stimuli given at intervals of 24 hr had a cumulative effect on both the population synaptic potential and spike of the dentate area. The potentiation could last up to 12 days. PTP after fornix stimulation is described in the section on septo-hippocampal projections. In vitro PTP was found in CA1, CA3, and the dentate area (2, 66, 169).

As regards the mechanisms of potentiation of the amplitude of the synaptic evoked potential, the most likely hypothesis is that it takes place due to a facilitated synaptic transmission. In this respect it is interesting to note that an accumulation of extracellular K^+ ions takes place during potentiation (73; see also 105, 144, 145). The question remains of how far the electrical stimuli being employed in the studies discussed above mimic physiological inputs. Further studies in unanaesthetized animals are necessary, aimed at evaluating the significance for behavior of these phenomena as a paradigm for learning and memory.

EXTRINSIC CONNECTIONS

Reports on septo-hippocampal connections in the rat (178) agree that the hippocampus receives projections from the medial septum. In some studies in the cat, however, it has been found that septal afferents to the hippocampus arise from both medial and lateral septal areas and are distributed to the dorsal and ventral hippocampus respectively (187). The question of which are the fields of projection of septal afferents within the hippocampus has been discussed by various authors in the rat (139, 160) and in the cat (101), but there is still no generally accepted view. The most recent and detailed findings on this subject (165) indicate that in the rat the medial septal nucleus projects primarily to the hilus of the dentate area and secondarily to the stratum oriens and radiatum of CA3; no significant projections were found in the molecular layer of the dentate area or in CA1. It has been reported (118) that the basket cells of the dentate may receive direct septal afferents as well. The electrophysiology of hippocampal inputs via the fornix system has been studied in detail by Spencer & Kandel (188, 189). According to Andersen et al (13), stimulation of the septo-hippocampal pathways in the rabbit leads to a type of extracellular field potential originating from the dentate area and also from the stratum pyramidale and the adjacent parts of apical dendrites of CA1; but as noted above, Rose et al (165) found no septal terminals in CA1 in the rat. Clearly there is not yet sufficient information on the physiology of the modes of activation of hippocampal neuronal populations by septal inputs. Recent anatomical data should lead to a new interest in this problem.

Inputs Originating in the Brain Stem

With classic anatomical techniques it has been difficult to individualize the brain stem afferents to the hippocampus. Nevertheless, ascending projections were demonstrated by Guillery (91) in the rat on the basis of degeneration studies, and by others using modern techniques (50, 138, 156, 178). Pasquier & Reinoso-Suarez (154) demonstrated ascending projections in the cat: (a) from neurons in the dorsal raphe with the same location as the serotonergic group B7, mainly to the dorsal hippocampus; (b) from the rostral part of locus coeruleus (noradrenergic) to the dorsal hippocampus; (c) from the nucleus centralis tegmenti superior (Bechterew) particularly to the ventral hippocampal regions. As regards the sites of termination of the above-mentioned ascending connections, the following has already been reported. Axons from raphe nuclei are concentrated on a narrow zone under the granule cells of the dentate area and in stratum lacunosum of CA1 (138). Axons from locus coeruleus (156, 178) project mostly around CA3 pyramidal cells and in the hilus of the dentate area. In the rat, pathways have been described originating from cells in the supra-mammillary region (178) and in the sub-mammillothalamic nuclei (153). In monkey and cat, a pathway has been found originating from the cerebellar fastigial nucleus (95).

Electrophysiological investigations combined with pharmacological manipulations have unraveled some interesting aspects of these brain stem afferents. The predominant type of response elicited by stimulation of the raphe nuclei (172) is a long-latency (100–150 msec) inhibition, probably mediated by oligo-synaptic pathways. It is likely that this pathway has a relay on the medial septal nucleus (50). Similarly, stimulation of locus coeruleus (173–176) produces long-lasting inhibition of spontaneous firing of hippocampal cells in the rat. This inhibition has a variable latency of about 50–150 msec. These inhibitory responses were antagonized by blockade of norepinephrine (NA) synthesis. Detailed electrophysiology of the pathway from the nucleus centralis tegmenti superior is not yet known. The pathway from the fastigial nucleus has been studied electrophysiologically using evoked potentials in monkeys and cats (95). These evoked potentials had a remarkably short latency and were found at widespread sites in the hippocampus. In this study no laminar field analysis nor cellular activity was recorded so that these evoked potentials are difficult to interpret. The existence of well-known correlates between the activity of the brain stem regions of origin of these ascending pathways and behavioral features such as sleep and arousal [raphe nuclei (182)], self-stimulation [locus coeruleus (176)], and motor control [fastigial nuclei (95)] leads naturally to speculations about the possible role of the hippocampus in those behaviors. The role of the putative neurotransmitters mentioned above in the normal synaptic transmission in the hippocampal formation remains to be clarified.

Inputs to the Entorhinal Cortex

An important part of the information that is passed to the hippocampal formation by way of the perforant path is derived from that which reaches the entorhinal cortex. Therefore, it is important to mention the main entorhinal inputs. For a detailed description see the series of articles of van Hoesen & Pandya (207–209). In at least the monkey, afferents to the entorhinal area come mainly from three neocortical areas: the ventral portion of the temporal lobe (area TH and adjoining areas), the prepyriform cortex (PPC), and the caudoventral portion of the frontal lobe (areas 12, 13, and also 14). Seltzer & Pandya (181) have noted that these cortical areas are connected to association areas for visual (51, 89), auditory (90), and somesthetic (107) modalities. Thus the entorhinal cortex is in a position to receive multi-synaptic cortico-cortical inputs of all sensory modalities coming from association areas of the frontal, parietal, temporal, and occipital lobes. One well-studied sensory input to the entorhinal cortex and hippocampal formation has an olfactory origin (39, 41, 52, 53, 78, 217). Wooley & Barron (228) found that the hippocampal evoked potentials to the olfactory bulb and PPC stimulation in rats showed a laminar profile similar, though not identical, to that described for the potential evoked by perforant path stimulation (79). From recent electrophysiological experiments in the cat, Habets et al (92) have concluded that the PPC inputs reach the hippocampus most likely along the perforant path that emerges from lateral entorhinal cortical areas corresponding to area 28b. A study by Yokota et al (230) provides information on intracellular (CA1 and CA3) responses to stimulations of the olfactory bulb in the unanaesthetized monkey. The responses were exclusively EPSPs but no associated spikes were recorded. However, in the cat Habets et al (92) have found units in both dentate, CA1, and subicular fields that were driven by PPC stimulation with initial discharge latencies of 18–20 msec; some of these units showed secondary inhibition probably caused by local inhibitory circuits. It should be noted that no studies have been made yet of hippocampal responses to natural olfactory stimuli. Besides the olfactory modality, other types of sensory inputs have been reviewed by MacLean (129). In the awake monkey none of 596 units recorded from the hippocampus were activated by visual stimuli (129, 130). Similarly auditory, somasthetic, or gustatory stimulation caused no hippocampal response; vagal stimulation, however, could elicit unit and field responses in the hippocampus (129). Cragg (52) has also described field potentials in the hippocampus in the cat in response to electrical stimulation of the vagus and of the lingual nerve; these probably follow a septo-hippocampal path quite distinct from the olfactory input.

OUTPUTS OF THE HIPPOCAMPAL FORMATION

Until recently it was generally assumed that the main hippocampal efferents (CA1 and CA3) would travel along the alveus and fimbria to be distributed by the pre- and post-commissural fornix system to several areas of the forebrain and midbrain. This view must be revised in the face of recent experimental evidence obtained with tracer techniques by Meibach & Siegel (135) and Swanson & Cowan (197) in the rat. The axons of CA1 and CA3 have 2 projection areas. One is the *lateral septal area,* which is reached only by way of the precommissural fornix; both CA1 and CA3 project to the lateral septum, the former ipsilaterally and the latter bilaterally. The other is the *subicular complex;* both CA1 and CA3 project to the subiculum. In addition, the anterior part of CA3 projects to the cingulate area and presubiculum; the intermediate part of CA3 projects to parasubiculum and entorhinal area; the anterior part of CA1 projects to the perirhinal area. The fimbria–fornix system does not contain only CA axons but also an important contribution from the subicular complex. Projections from the subicular complex (not from CA fields) are to the anterior and lateral thalamic nuclei (from pre-/parasubiculum), mammillary bodies (from the dorsal part of subiculum, pre-/parasubiculum), rostral hypothalamus, and other basal forebrain areas (from the ventral part of subiculum); the original papers should be consulted (135, 197). The same applies to the cortico-cortical projections of the subicular complex to the cingulate, entorhinal, perirhinal, and retrosplenial areas (197).

In the era before the new anatomic labeling techniques, Nauta (143, 202) emphasized that there are differences between species in the organization of the hippocampal projections; the same warning has been given by Swanson & Cowan (197). We cannot discuss here these species differences in any detail, nor the secondary projections from the septal and other target areas receiving efferents from the hippocampal formation (44, 54, 61, 62, 143, 161, 183, 184, 186, 202). The electrophysiology of the projections of the hippocampal formation is still fragmentary. Nevertheless, Andersen et al (9) concluded from electrophysiological experiments in the rabbit that the main output of the hippocampal pyramidal cells is differentiated. Only CA3 cells were shown to project along the fimbria precommissural fornix to the septum; CA1 cells project only to the subiculum. However, the generality of this conclusion has been questioned (135) since fibers originating in CA1 have been shown [in rat (135, 197)] to project through the precommissural fornix. Whether this difference is due to the species used is not clear. The electrophysiology of hippocampal projections to the septum has been studied by De France and collaborators (55–57), Edinger et al (68), and McLennan & Miller (134).

Stimulation of fimbria and fornix efferents in the rat caused excitatory responses in the larger cells in the lateral septal nucleus (LSN), distributed mainly in the dorsal regions of the LSN. From the latency (3–4 msec) and time course of the EPSPs it was concluded that the hippocampal efferents formed monosynaptic axo-dendritic contacts with the septal cells. The EPSPs were followed by a relatively long hyperpolarization. This should correspond to IPSPs most likely mediated via inhibitory interneurons in the LSN. Electrophysiological evidence for different topographical projections of dorsal and ventral hippocampal formation on the medio-lateral septal area was encountered (68). McLennan & Miller (134) found that single volleys to the fimbria could produce complete cessation of spontaneous activity of cells in the medial septal nucleus (MSN) that could last for periods ranging from 40 to 600 msec (mean: 260 msec). These responses were interpreted as being mediated by fibers impinging directly on inhibitory interneurons of the MSN. The authors draw the conclusion that fimbrial fibers can alter neural activity in the MSN in two ways: directly by local inhibitory interneurons, and indirectly via the lateral septum. The possibility that a closed circuit (hippocampus–septum–hippocampus) exists as a functional entity has been considered (58, 134) but has not yet been clarified.

The electrophysiology of the hippocampal output to the brain stem is even less clear than the hippocampo-septal relations. This is readily understandable; the differentiated projections of hippocampus and subicular complex have only recently become clearer. Nevertheless there have been a few investigations (e.g. 158) of the results of hippocampal stimulation on units of the "basal forebrain" (septal area, preoptic area, hypothalamus, etc). The great majority of units showed initial excitatory responses; only a small percentage were initially inhibited. Excitatory responses to fornix-fimbria stimulation in the mamillary bodies have also been found recently (115). However, these studies are not informative as regards the fields of origin of the stimulated hippocampal outputs. Recently acquired anatomical knowledge about the distinct origin of fornix-fimbria fibers engenders a need for more specific data on the relative importance of different projection systems from hippocampus and subicular complex to subcortical areas. In particular more knowledge about the influence of hippocampal efferents on hypothalamic areas involved in neuro-endocrine functions is necessary, in order to establish the possible role of the hippocampus in the control of these functions (37, 206).

PHYSIOLOGICAL PROCESSES UNDERLYING THE THETA RHYTHM

The hippocampal EEG, particularly the 4–7 c sec^{-1} activity or theta rhythm (87), is a signal that results from the synchronous activity of neurons in a large neural mass. It has been named Rhythmical Slow Activity (RSA) also, to avoid confusing the EEG nomenclature—particularly because in rodents it may reach frequencies of 10 c sec^{-1}. This activity has been recorded in several animals: rodent, rabbit, cat, dog, and also in primates, including man (38). However, it should be noted that the hippocampal EEG in several species presents considerable variability as regards not only frequency of the dominant rhythmic activity, but also abundance, stability, and reactivity. It should be noted that theta rhythms are not unique to the hippocampus; they may be found in other cortical areas. Besides RSA, the hippocampal EEG contains fast waves (frequencies higher than 15 Hz), which have been little studied (196, 37a). The presence of these higher frequency components is not characteristic of the "desynchronized" state only; they may also occur together with RSA. To what degree they are related to RSA has not yet been clarified.

RSA Field Potentials and Cell Activity in the Hippocampus

The general view is that the theta rhythm originates in hippocampal cells (88, 214). The fact that hippocampal pyramidal cells show sequences of EPSP-IPSPs where the latter have a long duration (100–300 msec) led Spencer & Kandel (189) to propose that those synaptic properties played an important role in the development of the theta rhythm. It has been proposed that the hippocampal theta rhythm depends on the phenomenon of phasing inhibition (14, 67). However Fujita & Sato (75) have shown that intracellularly recorded theta waves (both in CA1 and CA3 fields) behaved as EPSPs rather than as IPSPs when current pulses were injected. Fujita (74) noted also that multiple loci of dendritic spike generation could occur particularly during theta rhythm. This observation indicates the possibility that the presence of theta rhythm in hippocampal pyramidal cells may modify the input-output relations of the latter. Recently the question of which hippocampal fields are responsible for the generation of theta rhythm has been reexamined. In the curarized rabbit, Artemenko (21) found a phase reversal of theta waves of 180° in stratum radiatum, which he attributed to the dipole character of the CA1 pyramidal cell layer. The dipole would be caused by EPSPs in the basal dendrites of the pyramidal cells. However Winson (225), in the freely moving rat (or during REM sleep), found another type of profile with two maxima, a dorsal one in CA1, and a ventral one in the dentate area. Following the dorsal maximum there was a gradual phase shift, which reached 180° at the level of the hippocampal fissure. It was concluded that in rat there were two closely coupled generators of theta activity, approximately 180° out of phase—one in the dentate area and another in CA1. In a subsequent study in rabbit this finding was confirmed (32); moreover, an intracellular theta activity in dentate granule cells was reported, giving further evidence for a participation of these cells in the theta process. It appears that there are species differences (226, 227) at least between rat and rabbit, as regards the depth profile of theta in the hippocampal formation and the possible effect of curare on this process. The differences observed between species and the effect of drugs on theta rhythm discussed above may be due to differences in the distribution of two types of acetylcholine receptors in the hippocampal formation (33, 117, 159, 194). The validity of the studies of profiles of theta rhythm has not yet been checked on the basis of mathematical analysis of hippocampal field potentials as used in investigations of other brain structures (72, 162, 210).

Generation and Modulation of Hippocampal EEG

The fact that hippocampus cells are directly related to the field potential characteristic of the theta rhythm does not necessarily mean that the basic neural circuitry necessary and sufficient for the generation of the theta rhythm must exist within the hippocampus. Indeed the evidence as reviewed by Green (86) is that the hippocampal theta rhythm depends on septo-hippocampal connections. The question of whether hippocampal theta rhythm depends on entorhinal inputs has also been repeatedly asked, with less clear results (1). The subicular area has been considered to be crucial to the normal existence of RSA (45, 46). The medial septum appears, however, to act as a source of rhythmic cell discharges, which impose a theta-rhythmic activity in hippocampal cells. The hypothesis is (200) that an inhibitory feedback loop within the nucleus of the diagonal band of Broca may be responsible for transforming a random input ascending from mesodiencephalon into the theta pattern of firing. To quote Petsche et al (155): "It cannot be decided whether this septal region is a real pacemaker or is more of the nature of a relay station, because it is not known how B-units (units firing in bursts correlated with hippocampal theta waves) would behave if they were completely deafferented." The correlation between the firing of septal cells and hippocampal theta rhythm has been confirmed in several studies in rabbits (18, 128).

McLennan & Miller (134) have put in doubt the hypothesis of Tömbol & Petsche (200); they have assumed that the inhibitory feedback circuits would be situated in the lateral septum and not in the medial septum. It is worth noting that the McLennan & Miller data refer to the rat whereas the other studies were carried out in the rabbit. It is well-known that there are differences in frequency content of the hippocampal rhythmic activity between the two species. It may be that there are also functional anatomical differences in these two species as regards the organization of the septal-hippocampal subsystems responsible for theta rhythm. Anatomical study of the midline septum in several species (mouse, rat, cat, and dog) (43) has revealed differences among species. The hippocampal EEG can change its characteristics in a more or less predictable way. It has long been known that the arousal reaction of the rabbit is characterized by the occurrence of a clear theta rhythm in the hippocampal EEG (87), which contrasts with desynchronization in neocortical EEG. However, the hippocampal EEG response to a stimulus is not always revealed in the form of a typical theta rhythm. Thus Grastyán et al (83) reported that in the cat the hippocampal EEG is of the desynchronized type when the animal is presented with a novel, unconditioned stimulus. It is generally thought that there exist two types of hippocampal EEG responses: theta rhythm and desynchronized EEG (196, 201, 229).

Anchel & Lindsley (6) found support (in the cat) for the hypothesis that the two systems affecting hippocampal EEG are mediated by distinct anatomical pathways: one medially placed, which controls the generation of theta rhythm, and a lateral one following the medial forebrain bundle (MFB), which controls the generation of fast waves. Both systems originate in an area of the dorsolateral mesencephalic tegmentum adjacent to the central grey; this area may extend to the raphe tegmental nuclei (127). Since serotoninergic neurons are distributed mainly along the midline raphe system, they appear to be associated with the "desynchronizing" system; whereas catecholaminergic neurons are closely related to the locus coeruleus and other regions from which theta responses were elicited. In a recent study by the same group (223), however, it was noted that the organization of the ascending hypothalamic pathways may be more complex, and it was suggested that MFB ascending fibers may exert multiple influences in the septo-hippocampal system. Paiva et al (152) found that in the cat, RSA frequency increased as a function of stimulus strength; the authors were not able to conclude that separate "synchronizing" and "desynchronizing" systems controlling the hippocampal EEG exist. On the contrary, they concluded that desynchronization may occur as the result of too strong stimulation, which may differ from area to area. Thus the hippocampal EEG forms a continuum, which may be considered to run from *large amplitude irregular activity* (LIA), via RSA of gradually increasing frequency, to *small amplitude irregular activity* (SIA). Hence any segmentation of the EEG on the basis of visual inspection is arbitrary. An interesting way to obtain a higher degree of precision in the analysis of the brain stem-modulating hippocampal EEG systems would be to combine the electrophysiological investigations with anatomical characterization of the stimulated pathways using tracer techniques.

QUANTITATIVE ANALYSIS OF HIPPOCAMPAL SYSTEMS

We are still rather far from a general synthesis. However, a piecewise approach to this problem is becoming possible. Separate subsystems can be analyzed quantitatively, leading to the establishment of models of parts of the hippocampus. In this section we discuss a number of studies that have as common denominator the aim of integrating quantitative data in explicit models. We start from the population level in the sense of Freeman (72), i.e. with groups of interacting populations of neurons.

At the population level, the input-output relations of populations are defined and measured. These relations have been analyzed in terms of the ratio between stimulus strength and the height of the population spike response (11) for CA3 pyramidal cells and granule cells. The relation is approximately linear for weak stimuli, but levels off, i.e. saturates, for stronger stimuli. This may be due to the fact that stronger stimuli lead to an increase in synchrony of cell discharges, and thus make it difficult to count isolated spikes. Nevertheless, it may be concluded that within a certain range the height of the population spike is an adequate measure of the number of synchronously firing neurons. Such input-output relations have also been measured for the population EPSPs and spikes in CA1, CA3, and dentate granule cells in hippocampal slices in vitro (2). Alger & Teyler (2) determined the frequency response of the same cells (EPSPs and population spike), although only in the frequency range up to 15 sec^{-1}. CA3 cells showed the clearest increase of sensitivity as a function of frequency, with maximal responses between 8 and 15 sec^{-1}; CA1 showed the same trend; on the contrary, the dentate granule cells showed an attenuation of the type shown by low-pass filtering. The responses of CA1 and CA3 cannot, however, be described as phenomena of resonance on basis of the data available; indeed one would need to know the behavior of the cells above 15 sec^{-1}. The dynamics of another hippocampal system were investigated by Horowitz (99), who analyzed the relationship between the output of the population of pyramidal cells and dorsal fornix inputs (single pulses). As a measure of the population output the averaged evoked potential (AEP) and post-stimulus time histograms (PSTH) were computed. The AEPs presented damped oscillations. These oscillations were explained in terms of a model including an inhibitory feedback loop. The forward branch of this circuit is formed by the pyramidal cell population; the feedback branch is formed by the basket cells, which elicit IPSPs on the pyramidal cells. The model also included threshold elements and synaptic delays. This model was capable of predicting the oscillatory behavior of the AEPs, the effects of increasing the background level of activity and of the response to triple shock stimulation. Later this model was extended (100) to include excitatory feedback, for which there is experimental evidence (60, 120). In this way the conditions of instability of the simulated neuronal populations were investigated in order to predict their behavior in epileptogenic foci.

The same type of problem was analyzed by Dichter & Spencer (60); their model, which simulates a relatively small population of pyramidal cells, generates epileptiform discharges due to enhanced excitatory feedback. At the periphery of the focus there is less excitation and thus inhibition prevails, forming a ring around the focus and preventing its spatial spread. In this model the development of a seizure is seen as an escape of the interictal spike from the inhibitory ring. A more abstract model is that of Kilmer & McLardy (109), who attempted to establish a set of equations governing the functional organization of the neural elements in the CA3 subfield.

At the cartel level, where different populations and multiple inputs interact, a model has been presented (125, 152) based on quantitative studies of input-output relations of the septo-hippocampal system generating theta rhythm; it postulates that the process responsible for theta generation consists of at least 3 interacting neuronal populations: a main population receiving extrinsic excitatory inputs (random series of spikes); and both an inhibitory and an excitatory population incorporated in 2 feedback loops with the main population. Excitatory feedback was necessary to account for the frequency range and bandwidth of the theta rhythm. Desynchronization of hippocampal EEG could occur either by means of feed-forward or by means of separate modulating inputs fed directly to the inhibitory neural population.

Attempts are thus being made to initiate the study of quantitative physiology of hippocampal networks, but efforts in this direction are still scarce.

HIPPOCAMPUS AND BEHAVIOR

The relevance of studies based on lesions and electrical stimulation of hippocampus and/or fornix to theories about specific functions of the hippocampus is necessarily limited. Indeed in most such investigations, structures other than the hippocampus are certainly involved, namely the subicular complex, since the latter is both a recipient of hippocampal efferents and a source of subcortical (fornix) and cortical projections.

The Behavioral Effect of Dorsal Hippocampal Lesions

Several reviews exist on the subject of hippocampal lesions and lesions in the limbic system in general (4, 63, 64, 103, 110, 132).

It appears that hippocampally lesioned animals are not deficient in the acquisition of simple discrimination tasks. However, the acquired responses show more resistance to extinction, and the animals have greater difficulty in cue reversion than normals (26); this difficulty can be overcome, however, by special experimental designs (48, 93).

Several results obtained in animals with hippocampal or fornix lesions point in the direction of a dysfunction of estimation of place and time that goes beyond the lack of attention for new stimuli (76, 136, 149, 151a, 157).

In open fields to which they are not accustomed, hippocampally lesioned animals exhibit enhanced motor activity; but this is not the case in small cages or on treadmills (103). The motivational circumstances under which the animals are tested appear to be of crucial importance for the open field behavior shown (106). Only a few studies exist on the effects of hippocampal lesions upon social behavior (114, 137). It should be noted that most animal studies are concerned with lesions in the dorsal hippocampus. Some studies that compare the effects of lesions in the dorsal and the ventral hippocampus (25, 140, 185) show a differential effect of these lesions on some operant tasks. Thus generalization from dorsal to ventral lesions, and moreover extrapolation to the primate case, may be dubious. The effects of hippocampal lesions in humans have recently been discussed (42), particularly regarding memory defects.

The Correlation between Behavior and Hippocampus EEG

Recent literature is reviewed by Klemm (113). This section is therefore not exhaustive in its treatment of the large body of data available. Our aim is rather to illustrate some main streams in current research and to unify these in a descriptive model of the correlation between the properties of the hippocampal EEG and overt behavior.

Vanderwolf and his school have reported correlations (mainly in rats) between the occurrence of RSA and gross motor behavior such as walking, rearing, jumping, and swimming, while behaviors such as blinking, scratching, face washing, licking, chewing food, etc, were reported to be associated with hippocampal desynchronization. Amplitude and frequency of the RSA found during gross motor behavior are reported to be higher in proportion to the size or force of the movement (e.g. 34, 203–205, 221). Some of these observations have been confirmed in the guinea pig (166) and in the rat (225). Furthermore, it is well established that clear RSA occurs during REM sleep. Correlations have been found between increases in RSA frequency and eye movements during REM sleep in the rat (167). Studies in which spectra of the hippocampal EEG have been computed during various behaviors in the rat (47, 102) show that a significant RSA component of relatively low amplitude and frequency can exist in the hippocampus EEG of rats even during behaviors that according to Vanderwolf are correlated with a desynchronized hippocampal EEG.

In the dog it has also been shown that there exists a significant rhythmicity in the theta band during many types of motor activity (20). Modulations in amplitude and frequency have been studied in detail in relation to phasic motor acts such as the transition from standing still to walking (19, 108, 124, 209a). Modulations of RSA have been found even with simple stepping in a slowly moving dog (20); it has also been shown that the frequency and amplitude of the hippocampal EEG are positively correlated with the speed of walking on a treadmill. McFarland (133) reported analogous findings in the rat. Arnolds et al (20) showed that in dogs even a simple vestibular stimulus (linear acceleration) may induce RSA of high amplitude and frequency, and concomittant reflex extension of neck and legs. The frequency of RSA of rats swimming under water (and thus holding their breath) has been shown to be significantly lower than that of rats swimming and breathing with their heads above the water (220). These findings imply that the occurrence of muscle activity in the context of simple mechanisms (reflexes, stepping and breathing movements) is reflected in the properties of the hippocampal EEG. In contrast to dog and rat, in cat RSA has been reported to occur during "attentive immobility" (22, 49, 108a). However, RSA has been reported (221) in walking cats, and desynchronized EEG activity during eating and drinking. In the rabbit Harper (94) found a significant RSA component in the hippocampal EEG during sleep, tonic immobility, nonmovement, and movement. Kramis et al (116) reported low-frequency RSA during behavioral immobility and high-frequency RSA during gross motor behavior. Klemm (111, 112) found in rabbits a nonspecific correlation between RSA and EMG activity. In the awake unrestrained rabbits there occur also trains of RSA in correlation with all kinds of sensory stimulation. The response habituates upon stimulus repetition (204). Clearly there are differences in the incidence and in the characteristics of RSA in various species, in relation to different behaviors (224).

In our view, however, these data can be described by a single model. Essential is the assumption that the hippocampus EEG forms a continuum from LIA via RSA to SIA, as described above. Arguments for this idea can be derived from the several behavioral and electrophysiological studies discussed above (20, 40, 82, 108, 113, 152). The reviewed data show that RSA amplitude and frequency present a wide scale of possible values, which determine whether RSA will be evident in an EEG record or not. In neurophysiological terms, motor behavior and sensory inputs may be reflected in the degree of neural activity in brain stem structures (111, 112, 152), which influence the hippocampus through ascending pathways. The hippocampal EEG response to an increase in neural activity of sufficient strength in these pathways is oscillatory (a series of RSA waves with weak damping). Such increases may be induced by the initiation of motor acts and by unhabituated sensory stimuli. The fact that the system has weak damping explains why trains of RSA accompanying isolated movements or sensory stimuli usually extend in time beyond the duration of the behavioral event, although the frequency and amplitude may change. If a train of such phasic events occurs, the ringing RSA responses related to each of these events will overlap. In this way, for example, the succession of steps during locomotion gives rise to the hippocampal EEG correlates of stepping (20).

The generalization formulated above presumably holds for all species investigated. Interspecies differences in frequency band, in the range of RSA amplitudes, and in RSA signal-to-noise ratio may be accounted for by assuming that different animals have distinct set-points of the RSA generating system. In this respect desynchronization (SIA) may occur in one species more easily (at a lower threshold) than in another.

CONDITIONED BEHAVIOR AND HIPPOCAMPAL EEG   RSA has been reported to be correlated with the execution of many operant tasks involving motor behaviors. Insofar as the actual behavior has been described or can be inferred from the experimental paradigm, the validity of the correlation between hippocampal EEG and motor behavior in general appears to hold (e.g. 27, 28, 69, 221). Grastyán et al (82, 83) emphasized the relation between the occurrence of RSA and the orienting reflex in cats, which may be interpreted as well in terms of the continuum outlined above.

In our survey of the literature we found no experiments in which careful measurement showed overt behavior to be constant while the EEG changed in relation to the acquisition of a task. Therefore we did not find support for the interpretation of hippocampal EEG changes in terms of internal processes (119).

Hippocampal Unit Activity Related to Behavior

The research on this subject is still qualitative. The few relevant studies do not form a comprehensive set and the frequent lack of quantification of both brain activity and behavior makes it difficult to integrate these reports.

FREE BEHAVIOR AND UNIT ACTIVITY   Hippocampal units that fire in relation to the position a rat occupies in space have been reported (147, 148) and led to a theory of the hippocampus as a spatial map (141). Feder & Ranck (70) found various motor behaviors in rats to be associated with slow-wave RSA and rhythmical firing of units, while other behaviors such as eating, drinking, and grooming were correlated with irregular slow-wave activity and irregular unit firing. Ranck (164) reports, however, that only 25% of the investigated cells show such a firing pattern in bursts correlated with the hippocampus EEG. The other units were reported to fire in correlation with various complex classes of behavior.

CONDITIONED BEHAVIOR AND UNIT ACTIVITY   Hippocampal units appear to respond in complex ways to different kinds of stimuli. Their responses are critically dependent on the past history of the stimulus. This is the main conclusion from the work of Vinogradova and collaborators (211–213), who noted that the necessary property of a stimulus that fires CA3 units is its "novelty" and not its specific physical characteristics. The dynamics of these units' responses (habituation and dishabituation) appear to be similar to those of the orienting reflex. In contrast, CA1 units show much less habituation. In the studies of Vinogradova the role that septal afferents play in modulating the "novelty" responses of CA3 appears to be important. It would be useful to know more about the relations between these responses and the hippocampal theta rhythm.

The possibility that hippocampal cells preferably respond to stimuli in various phases of classical conditioning was extensively studied in rats by Olds and collaborators (150, 151, 177, 179, 180). Dentate units were shown not to respond to simple tones during pseudo-conditioning but to be the first to acquire a conditioned response when this tone became the conditioned stimulus; CA3 followed, and CA1 units were the last. Segal (171) believes that the conditioned responses of the hippocampal units may result from a process of hetero-synaptic facilitation. Thus their response to septal inputs may be facilitated by long-lasting EPSPs on their apical dendrites, evoked by entorhinal inputs. Berger et al (24) showed that hippocampal units (CA1, CA3, granules) in rabbits gave conditioned responses to a tone after pairing to a corneal air puff (unconditioned stimulus for the contraction of the nictitating membrane). The units did not respond to either the conditioned or unconditioned stimuli when presented alone. Therefore these responses of hippocampal units were contingent on a form of associative learning. Mays & Best (131) found, however, that hippocampal units in rats could respond to tones but that the majority of the responses habituated. Furthermore, the units showed clear changes in their firing pattern with "behavioral arousal," suggesting that changes in conditioning may be nonspecific (120a).

The Effects of Drugs and Electrical Stimulation upon Hippocampus EEG and Behavior

Drugs at low doses that suffice to change the hippocampal EEG appear to have no dramatic behavioral effects (198, 23).

Urban & de Wied (201a, 201b) have shown that hippocampal theta activity in the rat is modulated by neuropeptides that also affect conditioned behavior. Kramis et al reported a selective attenuating influence of systemic injection of atropine sulfate in rabbits and rats upon the lower frequency components of the hippocampal EEG (116). This effect might be attributed to the selective influence of atropine upon some of the pathways ascending to the hippocampus (33, 194).

Manipulation of the hippocampus EEG by means of electrical stimulation (34, 49, 84, 85, 215, 216, 218, 219) does not result in behavioral changes that are consistent with the changes induced in the EEG. The behavioral effects appear to be rather dependent upon the site of stimulation and upon stimulation parameters.

CONCLUDING REMARKS

The hippocampal formation is not a homogeneous structure. Different regions (defined according to the patterns of connections both intrinsically and extrinsically) and areas of different chemical specificity (heavy metals, neurotransmitters) lead to the division of the hippocampal formation into a number of fields, each with a specific pattern of connectivity. The basic intrinsic organization of the hippocampus is in the form of a set of parallel segments, or lamellas, that partly overlap. Its extrinsic connections are topographically organized along the hippocampal axis and with respect to the different fields: CA1, CA3, subiculum, pre/parasubiculum. Individual subsystems of the hippocampus receive inputs from different sources and have multiple target areas of projection. They constitute systems with multiple inputs and outputs. The hippocampus is thus a part of the cortex ideally placed to integrate signals from (*a*) sensory associative sources (entorhinal areas), and (*b*) brain stem areas related to sleep-arousal and sensory/motor processes. How this interaction takes place is a challenge for future research. Despite considerable advances in functional anatomical knowledge through tracer techniques and electrophysiological studies, it is not yet known what processes work on the incoming signals, nor what functions are served by the hippocampal output signals. For elucidation of the operations within the hippocampus and the relevance of this structure in behavior, it is important, in our view, to advance toward more quantitative functional anatomy. The results of such studies can be used to construct explicit models of the transfer of information in hippocampal subsystems. In the search for behavioral correlates it appears promising to make quantitative measurements of brain activity in relation to simple sensorimotor paradigms. Measurement of unit activity will be of great importance when it is possible to interpret such data as signals from neuronal populations integrated in hippocampal subsystems. Due to its relatively simple structure and its special position at the crossroads between cortico-cortical pathways and cortico-subcortical circuits, the hippocampus may eventually serve as a model for the study of cortical functions.

ACKNOWLEDGMENTS

The authors gratefully acknowledge the expert help of Geeske Kuntze and Hilda Wijnands, as well as the suggestions and criticisms of Alphons Habets and Ab van Rotterdam. The help of F. Lioni with the bibliography is also acknowledged. This work was partly supported by the Foundation for Medical Research (FUNGO), which is subsidized by the Netherlands Organization for the Advancement of Pure Research (ZWO).

Literature Cited

1. Adey, W. R., Dunlop, C. W., Hendrix, C. E. 1960. Hippocampal slow waves: Distribution and phase relationships in the course of approach learning. *Arch. Neurol.* 3:74–90
2. Alger, B. E., Teyler, T. J. 1976. Long-term and short-term plasticity in the CA1, CA3 and dentate regions of the rat hippocampal slice. *Brain Res.* 110:463–80
3. Alksne, J. F., Blackstad, T. W., Walberg, F., White, L. E. Jr. 1966. Electron microscopy of axon degeneration: A valuable tool in experimental neuroanatomy. *Ergeb. Anat. Entwicklungsgesch.* 39:1–32
4. Altman, J., Brunner, R. L., Bayer, S. A. 1973. The hippocampus and behavioral maturation. *Behav. Biol.* 8:557–96
5. Alvarez-Leefmans, F. J., Gardner-Medwin, A. R. 1975. Influences of the septum on the hippocampal dentate area which are unaccompanied by field potentials. *J. Physiol.* 249:14–15P
6. Anchel, H., Lindsley, D. B. 1972. Differentiation of two reticulo-hypothalamic systems regulating hippocampal activity. *Electroencephalogr. Clin. Neurophysiol.* 32:209–26
7. Andersen, P. 1960. Interhippocampal impulses. II: Apical dendritic activation of CA1 neurons. *Acta Physiol.Scand.* 48:178–208
8. Andersen, P. 1975. Organization of hippocampal neurons and their interconnections. See Ref. 104, Vol. 1, pp. 155–75
9. Andersen, P., Bland, B. H., Dudar, J. D. 1973. Organization of the hippocampal output. *Exp. Brain Res.* 17:152–68
10. Andersen, P., Bliss, T. V. P., Skrede, K. K. 1971. Lamellar organization of hippocampal excitatory pathways. *Exp. Brain Res.* 13:222–38
11. Andersen, P., Bliss, T. V. P., Skrede, K. K. 1971. Unit analysis of hippocampal population spikes. *Exp. Brain Res.* 13:208–22
12. Andersen, P., Bliss, T. V. P., Lømo, T., Olsen, L. I., Skrede, K. K. 1969. Lamellar organization of hippocampal excitatory pathways. *Acta Physiol. Scand.* 76:4A–5A
13. Andersen, P., Bruland, H., Kaada, B. R. 1961. Activation of the field CA1 of the hippocampus by septal stimulation. *Acta Physiol. Scand.* 51:29–40
14. Andersen, P., Eccles, J. C., Loyning, Y. 1963. Recurrent inhibition in the hippocampus with identification of the inhibitory cell and its synapses. *Nature* 198:540–42
15. Andersen, P., Eccles, J. C., Loyning, Y. 1964. Location of postsynaptic inhibitory synapses of hippocampal pyramids. *J. Neurophysiol.* 27:592–607
16. Andersen, P., Gross, G. N., Lømo, T., Sveen, O. 1969. Participation of inhibitory and excitatory interneurones in the control of hippocampal cortical output. In *The Interneuron*, ed. M. A. B. Brazier, pp. 415–65. Berkeley: Univ. Calif.
17. Andersen, P., Holmqvist, B., Voorhoeve, P. E. 1966. Excitatory synapses on hippocampal apical dendrites activated by entorhinal stimulation. *Acta Physiol. Scand.* 66:461–72
17a. Angevine, J. B. Jr. 1975. Development of the hippocampal region. See Ref. 104, Vol. 1, p. 65

18. Apostol, G., Creutzfeldt, O. D. 1974. Crosscorrelation between the activity of septal units and hippocampal EEG during arousal. *Brain Res.* 67:65–75

19. Arnolds, D. E. A. T., Lopes da Silva, F. H., Aitink, W., Kamp, A. 1975. Motor acts and firing of reticular neurons correlated with operantly reinforced theta shifts. *Brain Res.* 85:194–95

20. Arnolds, D. E. A. T., Lopes da Silva, F. H., Kamp, A., Aitink, J. W. 1977. Hippocampal EEG correlates with movement in dog. *Electroencephalogr. Clin. Neurophysiol.* 43:567 (Abstr.)

21. Artemenko, D. P. 1970. Laminar analysis of hippocampal potentials evoked by peripheral stimulation, *Neirofiziologiya* 2:434–38 (English translation)

22. Bennett, T. L. 1969. Evidence against the theory that hippocampal theta is a correlate of voluntary movement. *Commun. Behav. Biol.* 4:165–69

23. Bennett, T. L. 1973. The effects of centrally blocking hippocampal theta activity on learning and retention. *Behav. Biol.* 9:541–52

24. Berger, T. W., Alger, B., Thompson, R. F. 1976. Neuronal substrate of classical conditioning in the hippocampus. *Science* 192:483–85

25. Best, P. J., Orr, J. Jr. 1973. Effects of hippocampal lesions on passive avoidance and taste aversion conditioning. *Physiol. Behav.* 10:193–96

26. Black, A. H. 1975. Hippocampal electrical activity and behaviour. See Ref. 104, Vol. 2, pp. 129–63

27. Black, A. H., Young, G. A. 1972. Electrical activity of the hippocampus and cortex in dogs operantly trained to move and to hold still. *J. Comp. Physiol. Psychol.* 79:128–41

28. Black, A. H., Young, G. A., Batenchuk, C. 1970. Avoidance training of hippocampal theta waves in flaxedilized dogs and its relation to skeletal movement. *J. Comp. Physiol. Psychol.* 70: 15–24

29. Blackstad, T. W. 1956. Commissural connections of the hippocampal region in the rat with special reference to their mode of termination. *J. Comp. Neurol.* 105:417–537

30. Blackstad, T. W. 1976. A letter on the anatomy of hippocampus. Pers. commun.

31. Blackstad, T. W., Brink, K., Hem, J., Jeune, B. 1970. Distribution of hippocampal mossy fibres in the rat. An experimental study with silver impregnation methods. *J. Comp. Neurol.* 138:433–50

32. Bland, B. H., Andersen, P., Ganes, T. 1975. Two generators of hippocampal theta activity in rabbits. *Brain Res.* 94:199–218

33. Bland, B. H., Kostopoulos, G. K., Phillis, J. W. 1974. Acetylcholine sensitivity of hippocampal formation neurons. *Can. J. Physiol. Pharmacol.* 52:966–71

34. Bland, B. H., Vanderwolf, C. H. 1972. Electrical stimulation of the hippocampal formation: behavioural and bioelectrical effects. *Brain Res.* 43:89–106

35. Bliss, T. V. P., Gardner-Medwin, A. R. 1973. Long-lasting potentiation of synaptic transmission in the dentate area of the unanaesthetized rabbit following stimulation of the perforant path. *J. Physiol. London.* 232:357–74

36. Bliss, T. V. P., Lømo, T. 1973. Long-lasting potentiation of synaptic transmission in the dentate area of the anaesthetized rabbit following stimulation of the perforant path. *J. Physiol. London* 232:331–56

37. Bohus, B. 1975. The hippocampus and the pituitary-adrenal system hormones. See Ref. 104, Vol. 1, pp. 323–53

37a. Boudreau, J. C. 1966. Computer measurements of hippocampal fast activity in cats with chronically implanted electrodes. *Electroencephalogr. Clin. Neurophysiol.* 20:165–74

38. Brazier, M. A. B. 1970. Regional activities within the human hippocampus and hippocampal gyrus. *Exp. Neurol.* 26: 354–68

39. Brodal, A. 1947. The hippocampus and the sense of smell. *Brain* 70:179–222

40. Brown, B. B. 1968. Frequency and phase of hippocampal theta activity in the spontaneously behaving cat. *Electroencephalogr. Clin. Neurophysiol.* 24: 53–62

41. Buser, P., Bancaud, J., Talairach, J., Szikla, G. 1968. Interconnexions amygdalo-hippocampiques chez L'Homme. Étude physiologique au cours d' explorations stéréo-taxiques. *Rev. Neurol.* 119:283–88

42. Butters, N., Cermak, L. 1975. Some analyses of amnesic syndromes in brain-damaged patients. See Ref. 104, Vol. 2, pp. 377–409

43. Chronister, R. B., DeFrance, J. F., Sikes, R. W., Srebro, B., White, L. E. 1976. The midline septum Telencephali: A raphe. *Exp. Neurol.* 50:684–98

44. Chronister, R. B., Sikes, R. W., White, L. E. Jr. 1975. Post-commissural fornix; origin and distribution in the rodent. *Neurosci. Lett.* 1:199–202

45. Chronister, R. B., White, L. E. Jr. 1975. Fiber architecture of the hippocampal formation: anatomy, projections and structural significance. See Ref. 104, Vol. 1, pp. 9–39

46. Chronister, R. B., Zornetzer, S. F., Bernstein, J. J., White, L. E. Jr. 1974. Hippocampal theta rhythm, intrahippocampal formation contributions. Brain Res. 65:13–28

47. Coenen, A. M. L. 1975. Frequency analysis of rat hippocampal electrical activity. Physiol. Behav. 14:391–94

48. Cohen, J. S., Laroche, J. P. 1973. Effect of a physical barrier on response perseveration in hippocampal lesioned rats. Physiol. Behav. 10:485–90

49. Coleman, J. R., Lindsley, D. B. 1975. Hippocampal electrical correlates of free behaviour and behaviour induced by stimulation of two hypothalamic-hippocampal systems in the cat. Exp. Neurol. 49:506–28

50. Conrad, L. C. A., Leonard, C. M., Pfaff, D. W. 1974. Connections of the median and dorsal raphe nuclei in the rat: An autoradiographic and degeneration study. J. Comp. Neurol. 156:179–206

51. Cowey, A., Gross, C. G. 1970. Effects of foveal prestriate and inferotemporal lesions on visual discrimination by rhesus monkeys. Exp. Brain Res. 11:128–44

52. Cragg, B. G. 1960. Responses of the hippocampus to stimulation of the olfactory bulb and of various afferent nerves in five mammals. Exp. Neurol. 2:547–72

53. Cragg, B. G. 1961. Olfactory and other afferent connections of the hippocampus in the rabbit, rat and cat. Exp. Neurol. 3:588–600

54. Cruce, J. A. F. 1975. An autoradiographic study of the projections of the mammillothalamic tract in the rat. Brain Res. 85:211–19

55. DeFrance, J. F., Kitai, S. T., Shimono, T. 1973. Electrophysiological analysis of the hippocampal-septal projections: I. Response and topographical characteristics. Exp. Brain Res. 17:447–62

56. DeFrance, J. F., Kitai, S. T., Shimono, T. 1973. Electrophysiological analysis of the hippocampal-septal projections. II: Functional characteristics. Exp. Brain Res. 17:463–76

57. DeFrance, J. F., Yoshihara, H. 1975. Fimbria input to the nucleus accumbens septi. Brain Res. 90:159–63

58. DeFrance, J. F., Yoshihara, H., Chronister, R. B. 1976. Electrophysiological studies of the septal nuclei. I. The lateral septal region. Exp. Neurol. 53:399–419

59. Dichter, M., Spencer, W. A. 1969. Penicillin-induced interictal discharges from the cat hippocampus. I. Characteristics and topographic features. J. Neurophysiol. 32:649–62

60. Dichter, M., Spencer, W. A. 1969. Penicillin-induced interictal discharges from the cat hippocampus. II. Mechanisms underlying origin and restriction. J. Neurophysiol. 32:663–87

61. Domesick, V. B. 1969. Projections from the cingulate cortex in the rat. Brain Res. 12:296–320

62. Domesick, V. B. 1973. Thalamic projections in the cingulum bundle to the parahippocampal cortex of the rat. Anat. Rec. 175:308

63. Douglas, R. J. 1967. The hippocampus and behaviour. Psychol. Bull. 67:416–42

64. Douglas, R. J. 1972. Pavlovian conditioning and the brain. In Inhibition and Learning, ed. R. Boakes, M. Halliday, pp. 529–53. London: Academic

65. Douglas, R. M., Goddard, G. V. 1975. Long-term potentiation of the perforant path-granule cell synapse in the rat hippocampus. Brain Res. 86:205–15

66. Dudek, F. E., Deadwyler, S. A., Cotman, C. W., Lynch, G. 1976. Intracellular responses from granule cell layer in slices of rat hippocampus: perforant path synapse. J. Neurophysiol. 39:383–93

67. Eccles, J. C. 1965. Inhibition in thalamic and cortical neurones and its role in phasing neuronal discharges. Epilepsia 6:89–115

68. Edinger, H., Siegel, A., Troiano, R. 1973. Single unit analysis of the hippocampal projections to the septum in the cat. Exp. Neurol. 41:569–83

69. Elazar, Z., Adey, W. R. 1967. Spectral analysis of low frequency components in the electrical activity of the hippocampus during learning. Electroencephalogr. Clin. Neurophysiol. 23:225–40

70. Feder, R., Ranck, J. B. 1973. Studies on single neurons in dorsal hippocampal formation and septum in unrestrained rats. Part II. Hippocampal slow waves and theta cell firing during bar pressing and other behaviours. Exp. Neurol. 41:532–55

71. Fifková, E. 1975. Two types of terminal degeneration in the molecular layer of the dentate fascia following lesions of the entorhinal cortex. Brain Res. 96:169–75

72. Freeman, W. J. 1975. *Mass Action in the Nervous System.* New York: Academic. 489 pp.
73. Fritz, L. C., Gardner-Medwin, A. R. 1976. The effect of synaptic activation on the extracellular potassium concentration in the hippocampal dentate area, in vitro. *Brain Res.* 112:183–87
74. Fujita, Y. 1975. Two types of depolarizing after-potentials in hippocampal pyramidal cells of rabbits. *Brain Res.* 94:435–46
75. Fujita, Y., Sato, T. 1964. Intracellular records from hippocampal pyramidal cells in rabbit during theta rhythm activity. *J. Neurophysiol.* 27:1011–25
76. Gambarian, L. S., Koval, I. N. 1973. *The Hippocampus: Physiology and Morphology.* Jerewan: Armenian Acad. Sci. 101 pp. (English summary)
77. Geneser-Jensen, F. A., Haug, F. M. S., Danscher, G. 1974. Distribution of heavy metals in the hippocampal region of the guinea-pig. A light microscope study with Timm's sulfide silver method. *Z. Zellforsch. Mikrosk. Anat.* 147:441–78
78. Gloor, P. 1955. Electrophysiological studies on the connections of the amygdaloid nucleus in the cat. I. Neuronal organization of the amygdaloid projection system. *Electroencephalogr. Clin. Neurophysiol.* 7:223–42
79. Gloor, P., Vera, C. L., Sperti, L. 1963. Electrophysiological studies of hippocampal neurons. I. Configuration and laminar analysis of the "resting" potential gradient, of the main-transient response to perforant path, fimbrial and mossy fiber volleys and of "spontaneous" activity. *Electroencephalogr. Clin. Neurophysiol.* 15:353–78
80. Gloor, P., Vera, C. L., Sperti, L. 1964. Electrophysiological studies of hippocampal neurons. III. Responses of hippocampal neurons to repetitive perforant path volleys. *Electroencephalogr. Clin. Neurophysiol.* 17:353–70
81. Goldowitz, D., White, W. F., Steward, O., Lynch, G., Cotman, C. 1975. Anatomical evidence for a projection from the entorhinal cortex to the contralateral dentate gyrus of the rat. *Exp. Neurol.* 47:433–41
82. Grastyán, E., Karmos, G., Vereczkey, L., Kellényi, L. 1966. The hippocampal electrical correlates of the homeostatic regulation of motivation. *Electroencephalogr. Clin. Neurophysiol.* 21:34–53
83. Grastyán, E., Lissák, K., Madarász, I., Donhoffer, H. 1959. Hippocampal electrical activity during the development

of conditioned reflexes. *Electroencephalogr. Clin. Neurophysiol.* 11:409–30
84. Gray, J. A. 1972. Effects of septal driving of the hippocampal theta rhythm on resistance to extinction. *Physiol. Behav.* 8:481–90
85. Gray, J. A., Araujo-Silva M. T., Quintao, L. 1972. Resistance to extinction after partial reinforcement training with blocking of the hippocampal theta rhythm by septal stimulation. *Physiol. Behav.* 8:497–502
86. Green, J. D. 1964. The hippocampus. *Physiol. Rev.* 44:561–608
87. Green, J. D., Arduini, A. A. 1954. Hippocampal electrical activity in arousal. *J. Neurophysiol.* 17:533–57
88. Green, J. D., Maxwell, D. S., Petsche, H. 1961. Hippocampal electrical activity. III. Unitary events and genesis of slow waves. *Electroencephalogr. Clin. Neurophysiol.* 13:854–67
89. Gross, C. G., Bender, D. B., Rocha-Miranda, C. E. 1969. Visual receptive fields of neurons in inferotemporal cortex of the monkey. *Science* 166:1303–5
90. Gross, C. G., Schiller, P. H., Wells, C., Gerstein, G. L. 1967. Single unit activity in temporal association cortex of the monkey. *J. Neurophysiol* 30:833–43
91. Guillery, R. W. 1956. Degeneration in the post-commisural fornix and the mammillary peduncle of the rat. *J. Anat.* 90:350–70
92. Habets, A. M. M. C., Kleisma, M., Lopes da Silva, F. H., de Quartel, F. W., Tielen, A. M., Mollevanger, W. J. 1977. Evoked potentials of the hippocampus: a functional anatomical study using equipotential maps. *Electroencephalogr. Clin. Neurophysiol.* 43:567–68 (Abstr.)
93. Harley, C. W. 1972. Hippocampal lesions and two cue discrimination in the rat. *Physiol. Behav.* 9:343–48
94. Harper, R. M. 1971. Frequency changes in hippocampal electrical activity during movement and tonic immobility. *Physiol. Behav.* 7:55–58
95. Heath, R. G., Harper, J. W. 1974. Ascending projections of the cerebellar fastigial nucleus to the hippocampus, amygdala and other temporal lobe sites: Evoked potential and histological studies in monkeys and cats. *Exp. Neurol.* 45:268–87
96. Hjorth-Simonsen, A. 1971. Hippocampal efferents to the ipsilateral entorhinal area: An experimental study in the rat. *J. Comp. Neurol.* 142:417–38
97. Hjorth-Simonsen, A. 1972. Projection of the lateral part of the entorhinal area

to the hippocampus and fascia dentata. *J. Comp. Neurol.* 146:219–32

98. Hjorth-Simonsen, A., Jeune, B. 1972. Origin and termination of the hippocampal perforant path in the rat studied by silver impregnation. *J. Comp. Neurol.* 144:215–32

99. Horowitz, J. M. 1972. Evoked activity of single units and neural populations in the hippocampus of the cat. *Electroencephalogr. Clin. Neurophysiol.* 32:227–40

100. Horowitz, J. M., Freeman, W. J., Stoll, P. J. 1973. A neural network with a background level of excitation in the cat hippocampus. *Int. J. Neurosci.* 5:113–23

101. Ibata, Y., Desiraju, T., Pappas, G. D. 1971. Light and electron microscopic study of the projection of the medial septal nucleus to the hippocampus of the cat. *Exp. Neurol.* 33:103–22

102. Irmis, F. 1976. Hippocampal rhythmic slow theta activity in relation to certain muscle movements. *Electroencephalogr. Clin. Neurophys.* 41:553 (Abstr.)

103. Isaacson, R. L. 1974. *The Limbic System.* New York & London: Plenum. 292 pp.

104. Isaacson, R. L., Pribram, K. H., eds. 1975. *The Hippocampus,* Vol. 1: Structure and Development; Vol. 2: Neurophysiology and Behaviour. New York: Plenum. 415 pp., 445 pp.

105. Izquierdo, I., Vásquez, B. 1968. Field potentials in rat hippocampus: monosynaptic nature and heterosynaptic posttetanic potentiation. *Exp. Neurol.* 21:133–46

106. Jarrard, L. E., Bunnell, G. N. 1968. Open-field behaviour of hippocampal lesioned rats and hamsters. *J. Comp. Physiol. Psychol.* 66:500–502

107. Jones, E. G., Powell, T. P. S. 1970. An anatomical study of converging sensory pathways within the cerebral cortex of the monkey. *Brain* 93:793–820

108. Kamp, A., Lopes da Silva, F. H., van Leeuwen, W. S. 1971. Hippocampal frequency shifts in different behavioural situations. *Brain Res.* 31:287–94

108a. Kemp, I. R., Kaada, B. R. 1975. The relation of hippocampal theta activity to arousal, attentive behaviour and somato-motor movements in unrestrained cats. *Brain Res.* 95:323–42

109. Kilmer, W. L., McLardy, T. 1970. A model of hippocampal CA3 circuitry. *Int. J. Neurosci.* 1:107–12

110. Kimble, D. P. 1975. Choice behaviour in rats with hippocampal lesions. See Ref. 104, Vol. 2, pp. 309–26

111. Klemm, W. R. 1970. Correlation of hippocampal theta rhythm, muscle activity, and brain stem reticular formation activity. *Commun. Behav. Biol.* A. 5:147–51

112. Klemm, W. R. 1971. EEG and multiple-unit activity in limbic and motor systems during movement and immobility. *Physiol. Behav.* 7:337–43

113. Klemm, W. R. 1976. Physiological and behavioral significance of hippocampal rhythmic, slow activity. ("Theta Rhythm"). *Prog. Neurobiol. Oxford* 6:23–47

114. Kolb, B., Nonneman, A. J. 1974. Frontolimbic lesions and social behavior in the rat. *Physiol. Behav.* 13:637–43

115. Kostopoulos, G. K., Phillis, J. W. 1977. Mammillothalamic neurons activated antidromically and by stimulation of the fornix. *Brain Res.* 122:143–49

116. Kramis, R., Vanderwolf, C. H., Bland, B. H. 1975. Two types of hippocampal rhythmical slow activity in both the rabbit and the rat: relations to behaviour and effects of atropine, diethyl ether, urethane, and pento-barbital. *Exp. Neurol.* 49:58–85

117. Kuhar, M. J., Yamamura, H. I. 1975. Light autoradiographic localization of cholinergic muscarinic receptors in rat brain by specific binding of a potent antagonist. *Nature,* 253:560–61

118. Kul'tas, K. N., Smolikhina, T. I., Brazhnik, E. S., Vinogradova, O. S. 1974. The effect of cutting septal afferents on acetylcholinesterase activity in short-axon neurons of the hippocampus. *Dokl. Akad. Nauk SSSR Ser. Physiol.* 216:462–63 (In Russian)

119. Landfield, P. W., Tusa, R. J., McGaugh, J. L. 1973. Effects of posttrial hippocampal stimulation on memory storage and EEG activity. *Behav. Biol.* 8:485–505

120. Lebovitz, R. B., Dichter, M., Spencer, W. A. 1971. Recurrent excitation in the CA3 region of cat hippocampus. *Int. J. Neurosci.* 2:99–108

120a. Lidsky, T. I., Levine, M. S., MacGregor, S. Jr. 1974. Hippocampal units during orienting and arousal in rabbits. *Exp. Neurol.* 44:171–86

121. Lφmo, T. 1969. *Synaptic mechanisms and organization of the dentate area of the hippocampal formation.* Thesis. Inst. Neurophysiol., Univ. Oslo, Norway

122. Lφmo, T. 1971. Patterns of activation in a monosynaptic cortical pathway; the perforant path input to the dentate area

of the hippocampal formation. *Exp. Brain Res.* 12:18–45
123. Lømo, T. 1971. Potentiation of monosynaptic EPSP's in the perforant path dentate granule cell synapse. *Exp. Brain Res.* 12:46–63
124. Lopes da Silva, F. H., Kamp, A. 1969. Hippocampal theta frequency shifts and operant behaviour. *Electroencephalogr. Clin. Neurophysiol.* 26:133–43
125. Lopes da Silva, F. H., Van Rotterdam, A., Barts, P., Van Heusden, E., Burr, W. 1976. Models of neuronal populations: the basic mechanisms of rhythmicity. *Prog. Brain Res.* 45:281–308
126. Lorente de Nó, R. 1934. Studies on the structure of the cerebral cortex. II. Continuation of the study of the ammonic system. *J. Psychol. Neurol.* 46:113–77
127. Macadar, A. W., Chalupa, L. M., Lindsley, D. B. 1974. Differentiation of brain stem loci which affect hippocampal and neocortical electrical activity. *Exp. Neurol.* 43:499–514
128. Macadar, O., Roig, J. A., Monti, J. M., Budelli, R. 1970. The functional relationship between septal and hippocampal unit activity and hippocampal theta rhythm. *Physiol. Behav.* 5:1443–49
129. MacLean, P. D. 1975. An ongoing analysis of hippocampal inputs and outputs: microelectrode and neuroanatomical findings in squirrel monkeys. See Ref. 104, Vol. 1, pp. 177–211
130. MacLean, P. D., Yokota, T., Kinnard, M. A. 1968. Photically sustained on-responses of units in posterior hippocampal gyrus of awake monkeys. *J. Neurophysiol.* 31:870–83
131. Mays, L. F., Best, P. J. 1975. Hippocampal unit activity to tonal stimuli during arousal from sleep and in awake rats. *Exp. Neurol.* 47:268–79
132. McClearly, R. A. 1966. Response modulating functions of the limbic system. In *Progress in Physiology and Psychology,* Vol. 1, ed. E. Stellar, J. Sprague, pp. 210–272. New York: Academic
133. McFarland, W. L., Teitelbaum, H., Hedges, E. K. 1975. Relationship between hippocampal theta activity and running speed in the rat. *J. Comp. Physiol. Psychol.* 88:324–28
134. McLennan, H., Miller, J. J. 1974. The hippocampal control of neuronal discharges in the septum of the rat. *J. Physiol. London* 237:607–24
135. Meibach, R. C., Siegel, A. 1977. Efferent connections of the hippocampal formation in the rat. *Brain Res.* 124:197–224
136. Mering, T. A., Mukhin, E. I. 1973. Functional significance of the hippocampus. *Physiol. Behav.* 10:185–91
137. Michal, E. K. 1973. Effects of limbic lesions on behaviour sequences and courtship behaviour of male rats. (Rattus Norvegicus). *Behaviour* 44:264–85
138. Moore, R. Y., Halaris, A. E. 1975. Hippocampal innervation by serotonin neurons of the midbrain raphe in the rat. *J. Comp. Neurol.* 164:171–83
139. Mosko, S., Lynch, G., Cotman, C. W. 1973. Distribution of the septal projections to the hippocampal formation of the rat. *J. Comp. Neurol.* 152:163–74
140. Myhrer, T. 1975. Locomotor, avoidance, and maze behaviour in rats with selective disruption of hippocampal output. *J. Comp. Physiol. Psychol.* 89:759–77
141. Nadel, L., O'Keefe, J. 1974. The hippocampus in pieces and patches: an essay on modes of explanation in physiological psychology. In *Essays on the Nervous System. A Festschrift for Prof. J. Z. Young,* ed. R. Bellairs, E. G. Gray, pp. 367–90. Oxford: Clarendon Press
142. Nafstad, P. H. J. 1967. An electron microscope study on the termination of the perforant path fibres in the hippocampus and the fascia dentata. *Z. Zellforsch. Mikrosk. Anat.* 76:532–42
143. Nauta, W. J. H. 1956. An experimental study of the fornix system in the rat. *J. Comp. Neurol.* 104:247–72
144. Ogata, N. 1976. Mechanisms of the stereotyped high-frequency burst in hippocampal pyramidal neurons in vitro. *Brain Res.* 103:386–88
145. Ogata, N., Hori, N.,Katsuda, N. 1976. The correlation between extracellular potassium concentration and hippocampal epileptic activity in vitro. *Brain Res.* 110:371–75
146. Ogata, N., Ueno, S. 1976. Mode of activation of pyramidal neurons by mossy fibre stimulation in thin hippocampal slices in vitro. *Exp. Neurol.* 53:567–84
147. O'Keefe, J. 1976. Place units in the hippocampus of the freely moving rat. *Exp. Neurol.* 51:78–109
148. O'Keefe, J., Dostrovsky, J. 1971. The hippocampus as a spatial map: preliminary evidence from unit activity in the freely moving rat. *Brain Res.* 34:171–75
149. O'Keefe, J., Nadel, L., Keightley, S., Kill, D. 1975. Fornix lesions selectively abolish place learning in the rat. *Exp. Neurol.* 48:152–66
150. Olds, J., Disterhoft, J. F., Segal, M., Kornblith, C. L., Hirsh, R. 1972. Learning centres of rat brain mapped by

measuring latencies of conditioned responses. *J. Neurophysiol.* 35:202–19

151. Olds, J., Hirano, O. 1969. Conditioned responses of hippocampal and other neurons. *Electroencephalogr. Clin. Neurophysiol.* 26:159–66

151a. Olton, D. S., Samuelson, R. J. 1976. Remembrance of places passed: spatial memory in rats. *J. Exp. Psychol.* (Animal Behavioral Processes) 2:97–116

152. Paiva, T., Lopes da Silva, F. H., Mollevanger, W. 1976. Modulating systems of hippocampal EEG. *Electroencephalogr. Clin. Neurophysiol.* 40:470–80

153. Pasquier, D. A., Reinoso-Suarez, F. 1976. Direct projections from hypothalamus to hippocampus in the rat demonstrated by retrograde transport of horseradish peroxidase. *Brain Res.* 108:165–69

154. Pasquier, D. A., Reinoso-Suarez, F. 1977. Differential efferent connections of the brain stem to the hippocampus in the cat. *Brain Res.* 120:540–48

155. Petsche, H., Stumpf, C., Gogolak, G. 1962. The significance of the rabbit's septum as a relay station between the midbrain and the hippocampus. I. The control of hippocampus arousal activity by the septum cells. *Electroencephalogr. Clin. Neurophysiol.* 14:202–11

156. Pickel, V. M., Segal, M., Bloom, F. E. 1974. A radioautographic study of the efferent pathways of the nucleus locus coeruleus. *J. Comp. Neurol.* 155:15–42

157. Plunkett, R. P., Faulds, B. D., Albino, R. C. 1973. Place learning in hippocampectomized rats. *Bull. Psychon. Soc.* 2:79–80

158. Poletti, C. E., Kinnard, M. A., MacLean, P. D. 1973. Hippocampal influence on unit activity of hypothalamus, preoptic region and basal forebrain in awake, sitting squirrel monkeys. *J. Neurophysiol.* 36:308–24

159. Polz-Tejera, G., Schmidt, J., Karten, H. J. 1975. Autoradiographic localization of α-bungarotoxin-binding sites in the central nervous system. *Nature,* 258: 349–51

160. Raisman, G. 1966. The connections of the septum. *Brain* 89:317–48

161. Raisman, G., Cowan, W. M., Powell, T. P. S. 1966. An experimental analysis of the efferent projection of the hippocampus. *Brain* 89:83–108

162. Rall, W., Shepherd, G. M. 1968. Theoretical reconstruction of field potentials and dendro-dendritic synaptic interactions in olfactory bulb. *J. Neurophysiol.* 31:884–915

163. Ramón y Cajal, S. 1893. *The Structure of Ammon's Horn.* Transl. 1968 by L. M. Kraft. Springfield, Ill.: Thomas 78 pp.

164. Ranck, J. B. 1973. Studies on single neurons in dorsal hippocampal formation and septum in unrestrained rats. Part 1, Behavioural correlates and firing repertoire. *Exp. Neurol.* 41:461–529

165. Rose, A. M., Hattori, T., Fibiger, H. C. 1976. Analysis of the septohippocampal pathway by light and electron microscopic autoradiography. *Brain Res.* 108:170–74

166. Sainsbury, R. S. 1970. Hippocampal activity during natural behaviour in the guinea-pig. *Physiol. Behav.* 5:317–24

167. Sano, K., Iwahara, S., Senba, K., Sano, A., Yamazaki, S. 1973. Eye movements and hippocampal theta activity in rats. *Electroencephalogr. Clin. Neurophysiol.* 35:621–25

168. Schwartzkroin, P. A. 1975. Characteristics of CA1 neurons recorded intracellularly in the hippocampal in vitro slice preparation. *Brain Res.* 85:423–36

169. Schwartzkroin, P. A., Wester, K. 1975. Long-lasting facilitation of a synaptic potential following tetanization in the in vitro hippocampal slice. *Brain Res.* 89:107–19

170. Segal, M. 1972. Hippocampal unit responses to perforant path stimulation. *Exp. Neurol.* 35:541–46

171. Segal, M. 1973. *The hippocampus as a learning machine.* PhD thesis. Calif. Inst. Technol., Pasadena, Calif. 197 pp.

172. Segal, M. 1975. Physiological and pharmacological evidence for a serotonergic projection to the hippocampus. *Brain Res.* 94:115–31

173. Segal, M., Bloom, F. E. 1974. The action of norepinephrine in the rat hippocampus. I. Iontophoretic studies. *Brain Res.* 72:79–97

174. Segal, M., Bloom, F. E. 1974. The action of norepinephrine in the rat hippocampus. II. Activation of the input pathway. *Brain Res.* 72:99–114

175. Segal, M., Bloom, F. E. 1976. The action of norepinephrine in the rat hippocampus. III. Hippocampal cellular responses to locus coeruleus stimulation in the awake rat. *Brain Res.* 107:499–511

176. Segal, M., Bloom, F. E. 1976. The action of norepinephrine in the rat hippocampus. IV. The effects of locus coeruleus stimulation on evoked hippocampal unit activity. *Brain Res.* 107:513–25

177. Segal, M., Disterhoft, J. F., Olds, J. 1972. Hippocampal unit activity during classical aversive and appetitive conditioning. *Science* 175:792–94

178. Segal, M., Landis, S. 1974. Afferents to the hippocampus of the rat studied with the method of retrograde transport of horseradish peroxidase. *Brain Res.* 78:1–15

179. Segal, M., Olds, J. 1972. Behaviour of units in the hippocampal circuit of the rat during learning. *J. Neurophysiol.* 35:680–90

180. Segal, M., Olds, J. 1973. Activity of units in the hippocampal circuit of the rat during differential classical conditioning. *J. Comp. Physiol. Psychol.* 82:195–204

181. Seltzer, B., Pandya, D. N. 1976. Some cortical projections to the parahippocampal area in the rhesus monkey. *Exp. Neurol.* 50:146–60

182. Shen, Y.S., Nelson, J. P., Bloom, F. E. 1974. Discharge patterns of cat raphe neurons during sleep and waking. *Brain Res.* 73:263–76

183. Shipley, M. T., Sörensen, K. E. 1975. Evidence for an ipsilateral projection from the subiculum to the deep layers of the presubicular and entorhinal cortices in the guinea-pig. *Exp. Brain Res.* 23 (Suppl):190 (Abstr.)

184. Shipley, M. T., Sörensen, K. E. 1975. On the laminar organization of the anterior thalamus projections to the presubiculum in the guinea-pig. *Brain Res.* 86:473–77

185. Siegel, A., Flynn, J. P. 1968. Differential effects of electrical stimulation and lesions of the hippocampus and adjacent regions upon attack behaviour in cats. *Brain Res.* 7:252–67

186. Siegel, A., Tassoni, J. P. 1971. Differential efferent projections from the ventral and dorsal hippocampus of the cat. *Brain Behav. Evol.* 4:185–200

187. Siegel, A., Tassoni, J. P. 1971. Differential efferent projections of the lateral and medial septal nuclei to the hippocampus in the cat. *Brain Beh. Evol.* 4:201–19

188. Spencer, W. A., Kandel, E. R. 1961. Hippocampal neuron responses to selective activation of recurrent collaterals of hippocampofugal axons. *Exp. Neurol.* 4:149–61

189. Spencer, W. A., Kandel, E. R. 1968. Cellular and integrative properties of the hippocampal pyramidal cell and the comparative electrophysiology of cortical neurons. *Int. J. Neurol.* 6:266–96

190. Sperti, L., Gessi, T., Volta, F., Riva Sanseverino, E. 1970. Synaptic organization of commissural projections of the hippocampal region in the guinea-pig. I. Dorsal psalterium: Mode of activation of granule cells and CA1 pyramidal neurons. *Arch. Sci. Biol.* 54:141–82

191. Steward, O. 1976. Topographic organization of the projections from the entorhinal area to the hippocampal formation of the rat. *J. Comp. Neurol.* 167:285–314

192. Steward, O., Cotman, C. W., Lynch, G. S. 1974. Growth of a new fiber projection in the brain of adult rats: reinnervation of the dentate gyrus by the contralateral entorhinal cortex following ipsilateral entorhinal lesions. *Exp. Brain Res.* 20:45–66

193. Steward, O., White, W. F., Cotman, C. W., Lynch, G. 1976. Potentiation of excitatory synaptic transmission in the normal and in the reinnervated dentate gyrus. *Exp. Brain Res.* 26:423–41

194. Storm-Mathisen, J. 1977. Localization of transmitter candidates in the brain: the hippocampal formation as a model. *Prog. Neurobiol.* 8:119–81

195. Deleted in proof.

196. Stumpf, C. 1965. Drug action on the electrical activity of the hippocampus. *Int. Rev. Neurobiol.* 8:77–138

197. Swanson, L. W., Cowan, W. M. 1977. An autoradiographic study of the organization of the efferent connections of the hippocampal formation in the rat. *J. Comp. Neurol.* 172:49–84

198. Teitelbaum, H., Lee, J. F., Johannessen, J. N. 1975. Behaviourally evoked hippocampal theta waves: a cholinergic response. *Science* 188:1114–16

199. Teyler, T. J., Alger, B. E. 1976. Monosynaptic habituation in the vertebrate forebrain: The dentate gyrus examined in vitro. *Brain Res.* 115:413–25

200. Tömbol, T., Petsche, H. 1969. The histological organization of the pacemaker for the hippocampal theta rhythm in the rabbit. *Brain Res.* 12:414–26

201. Torii, S. 1961. Two types of pattern of hippocampal electrical activity induced by stimulation of hypothalamus and surrounding parts of rabbit's brain. *Jpn. J. Physiol.* 11:147–57

201a. Urban, I., de Wied, D. 1976. Changes in excitability of the theta activity generating substrate by ACTH4-10 in the rat. *Exp. Brain Res.* 24:325–34

201b. Urban, I., de Wied, D. 1977. Neuropeptides: effects on paradoxical sleep and theta rhythm in rats. *Physiol. Behav.* In press

202. Valenstein, E. S., Nauta, W. J. H. 1959. A comparison of the distribution of the fornix system on the rat, guinea-pig, cat and monkey. *J. Comp. Neurol.* 113: 337–63

203. Vanderwolf, C. H. 1969. Hippocampal electrical activity and voluntary movement in the rat. *Electroencephalogr. Clin. Neurophysiol.* 26:407–18

204. Vanderwolf, C. H., Bland, B. H., Whishaw, I. Q., 1973. Diencephalic, hippocampal and neocortical mechanisms in voluntary movement. In *Efferent Organization and the Integration of Behaviour,* ed. J. D. Maser, pp. 229–62. New York: Academic

205. Vanderwolf, C. H., Kramis, R., Gillespie, L. A., Bland, B. H. 1975. Hippocampal rhythmic slow activity and neocortical low-voltage fast activity: relations to behaviour. See Ref. 104, Vol. 2, pp. 101–28

206. Van Hartesveldt, C. 1975. The hippocampus and regulations of the hypothalamic-hypophyseal-adrenal cortical axis. See Ref. 104. Vol. 1, pp. 375–92

207. Van Hoesen, G. W., Pandya, D. N. 1975. Some connections of the entorhinal (area 28) and perirhinal (area 35) cortices of the rhesus monkey. I. Temporal lobe afferents. *Brain Res.* 95:1–24

208. Van Hoesen, G. W., Pandya, D. N. 1975. Some connections of the entorhinal (area 28) and perirhinal (area 35) cortices of the rhesus monkey. II. Frontal lobe afferents. *Brain Res.* 95:25–38

209. Van Hoesen, G. W., Pandya, D. N. 1975. Some connections of the entorhinal (area 28) and perirhinal (area 35) cortices of the rhesus monkey. III. Efferent connections. *Brain Res.* 95:39–59

209a. van Leeuwen, W. S., Kamp, A., Kok, M. L., de Quartel, F. M., Lopes da Silva, F. H., Tielen, A. M. 1967. Relations entre les activités électriques cérébrales du chien, son comportement et sa direction d'attention. *Actual. Neurophysiol.* 7:167–86

210. Van Rotterdam, A. 1973. A discrete formalism for the computation of extracellular potentials. *Kybernetik* 12: 223–28

211. Vinogradova, O. S. 1970. Registration of information and the limbic system. In *Short-term Changes in Neural Activity and Behaviour,* ed. G. Horn, Z. A. Hinde, pp. 95–140. London: Cambridge

212. Vinogradova, O. S. 1975. Functional organization of the limbic system in the process of registration of information:

Facts and hypotheses. See Ref. 104, Vol. 2, pp. 3–70

213. Vinogradova, O. S., Semyonova, T. P., Konovalov, V. Ph. 1970. Trace phenomena in single neurons of hippocampus and mammillary bodies. In *Biology of Memory,* ed. K. H. Pribram, pp. 191–221. New York: Academic.

214. Von Euler, C., Green, J. D. 1960. Excitation, inhibition and rhythmical activity in hippocampal pyramidal cells in rabbit. *Acta Physiol. Scand.* 48:110–25

215. Votaw, C. L. 1957. The hippocampus as a supplementary motor area. *Anat. Rec.* 127:382–83

216. Votaw, C. L. 1959. Certain functional and anatomical relations of the Cornu Ammonis of the Macaque monkey. I. functional relations. *J. Comp. Neurol.* 112:353–82

217. Way, J. S. 1962. An oscillographic study of afferent connections to the hippocampus in the cat (*Felis domesticus*). *Electroencephalogr. Clin. Neurophysiol.* 14:78–89

218. Whishaw, I. Q., Bland, B. H., Vanderwolf, C. H. 1972. Hippocampal activity, behaviour, self-stimulation and heart rate during electrical stimulation of the lateral hypothalamus. *J. Comp. Physiol. Psychol.* 79:115–27

219. Whishaw, I. Q., Nikkel, R. W. 1975. Anterior hypothalamic electrical stimulation and hippocampal EEG in the rat: suppressed EEG, locomotion, self-stimulation and inhibition of shock avoidance. *Behav. Biol.* 13:1–20

220. Whishaw, I. Q., Schallert, T. 1977. Hippocampal RSA (theta), apnea, bradycardia and effects of atropine during under water swimming in the rat. *Electroencephalogr. Clin. Neurophysiol.* 42: 389–96

221. Whishaw, I. Q., Vanderwolf, C. H. 1973. Hippocampal EEG and behaviour: changes in amplitude and frequency of RSA (Theta Rhythm) associated with spontaneous and learned movement patterns in rats and cats. *Behav. Biol.* 8:461–84

222. White, W. F., Goldowitz, D., Lynch, G., Cotman, C. W. 1976. Electrophysiological analysis of the projection from the contralateral entorhinal cortex to the dentate gyrus in normal rats. *Brain Res.* 114:201–09

223. Wilson, C. L., Motter, B. C., Lindsley, D. B. 1976. Influences of hypothalamic stimulation upon septal and hippocampal electrical activity in the cat. *Brain Res.* 107:55–68

224. Winson, J. 1972. Interspecies differences in the occurrence of theta. *Behav. Biol.* 7:479–87
225. Winson, J. 1974. Patterns of hippocampal theta rhythm in the freely moving rat. *Electroencephalogr. Clin. Neurophysiol.* 36:291–301
226. Winson, J. 1976. Hippocampal theta rhythm. I. Depth profiles in the curarized rat. *Brain Res.* 103:57–70
227. Winson, J. 1976. Hippocampal theta rhythm. II. Depth profiles in the freely moving rabbit. *Brain Res.* 103:71–79
228. Wooley, D. E., Barron, B. A. 1968. Hippocampal responses evoked by stimulation of the prepyriform cortex in the rat. *Electroencephalogr. Clin. Neurophysiol.* 24:63–74
229. Yokota, T., Fujimori, B. 1964. Effects of brain stem stimulation upon hippocampal electrical activity, somatomotor reflexes and autonomic functions. *Electroencephalogr. Clin. Neurophysiol.* 16:375–82
230. Yokota, T., Reeves, A. G., MacLean, P. D. 1970. Differential effects of septal and olfactory volleys on intracellular responses of hippocampal neurons in awake, sitting monkeys. *J. Neurophysiol.* 33:96–107
231. Zimmer, J., Hjorth-Simonsen, A. 1975. Crossed pathways from the entorhinal area to the fascia dentata. II. Provokable in rats. *J. Comp. Neurol.* 161:71–102

Ann. Rev. Physiol. 1978. 40:217–48
Copyright © 1978 by Annual Reviews Inc. All rights reserved

BRAINSTEM CONTROL OF SPINAL PAIN-TRANSMISSION NEURONS

❖1191

Howard L. Fields

Department of Neurology and Physiology, University of California,
San Francisco, California 94143

Allan I. Basbaum

Department of Anatomy, University of California,
San Francisco, California 94143

INTRODUCTION

Over the past several years information has been gathered in three major areas related to pain transmission and its modulation. The new information concerns first, the nature and properties of neurons that relay messages concerning noxious stimuli; second, the presence of an endogenous analgesia system mediated by a morphine-like substance; and, third, the existence of discrete brainstem sites which, when electrically stimulated, are capable of suppressing pain transmission.

The pharmacology of endogenous morphine-like substances (101, 134, 229, 230, 231) and the physiology of peripheral receptor mechanisms involved in pain transmission (154) have recently been reviewed. This review covers primarily anatomical and physiological work relevant to pain sensation and the neural mechanism of the analgesia produced by electrical and pharmacological manipulation of brainstem sites. The initial part of this review focuses on the organization of spinal-cord neurons that relay information concerning noxious stimulation. We concentrate on the literature available since Wall & Dubner's 1972 review in this journal (253).

217

0066-4278/78/0301-0217$01.00

PAIN-TRANSMISSION NEURONS

Organization of Spinal Gray Matter

Rexed (204) surveyed the cytoarchitecture of the spinal cord and showed that the dorsal horn could be described as an axially aligned column of six laminae, each lamina having cells with characteristic shapes and orientations.

With the advent of single unit recordings in the 1950s, physiological exploration of the dorsal horn became possible. Wall (252) discovered a physiological dorsoventral lamination of the dorsal horn in the cat. Within each lamina there is also a mediolateral somatotopic organization. Neurons responding at short latency to electrical stimulation of the skin were concentrated just ventral to lamina III. Many of the cells in this region have a narrow dynamic range of response to mechanical stimulation of hairs and skin. These neurons have been called lamina IV cells but may not be restricted to this anatomical zone. Ventral to these cells in a region roughly corresponding to Rexed's lamina V is a group of neurons which respond at somewhat longer latency to cutaneous electrical stimulation, have larger receptive fields and a somewhat higher threshold and wider dynamic range of response to mechanical stimuli than the lamina IV cells. Still deeper is a layer of cells with cutaneous receptive fields essentially similar to lamina V–type cells but having inputs from deep somatic receptors (joint, muscle, etc) as well.

Heavner & DeJong (114) found that many lamina IV cells only respond to hair bending. They also found a greater tendency toward multimodal convergence in deeper layers, though the lamination they found was less precise than reported by Wall.

Using electrical stimulation of peripheral nerves in barbiturate-anesthetized cats, Gregor & Zimmermann (104) did not confirm an increased latency for cells in deeper laminae of dorsal horn. These authors found no laminar separation of neurons according to whether they receive C-fiber input.

Using only light tactile stimuli, Brown et al (44) did not confirm Wall's observation that the receptive field size of a dorsal horn neuron and the latency of its discharge to cutaneous stimulation increases in deeper laminae. However, Brown only studied decerebrate animals and did not use higher stimulus intensities. Thus, his method would tend to minimize differences in field size among laminae. Furthermore, lamina V spinothalamic tract (STT) cells have been reported to have consistently larger receptive fields than lamina IV STT cells in chloralose-anesthetized monkeys (256).

Christensen & Perl (59) and later Cervero et al (57) were more successful in recording from neurons in lamina I. A large number of lamina I neurons have small receptive fields and are driven specifically by Aδ and C fiber primary afferents. Since earlier work had established that a subgroup of these small diameter afferents respond specifically to tissue damaging stimuli (31, 47) and since many lamina I cells have high thresholds for mechanical stimulation, Perl (187) suggested that these lamina I neurons form part of a specific pain-transmission system. This suggestion received support from Pomeranz's finding of ascending anterolateral quadrant fibers in cervical cord with high thresholds for mechanical stimulation (194) and from a later study indicating that a significant number of lamina I neurons contribute to ascending spinal cord tracts (137, 242). Subsequent research has confirmed that many lamina I cells respond selectively to higher intensity mechanical stimuli. Studies using adequate stimuli to the skin in the monkey (199, 256), cat (196, 197), and rat (169) have all confirmed that there is a group of neurons with high intensity mechanical thresholds concentrated in lamina I and that wide-dynamic-range neurons with noxious inputs are concentrated in lamina V.

Other cells in lamina I and substantia gelatinosa respond to innocuous thermal and mechanical stimuli (57, 115, 136). The relative numbers and precise locations of these cells are uncertain; however, Kumazawa & Perl (136) have presented evidence that neurons in these superficial layers of the dorsal horn form anatomical clusters corresponding to input from different peripheral receptor types. They propose that the substantia gelatinosa is an important relay for afferent input from small-diameter myelinated fibers (Aδ) and that the marginal zone (lamina I) receives input primarily from unmyelinated (C) fibers. They were unable to show, however, that substantia neurons contribute to ascending pathways.

This evidence for a differential projection of Aδ and C primary afferents receives support from a recent anatomical study (140). The extent of large-diameter primary afferent projections to superficial layers of the dorsal horn is unknown.

Thus the picture that emerges of the laminar organization of the dorsal horn with regard to cutaneous stimuli is as follows: In lamina I there is a group of neurons that have small receptive fields and relatively high mechanical thresholds. Deep to the substantia gelatinosa, concentrated in lamina IV, is a group of cells with low thresholds and a relatively narrow dynamic range of responses to cutaneous mechanical stimuli. Still deeper, concentrated in lamina V but spilling over into laminae IV and VI, are neurons with a wide dynamic range, many of which respond maximally to stimuli in the noxious range. These will be referred to as lamina V cells. Still more ventral are cells that receive proprioceptive as well as cutaneous inputs. These cells are located in deeper laminae V, VI, and dorsal VII. Cells deep to lamina VI are not organized in an obvious laminar arrangement.

These deeper cells have complex, multimodal inputs and their receptive fields are often topographically extensive and bilateral.

When Wall (252) first described a physiological laminar organization in the dorsal horn, he emphasized that the "fit" with Rexed's anatomical lamination was not precise. The borders between adjacent physiological lamina were neither sharp nor straight. In fact, the lamination is also difficult to discern anatomically. Few, if any, authors use Rexed's (204) somewhat unconventional tissue preparation for their cytoarchitectural studies. With contemporary histological techniques, the marginal zone and the substantia gelatinosa are easily recognized; but the borders that separate, and the subtle differences that characterize laminae III through VI are not easily recognizable. As Rexed pointed out, the clearest delineation of laminae is found in the kitten spinal cord, before extensive fiber proliferation and cell maturation obscure laminar boundaries. Difficulty in correlating physiological and anatomical laminae has led to the terms "lamina IV–" or "V–type" cells, which are purely physiological descriptions. Nevertheless, as Wall (252) and others (88, 114) have stated, in any given microelectrode penetration there is a dorsoventral ordering of cell types. However, except for lamina I and the substantia gelatinosa, this physiologically detectable organization has not yet been correlated with easily recognizable cytoarchitectural differences.

Thus Wall's original observation of a physiological laminar organization of the dorsal horn has been confirmed in several other laboratories. Wall's description must be expanded to include the important cells of lamina I, which have inputs from high threshold mechanoreceptors. The concept of a cascading convergence of input from lamina IV cells to lamina V cells to lamina VI cells has been neither confirmed nor conclusively disproved.

Ascending Systems

THE SPINOTHALAMIC TRACT (STT) (254)   That the STT is the classical pathway for pain has been a standard clinical and neuroanatomical teaching for over a century. This idea derives from the observation that lesions restricted to the anterolateral quadrant (ALQ) of the spinal cord cause a marked loss of pain sensation contralateral and caudal to the lesion (232). Clinical observations indicate that lesions anywhere along the course of the STT may lead to deficits in pain perception (55). Furthermore, Noordenbos & Wall (177) recently observed a patient with a subtotal spinal cord transection sparing only one ALQ. In this patient, contralateral pain sensation was preserved caudal to the lesion.

In the past several years a major breakthrough in physiological and anatomical techniques has provided more direct data concerning spinal neurons projecting to supraspinal sites. Using stimulating electrodes placed in the appropriate thalamic regions and recording from single neurons in the spinal cord, spinothalamic neurons have been identified by observing collision of orthodromically conducted action potentials with those elicited antidromically by activation of the thalamic stimulating electrode. Anatomical studies based on the retrograde transport of horseradish peroxidase (HRP) from the terminal field of a neuron to its soma (143), have produced additional evidence on the cells of origin of spinal projection systems.

The story is clearest for the primate spinothalamic tract (STT). In physiological experiments, Trevino et al (243) found STT cell bodies throughout the lumbar dorsal horn, with a concentration in laminae I, IV, V, and VI. Some cells were also distributed in medial lamina VII. In a preliminary physiological study Albe-Fessard (7, 8) confirmed the STT projection from the IV–VI region but did not report laminae I and VII cells. HRP injections have confirmed a diencephalic projection for cells located in I and IV through VII (6, 242) with some suggestion that intralaminar thalamus receives input specifically from lamina I (6).

The properties of STT neurons are consistent with their locations in dorsal horn (256). Thus, cells with high threshold inputs are found in lamina I and concentrated around lamina V. STT cells with input from deep receptors are more ventral.

Spinothalamic tract neurons in cat lumbosacral cord are less numerous than in primates (73). They are found mainly in laminae VII and VIII, with a few in IV–VI (7, 244). In cat cervical cord, STT cells are found in laminae IV, V and VI (73) and have properties appropriate for those laminae.

The few STT cells that have been recorded in cat thoracic cord were in laminae IV–VIII (110). Too few have been recorded from to generalize about their receptive field properties. HRP injections into cat thalamus largely confirm the location of STT neurons in laminae IV–VI of cervical, and medial laminae VI–VIII in lumbosacral cord (242). In addition, at all spinal levels there is a large STT projection from lamina I.

There are recent data available on rat spinothalamic tract. Giesler and colleagues (98), using physiological techniques, have confirmed the earlier observation (73) that a large component of rat STT neurons arises from the dorsal horn. Rat STT neurons have receptive field properties typical for their dorsal horn location (169).

Subsequent anatomical studies based on HRP injection into rat thalamus provide a more detailed picture of the thalamopetal afferents (97). Spinal cord cells projecting to the ventrobasal thalamus (VB) are concentrated in laminae IV and V of the dorsal horn. In contrast, spinothalamic tract cells terminating in the medial (intralaminar nuclei) and posterior thalamus originate more ventrally in medial laminae VI and VII. After injections into posterior thalamus (caudal to VB), labeled neurons are concentrated in the marginal layer of the spinal trigeminal nucleus caudalis but are much less common in the marginal layer of the dorsal horn (21). Except for a bilateral projection from the ventral horn of the rostral cervical cord (similar to the cat) (51, 242) almost all rat spinothalamic tract axons are crossed.

SPINORETICULAR PATHWAY (33, 253)   There is no question that the anterolateral quadrant is the major pain transmitting pathway in the primate spinal cord. This region, however, contains several ascending systems in addition to the spinothalamic tract. The spinoreticular projection constitutes a major subcomponent of the fibers of the anterolateral quadrant and there is recent evidence that a spinoreticulothalamic projection is an important alternative route for pain transmission.

Cats that have recovered from bilateral lesions of the medial brainstem reticular formation (MBRF) demonstrate a marked reduction in responsiveness to noxious stimulation (9). Furthermore, stimulation in MBRF produces escape behavior in cats (54) and MBRF neuronal activity is correlated with this escape behavior (53). Melzack & Casey (167) have proposed that the spinoreticular projection is part of a central pathway that ascends through medial thalamus and hypothalamus, and is associated with aversive-motivational aspects of pain perception. In contrast, other pathways such as the spinothalamic and spinocervical tract were proposed to contribute more to the sensory-discriminative aspects of pain.

There is no direct anatomical evidence on the precise location of spinal neurons projecting to the MBRF. In early studies using antidromic identification, neurons projecting to MBRF were only found in laminae VI, VII, and VIII of cat lumbar spinal cord (7, 91, 149). In a more extensive study (89), units were antidromically activated from the MBRF and additionally tested with a stimulating array traversing the midbrain to rule out a more rostral destination. Spinoreticular tract (SRT) neurons were defined as those activated from MBRF but not midbrain electrodes. In contrast to earlier studies, 8/24 cells were located in laminae IV and V, and 2/24 in lamina I. The properties of SRT neurons are characteristic for their location and are similar to those of primate STT neurons found in the same region of the spinal gray matter.

A large number of spinoreticular neurons have extensive, complex receptive fields, often bilateral. Many of these cells have multiple discontinuous receptive field components, some responding to both cutaneous and deep receptors. These cells are concentrated in laminae VII and VIII. Evidence indicates that some SRT cells of each receptive field category (cutaneous, deep, and extensive complex) transmit information about noxious stimulation.

SPINOCERVICAL TRACT (SCT)   Recent physiological studies have demonstrated that the SCT in both the cat and the monkey originates mainly from cells in laminae IV and V (45, 46). A small but significant number arise in lamina VI but very few arise from other laminae. HRP studies in the cat and the dog confirm these observations (65).

In the cat there is a topographic map of the body surface onto cells of origin of the SCT (46). A significant proportion of SCT cells respond maximally to stimuli in the noxious range (38, 39, 41). Brown & Franz (38) observed that SCT cells show a marked increase in discharge frequency at skin temperature in the noxious range. In fact, many cells that do not respond to noxious mechanical stimuli do respond to noxious heat, albeit variably (38, 39). This observation is consistent with the finding that 72% of SCT neurons receive C-fiber inputs (40).

Kennard (131) observed that bilateral lesions of the cat dorsolateral funiculus (DLF) including the SCT are required to block pain. We have recently confirmed these observations and further demonstrated that a cat with a lesion at thoracic levels sparing only a single DLF is not analgesic in the hindlimbs. Thus, in the cat, the SCT is a probable pain-transmission pathway. In the primate, however, the role of the SCT in pain transmission has been questioned (175).

DORSAL COLUMN PATHWAYS   The dorsal column medial lemniscal system is not generally associated with transmission of nociceptive information (178). In man, stimulation of the dorsal columns has been used for analgesia and usually produces a tingling or vibratory sensation (172, 224). In monkeys, stimulation of the dorsal columns inhibits dorsal horn cells with nociceptive inputs (92).

A dorsal column pathway potentially capable of transmitting information about noxious stimuli is, however, suggested by the finding in monkey that dorsal column lesions at thoracic levels decrease the forelimb force exerted to escape a noxious stimulus to the hindlimb (248).

Ascending fibers to the dorsal column nuclei (DCN) other than dorsal root afferents have been demonstrated in cats. These fibers ascend in the dorsal columns (12, 13, 210, 211, 246) and in the dorsolateral funiculus (67, 213, 240). In cervical and lumbar enlargements, cells projecting to the DCN are concentrated in lamina IV and medial lamina V, in regions that overlap with cells of origin of the spinocervical tract (212).

Angaut-Petit (12, 13) has described a C-fiber input to the nonprimary afferent axons in the dorsal columns, and Dart & Gordon have shown that some DCN neurons respond maximally to noxious stimulation (67). However, escape thresholds are unaffected by dorsal column lesions (248). Furthermore, since none of the DCN cells responding to noxious stimuli were shown to project to thalamus, they were assumed to be inhibitory interneurons (67). The post-synaptic dorsal column fibers probably have a modulating rather than a sensory-relay function. Thus, although noxious stimulation can activate some neurons in the dorsal columns and dorsal column nuclei, there is little evidence to support a role for the dorsal columns in rostral transmission of information concerning noxious stimuli.

PROPRIOSPINAL SYSTEM   The propriospinal system is a dense meshwork of short and long axons arising from spinal neurons and terminating within the spinal cord. There is evidence that this system is capable of transmitting information concerning noxious stimuli. After all spinal axons projecting directly to supraspinal sites are cut, a noxious stimulus can still elicit apparent pain behavior in the rat (16), the cat (129), the monkey (220), and probably in man (103, 185).

The persistence of pain following cordotomy has been attributed to the release of tonic inhibitory control of the propriospinal pathway (176). The diffuse character of the pain sensation that survives cordotomy may reflect the lack of topographic and modality specificity within the propriospinal pathway and its brainstem analog, the reticular formation (148).

Physiological studies of lumbar propriospinal axons in the cat have demonstrated that many respond to noxious stimuli of both somatic and visceral structures (90). Their receptive field properties indicate that propriospinal axons arise from neurons deep to lamina VI (111). It should be pointed out, however, that neurons whose axons contribute to major ascending pathways (e.g. spinoreticular and spinothalamic tracts) may also form propriospinal connections that could survive anterolateral cordotomy.

Unfortunately, there is no direct evidence available at present that would enable us to determine what role the propriospinal pathways play in pain transmission when other pathways are intact.

Identification of Spinal Neurons Transmitting Pain

It is reasonable to conclude that there are at least three major classes of spinal neurons capable of transmitting information concerning noxious peripheral stimuli to supraspinal sites. One class is located in medial laminae VI, VII, and VIII, has high threshold primary afferent inputs, and contributes to both spinothalamic and spinoreticular tracts. Unfortunately, the response properties of these cells have a topographical and modality complexity that makes systematic analysis of their central projections diffi-cult. The other two classes are concentrated in laminae I and V. The characteristic cell found in lamina I has a high threshold to mechanical stimuli and appears to receive its input largely, if not exclusively, from high-threshold Aδ and C polymodal nociceptor afferents. The class concen-trated in lamina V receives input from high-threshold peripheral afferents, but also from lower-threshold receptors, giving it a wider dynamic range of response to peripheral stimulation. The latter two classes contribute to the spinothalamic tract in the rat and the monkey and, to a lesser extent, in the cat.

It is not clear whether these latter two neuronal classes are functionally distinct or represent the extremes of a continuum. There is evidence sug-gesting independent central connections for lamina I and lamina V neurons. In the primate, lamina I (marginal layer) STT cells project to both ven-trobasal and medial thalamus, while lamina V STT cells project primarily to ventrobasal thalamus. In the rat, lamina V cells also project primarily to ventrobasal thalamus, whereas the thalamic projection from the marginal layer of the trigeminal complex is largely to the posterior nucleus.

Perl has argued that the existence of central transmission cells, predomi-nantly activated by a single receptor type, e.g. those found in lamina I, is strong evidence that pain is a primary sensation requiring only activation of this central labeled line (187). Yet wide-dynamic-range lamina V neurons also respond to noxious stimuli and contribute to the STT, SRT, and SCT, all of which play some role in pain sensation.

An interesting series of experiments has provided information on the question of which dorsal horn neuron types relay the pain message (160, 161, 198). The stimulus parameters required to produce reports of pain were studied in human subjects undergoing anterolateral cordotomy for treat-ment of painful conditions. Correct placement of the stimulating electrode was confirmed by a low electrical threshold for pain and by effective analgesia following lesions made at the stimulating site. At constant stimu-lus intensity, the probability of a report of pain increases linearly as stimulus frequency increases from 5 to 25 Hz. Increases in frequency above 25 Hz produce reports of increased intensity of pain. Using the technique devel-oped by Deutsch (71), the refractory period of fibers transmitting pain was found to range between 1.0 and 3.0 msec in the majority of subjects with about half being below 1.4 msec.

In a companion paper, monkey spinal dorsal horn neurons were anti-dromically activated from the ALQ (200). Significantly, the mean refrac-tory period for lamina I neurons was 4.7 msec compared to 1.5 msec for lamina IV and V neurons, suggesting that the latter are sufficient for pain perception. In addition, the conduction-velocity range of the compound action potential elicited by anterolateral quadrant stimulation at 300 μA was 56–120 m sec^{-1}. All lamina I cells found had conduction velocities less than 42 m sec^{-1} [but see (137)]. The threshold for producing pain in the majority of human subjects by anterolateral quadrant stimulation was lower than 300 μA. On the basis of these studies, Price & Mayer argue that the wide dynamic range cells of lamina IV and V are sufficient, in primates, to produce the sensation of pain. A role for lamina I cells in pain sensation, although probable, is less definite at the present time (199).

MEDIAL BRAINSTEM SPINOPETAL SYSTEMS

Anatomy and Physiology

Since Sherrington (225) first demonstrated that there is a tonic inhibition of cutaneous reflexes in decerebrate animals, numerous studies have been directed at determining the brainstem source of this inhibition. Much of the work has focused on the region of the medial medullary reticular formation, stimulation of which strongly inhibits both monosynaptic reflexes and transmission from high threshold receptors (the flexor reflex afferents, FRAs). Since the topic has recently been reviewed (195), only a brief description of the major descending systems is here provided, with emphasis on new anatomical findings. The role of presynaptic inhibition of primary afferents by descending pathways has been extensively discussed (222) and is not considered here.

Three descending bulbospinal inhibitory systems originating in the region of the medial bulbar reticular formation have been described. One system arises from the relatively dorsal nucleus reticularis gigantocellularis (Rgc) and descends in the ventral half of the spinal cord. The other two descend in the spinal dorsolateral funiculus. One of the latter is the raphe-spinal system, a monoaminergic pathway originating in the raphe nuclei (66, 233); the other is the dorsoreticulospinal system, which originates in juxta-raphe regions of ventromedial medulla (84, 85, 119).

The initial description of reticulospinal connections was based largely on retrograde chromatolytic studies (241) and anterograde degeneration studies (179, 193) in the cat. These studies demonstrated only pathways originating in the medulla and pons, coursing in the ventral cord, and terminating almost exclusively in ventral horn, laminae VII and VIII. Studies in the opossum and the monkey reveal a similar organization (28, 138, 156, 157).

Autoradiographic studies of bulbospinal projections in the cat corroborate and extend the above results (18, 19). Small injections of tritiated leucine in the dorsal part of the medullary reticular formation (Rgc) result in heavy labeling of motor-related sites of the medulla, including cranial nerve nuclei V, VI, VII, XII, and the medial accessory olive. The spinal projection is via the ventral cord. Termination within the cord is concentrated in laminae VII and VIII ipsilateral, and in VIII contralateral to the injection site. There is no projection to the dorsal horn.

Although this ventral reticulospinal pathway can account for some of the tonic inhibitory effects exerted by the brainstem on the spinal cord in decerebrate cats (127, 155) there is also a tonic inhibition of transmission from FRAs that is abolished by dorsolateral funiculus (DLF) lesions (119). Furthermore, DLF lesions release spinal cutaneous reflexes in the cat (76) and the monkey (58). Pharmacological studies indicate that at least part of this inhibition involves descending monaminergic pathways (82, 83). Both 5HT blockade (215, 216) and 5HT mediation (60) of bulbospinal inhibition have been described, but the resulting controversy is not discussed here since the effects were on monosynaptic reflexes. Since the source of most spinal cord serotonin is the medullary raphe nuclei (49, 66), it is likely that raphe-spinal neurons mediate this inhibition. Dahlstrom & Fuxe (66) described monaminergic bulbospinal fibers that originate in the raphe nuclei of the medulla and course in the dorsolateral funiculus. Retrograde chromatolytic changes in the raphe nuclei of the cat after DLF lesions confirm this raphe-spinal pathway (36). Furthermore, retrograde transport of horseradish peroxidase from spinal cord to nucleus raphe magnus is blocked by bilateral lesions of the DLF (20).

In addition to this monaminergic raphe-spinal system, part of the DLF-mediated inhibition must originate in the ventromedial medulla adjacent to the raphe since it is not totally abolished by large lesions of nucleus raphe magnus (83). It was originally assumed that the dorsal reticulospinal (i.e. juxta-raphe) system is polysynaptic; however, in the cat a unilateral lesion of the DLF rostral to a horseradish peroxidase (HRP) injection site in spinal cord prevents retrograde labeling in the ventromedial reticular formation just lateral to the raphe (20). This juxta-raphe region is thus the origin of Lundberg's dorsal reticulospinal system. These HRP studies also indicate that the number of rostral medullary neurons projecting to the spinal cord in the DLF is much greater than via ventral spinal pathways.

Autoradiographic analysis has extended knowledge of the origin and termination of DLF axons (18, 19). Leucine injections placed ventral to Rgc in the juxta-raphe ventromedial reticular formation [magnocellular tegmental field, according to Berman (29)] produce a distinct projection pattern. In addition to a small ipsilateral ventrolateral funiculus pathway, many fibers course in the DLF, and distribute to the dorsal horn at all spinal segments, chiefly ipsilateral to the injection. The heaviest terminal fields are found in the marginal zone (lamina I), the substantia gelatinosa (lamina II), and more ventrally in laminae V, medial VI, and VII. There is a comparable projection to spinal trigeminal nucleus caudalis. This terminal field pattern shows a close correspondence to the location of spinal and trigeminal neurons known to respond to noxious stimuli.

Injections into nucleus raphe magnus produce the same trigeminal nucleus and dorsal horn terminal fields, confirming the preliminary indications of fluorescence-histochemical studies (66). The failure of a recent autoradiographic study of raphe projections to appreciate this distinction was no doubt due to the large injections used (32). Thus, the ventromedial medullary reticular formation and the nucleus raphe magnus have largely overlapping descending projections. Both have descending projections that are distinct from those of Rgc, which descend in ventral spinal cord. The differential physiological effects of dorsal versus ventral stimulation in the medial medullary reticular formation (84, 85, 127) are presumably related to the different terminal distribution of axons originating from these two regions.

These studies indicate that the classical ventral quadrant reticulospinal system, which terminates primarily in structures related to motor outflow, accounts for only a small part of the medial medullospinal projection. There are at least two major systems in the dorsolateral funiculus; one, serotonergic and arising in nucleus raphe magnus; and the other, non-aminergic, arising in the juxta-raphe magnocellular tegmental field. The spinal and trigeminal terminals of both pathways clearly correspond to the location of neurons identified with afferent transmission. Some of these neurons are concentrated in laminae I and V of the dorsal horn and contribute to pathways identified with pain transmission.

Control of Spinal Neurons

Ascending pathways are modulated by powerful brainstem inhibitory influences (50, 107). Taub (237) demonstrated that electrical stimulation of deep cerebellar nuclei and of a wide region of the brainstem reticular formation inhibits axons in the DLF. The axons were presumed but not proven to be in the spinocervical tract. Using reversible spinal block in decerebrate cats, Wall showed a tonic brainstem inhibition of dorsal horn neurons (252). Cells of several types are inhibited, including those concentrated in lamina V, which repond maximally, but not exclusively, to noxious stimuli. This observation has been confirmed (112, 118) and extended to the high-threshold dorsal horn neurons concentrated in laminae I and II (57). Furthermore, there is a relatively selective tonic brainstem inhibition of C-fiber inputs to dorsal horn neurons (112).

In decerebrate cats, identified spinocervical tract (SCT) neurons were studied before and after reversible spinal block. When the spinal cord is blocked, SCT neurons respond to a wider range of stimulus modalities and intensities and most have a higher rate of spontaneous activity (37). Input from unmyelinated fibers is markedly suppressed in the decerebrate state (40, 41). Systematic study of cervical cord indicates that stimulation of the dorsolateral funiculus is particularly effective in suppressing transmission from high-threshold receptors to SCT neurons (42). Descending inhibition of SCT neurons can also be activated by orthodromic conduction through the dorsal column nuclei (43). Thus, the brainstem modulates SCT neurons with high-threshold inputs through a DLF pathway.

Spinothalamic tract (STT) neuron responses to nociceptive stimuli are inhibited by electrical stimulation of cat medullary reticular formation (164) and primate nucleus raphe magnus (23, 255). Peripheral stimulation of trigeminal afferents also inhibits cat STT neurons (165). Spinoreticular neurons are inhibited by electrical stimulation of the medullary reticular formation (91) and by vestibular inputs (62).

It is clear that the brainstem modulates neurons with nociceptive inputs in the spinal dorsal horn, including some contributing to ascending pain-transmission pathways. However, there has been no systematic mapping of the effective brainstem sites. The midbrain periaqueductal gray (182), the dorsal raphe (105), and the nucleus raphe magnus (NRM) (18, 88, 255) all inhibit dorsal horn neurons responding to noxious stimulation. LSD reverses the inhibition from dorsal raphe (105). Neurons inhibited by NRM stimulation are located in laminae I and V, where the spinal terminals of NRM fibers are concentrated (18, 88). The NRM-induced inhibition is reversed by DLF lesions (18, 88, 255).

These anatomical and physiological data indicate that certain brainstem regions are part of a system that modulates spinal pain-transmission neurons. The brainstem outflow pathway originates in the ventromedial medulla and descends in the spinal dorsolateral funiculus.

A BRAINSTEM ANALGESIC SYSTEM

Stimulation-Produced Analgesia (158, 159)

Profound analgesia is produced without general behavioral depression by electrical stimulation in the midbrain periaqueductal gray, particularly its ventrolateral aspect (150, 163, 205), and in periventricular thalamic sites (206). Stimulation in the medial forebrain bundle and lateral hypothalamus also reduces behavioral responses to noxious stimuli (15, 64, 207, 263).

Less extensively studied (although not necessarily less effective) sites are the caudate nucleus in the monkey (152, 221) and in man (86, 106); the septum in the primate (221), in man (99) and in the rat (35), the internal capsule and ventrobasal thalamic nucleus in man (2, 87), dorsal columns in man (e.g. 172, 224), and the primate cerebellum (226).

Some caution is necessary in interpreting these diverse reports. In some cases, reflex responses have been examined, most commonly tail flick; in others, shock titration schedules have been used. More complex analyses have been employed, including subjective evaluation of pain. Further, different stimulus parameters can markedly change the analgesic action of brain stimulation. Mayer & Liebeskind (158) have stressed that failure in different laboratories to confirm "analgesic" sites often depends on the behavioral tests used. One cannot overemphasize the difficulties that attend the assessment of pain in animals. However, it is clear that electrical stimulation in midline periventricular sites, of midbrain, thalamus, and hypothalamus can produce profound analgesia in a variety of species including man.

Analgesia after electrical stimulation of NRM in the cat (183, 184) and the rat (180, 202) has been reported. This is discussed in more detail below.

The Anatomy of Opiate Analgesia

DISTRIBUTION OF OPIATE RECEPTOR AND ENDORPHINS   It has recently been established that there are opiate receptors in the vertebrate central nervous system (101, 190, 230). The presence of receptor has taken on even greater significance with the discovery of endogenous brain ligands for it (101, 121, 122, 134). Here we focus on the anatomical distribution and functional significance of opiate receptors and endogenous opiate compounds (endorphins).

Although the anatomical distribution of the opiate receptor varies in different species, there are many common locations. In most species the highest concentrations of opiate receptor are found in the striatum (186, 191, 229). In monkeys and humans, however, limbic structures contain the highest levels, with moderate levels in the striatum (117,135). All species studied have moderately high levels of receptor in the midbrain, especially the periaqueductal gray. Cortical levels are consistently low.

The distribution of endorphins is more difficult to summarize. This is due to the presence of multiple forms in the brain [e.g. leu- and met-enkephalin (101,122,231)] and to the possibility that some endorphins are blood-borne (192). Furthermore, β-endorphin, a fragment of the pituitary hormone β-lipotropin, is a potent analgesic and strongly binds to the opiate receptor (63,153). In fact, met-enkephalin is identical to part of the β-endorphin molecule (101). Nevertheless, there is considerable overlap in the distribution of enkephalin and the opiate receptor. For example, in rabbits (122), ungulates (186), rats (186), and monkeys (228), the highest levels of enkephalin are found in the striatum. Moderate levels are found in the midbrain PAG and low levels in the cerebral cortex (227).

Of particular interest are recent autoradiographic studies of the opiate receptor (14,191), and immunofluorescent studies of leu-enkephalin (80). High concentrations of both are found in laminae I, II, and V of the spinal dorsal horn, and in the analogous spinal trigeminal site, nucleus caudalis. Furthermore, both are found in nucleus solitarius and the dorsal motor nucleus of the vagus. As will be described in detail, the marginal layer and substantia gelatinosa of dorsal horn and nucleus caudalis, the nucleus solitarius, and the dorsal motor nucleus of the vagus all receive a dense projection from nucleus raphe magnus of the medulla.

EFFECTIVE SITES FOR ANALGESIA BY OPIATE INJECTION   Intracerebral opiate microinjections in monkeys (27, 189) and rats (26, 125, 126, 150, 223, 245) and intraventricular injections in rabbits (239, 245, 249) have been used to map effective sites for behavioral analgesia. The most consistently effective sites are in the midbrain periaqueductal gray (PAG) and diencephalic periventricular gray. Using labeled opiate agonists, and controlling CSF flow within the ventricles, Herz et al demonstrated that the gray matter adjacent to the caudal part of the aqueduct and the rostral fourth ventricle are very effective sites for analgesia (116). Intracerebral opiate microinjection into the ventroposterolateral (VPL) nucleus of the primate thalamus is also effective (189), though only low levels of receptor are found there (135). Moderate levels of opiate receptor, however, are present in the VPL nucleus of human thalamus (117).

Although there is a correspondence between the effective sites for opiate microinjection, stimulation-produced analgesia, and the distribution of opiate receptor and enkephalin, there are some discrepancies. Within the PAG the best sites for opiate microinjection do not precisely correspond to the most effective sites for stimulation-produced analgesia (150). Furthermore, opiate microinjection into rat striatum does not produce analgesia even though the region is rich in opiate receptor (192, 261).

Dey & Feldberg (72) have suggested that morphine acts in a quite unexpected place. In cats, they demonstrated a reduction in response to noxious tail pressure when 200 μg morphine is infused near the ventral surface of the medulla. This site is more efficacious than fourth ventricle or cisterna magna but less than third ventricle. They proposed that morphine acts directly on the serotonergic fibers descending to the spinal cord. Unfortunately, cats are rendered relatively immobile by these infusions so it is not possible to be sure the response-reduction actually reflects analgesia. Furthermore, since reversal of the analgesia by antagonist administration was not attempted, a nonspecific effect cannot be ruled out.

LESIONS THAT BLOCK OPIATE ACTION   Midbrain lesions including PAG and dorsal raphe have been reported to block the analgesic effect of systemic opiates (74, 94, 214, 258). Lesions of medullary raphe nuclei, especially nucleus raphe magnus (NRM), also antagonize opiate analgesia (202, 250, 258).

Spontaneous hyperalgesia follows midbrain central tegmental tract lesions in cats (130, 168) but not lesions restricted to the PAG (168). Most investigators report that lesions of the PAG, particularly its ventrolateral part, produce a reduction in escape responses to noxious stimulation (109, 151). This observation is difficult to reconcile with an active role for the PAG in analgesic mechanisms, especially since the ventrolateral PAG is the best site for opiate microinjection and stimulation-produced analgesia. However, in these studies the lesions have been large and it is possible that with small lesions effects on pain transmission may be separable from those on opiate analgesia.

IONTOPHORETIC STUDIES   The data from iontophoretic studies are complicated. Although excitatory and inhibitory effects of iontophoresed opiate have been demonstrated in a variety of CNS loci, including neurons in reticular formation (Rgc) (34, 95, 108, 174), caudate nucleus (93, 174), cortex (93, 174, 218, 265), and raphe magnus (96), only the inhibitory effects are naloxone-reversible. Two notable exceptions are spinal Renshaw cells (68, 69) and hippocampal neurons (174). Though most neurons in cat PAG are inhibited by iontophoresed morphine, some are excited (naloxone not tested) (93, 96); multiunit recordings indicate naloxone-reversible excitation of large numbers of PAG neurons by systemic morphine in the awake rat (247). A more systematic study of the response of single neurons in PAG to systemic and local opiate application is necessary.

Direct Spinal Action of Opiate Drugs

A major unresolved issue concerning the physiology of opiate action is the degree to which the analgesia resulting from systemically administered opiates depends on a direct spinal action.

There is a very dense concentration of both opiate receptor (14, 141, 191) and leu-enkephalin (80) in superficial layers of the spinal dorsal horn. In acutely spinalized animals, systemic opiates produce marked naloxone-reversible inhibitory effects, primarily upon nociceptive inputs to dorsal horn neurons (30, 123, 132, 144, 145, 147, 236, 264). A similar effect on ascending spinal axons has been reported (128). This morphine-induced inhibition is not seen in decerebrate cats, presumably because the powerful tonic brainstem inhibition of dorsal horn neurons masks the effect (145, 146).

Iontophoretic application of opiates at spinal cord levels has provided somewhat confusing and inconsistent information. Thus, morphine inhibits both spontaneous activity and glutamate-evoked excitation of dorsal horn neurons responding to noxious stimulation (48). In only 3/9 neurons, however, was the effect reversed by naloxone. In a later study, Dostrovsky & Pomeranz (75) showed that morphine blocks the excitatory effect of excitatory putative transmitters; however the *same* effect was produced by dextrorphan and naloxone, implying that this morphine action is not pharmacologically relevant to opiate analgesia. Duggan et al (77) showed naloxone-reversible inhibition of laminae IV and V neurons by iontophoresis of morphine and met-enkephalin. This inhibition is seen when opiate is iontophoresed into the substantia gelatinosa (a region rich in enkephalin and opiate receptor) but not when iontophoresed near the cell body of the recorded neuron. Zieglgansberger & Bayerl (264), with extracellular recording, found consistent inhibition of spontaneous and pinch-evoked responses of dorsal horn neurons by iontophoresed and systemic morphine. In 75% of the cells, this effect was blocked by naloxone, either systemically or iontophoretically applied. With intracellular recording, primarily from motor neurons, they found that morphine at high iontophoretic currents (80 nA) inhibits neurons but that this effect is not naloxone-reversible. At lower currents (20–80 nA), a naloxone-reversible slowing of EPSP rate of rise was consistently observed. Unfortunately, these results could not be confirmed using systemic administration of morphine because of marked changes in blood pressure.

These iontophoretic studies demonstrate receptor-specific actions of opiates directly on spinal cord neurons. However, the mechanism and site of opiate action at this level are uncertain. Since morphine appears to have the same effect on motor neurons as on putative pain-transmission neurons, the question of local tissue concentrations becomes important in trying to decide whether a particular pharmacological action of opiates is relevant to analgesia. It is possible that the direct effects seen on spinal neurons require tissue concentrations of opiates in excess of those produced by systemic doses adequate for analgesia.

Yaksh & Rudy (259) found that morphine directly infused into the lumbar subarachnoid space of the rat produces behavioral analgesia restricted to the hindlimbs. Although the dose required for this effect was small (10 µg) the local concentration of drug might still have been quite high at the site of action. In the rabbit, no analgesic action was observed when morphine was injected intrathecally in the lumbar subarachnoid space (245).

In thinking about the significance of direct spinal actions of opiates it is important to keep in mind that there are two separate issues: First, do systemically administered opiates produce analgesia by a direct action on the spinal cord? Second, at what sites and under what conditions is the endorphin-mediated pain-suppression system activated? The studies discussed in the preceding section deal mainly with the first question.

A full understanding of the endogenous analgesia system depends on elucidation of brainstem connections and physiology. Even if the direct spinal action of opiates is significant for analgesia, the distribution of opiate receptor, enkephalin, and sites sensitive to opiate microinjection discussed above argues for endogenous analgesic system that is activated in the brainstem. In fact, the hypothesis that systemically administered morphine produces analgesia by a direct action at brainstem, rather than spinal sites, receives strong support from the finding that brainstem microinjection of small quantities of opiate antagonist blocks the analgesia produced by systemic injection of opiates (125, 126, 245, 249). Evidence reviewed below indicates that systemic opiates produce analgesia by acting on an endogenous brainstem system which, under physiological conditions, is activated by endorphins.

THE NEURONAL MECHANISM OF OPIATE AND STIMULATION-PRODUCED ANALGESIA

Evidence that a Pathway to Spinal Cord is Required for Opiate and Stimulation-Produced Analgesia

The inhibitory effect of systemic morphine (4 mg kg^{-1}) on the splanchnic evoked potential in spinal cord ventrolateral funiculus of the cat is abolished by transection of the cervical cord (217). Furthermore, stimulation-produced analgesia from the rat midbrain periaqueductal gray (PAG) is blocked caudal to a lesion of the spinal dorsolateral funiculus (DLF) (18, 22). A lesion in the DLF also blocks the analgesia produced by systemic administration of morphine (18, 22) or by microinjection of opiates directly into midbrain sites (171). Since electrical stimulation or opiate microinjection into brainstem sites inhibits spinal (182, 209, 235) and trigeminal (209, 262) neurons with nociceptive inputs, it is likely that opiate and stimulation-produced analgesia depend on a descending pathway through which the brainstem inhibits pain-transmission neurons.

Although descending connections from the midbrain periaqueductal gray (PAG) and medial diencephalic sites rich in endorphin and opiate receptor appear to mediate stimulation-produced and opiate analgesia, there is no evidence for a direct anatomical connection from PAG to spinal cord (20, 56, 133, 139). Studies using retrograde transport of horseradish peroxidase injected into the spinal cord of rats, cats, and monkeys, demonstrate large numbers of spinal projecting neurons throughout the brainstem but none in PAG (20). A corollary of these observations is that there is minimal overlap between regions rich in opiate receptor and/or endorphins and those with large numbers of spinal projecting cells. A connection between the two is required.

Pharmacological studies relating serotonin to opiate and stimulation-produced analgesia indicate that the midbrain–spinal cord connection includes a serotonergic medullary relay (3, 4, 113, 238, 257). Vogt's study (250) of 5,6-dihydroxy-tryptamine is of interest in this regard. This compound depletes spinal cord 5HT levels by destroying brainstem 5HT neurons and concomitantly blocks morphine's analgesic action. Thus, the central analgesic system requires intact transmission at 5HT synapses. Since the medullary raphe nuclei (49, 66) are the source of most medullospinal 5HT axons, recent work has focused on the role of this brain region, particularly the nucleus raphe magnus (NRM), in analgesic mechanisms.

Evidence that NRM is Involved in Analgesic Mechanisms

Stimulation of NRM elicits powerful analgesia which is reversed by naloxone (180, 183, 184, 202), suggesting involvement of an opiate-like transmitter. The close correspondence of opiate receptor, enkephalin levels, and the terminals of NRM axons in dorsal horn laminae I and II is consistent with this proposal. Furthermore, lesions of NRM block the analgesic action of opiates (202). LeBars et al (146) reported that stimulation of NRM inhibits spinal neurons responding to noxious stimulation. We confirmed these findings for neurons in laminae I and V and demonstrated that the inhibition is blocked by dorsolateral funiculus (DLF) lesions (88). Furthermore, NRM stimulation inhibits primate STT neurons through a DLF pathway (255). The observation that iontophoresis of 5HT inhibits high-threshold lamina I cells (203) is also consistent with a role for NRM in control of pain-transmission cells. It is not known whether the 5HT-mediated inhibition is exerted by a direct action on high-threshold dorsal horn neurons or by enkephalin-containing interneurons in the substantia gelatinosa. Some studies suggest a presynaptic effect mediated by 5HT terminals of raphe-spinal neurons (201). Since approximately half of the spinal cord opiate receptor disappears after dorsal rhizotomy in monkeys (141), it is possible that endorphins act on primary afferents, dorsal horn neurons, or both. Although the precise neuronal mechanism of opiate and stimulation-produced analgesia has not been established, it is clear that the NRM projection to spinal cord is essential.

If opiate analgesia is mediated by a direct inhibitory NRM projection to spinal cord, it should be possible to demonstrate activation of NRM neurons by systemic administration of opiates. Naloxone-reversible increases in single (70) and multiunit (180) NRM activity by systemic administration of opiates has been described in the rat. In the cat a number of NRM neurons, including some that project to spinal cord, are excited by intravenous administration of morphine (11). However, only inhibitory effects have been demonstrated by direct iontophoresis of opiates onto NRM neurons (96).

Since neither opiate receptor nor endorphin-containing terminals have been found in NRM, and since direct opiate injection into NRM does not produce analgesia (235), it is unlikely that the excitatory effect of systemic opiates is produced by a direct action on NRM neurons. This is consistent with the observation that some spinal projecting NRM neurons are activated by microinjection of opiate directly into midbrain sites (11).

SUMMARY AND CONCLUSIONS

The evidence reviewed above establishes the existence of powerful and relatively specific brainstem control of spinal pain-transmission neurons. Nucleus raphe magnus (NRM), and perhaps the adjacent nucleus reticularis magnocellularis (RMC) form the major brainstem outflow of this control system by a pathway in the dorsolateral funiculus. NRM and RMC terminate primarily in laminae I, II, and V in proximity to neurons known to receive input from small-diameter, high-threshold primary afferents. There is an analogous termination in the spinal trigeminal nucleus caudalis. Naloxone-reversible activation of NRM neurons by systemic opiates has been demonstrated, and the raphe-spinal pathway has been shown to specifically inhibit neurons in laminae I and V with high-threshold inputs. Primate spinothalamic tract neurons with high-threshold inputs are also inhibited by this pathway. There is some evidence that serotonin mediates this inhibition but the mechanism has not been established.

As proposed by Mayer & Price (159), at least part of the analgesia produced by electrical or opiate-induced activation of neurons in the PAG is mediated by this raphe-spinal system. This hypothesis is supported by several lines of evidence. There are direct anatomical connections between the PAG region and NRM (208, 234). Activation of NRM neurons is produced by electrical stimulation of PAG or by systemic opiate administration (11, 180, 181). Furthermore, DLF lesions that interrupt the raphe-spinal pathway block the analgesia produced by systemic opiates, by opiates injected directly into PAG or by electrical stimulation in PAG. These data indicate that opiates given systemically produce analgesia by an initial direct action on midbrain PAG, which results in activation of medullary raphe-spinal neurons that inhibit spinal dorsal horn pain-transmission neurons.

This proposal may accurately describe the CNS response to exogenously administered opiates; however it is probably an incomplete description of the normal operation of the neural system that produces analgesia. Naloxone reverses stimulation-produced analgesia in patients with chronic pain (1, 120), but in experimental situations, naloxone is either ineffective (260), or only partially blocks analgesia produced by stimulation of PAG (5, 188). Naloxone is more effective in blocking the analgesia produced by NRM stimulation (183). Although not reported to be present in significant amounts in NRM, both opiate receptor and endorphin are concentrated near small-diameter primary afferent and raphe-spinal terminals in the superficial layer of dorsal horn. If PAG produced its analgesic effect entirely through activation of NRM, naloxone should block PAG-induced analgesia at least as effectively as it blocks NRM-induced analgesia. If indeed it does not, a significant part of the PAG-induced analgesia is not mediated by NRM. The observation that bilateral DLF lesions are quite effective in blocking stimulation-produced analgesia from PAG raises the possibility that RMC [a major source of DLF medullospinal fibers (19, 20)] is involved in PAG-induced analgesia but that its action is not mediated by endorphins. Thus there may be two pharmacologically distinct pathways capable of producing analgesia: One, via NRM, is mediated by enkephalin, and would be blocked by naloxone or serotonin antagonists. The other, via RMC, is not mediated by enkephalin and would be resistant to both naloxone and serotonin antagonists. If these two pathways are activated in parallel by PAG stimulation, then naloxone should only partially reverse the analgesia resulting from stimulation of PAG. Stimulation of either NRM or RMC would be expected to produce analgesia, but only the former should be naloxone-reversible.

At present, the precise neuronal mechanism of the inhibition by NRM of spinal dorsal horn neurons is unknown. Although iontophoresed 5HT inhibits lamina I neurons, this could be either a presynaptic or post-synaptic effect. Intracellular recording will be necessary to resolve this question. Other problems to be resolved are the nature of the opiate effect on PAG neurons; details of the PAG to NRM connection; and the properties of other inputs to PAG, NRM, and RMC neurons.

The most intriguing questions, however, relate to the function and normal physiology of this control system. What activates it? What is its behavioral significance?

One approach to this problem is to study receptive-field properties of the component neurons of the modulatory system. Both NRM and PAG receive input from the medullary reticular formation (17, 61, 78, 79, 173), which receives convergent input from all modalities, especially somatosensory and auditory (2, 52, 219). Raphe neurons (including those in NRM) are sensitive to cutaneous temperature (170). Many raphe neurons, including some in NRM that are antidromically driven from cervical cord (i.e. raphe-spinal neurons), have large bilateral receptive fields and are maximally activated by noxious mechanical and thermal stimulation (10, 11, 170).

Although these studies have been carried out in decerebrate or anesthetized animals, they predict that somatosensory stimuli, especially of a thermal or noxious quality, delivered to one part of the body might produce analgesia in the same or other regions by activating this endogenous analgesia system. This mechanism has been proposed to underly ancient counterirritant measures involving thermal or noxious stimuli, such as acupuncture, moxibustion, and local heat (159, 166). It follows that narcotic-antagonists such as naloxone, by blocking endorphins, should at least partially reverse the analgesic action of such manipulations. In fact, naloxone has been reported to reverse acupuncture analgesia (162).

The behavioral effects of opiate-antagonists indicate that there is a tonic release of endorphin in awake, freely moving animals. Naloxone has been demonstrated to enhance spinal reflexes (100), and to shorten tail-flick (25) and hot-plate (124) response latency in the absence of any exogenous opiate treatment. Furthermore, in humans naloxone is consistently worse than placebo for postoperative pain (142). On the other hand, Goldstein and colleagues (102) found no effect of naloxone on shock-escape threshold, and naloxone alone has not been shown to affect pain threshold in normal human subjects (81, 162).

This controversy over whether opiate-antagonists produce effects in the absence of administered opiates is hampered by the lack of an adequate behavioral paradigm for pain. Thus, periventricular-gray stimulation can produce complete pain relief in patients with chronic illness but the relief is not associated with a consistent elevation of pain threshold (120). Furthermore, analgesic doses of morphine in man have little effect on pain threshold (24). These findings suggest that standard tests of pain threshold are not sensitive to the action of the endogenous analgesia system. A better understanding of the function of this endogenous analgesia system will depend on the development of new techniques for quantitative evaluation of both the sensory-discriminative and the affective-motivational aspects of pain.

ACKNOWLEDGMENTS

The authors would like to thank Edwina Latimer for editorial assistance. This work was supported by N.I.H. grants NS70777, NS11529, and NS05272.

Literature Cited

1. Adams, J. E. 1976. Naloxone reversal of analgesia produced by brain stimulation in the human. *Pain* 2:161–66
2. Adams, J. E., Hosobuchi, Y., Fields, H. L. 1974. Stimulation of internal capsule for relief of chronic pain. *J. Neurosurg.* 41:740–44
3. Akil, H., Liebeskind, J. C. 1975. Monoaminergic mechanisms of stimulation-produced analgesia. *Brain Res.* 94:279–96
4. Akil, H., Mayer, D. J. 1972. Antagonism of stimulation-produced analgesia by p-CPA, a serotonin synthesis inhibitor. *Brain Res.* 44:692–97
5. Akil, H., Mayer, D. J., Liebeskind, J. C. 1976. Antagonism of stimulation-produced analgesia by naloxone, a narcotic antagonist. *Science* 191:961–62
6. Albe-Fessard, D., Boivie, J., Grant, G., Levante, A. 1975. Labelling of cells in the medulla oblongata and the spinal cord of the monkey after injections of horseradish peroxidase in the thalamus. *Neurosci. Lett.* 1:75–80
7. Albe-Fessard, D., Levante, A., Lamour, Y. 1974. Origin of spinothalamic and spinoreticular pathways in cats and monkeys. In *Advances in Neurology,* ed. J. J. Bonica, 4:147–170. New York: Raven Press. 850 pp.
8. Albe-Fessard, D., Levante, A., Lamour, Y. 1974. Origin of spinothalamic tract in monkeys. *Brain Res.* 65:503–9
9. Anderson, R. V., Pearl, G. S. 1975. Long term increases in nociceptive thresholds following lesions in feline nucleus reticularis gigantocellularis. *Abstr. 1st World Congr. Pain:*70
10. Anderson, S. D., Basbaum, A. I., Fields, H. L. 1977. Response of medullary raphe neurons to peripheral stimulation and to systemic opiates. *Brain Res.* 123:363–68
11. Anderson, S. D., Fields, H. L. 1977. Raphe-spinal neurons: responses to systemic and intracerebral opiates. *Neurosci. Abstr.* 3:In press
12. Angaut-Petit, D. 1975. The dorsal column system: I. Existence of long ascending postsynaptic fibers in the cat's fasciculus gracilis. *Exp. Brain Res.* 22:457–70
13. Angaut-Petit, D. 1975. The dorsal column system: II. Functional properties and bulbar relay of the postsynaptic fibers of the cat's fasciculus gracilis. *Exp. Brain Res.* 22:471–94
14. Atweh, S. F., Kuhar, M. J. 1977 Autoradiographic localization of opiate receptors in rat brain. I. Spinal cord and lower medulla. *Brain Res.* 124:53–67
15. Balagura, S., Ralph, T. 1973. The analgesic effect of electrical stimulation of the diencephalon and mesencephalon. *Brain Res.* 60:369–79
16. Basbaum, A. I. 1973. Conduction of the effects of noxious stimulation by short fiber multisynaptic systems on the spinal cord of the rat. *Exp. Neurol.* 40:699–716
17. Basbaum, A. I., Clanton, C. H., Fields, H. L. 1976. Ascending projections of nucleus raphe magnus in the cat. An autoradiographic study. *Anat. Rec.* 184:354
18. Basbaum, A. I., Clanton, C. H., Fields, H. L. 1976. Opiate and stimulus-produced analgesia: functional anatomy of a medullospinal pathway. *Proc. Natl. Acad. Sci. USA* 73:4685–88
19. Basbaum, A. I., Clanton, C. H., Fields, H. L. 1977. Three bulbospinal pathways from the rostral medulla of the cat. An autoradiographic study. *J. Comp. Neurol.* In press
20. Basbaum, A. I., Fields, H. L. 1977. The dorsolateral funiculus of the spinal cord: a major route for descending brainstem control. *Neurosci. Abstr.* 3:In press
21. Basbaum, A. I., Giesler, G. J., Menetrey, D. 1977. Medullothalamic projections in the rat. *Anat. Rec.* 187:531
22. Basbaum, A. I., Marley, N. J. E., O'Keefe, J., Clanton, C. H. 1977. Reversal of morphine and stimulus-produced analgesia by subtotal spinal cord lesions. *Pain* 3:43–56
23. Beall, J. E., Martin, R. F., Applebaum, A. E., Willis, W. D. 1976. Inhibition of primate spinothalamic tract neurons by stimulation in the region of the nucleus raphe magnus. *Brain Res.* 114:328–33
24. Beecher, H. K. 1959. *Measurement of Subjective Responses: Quantitative Effects of Drugs.* New York: Oxford. 494 pp.
25. Bell, C., Sierra, G., Buendia, N., Segundo, J. P. 1964. Sensory properties of neurons in the mesencephalic reticular formation. *J. Neurophysiol.* 27:961–87
26. Belluzzi, J. D., Grant, N., Garsky, V., Sarantakis, D., Wise, C. D., Stein, L. 1976. Analgesia induced *in vivo* by central administration of enkephalin in rat. *Nature* 260:625–26
27. Bennett, C. T., Hulsebus, R. C., Bevan, T. E. 1976. Signal-detection analysis of changes in nociception in the monkey following opiate administration to spe-

cific brain areas. *Neurosci. Abstr.* 2:565
28. Beran, R. L., Martin, G. F. 1971. Reticulospinal fibers of the opossum, *Didelphis virginiana. J. Comp. Neurol.* 141:453–66
29. Berman, A. L. 1968. *The Brain Stem of the Cat.* Madison: University of Wisconsin. 175 pp.
30. Besson, J. M., Wyon-Maillard, M. C., Benoist, J. M., Conseiller, C., Hamann, K. F. 1973. Effects of phenoperidine on lamina V cells in the cat dorsal horn. *J. Pharmacol. Exp. Ther.* 187:239–45
31. Bessou, P., Perl, E. R. 1969. Response of cutaneous sensory units with unmyelinated fibers to noxious stimulation. *J. Neurophysiol.* 32:1025–43
32. Bobillier, P., Seguin, S., Petitjean, F., Salvert, D., Touret, M., Jouvet, M. 1976. The raphe nuclei of the cat brain stem: a topographical atlas of their efferent projections as revealed by autoradiography. *Brain Res.* 113:449–86
33. Bowsher, D. 1976. The role of the reticular formation in responses to noxious stimulation. *Pain* 2:361–78
34. Bradley, P. B., Briggs, I., Gayton, R. J., Lambert, L. A. 1976. Effects of microiontophoretically applied methionine-enkephalin on single neurons in rat brainstem. *Nature* 261:425–26
35. Breglio, V., Anderson, D. C., Merrill, H. K. 1970. Alteration in foot-shock threshold by low-level septal brain stimulation. *Physiol. Behav.* 5:715–20
36. Brodal, A., Taber, E., Walberg, F. 1960. The raphe nuclei of the brainstem in the cat. II. Efferent connections. *J. Comp. Neurol.* 114:239–60
37. Brown, A. G. 1971. Effects of descending impulses on transmission through the spinocervical tract. *J. Physiol.* 219:103–25
38. Brown, A. G., Franz, D. N. 1969. Responses of spinocervical tract neurones to natural stimulation of identified cutaneous receptors. *Exp. Brain Res.* 7:231–49
39. Brown, A. G., Franz, D. N. 1970. Patterns of response in spinocervical tract neurones to different stimuli of long duration. *Brain Res.* 17:156–60
40. Brown, A. G., Hamann, W. C., Martin, H. F. III. 1973. Descending influences on spinocervical tract cell discharges evoked by non-myelinated cutaneous afferent nerve fibres. *Brain Res.* 53:218–21
41. Brown, A. G., Hamann, W. C., Martin, H. F. III. 1975. Effects of activity in non-myelinated afferent fibres on the spinocervical tract. *Brain Res.* 98:243–49
42. Brown, A. G., Kirk, E. J., Martin, H. F. III 1973. Descending and segmental inhibition of transmission through the spinocervical tract. *J. Physiol.* 230:689–705
43. Brown, A. G., Martin, H. F. III 1973. Activation of descending control of the spinocervical tract by impulses ascending the dorsal columns and relaying through the dorsal column nuclei. *J. Physiol.* 235:535–50
44. Brown, P. B., Fuchs, J. L., Tapper, D. N. 1975. Parametric studies of dorsal horn neurons responding to tactile stimulation. *J. Neurophysiol.* 38:19–25
45. Bryan, R. N., Coulter, J. D., Willis, W. D. 1974. Cells of origin of the spinocervical tract in the monkey. *Exp. Neurol.* 42:574–86
46. Bryan, R. N., Trevino, D. L., Coulter, J. D., Willis, W. D. 1973. Location and somatotopic organization of the cells of origin of the spinocervical tract. *Exp. Brain Res.* 17:177–89
47. Burgess, P. R., Perl, E. R. 1967. Myelinated afferents responding specifically to noxious stimulation of the skin. *J. Physiol. London* 190:541–62
48. Calvillo, O., Henry, J. L., Neuman, R. S. 1974. Effects of morphine and naloxone on dorsal horn neurones in the cat. *Can. J. Physiol. Pharmacol.* 52:1207–11
49. Carlsson, A., Falck, B., Fuxe, K., Hillarp, N. -A. 1964. Cellular localization of monoamines in the spinal cord. *Acta Physiol. Scand.* 60:112–19
50. Carpenter, D., Engberg, I., Lundberg, A. 1965. Differential supraspinal control of inhibitory and excitatory actions from the FRA to ascending spinal pathways. *Acta. Physiol. Scand.* 63:103–10
51. Carstens, E., Trevino, D. L. 1976. A projection from upper cervical spinal cord to ipsilateral thalamus in cat and monkey: a new somatosensory relay from the body? *Neurosci. Abstr.* 2:971
52. Casey, K. L. 1969. Somatic stimuli, spinal pathways, and size of cutaneous fibers influencing unit activity in the medial medullary reticular formation. *Exp. Neurol.* 25:35–56
53. Casey, K. L. 1971. Responses of bulboreticular units to somatic stimuli eliciting escape behavior in the cat. *Int. J. Neurosci.* 2:15–28
54. Casey, K. L. 1971. Escape elicited by bulboreticular stimulation in the cat. *Int. J. Neurosci.* 2:29–34
55. Cassinari, V., Pagni, C. A. 1969. *Cen-*

tral Pain. Cambridge: Harvard Univ. Press. 192 pp.

56. Castiglioni, A. J., Gallaway, M. C., Coulter, J. D. 1977. Origins of brainstem connections to spinal cord in monkey. *Anat. Rec.* 187:547

57. Cervero, F., Iggo, A., Ogawa, H. 1976. Nociceptor-driven dorsal horn neurones in the lumbar spinal cord of the cat. *Pain* 2:5–24

58. Chambers, W. W., Liu, C. N., McCouch, G. P. 1970. Cutaneous reflexes and pathways affecting them in the monkey. *Exp. Neurol.* 28:243–56

59. Christensen, B. R., Perl, E. R. 1970. Spinal neurons specifically excited by noxious or thermal stimuli. *J. Neurophysiol.* 33:293–307

60. Clineschmidt, B. V., Anderson, E. G. 1970. The blockade of bulbospinal inhibition by 5-Hydroxytryptamine antagonists. *Exp. Brain Res.* 11:175–86

61. Couch, J. R. 1976. Further evidence for a possible excitatory serotoninergic synapse on raphe neurons of pons and lower midbrain. *Life Sci.* 19:761–68

62. Coulter, J. D., Mergner, T., Pompeiano, O. 1974. Macular influences on ascending spinoreticular neurons located in the cervical cord. *Brain Res.* 82:322–27

63. Cox, B. M., Goldstein, A., Li, C. H. 1976. Opioid activity of a peptide, β-lipotropin-(61–91), derived from β-lipotropin. *Proc. Natl. Acad. Sci. USA* 73:1821–23

64. Cox, V. C., Valenstein, E. S. 1965. Attenuation of aversive properties of peripheral shock by hypothalamic stimulation. *Science* 149:323–25

65. Craig, A. D. 1976. Spinocervical tract cells in cat and dog labeled by the retrograde transport of horseradish peroxidase. *Neurosci. Lett.* 3:173–78

66. Dahlstrom, A., Fuxe, K. 1965. Evidence for the existence of monoamine neurons in the central nervous system. *Acta. Physiol. Scand.* 64(Suppl. 247):1–30

67. Dart, A. M., Gordon, G. 1973. Some properties of spinal connections of the cat's dorsal column nuclei which do not involve the dorsal columns. *Brain Res.* 58:61–68

68. Davies, J. 1976. Effects of morphine and naloxone on Renshaw cells and spinal interneurones in morphine dependent and non-dependent rats. *Brain Res.* 113:311–26

69. Davies, J., Dray, A. 1976. Effects of enkephalin and morphine on Renshaw cells in feline spinal cord. *Nature* 262:603–4

70. Deakin, J. F. W., Dickenson, A. H., Dostrovsky, J. O. 1977. Morphine effects on rat raphe magnus neurones. *J. Physiol.* 267:46–47P

71. Deutsch, J. A. 1964. Behavioral measurement of the neural refractory period and its application to self-stimulation. *J. Comp. Physiol. Psychol.* 58:1–9

72. Dey, P. K., Feldberg, W. 1976. Analgesia produced by morphine when acting from the liquor space. *Br. J. Pharmacol.* 58:383–93

73. Dilly, P. N., Wall, P. D., Webster, K. E. 1968. Cells of origin of the spinothalamic tract in the cat and rat. *Exp. Neurol.* 21:550–62

74. Dostrovsky, J. O., Deakin, J. F. W. 1977. Periaqueductal gray lesions reduce morphine analgesia in the rat. *Neurosc. Lett.* 4:99–103

75. Dostrovsky, J. O., Pomeranz, B. 1976. Interaction of iontophoretically applied morphine with responses of interneurons in cat spinal cord. *Exp. Neurol.* 52:325–38

76. Dougherty, M., Shea, S., Liu, C. N., Chambers, W. W. 1970. Effects of spinal cord lesions on cutaneously elicited reflexes in the decerebrate cat. Tonic bulbospinal and spinobulbar inhibitory systems. *Exp. Neurol.* 26:551–70

77. Duggan, A. W., Hall, J. G., Headley, P. M. 1976. Morphine, enkephalin and the substantia gelatinosa. *Nature* 264:456–58

78. Edwards, S. B. 1975. Autoradiographic studies of the projections of the midbrain reticular formation: descending projections of nucleus cuneiformis. *J. Comp. Neurol.* 161:341–58

79. Edwards, S. B., de Olmos, J. S. 1976. Autoradiographic studies of the projections of the midbrain reticular formation: ascending projections of nucleus cuneiformis. *J. Comp. Neurol.* 165:417–32

80. Elde, R., Hokfelt, T., Johansson, O., Terenius, L. 1976. Immunohistochemical studies using antibodies to leu-enkephalin: initial observations on the nervous system of the rat. *Neuroscience* 1:349–51

81. El-Sobky, A., Dostrovsky, J. O., Wall, P. D. 1976. Lack of effect of naloxone on pain perception in humans. *Nature* 263:783–84

82. Engberg, I., Lundberg, A., Ryall, R. W. 1968. The effect of reserpine on transmission in the spinal cord. *Acta. Physiol. Scand.* 72:115–22

83. Engberg, I., Lundberg, A., Ryall, R. W. 1968. Is the tonic decerebrate inhibition

of reflex paths mediated by monoaminergic pathways? *Acta Physiol. Scand.* 72:123–33

84. Engberg, I., Lundberg, A., Ryall, R. W. 1968. Reticulospinal inhibition of transmission in reflex pathways. *J. Physiol.* 194:201–23

85. Engberg, I., Lundberg, A., Ryall, R. W. 1968. Reticulospinal inhibition of interneurones. *J. Physiol.* 194:225–36

86. Ervin, F. R., Brown, C. E., Mark, V. H. 1966. Striatal influence on facial pain. *Confin. Neurol.* 27:75–90

87. Fields, H. L., Adams, J. E. 1974. Pain after cortical injury relieved by electrical stimulation of the internal capsule. *Brain* 97:169–78

88. Fields, H. L., Basbaum, A. I., Clanton, C. H., Anderson, S. D. 1977. Nucleus raphe magnus inhibition of spinal cord dorsal horn neurons. *Brain Res.* 126: 441–53

89. Fields, H. L., Clanton, C. M., Anderson, S. D. 1977. Somatosensory properties of spinoreticular neurons in the cat. *Brain Res.* 120:49–66

90. Fields, H. L., Partridge, L. D. Jr., Winter, D. L. 1970. Somatic and visceral receptive field properties of fibers in ventral quadrant white matter of the cat spinal cord. *J. Neurophysiol.* 33:827–37

91. Fields, H. L., Wagner, G. M., Anderson, S. D. 1975. Some properties of spinal neurons projecting to the medial brain stem reticular formation. *Exp. Neurol.* 47:118–34

92. Foreman, R. D., Beall, J. E., Applebaum, A. E., Coulter, J. D., Willis, W. D. 1976. Effects of dorsal column stimulation on primate spinothalamic tract neurons. *J. Neurophysiol.* 39: 534–46

93. Frederickson, R. C. A., Norris, F. H. 1976. Enkephalin-induced depression of single neurons in brain areas with opiate receptors—antagonism by naloxone. *Science* 194:440–42

94. Garau, L., Mulas, M. L., Pepeu, G. 1975. The influence of raphe lesions on the effect of morphine on nociception and cortical Ach output. *Neuropharmacology* 14:259–63

95. Gent, J. P., Wolstencroft, J. H. 1976. Effects of methionine-enkephalin and leucine-enkephalin compared with those of morphine on brain stem neurones in cat. *Nature* 261:426–27

96. Gent, J. P., Wolstencroft, J. H. 1976. In *Opiates and Endogenous Opioid Peptides,* ed. H. W. Kosterlitz, 217–224. Amsterdam: North Holland. 456 pp.

97. Giesler, G. J., Basbaum, A. I., Menetrey, D. 1977. Projections and origins spinothalamic tract in the rat: an HRP study. *Neurosci. Abstr.* 3:In press

98. Giesler, G. J., Menetrey, D., Guilbaud, G., Besson, J. M. 1976. Lumbar cord neurons at the origin of the spinothalamic tract in the rat. *Brain Res.* 118:320–24

99. Gol, A. 1967. Relief of pain by electrical stimulation of the septal area. *J. Neurol. Sci.* 5:115–20

100. Goldfarb, J., Hu, J. W. 1976. Enhancement of reflexes by naloxone in spinal cats. *Neuropharmacology* 15:785–92

101. Goldstein, A. 1976. Opioid peptides (endorphins) in pituitary and brain. *Science* 193:1081–86

102. Goldstein, A., Pryor, G. T., Otis, L. S., Larsen, F. 1976. On the role of endogenous opioid peptides: failure of naloxone to influence shock escape threshold in the rat. *Life Sci.* 18:599–604

103. Graf, C. J. 1960. Consideration in loss of sensory level after bilateral cervical cordotomy. *Arch. Neurol.* 3:410–15

104. Gregor, M., Zimmermann, M. 1972. Characteristics of spinal neurones responding to cutaneous myelinated and unmyelinated fibres. *J. Physiol.* 221: 555–76

105. Guilbaud, G., Besson, J. M., Oliveras, J. L., Liebeskind, J. C. 1973. Suppression by LSD of the inhibitory effect exerted by dorsal raphe stimulation on certain spinal cord interneurons in the cat. *Brain Res.* 61:417–22

106. Gybels, J., Cosyns, P. 1976. In *Sensory Functions of the Skin,* ed. Y. Zotterman, pp. 531–48. Oxford:Pergamon. 607 pp.

107. Hagbarth, K. E., Kerr, D. I. B. 1954. Central influences on spinal afferent conduction. *J. Neurophysiol.* 17:295–307

108. Haigler, H. J. 1976. Morphine: ability to block neuronal activity evoked by a nociceptive stimulus. *Life Sci.* 19: 841–58

109. Halpern, M. 1968. Effects of midbrain central gray matter lesions on escape-avoidance behavior in rats. *Physiol. Behav.* 3:171–78

110. Hancock, M. B., Foreman, R. D., Willis, W. D. 1975. Convergence of visceral and cutaneous input onto spinothalamic tract cells in the thoracic spinal cord of the cat. *Exp. Neurol.* 47: 240–48

111. Hancock, M. B., Rigamonti, D. D., Bryan, R. N. 1973. Convergence in the lumbar spinal cord of pathways ac-

tivated by splanchnic nerve and hind-limb cutaneous nerve stimulation. *Exp. Neurol.* 38:337–48

112. Handwerker, H. O., Iggo, A., Zimmermann, M. 1975. Segmental and supraspinal actions on dorsal horn neurons responding to noxious and non-noxious skin stimuli. *Pain* 1:147–65

113. Hayes, R. L., Newlon, P. G., Rosecrans, J. A., Mayer, D. J. 1977. Reduction of stimulation-produced analgesia by lysergic acid diethylamide, a depressor of serotonergic neural activity. *Brain Res.* 122:367–72

114. Heavner, J. E., DeJong, R. H. 1973. Spinal cord neuron response to natural stimuli. A microelectrode study. *Exp. Neurol.* 39:293–306

115. Hellon, R. F., Misra, N. K. 1973. Neurones in the dorsal horn responding to scrotal skin temperature changes. *J. Physiol. London* 232:375–88

116. Herz, A., Albus, K., Metys, J., Schubert, P., Teschemacher, H. 1970. On the central sites for the antinociceptive action of morphine and fentanyl. *Neuropharmacology* 9:539–51

117. Hiller, J. M., Pearson, J., Simon, E. J. 1973. Distribution of stereospecific binding of the potent narcotic analgesic etorphine in the human brain: predominance in the limbic system. *Res. Commun. Chem. Pathol. Pharmacol.* 6:1052–62

118. Hillman, P., Wall, P. D. 1969. Inhibitory and excitatory factors influencing the receptive fields of lamina 5 spinal cord cells. *Exp. Brain Res.* 9:284–306

119. Holmqvist, B., Lundberg, A. 1959. On the organization of the supraspinal inhibitory control of interneurones of various spinal reflex arcs. *Arch. Ital. Biol.* 97:340–56

120. Hosobuchi, Y., Adams, J. E., Linchitz, R. 1977. Pain relief by electrical stimulation of the central gray matter in humans and its reversal by naloxone. *Science* 197:183–86

121. Hughes, J. 1975. Isolation of an endogenous compound from the brain with pharmacological properties similar to morphine. *Brain Res.* 88:295–308

122. Hughes, J., Smith, T. W., Kosterlitz, H. W., Fothergill, L. A., Morgan, B. A., Morris, H. R. 1975. Identification of two related pentapeptides from the brain with potent opiate agonist activity. *Nature* 258:577–79

123. Iwata, N., Sakai, Y. 1971. Effects of fentanyl upon the spinal interneurons activated by A_δ afferent fibers of the cu-taneous nerve of the cat. *Jpn. J. Pharmacol.* 21:413–16

124. Jacob, J. J., Tremblay, E. C., Colombel, M. C. 1974. *Psychopharmacologia* 37:217–23

125. Jacquet, Y. F., Lajtha, A. 1974. Paradoxical effects after microinjection of morphine in the periaqueductal gray matter in the rat. *Science* 185:1055–57

126. Jacquet, Y. F., Lajtha, A. 1976. The periaqueductal gray: site of morphine analgesia and tolerance as shown by 2-way cross tolerance between systemic and intracerebral injections. *Brain Res.* 103:501–13

127. Jankowska, E., Lund, S., Lundberg, A., Pompeiano, O. 1968. Inhibitory effects evoked through ventral reticulospinal pathways. *Arch. Ital. Biol.* 106:124–40

128. Jurna, I., Grossmann, W. 1976. The effect of morphine on the activity evoked in ventrolateral tract axons of the cat spinal cord. *Exp. Brain Res.* 24:473–84

129. Karplus, J. P., Kreidl, A. 1914. Ein Beitrag zur Kenntnis der Schmerzleitung in Ruckenmark. *Pfluegers Arch.* 158:275–87

130. Kelly, D. D., Glusman, M. 1968. Aversive thresholds following midbrain lesions. *J. Comp. Physiol. Psychol.* 66:25–34

131. Kennard, M. A. 1954. The course of ascending fibers in the spinal cord of the cat essential to the recognition of painful stimuli. *J. Comp. Neurol.* 100:511–24

132. Kitahata, L. M., Kosaka, Y., Taub, A., Bonikos, K., Hoffert, M. 1974. Lamina specific suppression of dorsal horn unit activity by morphine sulfate. *Anesthesiology* 41:39–48

133. Kneisley, L. W., Biber, M. P., Lavail, J. H. 1976. Brainstem projections to the spinal cord using retrograde transport of horseradish peroxidase in rhesus monkey. *Neurology* 26:350

134. Kosterlitz, H. W., ed. 1977. *Opiates and Endogenous Opioid Peptides.* Amsterdam: North-Holland. 456 pp.

135. Kuhar, M. J., Pert, C. B., Snyder, S. H. 1973. Regional distribution of opiate receptor binding in monkey and human brain. *Nature* 245:447–50

136. Kumazawa, T., Perl, E. R. 1976. In *Sensory Functions of the Skin,* ed. Y. Zotterman, 67–89. Oxford: Pergamon. 607 pp.

137. Kumazawa, T., Perl, E. R., Burgess, P. R., Whitehorn, D. 1975. Ascending projections from marginal zone (lamina

1) neurons of the spinal dorsal horn. *J. Comp. Neurol.* 162:1–11

138. Kuypers, H. G. J. M., Fleming, W. R., Farinholt, J. W. 1962. Subcortical projections in the rhesus monkey. *J. Comp. Neurol.* 118:107–37

139. Kuypers, H. G. J. M., Maisky, V. A. 1975. Retrograde axonal transport of horseradish peroxidase from spinal cord to brain stem cell groups in the cat. *Neurosci. Lett.* 1:9–14

140. LaMotte, C. 1977. Distribution of the tract of Lissaver and the dorsal root fibers in the primate cord. *J. Comp. Neurol.* 172:529–61

141. LaMotte, C., Pert, C. B., Snyder, S. H. 1976. Opiate receptor binding in primate spinal cord: distribution and changes after dorsal root section. *Brain Res.* 112:407–12

142. Lasagna, L. 1965. Drug interaction in the field of analgesic drugs. *Proc. Soc. Exp. Biol. Med.* 58:978–983.

143. Lavail, J. H., Winston, R. R., Tish, A. 1973. A method based on retrograde axonal transport of protein for identification of cell bodies of origin of axons terminating within the CNS. *Brain Res.* 58:470–77

144. LeBars, D., Guilbaud, G., Jurna, I., Besson, J. M. 1976. Differential effects of morphine on responses of dorsal horn lamina V type cells elicited by A and C fibre stimulation in the spinal cat. *Brain Res.* 115:518–24

145. LeBars, D., Menetrey, D., Besson, J. M. 1976. Effects of morphine upon the lamina V type cell activity in the dorsal horn of the decerebrate cat. *Brain Res.* 113:293–310

146. LeBars, D., Menetrey, D., Conseiller, C., Besson, J. M. 1974. Comparaison, chez le chat spinal et le chat decerebre, des effets de la morphine sur les activites des interneurones de type V de la corne dorsale de la moelle. *C. R. H. Acad. Sci.* 279:1369–71

147. LeBars, D., Menetrey, D., Conseiller, C., Besson, J. M. 1975. Depressive effects of morphine upon lamina V cell activities in the dorsal horn of the spinal cat. *Brain Res.* 98:261–77

148. Leontovitch, T. D., Zhukova, G. P. 1963. The specificity of the neuronal structure and topography of the reticular formation in the brain and spinal cord of carnivora. *J. Comp. Neurol.* 121:347–80

149. Levante, A., Albe-Fessard, D. 1972. Localization dans les couches VII et VIII de Rexed des cellules d'origine d'un fosceau spino-reticulaire croise. *C. R. Acad. Sci. Paris* 274:3007–10

150. Lewis, V. A., Gebhart, G. F. 1977. Evaluation of the periaqueductal central gray (PAG) as a morphine-specific locus of action and examination of morphine-induced and stimulation-produced analgesia at coincident PAG loci. *Brain Res.* 124:283–303

151. Liebman, J. M., Mayer, D. J., Liebeskind, J. C. 1970. Mesencephalic central gray lesions and fear-motivated behavior in rats. *Brain Res.* 23:353–70

152. Lineberry, C. G., Vierck, C. J. 1975. Attenuation of pain reactivity by caudate nucleus stimulation in monkeys. *Brain Res.* 98:110–34

153. Loh, H. H., Tseng, L. F., Wei, E., Li, C. H. 1976. β-Endorphin is a potent analgesic agent. *Proc. Natl. Acad. Sci. USA* 73:2895–98

154. Lynn, B. 1975. Somatosensory receptors and their CNS connections. *Ann. Rev. Physiol.* 37:105–127

155. Magoun, H. W., Rhines, R. 1946. An inhibitory mechanism in the bulbar reticular formation. *J. Neurophysiol.* 9:165–71

156. Martin, G. F., Beattie, M. S., Bresnahan, J. C., Henkel, C. K. 1975. Cortical and brain stem projections to the spinal cord of the American opossum (Didelphis marsupialis virginiana). *Brain Behav. Evol.* 12:270–310

157. Martin, G. F., Dom, R. 1971. Reticulospinal fibers of the opossum, Didelphis virginiana II. Course, caudal extent, and distribution. *J. Comp. Neurol.* 141:467–84

158. Mayer, D. J., Liebeskind, J. C. 1974. Pain reduction by focal electrical stimulation of the brain: an anatomical and behavioral analysis. *Brain Res.* 68:73–93

159. Mayer, D. J., Price, D. D. 1976. Central nervous system mechanisms of analgesia. *Pain* 2:379–404

160. Mayer, D. J., Price, D. D., Becker, D. P., Young, H. F. 1975. Threshold for pain from anterolateral quadrant stimulation as a predictor of success of percutaneous cordotomy for relief of pain. *J. Neurosurg.* 43:445–47

161. Mayer, D. J., Price, D. D., Becker, D. P. 1975. Neurophysiological characterization of the anterolateral spinal cord neurons contributing to pain perception in man. *Pain* 1:51–58

162. Mayer, D. J., Price, D. D., Rafii, A. 1977. Antagonism of acupuncture analgesia in man by the narcotic antagonist naloxone. *Brain Res.* 121:360–73

163. Mayer, D. J., Wolfe, T. L., Akil, H., Carder, B., Liebeskind, J. C. 1971. Analgesia from electrical stimulation in the brainstem of the rat. *Science* 174: 1351–54

164. McCreery, D. B., Bloedel, J. R. 1975. Reduction of the response of cat spinothalamic neurons to graded mechanical stimuli by electrical stimulation of the lower brain stem. *Brain Res.* 97:151–56

165. McCreery, D. B., Bloedel, J. R. 1976. Effect of trigeminal stimulation on the excitability of cat spinothalamic tract neurons. *Brain Res.* 117:136–40

166. Melzack, R., ed. 1973. *The Puzzle of Pain.* New York: Basic Books. 232 pp.

167. Melzack, R., Casey, K. L. 1968. In *The Skin Senses,* ed. D. Kenshalo, 423–43. Springfield, Ill.: Thomas. 636 pp.

168. Melzack, R., Stotler, W. A., Livingston, W. K. 1958. Effects of discrete brainstem lesions in cats on perception of noxious stimulation. *J. Neurophysiol.* 21:353–67

169. Menetrey, D., Giesler, G. J. Jr., Besson, J. M. 1977. An analysis of response properties of spinal cord dorsal horn neurones to non-noxious and noxious stimuli in the spinal rat. *Exp. Brain Res.* 27:15–33

170. Moolenaar, G. -M., Holloway, J. A., Trouth, C. O. 1976. Responses of caudal raphe neurons to peripheral somatic stimulation. *Exp. Neurol.* 53:304–13

171. Murfin, R., Bennett, J., Mayer, D. J. 1976. The effect of dorsolateral spinal cord (DLF) lesions on analgesia from morphine microinjected into the periaqueductal gray matter (PAG) of the rat. *Neurosci. Abstr.* 2:946

172. Nashold, B. S., Friedman, H. 1972. Dorsal column stimulation for relief of pain. Preliminary report on 30 patients. *J. Neurosurg.* 36:590–97

173. Nauta, W. J. H., Kuypers, H. G. J. M. 1958. In *Henry Ford International Symposium, The Reticular Formation of the Brain,* ed. H. H. Jasper, 3–30. Boston: Little, Brown. 766 pp.

174. Nicoll, R. A., Siggins, G. R., Ling, N., Bloom, F. E., Guillemin, R. 1977. Neuronal actions of endorphins and enkephalins among brain regions: a comparative microiontophoretic study. *Proc. Natl. Acad. Sci. USA* 74:2584–89

175. Nijensohn, D. E., Kerr, F. W. L. 1975. The ascending projections of the dorsolateral funiculus of the spinal cord in the primate. *J. Comp. Neurol.* 161: 459–70

176. Noordenbos, W. 1959. *Pain.* Amsterdam: Elsevier. 182 pp.

177. Noordenbos, W., Wall, P. D. 1976. Diverse sensory functions with an almost totally divided spinal cord. A case of spinal cord transection with preservation of part of one anterolateral quandrant. *Pain* 2:185–95

178. Norton, A. C. 1973. *The Dorsal Column System of the Spinal Cord.* Los Angeles: UCLA Brain Information Service. 180 pp.

179. Nyberg-Hansen, R. 1965. Site and mode of termination of reticulospinal fibers in the cat. *J. Comp. Neurol.* 124: 71–100

180. Oleson, T. D., Liebeskind, J. C. 1975. Relationship of neural activity in the raphe nuclei of the rat to brain stimulation-produced analgesia. *Physiologist* 18:338

181. Oleson, T. D., Twombly, D. A., Liebeskind, J. C. 1977. Effects of pain-attenuating brain stimulation and morphine on electrical activity in the raphe nuclei of the awake rat. *Pain.* In press

182. Oliveras, J. L., Besson, J. M., Guilbaud, G., Liebeskind, J. C. 1974. Behavioral and electrophysiological evidence of pain inhibition from midbrain stimulation in the cat. *Exp. Brain Res.* 20: 32–44

183. Oliveras, J. L., Hosobuchi, Y., Redjemi, F., Guilbaud, G., Besson, J. M. 1977. Opiate antagonist, naloxone, strongly reduces analgesia induced by stimulation of a raphe nucleus (centralis inferior). *Brain Res.* 120:221–29

184. Oliveras, J. L., Redjemi, F., Guilbaud, G., Besson, J. M. 1975. Analgesia induced by electrical stimulation of the inferior centralis nucleus of the raphe in the cat. *Pain* 1:139–45

185. Papo, I., Caruselli, G. 1970. The pain threshold after spinothalamic tractotomy. *Neurochirurgia* 16:513–24

186. Pasternak, G. W., Goodman, R., Snyder, S. H. 1975. An endogenous morphine-like factor in mammalian brain. *Life Sci.* 16:1765–69

187. Perl, E. R. 1971. Is pain a specific sensation? *J. Psychiatr. Res.* 8:273–87

188. Pert, A., Walter, M. 1976. Comparison between reversal of morphine and electrical stimulation induced analgesia in the rat mesencephalon. *Life Sci.* 19: 1023–32

189. Pert, A., Yaksh, T. 1974. Sites of morphine induced analgesia in the primate brain: relation to pain pathways. *Brain Res.* 80:135–40

190. Pert, C. B., Aposhian, D., Snyder, S. H. 1974. Phylogentic distribution of opiate receptor binding. *Brain Res.* 75:356–61

191. Pert, C. B., Kuhar, M. J., Snyder, S. H. 1976. Opiate receptor: autoradiographic localization in rat brain. *Proc. Natl. Acad. Sci. USA* 73:3729–33
192. Pert, C. B., Pert, A., Tallman, J. F. 1976. Isolation of a novel endogenous opiate analgesic from human blood. *Proc. Natl. Acad. Sci. USA* 73:2226–30
193. Petras, J. M. 1967. Cortical, tectal and tegmental fiber connections in the spinal cord of the cat. *Brain Res.* 6:275–324
194. Pomeranz, B. 1973. Specific nociceptive fibers projecting from spinal cord neurons to the brain: a possible pathway for pain. *Brain Res.* 50:447–51
195. Pompeiano, O. 1973. *Handbook of Sensory Physiology, Somatosensory System,* ed. A. Iggo, 2:381–488. Berlin: Springer 851 pp.
196. Price, D. D., Browe, A. C. 1973. Responses of spinal cord neurons to graded noxious and non-noxious stimuli. *Brain Res.* 64:425–29
197. Price, D. D., Browe, A. C. 1975. Spinal cord coding of graded non-noxious and noxious temperature increases. *Exp. Neurol.* 48:201–21
198. Price, D. D., Dubner, R. 1977. Neurons that subserve the sensory-discriminative aspects of pain. *Pain.* In press
199. Price, D. D., Mayer, D. J. 1974. Physiological laminar organization of the dorsal horn of M. mulatta. *Brain Res.* 79:321–25
200. Price, D. D., Mayer, D. J. 1975. Neurophysiological characterization of the anterolateral quadrant neurons subserving pain in M. mulatta. *Pain* 1:59–72
201. Proudfit, H. K., Anderson, E. G. 1974. New long latency bulbospinal evoked potentials blocked by serotonin antagonists. *Brain Res.* 65:542–46
202. Proudfit, H. K., Anderson, E. G. 1975. Morphine analgesia: blockade by raphe magnus lesions. *Brain Res.* 98:612–18
203. Randic, M., Yu, H. H. 1976. Effects of 5-hydroxytryptamine and bradykinin in cat dorsal horn neurones activated by noxious stimuli. *Brain Res.* 111:197–203
204. Rexed, B. 1952. The cytoarchitectonic organization of the spinal cord in the cat. *J. Comp. Neurol.* 96:415–96
205. Reynolds, D. V. 1969. Surgery in the rat during electrical analgesia induced by focal brain stimulation. *Science,* 164:444–45
206. Rhodes, D. L. 1975. *A Behavioral Investigation of Pain Responsiveness Following Electrical Stimulation of the Rostral Brain Stem of the Rat.* PhD Dissertation. Univ. Calif., Los Angeles

207. Rose, M. D. 1974. Pain-reducing properties of rewarding electrical brain stimulation in the rat. *J. Comp. Physiol. Psychol.* 87:607–17
208. Ruda, M. 1975. *Autoradiographic Study of the Efferent Projections of the Midbrain Central Gray of the Cat.* PhD Dissertation. Univ. Pennsylvania, Philadelphia. 73 pp.
209. Ruda, M. A., Hayes, R. L., Price, D. D., Hu, J. W., Dubner, R. 1976. Inhibition of nociceptive reflexes in the primate by electrical stimulation or narcotic microinjection at medial mesencephalic and diencephalic sites: behavioral and electrophysiological analyses. *Neurosci. Abstr.* 2:952
210. Rustioni, A. 1973. Non-primary afferents to the nucleus gracilis from the lumbar cord of the cat. *Brain Res.* 51:81–95
211. Rustioni, A. 1974. Non-primary afferents to the cuneate nucleus in the brachial dorsal funiculus of the cat. *Brain Res.* 75:247–59
212. Rustioni, A., Kaufman, A. B. 1977. Identification of cells of origin of non-primary afferents to the dorsal column nuclei of the cat. *Exp. Brain Res.* 27:1–14
213. Rustioni, A., Molenaar, I. 1975. Dorsal column nuclei afferents in the lateral funiculus of the cat: distribution pattern and absence of sprouting after chronic deafferentation. *Exp. Brain. Res.* 23:1–12
214. Samanin, R., Gumulka, W., Valzelli, L. 1970. Reduced effect of morphine in midbrain raphe lesioned rats. *Eur. J. Pharmacol.* 10:339–43
215. Sastry, B. S. R., Sinclair, J. G. 1976. The blockade of presynaptic and postsynaptic bulbospinal inhibition of the cat spinal monosynaptic reflex by imipramine. *Brain Res.* 110:399–402
216. Sastry, B. S. R., Sinclair, J. G. 1976. Serotonin involvement in the blockade of bulbospinal inhibition of the spinal monosynaptic reflex. *Brain Res.* 115:427–36
217. Satoh, M., Takagi, H. 1971. Enhancement by morphine of the central descending inhibitory influence on spinal sensory transmission. *Eur. J. Pharmacol.* 114:60–65
218. Satoh, M., Zieglgansberger, W., Herz, A. 1976. Actions of opiates upon single unit activity in the cortex of naive and tolerant rats. *Brain Res.* 115:99–110
219. Scheibel, M., Scheibel, A., Mollica, A., Moruzzi, G. 1954. Convergence and interaction of afferent impulses on single

units of reticular formation. *J. Neurophysiol.* 18:309–29

220. Schiff, M. 1854. Sur la transmission des impressions sensitives dans la moelle epiniere. *C. R. Seances Soc. Biol.* 38:926–30

221. Schmidek, H. H., Fohanno, D., Ervin, F. R., Sweet, W. H. 1971. Pain threshold alterations by brain stimulation in the monkey. *J. Neurosurg.* 35:715–22

222. Schmidt, R. F. 1973. *Somatosensory System,* ed. A. Iggo, 2:151–206. Berlin: Springer. 851 pp.

223. Sharpe, L. G., Garnett, J. E., Cicero, T. J. 1974. Analgesia and hyperreactivity produced by intracranial microinjection of morphine into the periaqueductal gray. *Behav. Biol.* 11:303–13

224. Shealy, C. N., Mortimer, J. T., Hagfors, N. R. 1970. Dorsal column electroanalgesia. *J. Neurosurg.* 32:560–64

225. Sherrington, C. 1906. *The Integrative Action of the Nervous System.* New Haven: Yale. 433 pp.

226. Siegel, P., Wepsic, J. G. 1974. Alteration of nociception by stimulation of cerebellar structures in the monkey. *Physiol. Behav.* 13:189–94

227. Simantov, R., Goodman, R., Aposhian, D., Snyder, S. H. 1976. Phylogenetic distribution of a morphine-like peptide (enkephalin). *Brain Res.* 111:204–11

228. Simantov, R., Kuhar, M. J., Pasternak, G. W., Snyder, S. H. 1976. The regional distribution of a morphine-like factor enkephalin in monkey brain. *Brain Res.* 106:189–97

229. Snyder, S. H. 1975. Opiate receptor in normal and drug altered brain function. *Nature* 257:185–89

230. Snyder, S. H., Matthysse, S., eds. 1975. *Neurosci. Res. Program Bull.* 13:166

231. Snyder, S. H., Simantov, R. 1977. The opiate receptor and opioid peptides. *J. Neurochem.* 28:13–20

232. Spiller, W. G., Martin, E. 1921. The treatment of persistent pain of organic origin in the lower part of the body by division of the anterolateral column of the spinal cord. *J. Am. Med. Ass.* 58:1489–90

233. Taber, E., Brodal, A., Walberg, F. 1960. The raphe nuclei of the brainstem in the cat. I. Normal topography and cytoarchitecture and general discussion. *J. Comp. Neurol.* 114:161–88

234. Taber-Pierce, E., Foote, W. E., Hobson, J. A. 1976. The efferent connection of the nucleus raphe dorsalis. *Brain Res.* 107:137–44

235. Takagi, H., Doi, T., Akaiki, A. 1976. In *Opiates and Endogenous Opioid Peptides,* ed. H. W. Kosterlitz, 191–198. Amsterdam: North-Holland. 456 pp.

236. Takagi, H., Doi, T., Kawasaki, K. 1975. Effects of morphine, L-dopa and Tetrabenazine on the lamina V cells of spinal dorsal horn. *Life Sci.* 17:67–72

237. Taub, A. 1964. Local, segmental and supraspinal interaction with a dorsolateral spinal cutaneous afferent system. *Exp. Neurol.* 10:357–74

238. Tenen, S. S. 1968. Antagonism of the analgesic effect of morphine and other drugs by p-Chlorophenylalanine, a serotonin depletor. *Psychopharmacologia* 12:278–85

239. Teschemacher, H. J., Schubert, P., Herz, A. 1973. Autoradiographic studies concerning the supraspinal site of the antinociceptive action of morphine when inhibiting the hindleg flexor reflex in rabbits. *Neuropharmacology* 12:123–31

240. Tomasulo, K. C., Emmers, R. 1972. Activation of neurons in the gracile nucleus by two afferent pathways in the rat. *Exp. Neurol.* 36:197–206

241. Torvik, A., Brodal, A. 1957. The origin of reticulospinal fibers in the cat. *Anat. Rec.* 128:113–38

242. Trevino, D. L., Carstens, E. 1975. Confirmation of the location of spinothalmic neurons in the cat and monkey by the retrograde transport of horseradish peroxidase. *Brain Res.* 98:177–82

243. Trevino, D. L., Coulter, J. D., Willis, W. D. 1973. Location of cells of origin of spinothalamic tract in lumbar enlargement of the monkey. *J. Neurophysiol.* 36:750–61

244. Trevino, D. L., Maunz, R. A., Bryan, R. N., Willis, W. D. 1972. Location of cells of origin of the spinothalamic tract in the lumbar enlargement of cat. *Exp. Neurol.* 34:64–77

245. Tsou, K., Jang, C. S. 1964. Studies on the site of analgesic action of morphine by intracerebral microinjections. *Sci. Sin.* 13:1099–1109

246. Uddenberg, N. 1968. Functional organization of long second order afferents in the dorsal funiculus. *Exp. Brain Res.* 4:377–82

247. Urca, G., Frenk, H., Liebeskind, J. C., Taylor, A. N. 1977. Morphine and enkephalin: analgesic and epileptic properties. *Science* 197:83–86

248. Vierck, C. J. Jr., Hamilton, D. M., Thornby, J. I. 1971. Pain reactivity of monkeys after lesions to the dorsal lateral columns of the spinal cord. *Exp. Brain Res.* 13:140–58

249. Vigouret, J., Teschemacher, H. J., Albus, K., Herz, A. 1973. Differentiation between spinal and supraspinal sites of action of morphine when inhibiting the hindleg flexor reflex in rabbits. *Neuropharmacology* 12:111–21

250. Vogt, M. 1974. The effect of lowering the 5-hydroxytryptamine content of the rat spinal cord on analgesia produced by morphine. *J. Physiol.* 236:483–98

251. Walker, J. M., Berntson, G. G., Sandman, C. A., Coy, D. H., Schally, A. V., Kastin, A. J. 1977. An analog of enkephalin having prolonged opiate-like effects in vivo. *Science* 196:85–87

252. Wall, P. D. 1967. The laminar organization of dorsal horn and effects of descending impulses. *J. Physiol.* 188: 403–23

253. Wall, P. D., Dubner, R. 1972. Somatosensory pathways. *Ann. Rev. Physiol.* 34:315–36

254. Willis, W. D. 1976. In *Advances in Pain Research and Therapy,* ed. J. J. Bonica, D. G. Albe-Fessard 1:215–23. New York: Raven. 1012 pp.

255. Willis, W. D., Haber, L. H., Martin, R. F. 1977. Inhibition of spinothalamic tract cells and interneurons by brainstem stimulation in the monkey. In press

256. Willis, W. D., Trevino, D. L., Coulter, J. D., Maunz, R. A. 1974. Responses of primate spinothalamic tract neurons to natural stimulation of hindlimb. *J. Neurophysiol.* 37:358–72

257. Yaksh, T. L., DuChateau, J. C., Rudy, T. A. 1976. Antagonism by methysergide and cinanserin of the antinociceptive action of morphine administered into the periaqueductal gray. *Brain Res.* 104:367–72

258. Yaksh, T. L., Plant, R. L., Rudy, T. A. 1977. Studies on the antagonism by raphe lesions of the antinociceptive action of systemic morphine. *Eur. J. Pharmacol.* 41:399–408

259. Yaksh, T. L., Rudy, T. A. 1976. Analgesia mediated by a direct spinal action of narcotics. *Science* 192: 1357–58

260. Yaksh, T. L., Yeung, J. C., Rudy, T. A. 1976. An inability to antagonize with naloxone the elevated nociceptive thresholds resulting from electrical stimulation of the mesencephalic central gray. *Life Sci.* 18:1193–98

261. Yaksh, T. L., Yeung, J. C., Rudy, T. A. 1976. Systematic examination in the rat of brain sites sensitive to the direct application of morphine: observation of differential effects within the periaqueductal gray. *Brain Res.* 114:83–103

262. Yokota, T., Hashimoto, S. 1976. Periaqueductal gray and tooth pulp afferent interaction on units in caudal medulla oblongata. *Brain Res.* 117: 508–12

263. Yunger, L. M., Harvey, J. A., Lorens, S. A. 1973. Dissociation of the analgesic and rewarding effects of brain stimulation in the rat. *Physiol. Behav.* 10: 909–13

264. Zieglgansberger, W., Bayerl, H. 1976. The mechanism of inhibition of neuronal activity by opiates in the spinal cord of cat. *Brain Res.* 115:111–28

265. Zieglgansberger, W., Fry, J. P., Herz, A., Moroder, L., Wunsch, E. 1976. Enkephalin-induced inhibition of cortical neurones and the lack of this effect in morphine tolerant/dependent rats. *Brain Res.* 115:160–64

Ann. Rev. Physiol. 1978. 40:249–77
Copyright © 1978 by Annual Reviews Inc. All rights reserved

STUDIES OF ISOLATED
RENAL TUBULES IN VITRO

❖1192

Jared J. Grantham

James M. Irish III

Dennis A. Hall

Department of Medicine, Division of Nephrology, University of Kansas
School of Medicine, Kansas City, Kansas 66103

INTRODUCTION

The conversion of blood into urine is a hallowed function of the kidney. In high forms of life the kidneys contain minute epithelial tubules in a complex array through which the blood filtrate passes in the quiet ritual of urine formation. Over the years a number of experimental approaches have been used to determine how urine is made. From the clearance method, a highly indirect approach, we learned that blood solutes may be filtered, absorbed, and secreted. The so-called "stop-flow" method helped to localize certain transport processes to proximal and distal regions of the renal tubule. The micropuncture technique, adapted for in situ work, served to locate discrete transport processes more clearly. Nevertheless, all of the foregoing methods have been inadequate to study nephron segments buried within the substance of the kidney or to define specific mechanisms of salt and water transport across the different segments of nephron.

Frustrated by the relatively indirect approaches of the day, Dr. Maurice (Moe) Burg of the National Institutes of Health conceived the idea that living tubules should be removed from the kidney and studied in vitro, as one might perfuse an isolated segment of the bowel (12). The initial attempts to perfuse tubules with glass pipets were unsuccessful. The short segments of proximal tubule had been retrieved from a suspension of rabbit kidney cortex prepared by enzymatic digestion with collagenase. Collagenase re-

249

0066-4278/78/0301-0249$01.00

moved the tubule basement membrane (91); consequently, perfusion of fluid into the lumen caused the tubule wall to rupture. An attempt was finally made to dissect the tubules without enzymatic treatment, and Providence smiled. Of all the laboratory species that might have been tried first, the rabbit, an animal cursed by Homer Smith, was chosen; it subsequently proved to be the only laboratory mammal from which tubules could be conveniently dissected. Segments of proximal and collecting tubules were perfused and the perfusate collected at the other end for analysis. The ominously complex kidney had been reduced to its fundamental components. In the 13 years since its initial use, the isolated tubule method has been adopted by numerous laboratories in the United States and several other countries. With the exception of the glomerulus, every segment of the nephron has been dissected, perfused, and studied.

Two recent papers survey the methods, the analytical approaches, and some of the problems encountered in isolated tubule work (27, 103). In this review we assemble a complete bibliography of the published data on single isolated tubules. Further, we attempt to provide a concise summary of the more important contributions the new approach has made to the understanding of tubule function.

PROXIMAL CONVOLUTED TUBULE

The proximal convoluted tubules of adult rabbit kidneys are several millimeters long. Segments 0.5–2.2 mm in length have been perfused in vitro (19, 86, 87, 113). The outer diameter depends on the transmembrane hydrostatic pressure. At 10 cm H_2O the outside diameter averaged 40 μm and the luminal diameter 25 μm (119). There are approximately eight cells around the circumference of the proximal convoluted tubule. A basement membrane surrounds the epithelial cells and apparently provides the principal scaffold on which the cells rest.

The epithelium is columnar with a prominent brush border and many basilar infoldings. Recent studies have indicated that the surface area of the brush border is the same as the lateral cell surface in the proximal convoluted tubule (118). The complicated interdigitation of adjacent tubule cells has mystified researchers interested in function for a number of years. Recently Welling & Welling (119) have performed an exhaustive morphometric study of isolated proximal tubules and have provided a splendid three-dimensional model of the intercellular channels. From their work it is clear that the intercellular space is not a simple rectangle, as conventionally depicted in most schematic diagrams, but rather the channel is in the shape of an exponential horn. The shape has an important bearing on the linear velocity of fluid flow in the channel.

The hydraulic permeability has been determined for intact proximal convoluted and straight tubules and for their respective basement membranes (116). The conductance of the basement membrane exceeds that of the intact epithelium by two orders of magnitude.

On the basis of electrophysiologic studies, the proximal convoluted tubule can be characterized as a very leaky epithelium. The transepithelial resistance is relatively low in the proximal convoluted tubule (6.1 Ωcm^2), reflecting the ionic leakiness of the epithelium (92). Large electrical and chemical concentration gradients cannot be maintained, and in fact, in an early study, no spontaneous electrical potential difference was detected (18). However, improved insulation at the perfusion end uncovered a small electrical potential difference of 3.8 mV lumen-negative (20), a value that has been repeatedly confirmed (24, 78, 86).

Fluid Absorption

The proximal tubule absorbs approximately 70% of the ultrafiltrate formed by the glomerulus. Chonko et al (28) performed micropuncture studies in New Zealand white rabbits of the same strain used for in vitro perfusion studies. The single nephron glomerular filtration rate was 21 nl min^{-1} and fluid absorption rate was about 1.9 nl mm^{-1} min^{-1} in superficial proximal convoluted tubules on the average.

In the pioneering studies of tubules in vitro, researchers attempted to simulate the fluid environment of tubules in vivo by using normal rabbit serum for the bath and an ultrafiltrate of serum for the perfusate. Under these conditions the average rate of fluid absorption was 1.18 nl mm^{-1} min^{-1} in the proximal convoluted tubule (19). In succeeding years the average rate of net fluid absorption reported from many laboratories has been about 1 nl mm^{-1} min^{-1} in adult animals and may be as low as 0.3 nl mm^{-1} min^{-1} in immature rabbits (90). It should be noted that the absorption rate of a single isolated convoluted tubule may range from 0.8 to 3.5 nl mm^{-1} min^{-1}. This scatter in basal rates of fluid absorption probably reflects intrinsic variation among tubules as much as unstable experimental conditions among researchers.

Several factors have been found to modify the rate of fluid absorption in otherwise normal tubules. Normal body temperature for the rabbit is 39.5°C (103), but by convention most studies of isolated proximal tubules have been conducted at 37°C. It may be interesting to learn of the effect of normal body temperature on fluid absorption in isolated proximal tubules. A reduction of temperature below 37°C has been repeatedly shown to depress active transport processes in kidney tissue. In isolated tubules perfused with ultrafiltrate and bathed in rabbit serum, reduction of temperature from 37°C to 25°C depressed but did not stop fluid absorption (46).

Further cooling to 15° eliminated fluid absorption completely (19). Cooling to 5°C blocked the adjustment of proximal tubule cell volume in hypotonic media (34).

Dennis, Woodhall & Robinson (36) have called attention to the important influence of the environmental pH on fluid absorption in convoluted tubules. Fluid absorption was maintained relatively constant if bath pH was kept between 7.3 and 7.5. On the alkaline side of the pH range however, there were a marked decrease in fluid absorption. The tubules appeared to tolerate acid better than alkaline pH. It is clear from these studies that pH must be regulated within rather narrow limits in studies of isolated tubules.

Burg & Orloff (19) examined the effect of perfusion rate and transtubule pressure and found that neither factor significantly altered the basal rate of fluid absorption. Although they did not emphasize it in their original study, they found that fluid absorption did increase slightly when lumen perfusion rate was raised from 8 to 19 nl min^{-1}, or when the transtubule hydrostatic pressure was increased. Kokko and his collaborators have looked more closely at the dependence of fluid absorption on perfusion rate and transtubule hydrostatic pressure. In their initial survey, potential difference was used as an indirect reflection of solute absorption in the proximal convoluted tubule. Kokko & Rector (87) observed that as perfusion rate dropped below 10 nl min^{-1}, the potential difference approached zero. To overcome the criticism that potential difference is a poor indicator of fluid absorption (24), Imai, Seldin & Kokko (72) reexamined the effect of flow rate on fluid absorption. The rate of fluid absorption increased steadily as perfusion rate was raised from 2 to 11 nl min^{-1}. At faster perfusion rates, fluid absorption did not increase further.

Recent studies by Horster & Larsson (66) and the earlier report by Burg & Orloff (19) indicate that transtubule hydrostatic pressure may modify fluid absorption to a small but significant degree. Although Grantham, Qualizza & Welling (54) found no effect of pressure on fluid absorption in early studies, more recent unpublished work utilizing a more sensitive method for measuring volume absorption (53) showed that elevated transtubule hydrostatic pressure definitely increased net fluid absorption. In the final analysis it appears that perfusion rate and hydrostatic pressure may independently affect the rate of fluid absorption in isolated tubules to an appreciable extent.

The composition of the perfusate and its role in altering fluid absorption has been examined in considerable detail. Kokko & Rector (87) noted that at very slow perfusion rates, transmembrane electrical potential of the proximal convoluted tubule approached zero, suggesting to these researchers that consumption of some of the constitutents in the perfusate might contribute to the observed change in the potential difference. Removal of glucose, alanine, and bicarbonate from the perfusate, individually or in concert, produced significant changes in potential difference. Clearly the transepithelial electrical potential difference depended on the luminal concentration of the solutes. The relation between changes in potential difference and fluid absorption was inferred but not tested in these studies. Cardinal and co-workers (24) also evaluated the effect of luminal solutes on both transtubule potential difference and fluid absorption. Removal of alanine, glucose, and bicarbonate from the perfusate resulted in a marked decrease in fluid absorption. Importantly, these investigators were able to dissociate the potential difference from changes in fluid absorption.

Burg and associates (21) tested further the influence of organic solutes on fluid absorption in proximal convoluted tubules. Removal of alanine, citrate, glucose, and lactate from the perfusate decreased absorption significantly. Addition of alanine, glucose, lactate, or citrate individually to the perfusate caused an incremental increase in fluid absorption. By contrast, selective removal of the same solutes from the bath had no effect. When α-methyl-D-glucoside and cycloleucine (which are transported but not metabolized) were added to the perfusate, fluid absorption increased. Thus, glucose and amino acids probably facilitate sodium transport and fluid absorption directly rather than by simply providing fuel for cell metabolism.

Sodium, potassium, chloride, and bicarbonate are the dominant ions in the perfusate and bath. Burg & Green (16) noted the effect on fluid absorption of removing these ions selectively from the bath and/or the perfusate. Complete replacement of sodium in the bath and perfusate with choline, tetramethylammonium, or lithium eliminated fluid absorption, a clear indication that active sodium transport is a dominant force in the absorption of fluid in the proximal tubule. Removal of potassium from the bath stopped fluid absorption, whereas excluding the cation from the lumen had little effect. The effect of potassium removal on volume absorption is probably indirect, and mediated through a decrease in active sodium transport at the peritubular membrane. Replacement of chloride with either nitrate or perchlorate in bath and perfusate caused fluid absorption to decrease only modestly; consequently, active chloride transport is not a significant power in the convoluted tubule.

Efforts to define the importance of bicarbonate in the absorption of fluid in isolated perfused convoluted tubules (and pars recta for that matter) have produced some interesting meandering in the recent literature. In a preliminary report, Kokko, Rector & Seldin (89) observed that removal of bicarbonate from the perfusate and bath caused fluid absorption to decrease precipitously. By contrast Cardinal et al (24) could detect no decrease in fluid absorption when bicarbonate was eliminated in their experiments. In more recent studies from the same laboratory, Burg & Green (16) detected a significant decrease in absorption upon the removal of bicarbonate, a result confirmed recently by Dennis (35). At this juncture there is general agreement within the microperfusion crowd that removal of bicarbonate significantly reduces fluid absorption.

It has been suggested that physical factors may modify the rate of fluid absorption in the proximal nephron. The influence of peritubular protein concentration has been investigated in perfused tubules by several laboratories. Imai & Kokko (68) found that fluid absorption in proximal convoluted tubules decreased 50% when protein was removed from the bath (ultrafiltrate of serum substituted for whole serum). Conversely, fluid absorption increased when the peritubular protein concentration was raised from 6.0 to 12.5 g dl^{-1}. Shortly thereafter, Grantham, Qualizza & Welling (54) confirmed that peritubular protein concentration was a determinant of fluid absorption in proximal tubules. Horster, Burg & colleagues (65) contested the notion that protein concentration in the bathing fluid had an effect on fluid absorption in convoluted tubules in vitro. In response to this challenge Imai & Kokko (70) performed additional experiments, from which they drew the same conclusion as previously; namely, that fluid absorption was dependent on the concentrations of oncotic material in the bath. Grantham and co-workers repeated, but did not publish, their studies on the effect of peritubular protein with the same result as before. In the meantime, Horster & Larsson (66) and Burg et al (21) reevaluated the effect of protein on fluid absorption and acknowledged that peritubular protein concentration indeed has a significant impact on fluid absorption in convoluted tubules.

Grantham, Qualizza & Welling (54) suggested that protein might exert its effect by generating an osmotic force across the basement membrane. However, recent work shows that the basement membrane is highly permeable to protein (112). Moreover, Tisher & Kokko (112) found the intercellular spaces were more dilated in the presence of normal peritubular protein concentration than in the absence of protein. It is suggested that the protein effect may be across the tight junction or the plasma membrane.

Hamburger, Lawson & Schwartz (61) observed a significant decrease in fluid absorption when proximal convoluted tubules were exposed to parathyroid hormone (PTH), a result confirmed by Dennis (35). PTH apparently acts principally from the peritubular side of the cells. The adenylate cyclase activity of single proximal tubules is stimulated by PTH (25, 73). In the perfused proximal convoluted tubules fluid absorption decreased reversibly in response to dibutyryl cyclic 3',5'-adenosine monophosphate (cAMP) (60) and another cAMP analog, 8-[p-chlorophenylthio]-cAMP (76). Thus, the hormone is thought to act through the intermediacy of cAMP.

Bicarbonate must be present in the perfusate for PTH to exert any influence on fluid absorption (35). A decrease in fluid absorption equivalent to that caused by PTH was found when bicarbonate was removed from the perfusate. The relationship between bicarbonate and PTH is interesting, but apparently cannot be explained simply by a hormonal inhibition of carbonic anhydrase.

Solute Transport

The leakiness of the proximal convoluted tubule can be seen clearly in the analysis of bidirectional sodium fluxes in isolated tubules at 37°C. The net sodium flux from lumen to bath was only 20% of the unidirectional flux from lumen to bath (86). When a raffinose solution was perfused the steady-state concentration gradient for sodium was about 34 meq l^{-1}. The unidirectional flux of sodium from lumen to bath appears to vary directly with perfusion rate and is dependent on the presence of alanine and glucose in the perfusate.

Phosphate transport occurs thoroughout the proximal tubule although the major portion is absorbed in the convoluted segment (36). The flux ratio asymmetry is striking for phosphate, approximately 13:1; the passive permeability from bath to lumen is relatively low. Phosphate is probably absorbed by active transport, although the exact mechanism has not been defined.

Glucose transport, aside from its role in proximal fluid absorption, has been studied by Tune & Burg (113). The net movement of glucose from lumen to bath appears to require active transport across the luminal membrane since the cell concentration of glucose apparently exceeds that in the lumen. The permeability of the peritubular membrane to glucose is approximately four times greater than that of the luminal membrane. Glucose transport has also been examined in the proximal tubule of the snake kidney (6); the results provide interesting contrast to glucose transport in the rabbit kidney (113). The distal-proximal snake tubule, comparable to the pars recta of the rabbit, has twice the capacity of the proximal-proximal tubule to absorb glucose. The site of active transport is probably at the peritubular membrane, rather than at the luminal membrane.

Urea absorption in the proximal convoluted tubule is passive (83). The reflection coefficient for urea is greater than for sodium chloride. Unlike sodium and chloride fluxes, urea flux from lumen to bath is relatively unaffected by changes in perfusion rate (72).

Proteins and peptides are also transported by convoluted tubules in vitro. Proximal convoluted tubules transport perfused albumin from the luminal fluid to the bath (9). Uptake of albumin takes place across the luminal membrane, possibly by vesicular transport. Although movement of albumin from lumen to bath has not been measured directly, autoradiographs of labelled albumin indicate that the protein moves through the cell into the peritubular medium. Movement of albumin from the bath into the cells is negligible (8). Endocytosis is probably the primary mode of insulin transport (10).

Organic acid transport has been demonstrated in the proximal convoluted tubule; however, most investigators have foresaken this segment for the more striking proximal straight tubule. Para-aminohippurate (PAH) secretion has been observed in proximal convoluted tubules or their counterparts obtained from rabbit (53, 114), snake (30–33), and frog (75). Fluid secretion induced by PAH, so prominent in rabbit proximal straight tubules, has not been observed in proximal convoluted tubules. It should be noted that although fluid secretion did not occur in the proximal convoluted tubule in response to PAH transport, fluid absorption was significantly depressed by the aryl acid (53).

Effect of Drugs on the Proximal Tubule

Ouabain diminishes fluid absorption in the proximal tubule (19, 46). This finding has been repeatedly confirmed in both the convoluted and straight proximal tubule and is used regularly at the termination of experiments to verify that salt and water absorption was in fact due to active rather than passive forces. Ouabain rapidly changes the electrolyte composition of the cells (51). Several diuretics, including acetazolamide, chlorothiazide, and furosemide, when added to the bath, significantly depressed fluid absorption along the proximal tubule (35, 46, 102). Phloretin selectively inhibited urea transport (81) whereas the glycoside, phlorizin, blocked glucose transport (6). Probenecid is a potent inhibitor of organic acid secretion (29, 32, 50, 53).

Heterogeneity of Proximal Tubules

There is a new awareness of functional heterogeneity in the nephron stemming in large measure from studies utilizing single isolate perfused tubules. It is clear that proximal nephrons are different from one end to the other and nephrons whose glomeruli are superficial are different from those whose glomeruli are deep in the cortex. Burg & Orloff (19) were the first to point out the difference in the rate of fluid absorption between the proximal convoluted and proximal straight tubule. Tune, Burg & Patlak (114) noted the difference between the rate of PAH transport in the proximal convoluted and straight tubules. Recently, Woodhall et al (120) observed that different portions of the pars recta may secrete PAH to a variable extent. Jacobson & Kokko (78) observed that the first millimeter of the superficial proximal convoluted tubule is more permeable to sodium than to chloride. Conversely, in the remaining portion of the superficial tubule the relation between the sodium and chloride permeabilities is reversed. In contrast to the superficial proximal convoluted tubule, the juxtamedullary proximal convoluted tubule is more permeable to sodium than to chloride along its entire length. Hamburger, Lawson & Schwartz (61) found that fluid absorption in the more distal portion of the superficial proximal convoluted tubule is strikingly reduced to rates near those observed in the pars recta.

Heterogeneity has also been observed with reference to sodium and chloride permeabilities in the pars recta. In the superficial proximal straight tubule, chloride permeability is twice the sodium permeability. The relative permeabilities to anion and cation are reversed in the juxtamedullary proximal straight tubules. Bicarbonate absorption is more rapid in the juxtamedullary proximal straight than in the superficial proximal straight tubule (115).

PARS RECTA

The proximal straight tubules are, as their name implies, relatively straight, at least in comparison to proximal convoluted tubules. Most of the studies of function have been made in pars recta from relatively superficial nephrons. Tubules used for in vitro perfusion studies have ranged between 0.3 and 4.1 mm (51, 54, 81, 113, 114) in length. Tubules perfused at 10 cm H_2O have a nominal outer diameter of 38 μm and a lumen diameter of 28 μm. The epithelium is cuboidal with well developed brush borders and fewer basilar infoldings than in the proximal convoluted tubule.

Electrophysiologic studies suggest that the proximal straight tubules are electrically tighter than the convoluted segments (92).

Fluid Absorption

When bathed in serum and perfused with an ultrafiltrate of serum, proximal straight tubules absorb fluid at about one half the rate of proximal convoluted tubules (19, 36, 60). Decreased ambient temperature (105), altered peritubular protein concentration (54), and changes in hydrostatic pressure and flow rate (19) affected fluid absorption to an extent similar to convoluted tubules.

Removal of glucose and alanine from the perfusion solution produced no change in fluid absorption or transepithelial potential difference in the proximal straight tubule (107), a finding in marked contrast to the proximal convoluted tubule (24, 84). Elimination of acetate from the perfusate did not alter the transepithelial potential difference or rate of fluid absorption (102).

The influence of bicarbonate on fluid absorption is not entirely clear. Schafer, Troutman & Andreoli initially found that removal of bicarbonate from the lumen had no effect on fluid absorption (107). More recent unpublished studies by this group indicates, however, that removal of bicarbonate decreases fluid absorption. Dennis (35) found that elimination of bicarbonate from lumen and bath decreased fluid absorption by 36%. Schafer, Patlak & Andreoli (105) have suggested a critical role for bicarbonate in fluid transport in this segment. Lumen solutes and fluid may be absorbed by solvent drag owing to a higher reflection coefficient for bicarbonate than for more permeable anions. It is clear however that a bicarbonate gradient is not the sole driving force for fluid transport since the rate of fluid absorption is actually higher when the perfusate contains bicarbonate than when this anion is removed. Thus active sodium transport is probably the dominant force driving fluid absorption when the proximal straight tubule is exposed to symmetrical concentrations of bicarbonate. Bicarbonate gradients may have a role in fluid absorption in vivo where urinary acidification in convoluted segments reduces the luminal bicarbonate concentration entering the pars recta.

The possible effect of parathyroid hormone on fluid absorption in the proximal straight tubule needs to be clarified. Although stimulation of adenylate cyclase activity by PTH has been documented in rabbit proximal straight tubules, Hamburger and co-workers did not observe decreased fluid absorption in response to either dibutyryl cAMP (60) or PTH (61). However, in studies from another laboratory (35), PTH significantly decreased fluid absorption in the proximal straight tubule. The reason for the discrepancy between these results is not apparent.

Solute Transport

In general, solute transport is slower in the proximal straight tubule than in the proximal convoluted tubule, with some notable exceptions.

Unidirectional sodium flux in the proximal straight tubule averaged about 20% of the sodium flux in the proximal convoluted tubule (107). The concentration of sodium in the perfused fluid and the collected fluid was equal, indicating isotonic sodium absorption. The apparent sodium permeability of proximal straight tubule from superficial nephrons was less than half that of straight tubules from juxtamedually nephrons (80).

Chloride absorption in the proximal straight tubule can be accounted for by passive movement down an electrochemical gradient. Proximal straight tubules generate a chloride gradient when perfused with a bicarbonate concentration equal to the bath (35). The apparent permeability to chloride is greater in the superficial than in the juxtamedullary proximal straight tubule (80).

In the superficial proximal straight tubule the bicarbonate flux from lumen to bath exceeded the flux from bath to lumen indicating net absorption (115). Bicarbonate absorption was twice as rapid in the juxtamedullary proximal straight tubule. According to Warnock & Burg (115) the pars recta is 2.9 times more permeable to chloride than to bicarbonate; Schafer, Troutman & Andreoli (107) found that permeability between the anions differed by a factor of 18. The discrepancy in results is probably related to the poor sensitivity of the current electrical methods used to assess relative conductance to ions.

The rate of phosphate transport in the pars recta is 31% of that observed in the proximal straight tubule (36).

Glucose is absorbed in the proximal straight tubule at a rate approximately 8% of that in the proximal convoluted tubule (113). When exposed to the same perfused load of glucose, the proximal convoluted tubule absorbed 85–90%, whereas the proximal straight tubule absorbed only 25% of the glucose.

Kawamura & Kokko (81) have found evidence for active urea secretion in the proximal straight tubule. The apparent permeability from bath to lumen was twice that from lumen to bath for both superficial and juxtamedullary segments. Sodium cyanide and phloretin reduced the bath-to-lumen permeability but did not affect lumen-to-bath permeability. Urea secretion occurred against a small transtubule difference in concentration. The urea reflection coefficient was 1.0 for both straight segments. The urea secretory mechanism in the proximal straight tubule fits comfortably into the passive model for countercurrent multiplication (88).

Small peptides circulating in the plasma are filtered at the glomerulus and metabolized by the nephron. Peterson et al (94) investigated the role of the proximal straight tubule in the metabolism of angiotensin II and oxytocin. The pars recta absorbed 30% of the angiotensin and 8.6% of the oxytocin loads perfused into the lumen. Hydrolysis of the angiotensin II must have occurred in the pars recta in the course of peptide absorption since the isotope recovered from the cells migrated chromatographically as a single amino acid, isoleucine (94). It is suggested that angiotensin hydrolysis occurred within the lumen by hydrolytic enzymes in the brush border. There was no hydrolysis of oxytocin in the pars recta.

Although active para-aminohippurate (PAH) secretion was reported in the inaugural report on isolated tubules (12), the first in-depth analysis of organic acid transport was presented in the classic paper by Tune, Burg & Patlak (114). Active PAH secretion occurred most avidly in the proximal straight tubule although it was observed throughout the length of the proximal tubule. PAH concentrations were consistently higher in the cells than in the collected fluid or the bath, and the luminal membrane was 16 times more permeable to PAH than the peritubular membrane. On the basis of these results, Tune, Burg & Patlak proposed a model which holds that active PAH transport proceeds across the peritubular membrane with diffusion of the organic acid across the luminal membrane into the urine. This model of PAH secretion has been widely, though not universally, accepted by renal physiologists.

Grantham, Qualizza & Irwin (53) found that PAH in the bathing medium caused net fluid secretion in nonperfused proximal straight tubules. Although the rate of fluid secretion depended on the amount of PAH transported, the concentration of organic acid in the secreted fluid was reasonably constant at about 40 mM. The maximal rate of fluid secretion was about 0.1 nl mm^{-1} min^{-1} in tubules exposed to PAH. It is suggested that active PAH secretion accounts for the secretion of fluid in nonperfused pars recta. Proximal straight tubules also secreted fluid when bathed in human uremic serum (50), or a variety of organic acids (95).

The PAH transport system has also been extensively investigated in the garter snake. Active PAH secretion occurred primarily in the distal-proximal tubule (30), comparable to the rabbit proximal straight tubule, at a rate 28% of that observed in the rabbit (114). The rate of PAH secretion was dependent on the potassium (31, 32) and sodium (33) concentrations of the bath.

The rate of PAH transport in bullfrog tubules was similar in the proximal-proximal and intermediate-proximal segments (75), in contrast to PAH secretion in the snake (30) and rabbit (114). Urea inhibited PAH transport in this species.

Dantzler (29) observed active secretion of urate in the snake distal-proximal tubule. Removal of potassium from the bath eliminated active urate transport (96). Surprisingly, however, urate secretion was remarkably insensitive to inhibition by ouabain. Dantzler (30) has suggested that urate and PAH may be secreted by independent mechanisms in the snake.

Burg & Weller (23) detected active iodopyracet secretion in proximal tubules obtained from the flounder. Transport in this species seemed to fit the model for PAH transport proposed by Tune, Burg & Patlak (114).

THIN DESCENDING LIMB OF HENLE'S LOOP

As the name suggests, this segment of the nephron has a small external diameter. The cells lining the tubule are extremely thin and have nuclei that project into the lumen. The projecting nuclei are the principal determinant of the effective lumen diameter and the resistance to flow (117).

Functional studies of isolated perfused thin descending limbs have been conducted by Kokko (82, 83) and Rocha & Kokko (98). The thin descending limb had a low permeability to sodium, potassium, and urea but a very high permeability to water, greater than that observed for any other segment (Table 1). There was no evidence for active solute or isotonic fluid absorption in this segment. These observations were central to the thesis later proposed by Kokko & Rector that countercurrent multiplication in the inner medulla may occur by passive mechanisms (88).

THIN ASCENDING LIMB OF HENLE'S LOOP

The thin ascending limb is morphologically similar to the thin descending limb, but its permeability characteristics are markedly different. This segment has been examined in isolated tubules by Imai & Kokko in the rabbit (69, 71) and, more recently, by Imai in the rat and hamster (67). Tubule segments from all species were impermeable to water, while the permeabilities to sodium, chloride, and urea were relatively high compared to other segments of the nephron. The urea permeability, although high, was much lower than the permeability to sodium chloride.

Given the observed permeability characteristics and the composition of luminal fluid and interstitium thought to occur in vivo, Imai & Kokko

Table 1 Features of transport in isolated tubules at $37°C$

Segment[a]	Lp (cm sec^{-1} atm^{-1} × 10^7)	Urea permeability (cm sec^{-1} × 10^5)	Net sodium absorption (peq cm^{-1} sec^{-1})
PCT	290–630 (86)[b]	2.5–6.6 (68, 72, 83)	28 (86)
PST	—	—	—
superficial	—	1.4 (81)	10 (107)
juxtamedullary	—	2.1 (81)	—
Thin DLH	1,665 (82)	1.5 (83)	—
Thin ALH	9 (69)	6.7 (69)	—
Thick ALH	4–8 (13, 97)	0.9 (99)	13 (13)
DCT	0 (55)	—	—
Collecting tubule			
vasopressin –	40 (5)	0.3 (99)	—
vasopressin +	316 (5)	0.3 (99)	—
aldosterone –	—	—	9 (111)
aldosterone +	—	—	26 (108)
Collecting duct			
vasopressin –	—	2.2 (99)	—
vasopressin +	48 (99)	2.4 (99)	—

[a] Abbreviations used: PCT, proximal convoluted tubule; PST, proximal straight tubule; DLH, descending limb of Henle; ALH, ascending limb of Henle.
[b] Sources indicated in parentheses.

tested experimentally (69) the notion that urine could be diluted in this medullary segment without active transport. Tubules were perfused with a sodium chloride solution in the presence of an isosmotic bath of low sodium and high urea concentration. Indeed, sodium efflux exceeded urea influx to yield a hypotonic effluent in the absence of active transport. Active transport was rigorously excluded by the observations that in the absence of imposed solute gradients (a) no net fluid absorption occurred, (b) no electrical potential difference was detected, and (c) there was no decrease in collected fluid osmolality. When salt gradients were imposed, net sodium flux was consistent with simple passive diffusion (71). Chloride movement, on the other hand, may involve facilitated as well as simple passive diffusion.

In the final analysis, this elegant series of experiments has provided a satisfactory explanation for the mechanism by which a morphologically unimpressive epithelium can participate in the process of urinary dilution through the utilization of solute concentration gradients generated in more remote regions of the kidney (79, 88).

THICK ASCENDING LIMB OF HENLE'S LOOP

In one respect the thick ascending limb is misnamed, for it is in fact the smallest of the tubules in the cortex. The medullary portion has an external diameter of 33 μm and a cell height of 4 μm, and the cortical portion is somewhat smaller.

The unique functional characteristics of this interesting segment were described almost simultaneously by Burg & Green (13), who studied the cortical portion, and Rocha and Kokko (97), who evaluated the medullary portion of the thick limb. It is interesting to note that the transport features of both cortical and medullary portions were found to be virtually identical.

Although sodium chloride was avidly absorbed, there was no evidence of fluid absorption coupled to the solute transport, probably due to the vanishingly low water permeability. Perhaps the most striking new feature of the epithelium was revealed in the finding that salt was absorbed in association with an electrical potential difference that was definitely lumen positive. The unique polarity of the potential difference suggested that anion rather than cation might be the ionic species actively transported. The potential was clearly dependent on chloride ions; replacement of sodium chloride with choline chloride had relatively little effect on the potential. Thus chloride was apparently transported actively against both a concentration and an electrical gradient. The observed sodium concentration gradient was consistent with passive movement in response to the lumen positive potential difference. However, in spite of a measured concentration gradient consistent with a passive mechanism of transport, flux ratios for labelled sodium were higher than predicted for a purely passive distribution. Thus, while sodium transport may not be entirely passive, active cation transport could conceivably contribute only a minor portion to net solute absorption.

The urea permeability of the thick ascending limb is low and unresponsive to vasopressin (99). It has been stated that the permeability to water does not respond to vasopressin either (99), but we could not find data in the published literature to support such a claim.

A segment analogous to the thick ascending limb, the "diluting segment" of the frog, toad, and salamander, has been examined in vitro by Stoner (110). The "diluting segment" of these amphibian species is comparable to the mammalian counterpart; it is impermeable to water, reabsorbs sodium chloride actively, and has a lumen positive potential difference that is decreased by ouabain and replacement of chloride ions in the bulk phase solutions. As observed in mammalian thick limbs, sodium chloride transport and the positive potential difference were diminished by luminal furosemide but not by amiloride. In view of the similarities to the mammalian thick limb, it is interesting that evidence for active potassium secretion was also obtained in the amphibian segment.

No functional differences between the medullary and cortical portions of the rabbit thick ascending limb have as yet been observed. A possible functional difference between these portions is suggested, however, by recent studies of adenylate cyclase activation by various hormones in nephron segments in vitro. While calcitonin stimulated adenylate cyclase activity in both the cortical and medullary portions of the thick limb (26), parathyroid hormone only stimulated adenylate cyclase in the cortical portion (25), and vasopressin stimulated adenylate cyclase primarily in the medullary portion (74). However, the functional significance of these findings may be questioned because of the high concentrations of hormone required to stimulate adenylate cyclase.

Diuretics in the Thick Ascending Limb

Studies of isolated perfused thick ascending limbs have provided a clearer understanding of how the potent "loop" diuretics inhibit salt transport. Burg and his associates examined the effect of the "loop" diuretics furosemide (22), the water soluble mercurial mersalyl (14), and the cysteine adduct of ethacrynic acid (15) in thick ascending limbs. Rocha & Kokko have also examined the effect of furosemide in this segment (85). A key observation of these studies was the finding that the diuretics were more than ten times more potent from the luminal, as opposed to the blood, side of the tubules. Perfusion of these compounds into the lumen resulted in a rapid and reversible decrease in the potential difference and a concurrent decrease in net chloride flux, suggesting a dominant effect on active chloride transport. Amiloride, a potent inhibitor of active sodium transport in the collecting tubule, had no effect on the thick ascending limb (111).

The observations on the luminal site of action of the "loop" diuretics, together with earlier findings in intact animals that probenecid completely blocked the natriuresis of furosemide, led Burg to suggest that the therapeutic efficacy and low incidence of toxicity of these drugs may be attributed to their effect on chloride transport, rather than sodium transport, and to the high concentration achieved at the site of action in the kidney (11).

DISTAL CONVOLUTED TUBULE

The distal convoluted tubule is very short in the rabbit (0.3–0.8 mm) and this tiny tubule has attracted only a few hardy explorers (55, 57). They have observed a relatively high electrical potential difference which is oriented lumen negative. This potential difference is not increased by mineralocorticoids and is not affected by spironolactone or triamterene. The tubules are also impermeable to water and unresponsive to vasopressin. These data are in agreement with the recent observation that the adenylate cyclase activity of the distal convoluted tubule is unresponsive to vasopressin (74). In this context, however, it should be noted that the functional studies with vasopressin were conducted at 37°C rather than 25°C. At the lower temperature, collecting tubules routinely respond to vasopressin in vitro, whereas at 37°C, the collecting tubules become refractory to the hormone (59). It may be instructive to reevaluate the effect of vasopressin on the water permeability of distal convoluted tubules at different ambient temperatures.

COLLECTING TUBULE

Collecting tubules traverse both the cortex and medulla and ultimately merge in the inner medulla to form collecting ducts. The collecting system, including both tubules and ducts, is of different embryologic origin than more proximal portions of the nephron and differs functionally from other segments in its responsiveness to vasopressin. In fact, the dependable and dramatic response to antidiuretic hormone and the high electrical potential difference made this a favorite segment for the early studies of perfused tubules.

The cells of this epithelium are of two types: the predominant light cells, and the less common intercalated or dark cells. The dark cells are more common in the cortex and gradually decrease in number as the tubule approaches the inner medulla. The morphologic heterogeneity in the distribution of dark cells between the cortical and medullary portions of the collecting tubule is not reflected in differences in water permeability, urea permeability, or vasopressin responsiveness. However, preliminary evidence suggests that there are significant differences in electrolyte transport between the two portions of the collecting tubule, and this difference correlates with the relative frequency of light and dark cells (109). On a cautionary note, it should be pointed out that any functional difference would correlate with frequency of dark cells, and would not necessarily indicate a cause-effect relationship.

The epithelial layer of the collecting tubule is "tight" both morphologically and functionally. The permeability to solutes and water is exceedingly low, and large differences in solute concentration can be maintained across the tubule wall. The measured electrical resistance is also high as would be predicted from the permeability characteristics. The original estimate of electrical resistance (18) was probably invalid because an electrical short circuit existed at the collecting end and the experimental method altered core resistance. When the experimental method was changed to keep core resistance constant and Sylgard was introduced to insulate the collecting end, electrical resistance was indeed found to be high at both 25°C (867 Ωcm^2) (64) and 37°C ($266\Omega cm^2$) (111). The electrical resistance is thought to be determined principally by tight junctions (63).

Fluid Absorption

Unlike most other segments of the nephron, fluid absorption in the collecting tubule is not necessarily coupled to active solute absorption. Fluid absorption only occurs in response to an osmotic gradient and is apparently passive since it continues unaltered when ouabain is added (49). Even with a gradient, significant fluid absorption only occurs in the presence of vasopressin. In the absence of hormone, active solute absorption may lead to the dilution of the luminal fluid (62). Vasopressin exerts its effect on fluid absorption by altering the water permeability of the epithelial layer and thus the rate of fluid movement at any given osmotic gradient. Vasopressin itself has no effect on net fluid absorption in the absence of an imposed gradient, although its effect on water permeability can be detected by measuring the diffusional flux of tritiated water (17, 47, 100).

Since net fluid absorption is dependent on the osmotic gradient as well as the presence of vasopressin, experimental results have generally been reported in terms of hydraulic water permeability, Lp, which takes the gradient into account. Early reports used several different methods to estimate the mean osmotic gradient since the profile of luminal osmolality along the length of the tubule had not been defined. Recently, however, three groups (5, 27, 38) have independently derived a formula which gives a precise value for Lp in perfused tubules:

$$Lp = \frac{-V^O C^O}{RTA} \left[\frac{C^O - C^L}{C^O \, C^L \, C^b} + \frac{1}{(C^b)^2} \ln \frac{(C^L - C^b) \, C^O}{(C^O - C^b) \, C^L} \right]$$

in terms of the absolute temperature, T; gas constant, R; surface area, A; perfusion rate V^O; and the osmotic concentrations of the bath, C^b; perfusate, C^O; and collected fluid C^L. This formula (and its equivalent in the other citations) is based on the assumption that the reflection coefficient is 1.0 for the solute determining the gradient and that there is no net change in the quantity of luminal solute.

The initial study by Grantham & Burg (47), conducted at 25°C, established that the cortical collecting tubule is responsive to vasopressin as well as cAMP, the postulated mediator of vasopressin action. They also observed that vasopressin was effective only from the blood side of the tubule. In the absence of vasopressin, collecting tubules have a small, but detectable permeability to water (5, 58, 106). Tubules are exquisitely sensitive to the hormone, responding to as little as 0.25 μU ml^{-1} (52), and achieve a maximal increase in permeability at concentrations in the physiologic range (52, 58, 100). The response to maximally effective concentrations of vasopressin has been similar in various studies conducted at 25°C both in the human (4) and in the rabbit, where results range from 105 X 10^{-7} to 150 X 10^{-7} cm sec^{-1} atm^{-1} (47, 58, 100). Even though a plateau is observed in the dose–response relationship with vasopressin, water permeability can be increased further by adding a cAMP phosphodiesterase inhibitor or by using a powerful cAMP analog (58).

Studies conducted at 37°C, as opposed to 25°C, are difficult to interpret because of the recent observation that collecting tubules become progressively and irreversibly insensitive to the hormone (59). The nature of this progressive insensitivity has not been established, but it may be related to the utilization of some substrate between the generation of cAMP and the ultimate change in membrane permeability. Regardless of the mechanism, this observation should signal researchers to be cautious in the examination and interpretation of hormone effects on renal tubules studied at 37°C.

The paths of transtubular water flow in response to vasopressin have been adduced from morphologic studies (43, 49). In the absence of vasopressin, cells swelled only when the bathing medium was hypotonic, indicating that the permeability barrier to water was located at the luminal border. In the presence of vasopressin, osmotic fluid absorption was accompanied by cell swelling and the development of dilated intercellular spaces. The intercellular spaces developed only when water flow occurred in the absorptive direction (lumen to bath) and were observed even when net transtubular flow was prevented by collapsing the lumen. It was therefore concluded that during water absorption, water enters the cell at the luminal membrane and exits from the sides as well as the base of the cell. Flow through tight junctions was excluded since the diameter of aqueous channels required to support the observed absorption, 42 Å (45), could not be confirmed by electron microscopy. Furthermore, vasopressin clearly has an effect on the cell membrane as indicated by an increase in mechanical deformability (44). Studies of osmotic flow rectification (106) support the conclusion derived from morphologic data that water flow through tight junctions is trivial.

The nature of water permeation through the luminal cell membrane, both with and without added vasopressin, has been examined by Schafer, Andreoli, and colleagues (5, 100, 101, 104). They have reasoned that the increase in the ratio of hydraulic and diffusional permeabilities cannot be explained by an increase in the diameter of pores in the luminal membrane, because the pore size required would be too large to limit the diffusion of small solutes, such as urea, to which the tubules are impermeable. The presence of significant unstirred layers has been offered as an alternative explanation for the discrepancy between diffusional and hydraulic water permeability. Schafer & Andreoli (101) made clever use of lipophilic solutes, which traverse the cell membrane by diffusion rather than by pores, and observed that unstirred layers were, in fact, present. However, since significant unstirred layers in the bulk phase solutions on both sides of the cell and in the intercellular space were excluded, the authors concluded that the cell cytoplasm itself was an unstirred layer, equivalent to a layer of water 25 times thicker than the actual cell layer (100, 101, 104). Since the diffusional resistance attributed to unstirred layers was similar for lipophilic solutes and water, they also concluded that both substances traverse the cell layer primarily by diffusion. They have argued further, based on data with osmotic transients and activation energies, that only a portion of the membrane is permeable to water and that vasopressin increases the area or number of sites available for water diffusion. Similarly, moderately lipophilic solutes, whose permeability is also increased by vasopressin, cross the membrane at discrete sites. The increased rate of permeation of lipophilic solutes after vasopressin indicates an increase in the area or number of sites and does not imply a change in the lipid composition or liquidity of the lipid matrix of the cell membrane (5).

Pharmacologic agents that might affect the vasopressin response of collecting tubules have been studied infrequently. In an early study, Grantham & Orloff (52) found that the prostaglandin PGE_1 could inhibit or reverse an established effect of vasopressin. The response to cAMP, on the other hand, was not inhibited by PGE_1. Since PGE_1 itself had a small effect on water permeability, and this effect could be enhanced by theophylline, the authors concluded that PGE_1 blocked the interaction of vasopressin with the receptor. Although PGE_1, rather than the naturally occuring PGE_2, was used, this study provided one of the first clues to a role for prostaglandins in the action of renal hormones. On the basis of this study, Grantham & Orloff suggested that endogenous prostaglandins might serve to modulate vasopressin action in vivo, a notion for which additional support has been obtained recently.

Ethacrynic acid (2) and furosemide (1) have been found to inhibit the effect of vasopressin on water permeability. However, the effect of cAMP on water permeability is not affected by ethacrynic acid. Since the inhibitory effect can be overcome with supramaximal concentrations of vasopressin, these agents apparently inhibit the binding of vasopressin to its receptor.

Cytochalasin B, a drug that interferes with microfilaments, appears to enhance the effect of vasopressin (3). By contrast, colchicine, which disrupts cytoplasmic microtubules, appears to inhibit the effect of vasopressin (3). A rigorous assessment of the effect of these interesting compounds on hormone action has not been published.

Solute Transport

Urea is transported to a minimal extent in the collecting tubule. In the first published study of collecting tubules, urea permeability was found to be quite low and did not change when vasopressin was added to the bathing medium (47). In subsequent work from the same laboratory, a significant artifact in this early study was eliminated by insulating the distal end of the tubule with the potting resin Sylgard (17). From this study it was learned that the permeability to urea was even lower, by an order of magnitude, than estimated originally; however, vasopressin had no effect on the permeability to urea or other related compounds (thiourea and acetamide). Virtually identical results have been obtained subsequently in outer medullary collecting tubules (99, 101) and, moreover, the permeability barrier for urea has been localized to the luminal cell border (101). The extremely low urea permeability of collecting tubules is a necessary element in urea recycling within the inner medulla and papilla and an essential component in the passive mechanism of urine concentration proposed by Kokko & Rector (88).

The observation that collecting tubules develop an electrical potential difference in the absence of imposed solute gradients provided the first evidence that active solute transport may occur in this segment (18). In tubules taken from rabbits on a regular laboratory diet, the electrical potential was usually oriented lumen-negative, but it was unstable and highly variable in magnitude when the tubules were first attached to the pipets. The electrical potential ultimately reached a steady value 80–100 min later. In the stable period, the potential difference averaged -25 ± 3 mV. Ouabain abolished or even reversed the polarity of the potential. It was also observed that the potential difference was extremely sensitive to intraluminal hydrostatic pressure. Since electrical resistance did not change when intraluminal pressure was increased, active electrolyte transport was apparently affected (18, 55, 64).

Evidence for active electrolyte transport in the perfused collecting tubule was obtained by Grantham, Burg & Orloff (48). Under slow flow conditions, sodium efflux from the lumen approximately equalled the rate of potassium influx and both fluxes were dependent on the presence of luminal sodium and bath potassium. With prolonged contact times, luminal sodium concentration could be reduced to 13 meq l^{-1} and potassium concentration increased to 136 meq l^{-1}. The concentration of potassium in the collected fluid was higher than could be accounted for by electrical forces alone; thus, it was suggested that potassium was actively secreted. Sodium, on the other hand, was clearly absorbed against a strong electrochemical gradient.

The apparent equivalence of sodium efflux and potassium influx observed in this study should not be taken as evidence for a strict 1:1 exchange of sodium for potassium. Although an approximate 1:1 ratio is observed at slow flow rates (48, 111), at higher flow rates the ratio of sodium absorption to potassium secretion may be 4:1, 6:1, or other intermediate ratios (93, 111). The nature of the effect of flow rate on the relative rates of sodium and potassium transport has not been established. Even though the rate of potassium transport is less than the rate of sodium transport under these conditions, potassium transport is probably still active since the observed rate of transport is greater than can be accounted for by the electrical potential (93, 111). However, the possible role of single file diffusion as an alternative explanation for potassium transport has not been excluded.

A number of factors have been shown to influence the rate of electrolyte transport in collecting tubules. As might be expected, an increase in temperature from 25° to 37°C is associated with an accelerated rate of transport for both sodium (from approximately 2.5 to 8.5 peq cm^{-1} sec^{-1}) (42, 93, 111) and potassium (from approximately 0.5 to 2.2 peq cm^{-1} sec^{-1}) (93, 111). The electrical potential difference, -35 ± 3 mV, is also somewhat higher than that observed at 25°C in animals on an ordinary laboratory diet (42, 48, 93, 111).

The influence of dietary sodium and potassium on potential difference in isolated tubules was examined by Frindt & Burg in studies conducted at 25°C (42). In general, the potential difference was more negative in the animals fed a high-potassium–low-sodium diet than in animals fed regular laboratory chow. The effect of diet on electrical potential difference is probably mediated by an increase in mineralocorticoid secretion since a hundred-fold increase in serum aldosterone concentration was observed in animals on the low-sodium–high-potassium diet as compared to the animals on an ordinary diet (55). Higher potential differences are also observed when animals are treated with desoxycorticosterone acetate (DOCA) for several days prior to dissection of the nephron segments (55, 93).

The experimental animals do not have to be pre-treated with DOCA to demonstrate an effect of mineralocorticoids on electrolyte transport. Addition of d-aldosterone to either lumen or bath causes the potential difference to increase within 10–20 min and the maximal effects are seen after 116 min. The latent period and the magnitude of the aldosterone effect are strongly temperature-dependent (57). In recent work, O'Neil & Helman (93) have examined the effect of DOCA pre-treatment on both the electrical potential difference and solute transport at 25°C. They found an increased rate of sodium transport, but potassium transport was enhanced to an even greater degree. The higher electrical potential difference was due not only to an increased rate of sodium and potassium transport, but also to an 80% decrease in chloride conductance. The reduced chloride conductance is presumably due to decreased shunting through tight junctions. Further studies with current-voltage plots suggested that DOCA had no effect on the electromotive force of the sodium and potassium pumps, but rather had an effect on the resistance to flow of these ions across the membrane.

In studies conducted at 25°C and with slow flow rates, DOCA pre-treatment had little effect on net solute transport since the increased rates of sodium and potassium transport were in opposite directions (93). This may not be true in studies conducted at 37°C since recent evidence indicates that the luminal fluid is diluted under these conditions (62). Whether the increase in net solute absorption is due to the higher temperature or to the perfusion rate is not clear. At any rate, the sodium absorption observed at 37°C in DOCA-treated animals is exceedingly high: 25.5 peq cm^{-1} sec^{-1} (108). This value is close to the rate of sodium absorption observed in the proximal convoluted tubule (Table 1). With this high rate of sodium transport, the collecting tubule could obviously be a major factor in the control of sodium balance in the intact animal. These data are consistent with the currently held view of the role of the collecting tubule in renal physiology. Once considered a mere conduit from the distal convoluted tubule to the renal pelvis, an increasingly important role has been assigned to the collecting tubule as the final regulator of sodium and potassium balance.

Vasopressin has a peculiar effect on the electrical potential and solute transport. When the hormone is added to the bathing medium, electrical potential difference increases for approximately 30 min, then decreases steadily to levels below the control (18, 42). When vasopressin is removed, the potential difference returns to the control level. Vasopressin has no effect on the electrical resistance (64) and the transient increase in potential is accompanied by a transient increase in sodium transport (42). The transient nature of the change in potential difference and sodium transport is perplexing, especially since there is a sustained increase in water permeability under the same conditions.

The effect of some other humoral factors on electrolyte transport has been examined in a few studies. Prostaglandins, which are natriuretic in vivo, had no effect on sodium transport in tubules obtained from rabbits on a normal diet (41). In contrast, PGE_2 caused a significant decrease in net sodium transport in tubules obtained from animals pre-treated with DOCA (108). A natriuretic factor obtained from patients with renal failure has been shown to inhibit the potential difference and sodium transport in this segment, suggesting that the increased fractional excretion of sodium in uremia may be due to the effect of a humoral substance on the collecting tubule (40).

Surprisingly few studies have examined the effect of diuretics in isolated collecting tubules. Furosemide does not alter electrolyte transport in this segment (22). Triamterene, effective only from the blood side of the tubule, can abolish the lumen-negative potential difference. Spironolactone also inhibits the potential difference in DOCA-treated animals and can prevent the increase in potential difference following aldosterone administration (57). The most thoroughly studied inhibitor of sodium transport is the experimental diuretic, amiloride. Addition of this drug to the perfusate immediately decreases active sodium and potassium transport, decreases the permeability to both electrolytes, and increases the electrical resistance of the epithelial layer (111). These effects are readily reversible when amiloride is removed. The effects of other diuretics, such as the thiazides, have not been reported.

Intraluminal pH may importantly influence the rate of potassium secretion. In studies conducted at 37°C, a reduction of lumen pH from 7.4 to 6.8 resulted in a 47% decrease in potassium secretion but only a 5% decrease in sodium transport (7). The transtubular potential difference increased in response to lumen acidification, presumably due to the reduction in potassium secretion. Thus, lumen acidification may play a role in the reduced potassium secretion observed in systemic acidosis in vivo. Although acidification of the bath, rather than the perfusate, was initially reported to have an effect on electrical potential difference (37), this observation was not confirmed (7).

The lumen-negative potential difference in collecting tubules has generally been associated with active cation transport from lumen to bath. However, a clearly lumen-positive potential difference has been observed in many tubules taken from rabbits on a normal diet (42, 55, 93), and occasionally after ouabain or amiloride (18, 55, 111). It has been consistently observed in human collecting tubules (77). The cause of this positive potential difference is not clear. In tubules exposed to amiloride, the positive potential was dependent on the presence of CO_2 or an acid bath. Furthermore, the magnitude of the potential was decreased by acetazolamide, suggesting that active hydrogen ion secretion might contribute to the generation of the positive potential. Active chloride transport from lumen to bath seemed unlikely, since replacement of chloride ions with sulfate had no effect on the potential (111). Somewhat different results have been obtained recently by Gross and colleagues (56). The positive potential observed in tubules obtained from rabbits on a high salt diet was only partially inhibited by acetazolamide and was dependent on the presence of chloride ions, suggesting active chloride absorption rather than hydrogen ion secretion as the cause of the positive potential. The reason for these differing results has not been established.

COLLECTING DUCT

Collecting ducts derive from the merging of collecting tubules in the inner medulla and papilla. Isolated collecting duct cells can be obtained as a relatively pure collection for study of certain transport processes (39). However, the ducts are difficult to perfuse in vitro because the diameter of the tubule is highly variable, the distance between branches is relatively short, and the interstitial tissue makes dissection difficult. Nevertheless, in spite of the difficulties, one study of perfused collecting ducts has been published (99). The most important feature of this study was the observation that urea permeability was an order of magnitude greater than that observed in cortical and outer medullary collecting tubules. Urea permeability did not increase when vasopressin was added to the bathing medium. The higher urea permeability observed in this segment is essential for urea recycling in the inner medulla and papilla.

In the absence of vasopressin, the diffusional water permeability was similar to that found in cortical and outer medullary collecting tubules. In the presence of vasopressin, the increase in water permeability was much less than that observed in the collecting tubule. It should be noted that the collecting duct experiments were conducted at 37°C. Therefore the results should be interpreted with caution in view of the progressive insensitivity to vasopressin observed in the collecting tubule at 37°C (59).

CONCLUSIONS

Studies of single isolated tubules in vitro have contributed several important new findings about the nature of renal function. The mechanism of salt absorption in the ascending limb of Henle, the heterogeneity of transport in the proximal tubule, the cellular basis of hormone action in the collecting tubule, and the permeability characteristics of the loop of Henle are but a few examples. It must be acknowledged, however, that the highly integrated process of urine formation cannot be adduced exclusively from studies of isolated segments. The function of each part ultimately must be viewed and studied in the context of the intact whole kidney. Thus the isolated tubule approach complements, but does not supplant, the more traditional techniques of inquiry.

There is obviously much more to be learned about the cellular biology of renal tubules. With better analytical methods and newer investigative strategies there is reason to believe that research on isolated renal tubules may yield answers to some very basic questions about the nature of active solute transport and membrane permeation.

ACKNOWLEDGMENTS

We gratefully acknowledge the secretarial assistance of Alice Dworzack, Judy Irish, and Karen Robson.

Literature Cited

1. Abramow, M. 1974. Tubular functions studied by microperfusion of isolated renal tubules. In *Advances in Nephrology,* ed. J. Hamburger, J. Crosnier, M. H. Maxwell, 3:275–88. Chicago: Yearbook Medical Publisher. 356 pp.
2. Abramow, M. 1974. Effects of ethacrynic acid on the isolated collecting tubule. *J. Clin. Invest.* 53:796–804
3. Abramow, M. 1976. Effect of vasopressin on water transport in the kidney: possible role of microtubules and microfilaments. In *Intestinal Ion Transport,* ed. J. W. L. Robinson, pp. 173–88. Baltimore: University Park Press. 405 pp.
4. Abramow, M., Dratwa, M. 1974. Effect of vasopressin on the isolated human collecting duct. *Nature* 250:492–93
5. Al-Zahid, G., Schafer, J. A., Troutman, S. L., Andreoli, T. E. 1977. Effect of antidiuretic hormone on water and solute permeation, and the activation energies for these processes, in mammalian cortical collecting tubules. *J. Membrane Biol.* 31:103–129
6. Barfuss, D. W., Dantzler, W. H. 1976. Glucose transport in isolated perfused proximal tubules of snake kidney. *Am. J. Physiol.* 231:1716–28

7. Boudry, J. F., Stoner, L. C., Burg, M. B. 1976. Effect of acid lumen pH on potassium transport in renal cortical collecting tubules. *Am. J. Physiol.* 230:239–44
8. Bourdeau, J. E., Carone, F. A. 1973. Contraluminal serum albumin uptake in isolated perfused renal tubules. *Am. J. Physiol.* 224:399–404
9. Bourdeau, J. E., Carone, F. A., Ganote, C. E. 1972. Serum albumin uptake in isolated perfused renal tubules. *J. Cell Biol.* 54:382–98
10. Bourdeau, J. E., Chen, E. R. Y., Carone, F. A. 1973. Insulin uptake in the renal proximal tubule. *Am. J. Physiol.* 225:1399–1404
11. Burg, M. B. 1976. Tubular chloride transport and the mode of action of some diuretics. *Kidney Int.* 9:189–97
12. Burg, M., Grantham, J., Abramow, M., Orloff, J. 1966. Preparation and study of fragments of single rabbit nephrons. *Am. J. Physiol.* 210:1293–98
13. Burg, M. B., Green, N. 1973. Function of the thick ascending limb of Henle's loop. *Am. J. Physiol.* 224:659–68
14. Burg, M., Green, N. 1973. Effect of mersalyl on the thick ascending limb of Henle's loop. *Kidney Int.* 4:245–51
15. Burg, M., Green, N. 1973. Effect of ethacrynic acid on the thick ascending

limb of Henle's loop. *Kidney Int.* 4:301–8

16. Burg, M. B., Green, N. 1976. Role of monovalent ions in the reabsorption of fluid by isolated perfused proximal renal tubules of the rabbit. *Kidney Int.* 10:221–28

17. Burg, M., Helman, S., Grantham, J., Orloff, J. 1968. Effect of vasopressin on the permeability of isolated rabbit cortical collecting tubules to urea, acetamide, and thiourea. In *Urea and the Kidney.* ed. B. Schmidt-Nielsen, D. W. S. Kerr, pp. 193–99. Amsterdam: Excerpta Medica Foundation. 495 pp.

18. Burg, M. B., Isaacson, L., Grantham, J., Orloff, J. 1968. Electrical properties of isolated perfused rabbit renal tubules. *Am. J. Physiol.* 215:788–94

19. Burg, M. B., Orloff, J. 1968. Control of fluid absorption in the renal proximal tubules. *J. Clin. Invest.* 47:2016–24

20. Burg, M. B., Orloff, J. 1970. Electrical potential difference across proximal convoluted tubules. *Am. J. Physiol.* 219:1714–16

21. Burg, M., Patlak, C., Green, N., Villey, D. 1976. Organic solutes in fluid absorption by renal proximal convoluted tubules. *Am. J. Physiol.* 231:627–37

22. Burg, M., Stoner, L., Cardinal, J., Green, N. 1973. Furosemide effect on isolated perfused tubules. *Am. J. Physiol.* 225:119–24

23. Burg, M. B., Weller, P. F. 1969. Iodopyracet transport by isolated perfused flounder proximal renal tubules. *Am. J. Physiol.* 217:1053–56

24. Cardinal, J., Lutz, M., Burg, M. B., Orloff, J. 1975. Lack of relationship of potential difference to fluid absorption in the proximal renal tubule. *Kidney Int.* 7:94–102

25. Chabardès, D., Imbert, M., Clique, A., Montégut, M., Morel, F. 1975. PTH sensitive adenyl cyclase activity in different segments of the rabbit nephron. *Pflügers Arch.* 354:229–39

26. Chabardès, D., Imbert-Teboul, M., Montégut, M., Clique, A., Morel, F. 1976. Distribution of calcitonin-sensitive adenylate cyclase activity along the rabbit kidney tubule. *Proc. Natl. Acad. Sci. USA* 73:3608–12

27. Chonko, A. M., Irish, J. M. III, Welling, D. J. Microperfusion of isolated tubules. In *Methods in Pharmacology, Vol 4B: Renal Pharmacology,* ed. M. Martinez-Maldonado. New York: Plenum. In press.

28. Chonko, A. M., Osgood, R. W., Nickel, A. E., Ferris, T. F., Stein, J. H. 1975. The measurement of nephron filtration rate and absolute reabsorption in the proximal tubule of the rabbit kidney. *J. Clin. Invest.* 56:232–35

29. Dantzler, W. H. 1973. Characteristics of urate transport by isolated perfused snake proximal renal tubules. *Am. J. Physiol.* 224:445–53

30. Dantzler, W. H. 1974. PAH transport by snake proximal renal tubules: Differences from urate transport. *Am. J. Physiol.* 226:634–41

31. Dantzler, W. H. 1974. K^+ effects on PAH transport and membrane permeabilities in isolated snake renal tubules. *Am. J. Physiol.* 227:1361–70

32. Dantzler, W. H., Bentley, S. K. 1975. High K^+ effects on PAH transport and permeabilities in isolated snake renal tubules. *Am. J. Physiol.* 229:191–99

33. Dantzler, W. H., Bentley, S. K. 1976. Low Na^+ effects on PAH transport in isolated snake renal tubules. *Am. J. Physiol.* 230:256–62

34. Dellasega, M., Grantham, J. J. 1973. Regulation of renal tubule cell volume in hypotonic media. *Am. J. Physiol.* 224:1288–94

35. Dennis, V. W. 1976. Influence of bicarbonate on parathyroid hormone-induced changes in fluid absorption by the proximal tubule. *Kidney Int.* 10:373–80

36. Dennis, V. W., Woodhall, P. B., Robinson, R. R. 1976. Characteristics of phosphate transport in isolated proximal tubule. *Am. J. Physiol.* 231:979–85

37. Douglas, R. J., Isaacson, L. C. 1972. Peritubular pH and transtubular potentials in isolated perfused cortical collecting ducts of rabbit kidney. *J. Physiol.* 221:645–55

38. DuBois, R., Verniory, A., Abramow, M. 1976. Computation of the osmotic water permeability of perfused tubule segments. *Kidney Int.* 10:478–79

39. Dworzack, K. L., Grantham, J. J. 1975. Preparation of renal papillary collecting duct cells for study *in vitro. Kidney Int.* 8:191–94

40. Fine, L. G., Bourgoignie, J. J., Hwang, K. H., Bricker, N. S. 1976. On the influence of the natriuretic factor from patients with chronic uremia on the bioelectric properties and sodium transport of the isolated mammalian collecting tubule. *J. Clin. Invest.* 58:500–597

41. Fine, L. G., Trizna, W. 1977. Influence of prostaglandins on sodium transport of isolated medullary nephron segments. *Am. J. Physiol.* 132:F383–90

42. Frindt, G., Burg, M. B. 1972. Effect of vasopressin on sodium transport in renal cortical collecting tubules. *Kidney Int.* 1:224–31

43. Ganote, C. E., Grantham, J. J., Moses, H. L., Burg, M. B., Orloff, J. 1968. Ultrastructural studies of vasopressin effect on isolated perfused renal collecting tubules of the rabbit. *J. Cell Biol.* 36:355–67

44. Grantham, J. J. 1970. Vasopressin: Effect on deformability of urinary surface of collecting duct cells. *Science* 168:1093–95

45. Grantham, J. J. 1971. Mode of water transport in mammalian renal collecting tubules. *Fed. Proc.* 30:14–21

46. Grantham, J. J. 1972. Sodium transport in isolated renal tubules. In *Modern Diuretic Therapy in the Treatment of Cardiovascular and Renal Disease*, ed. A. F. Lant, G. M. Wilson, pp. 220–28. Amsterdam: Exerpta Medica International, 365 pp.

47. Grantham, J. J., Burg, M. B. 1966. Effect of vasopressin and cyclic AMP on permeability of isolated collecting tubules. *Am. J. Physiol.* 211:255–59

48. Grantham, J. J., Burg, M. B., Orloff, J. 1970. The nature of transtubular Na and K transport in isolated rabbit renal collecting tubules. *J. Clin. Invest.* 49:1815–26

49. Grantham, J. J., Ganote, C. E., Burg, M. B., Orloff, J. 1969. Paths of transtubular water flow in isolated renal collecting tubules. *J. Cell Biol.* 41:562–76

50. Grantham, J. J., Irwin, R. L., Qualizza, P. B., Tucker, D. R., Whittier, F. C. 1973. Fluid secretion in isolated proximal straight renal tubules. *J. Clin. Invest.* 52:2441–50

51. Grantham, J. J., Lowe, C. M., Dellasega, M., Cole, B. R. 1977. Effect of hypotonic medium on K and Na content of proximal renal tubules. *Am. J. Physiol.* 232:F42–F49

52. Grantham, J. J., Orloff, J. 1968. Effect of prostaglandin E_1 on the permeability response of the isolated collecting tubule to vasopressin, adenosine 3'5'-monophosphate, and theophylline. *J. Clin. Invest.* 47:1154–61

53. Grantham, J. J., Qualizza, P. B., Irwin, R. L. 1974. Net fluid secretion in proximal straight renal tubules in vitro: role of PAH. *Am. J. Physiol.* 226:191–97

54. Grantham, J. J., Qualizza, P. B., Welling, L. W. 1972. Influence of serum proteins on net fluid reabsorption of isolated proximal tubules. *Kidney Int.* 2:66–75

55. Gross, J. B., Imai, M., Kokko, J. P. 1975. A functional comparison of the cortical collecting tubule and the distal convoluted tubule. *J. Clin. Invest.* 55:1284–94

56. Gross, J. B., Jacobson, H. R., Kawamura, S., Kokko, J. P. 1975. Demonstration of electrogenic chloride transport in rabbit cortical collecting tubules (CCT). *Kidney Int.* 8:477 (Abstr.)

57. Gross, J. B., Kokko, J. P. 1977. Effects of aldosterone and potassium-sparing diuretics on electrical potential differences across the distal nephron. *J. Clin. Invest.* 59:82–89

58. Hall, D. A., Barnes, L. D., Dousa, T. P. 1977. Cyclic AMP in action of antidiuretic hormone: Effects of exogenous cyclic AMP and its new analog. *Am. J. Physiol.* 232:F368–76

59. Hall, D. A., Grantham, J. J. 1977. Transient response to vasopressin in isolated perfused rabbit cortical collecting tubules. *Fed. Proc.* 36:592 (Abstr.)

60. Hamburger, R. J., Lawson, N. L., Dennis, V. W. 1974. Effects of cyclic adenosine nucleotides on fluid absorption by different segments of proximal tubule. *Am. J. Physiol.* 227:396–401

61. Hamburger, R. J., Lawson, N. L., Schwartz, J. H. 1976. Response to parathyroid hormone in defined segments of proximal tubule. *Am. J. Physiol.* 230:286–90

62. Hanley, M. J., Kokko, J. P. 1977. Characteristics of chloride transport across the rabbit cortical collecting tubule (CCT): Response to desoxycorticosterone (DOCA). *Clin. Res.* 25:506A (Abstr.)

63. Helman, S. I. 1972. Determination of electrical resistance of the isolated cortical collecting tubule and its possible anatomical location. *Yale J. Biol. Med.* 45:339–45

64. Helman, S. I., Grantham, J. J., Burg, M. B. 1971. Effect of vasopressin on electrical resistance of renal cortical collecting tubules. *Am. J. Physiol.* 220:1825–32

65. Horster, M., Burg, M., Potts, D., Orloff, J. 1973. Fluid absorption by proximal tubules in the absence of a colloid osmotic gradient. *Kidney Int.* 4:6–11

66. Horster, M., Larsson, L. 1976. Mechanisms of fluid absorption during proximal tubule development. *Kidney Int.* 10:348–63

67. Imai, M. 1977. Function of the thin ascending limb of Henle of rats and ham-

sters perfused in vitro. *Am. J. Physiol.* 232:F201–F209

68. Imai, M., Kokko, J. P. 1972. Effect of peritubular protein concentration on reabsorption of sodium and water in isolated perfused proximal tubules. *J. Clin. Invest.* 51:314–25

69. Imai, M., Kokko, J. P. 1974. Sodium chloride, urea, and water transport in the thin ascending limb of Henle. *J. Clin. Invest.* 53:393–402

70. Imai, M., Kokko, J. P. 1974. Transtubular oncotic pressure gradients and net fluid transport in isolated proximal tubules. *Kidney Int.* 6:138–45

71. Imai, M., Kokko, J. P. 1976. Mechanism of sodium and chloride transport in the thin ascending limb of Henle. *J. Clin. Invest.* 58:1054–60

72. Imai, M., Seldin, D. W., Kokko, J. P. 1977. Effect of perfusion rate on the fluxes of water, sodium, chloride and urea across the proximal convoluted tubule. *Kidney Int.* 11:18–27

73. Imbert, M., Charbardès, D., Montégut, M., Clique, A., Morel, F. 1975. Adenylate cyclase activity along rabbit nephron as measured in single isolated segments. *Pflügers Arch.* 354:213–28

74. Imbert, M., Charbardès, D., Montégut, M., Clique, A., Morel, F. 1975. Vasopressin dependent adenylate cyclase in single segments of rabbit kidney tubule. *Pflügers Arch.* 357:173–86

75. Irish, J. M. III, Dantzler, W. H. 1976. PAH transport and fluid absorption by isolated perfused frog proximal renal tubules. *Am. J. Physiol.* 230:1509–16

76. Jacobson, H. R. 1977. Effect of 8-[p-chlorophenylthio] cyclic AMP (ClPheS-cAMP) on proximal tubular reabsorption. *Clin. Res.* 25:436A (Abstr.)

77. Jacobson, H. R., Gross, J. B., Kawamura, S., Waters, J. D., Kokko, J. P. 1976. Electrophysiological study of isolated perfused human collecting ducts. Ion dependency of the transepithelial potential difference. *J. Clin. Invest.* 58:1233–39

78. Jacobson, H. R., Kokko, J. P. 1976. Intrinsic differences in various segments of the proximal convoluted tubule. *J. Clin. Invest.* 57:818–25

79. Jamison, R. L., Maffly, R. H. 1976. The urinary concentrating mechanism. *N. Engl. J. Med.* 295:1059–67

80. Kawamura, S., Imai, M., Seldin, D. W., Kokko, J. P. 1975. Characteristics of salt and water transport in superficial and juxtamedullary straight segments

of proximal tubules. *J. Clin. Invest.* 55:1269–77

81. Kawamura, S., Kokko, J. P. 1976. Urea secretion by the straight segment of the proximal tubule. *J. Clin. Invest.* 58:604–12

82. Kokko, J. P. 1970. Sodium chloride and water transport in the descending limb of Henle. *J. Clin. Invest.* 49:1838–46

83. Kokko, J. P. 1972. Urea transport in the proximal tubule and the descending limb of Henle. *J. Clin. Invest.* 51:1999–2008

84. Kokko, J. P. 1973. Proximal tubule potential difference. *J. Clin. Invest.* 52:1362–67

85. Kokko, J. P. 1974. Membrane characteristics governing salt and water transport in the loop of Henle. *Fed. Proc.* 33:25–30

86. Kokko, J. P., Burg, M. B., Orloff, J. 1971. Characteristics of NaCl and water transport in the renal proximal tubule. *J. Clinc. Invest.* 50:69–76

87. Kokko, J. P., Rector, F. C. 1971. Flow dependence of transtubular potential difference in isolated perfused segments of rabbit proximal convoluted tubule. *J. Clin. Invest.* 50:2745–50

88. Kokko, J. P., Rector, F. C. Jr. 1972. Countercurrent multiplication system without active transport in inner medulla. *Kidney Int.* 2:214–23

89. Kokko, J. P., Rector, F. C., Seldin, D. W. 1970. Mechanism of salt and water reabsorption in proximal convoluted tubule (PCT). *Fourth Annu. Meet. Am. Soc. Nephrol. Abstr.:* 42 (Abstr.)

90. Larsson, L., Horster, M. 1976. Ultrastructure and net fluid transport in isolated perfused developing proximal tubules. *J. Ultrastruct. Res.* 54:276–85

91. Linshaw, M. A., Stapleton, F. B. 1976. Estimation of intracellular macromolecular osmotic pressure of renal tubules. *Kidney Int.* 10:591 (Abstr.)

92. Lutz, M. D., Cardinal, J., Burg, M. B. 1973. Electrical resistance of renal proximal tubule perfused in vitro. *Am. J. Physiol.* 225:729–34

93. O'Neil, R. G., Helman, S. I. 1976. Influence of DOCA on ion conductances of cortical collecting tubules. *Kidney Int.* 10:594 (Abstr.)

94. Peterson, D. R., Oparil, S., Flouret, G., Carone, F. A. 1977. Handling of angiotensin II and oxytocin by renal tubular segments perfused in vitro. *Am. J. Physiol.* 232:F319–25

95. Porter, R. D., Cathcart-Rake, W. F., Wan, S. H., Whittier, F. C., Grantham, J. J. 1975. Secretory activity and aryl

acid content of serum, urine, and cerebrospinal fluid in normal and uremic man. *J. Lab. Clin. Med.* 85:723–33

96. Randle, H. W., Dantzler, W. H. 1973. Effects of K^+ and Na^+ on urate transport by isolated perfused snake renal tubules. *Am. J. Physiol.* 225:1206–14

97. Rocha, A. S., Kokko, J. P. 1973. Sodium chloride and water transport in the medullary thick ascending limb of Henle. *J. Clin. Invest.* 52:612–23

98. Rocha, A. S., Kokko, J. P. 1973. Membrane characteristics regulating potassium transport out of the isolated perfused descending limb of Henle. *Kidney Int.* 4:326–30

99. Rocha, A. S., Kokko, J. P. 1974. Permeability of medullary nephron segments to urea and water: Effect on vasopressin. *Kidney Int.* 6:379–87

100. Schafer, J. A., Andreoli, T. E. 1972. Cellular constraints to diffusion. *J. Clin. Invest.* 51:1264–78

101. Schafer, J. A., Andreoli, T. E. 1972. The effect of antidiuretic hormone on solute flows in mammalian collecting tubules. *J. Clin. Invest.* 51:1279–86

102. Schafer, J. A., Andreoli, T. E. 1976. Anion transport processes in the mammalian superficial proximal straight tubule. *J. Clin. Invest.* 58:500–513

103. Schafer, J. A., Andreoli, T. E. 1977. Perfusion of isolated mammalian renal tubules. In *Transport Across Biologic Membranes*, Vol. IV, ed. D. C. Tosteson, G. H. Giebisch, H. H. Ussing. New York: Springer. In press

104. Schafer, J. A., Patlak, C. S., Andreoli, T. E. 1974. Osmosis in cortical collecting tubules: A theoretical and experimental analysis of the osmotic transient phenomenon. *J. Gen. Physiol.* 64:201–27

105. Schafer, J. A., Patlak, C. S., Andreoli, T. E. 1975. A component of fluid absorption linked to passive ion flows in the superficial pars recta. *J. Gen. Physiol.* 66:445–71

106. Schafer, J. A., Troutman, S. L., Andreoli, T. E. 1974. Osmosis in cortical collecting tubules: ADH-independent osmotic flow rectification. *J. Gen. Physiol.* 64:228–40

107. Schafer, J. A., Troutman, S. L., Andreoli, T. E. 1974. Volume reabsorption, transepithelial potential differences, and ionic permeability properties in mammalian superficial proximal

straight tubules. *J. Gen. Physiol.* 64:582–607

108. Stokes, J. B., Kokko, J. P. 1976. Effects of prostaglandin E_2 (PGE_2) on Na^+ transport across the rabbit cortical collecting tubule (CCT). *Kidney Int.* 10:600 (Abstr.)

109. Stokes, J. B., Tisher, C. C., Kokko, J. P. 1977. Heterogeneity of structure and function in the rabbit collecting tubule. *Clin. Res.* 25:449A (Abstr.)

110. Stoner, L. C. Isolated, perfused amphibian renal tubules: The diluting segment. *Am. J. Physiol.* In press

111. Stoner, L. C., Burg, M. B., Orloff, J. 1974. Ion transport in cortical collecting tubule: Effect of amiloride. *Am. J. Physiol.* 227:453–59

112. Tisher, C. C., Kokko, J. P. 1974. Relationship between peritubular oncotic pressure gradients and morphology in isolated proximal tubules. *Kidney Int.* 6:146–56

113. Tune, B. M., Burg, M. B. 1971. Glucose transport by proximal renal tubules. *Am. J. Physiol.* 221:580–85

114. Tune, B. M., Burg, M. B., Patlak, C. S. 1969. Characteristics of p-aminohippurate transport in proximal renal tubules. *Am. J. Physiol.* 217:1057–63

115. Warnock, D. G., Burg, M. B. 1977. Urinary acidification: CO_2 transport by the rabbit proximal straight tubule. *Am. J. Physiol.* 232:F20–F25

116. Welling, L. W., Grantham, J. J. 1972. Physical properties of isolated perfused renal tubules and tubular basement membranes. *J. Clin. Invest.* 51:1063–75

117. Welling, L. W., Welling, D. J. 1975. Pressure–flow–diameter relationships in isolated perfused thin limb of Henle. *Am. J. Physiol.* 229:1–7

118. Welling, L. W., Welling, D. J. 1975. Surface areas of brush border and lateral cell walls in the rabbit proximal nephron. *Kidney Int.* 8:343–48

119. Welling, L. W., Welling, D. J. 1976. Shape of epithelial cells and intercellular channels in the rabbit proximal nephron. *Kidney Int.* 9:385–94

120. Woodhall, P. B., Tisher, C. C., Simonton, C. A., Robinson, R. R. 1976. Relationship between p-aminohippurate (PAH) secretion and cellular morphology in superficial (SF) and juxtamedullary (JM) proximal tubules (PT). *Clin. Res.* 24:417A (Abstr.)

Ann. Rev. Physiol. 1978. 40:279–306
Copyright © 1978 by Annual Reviews Inc. All rights reserved

SEXUAL DIFFERENTIATION   ❖1193

Jean D. Wilson

Department of Internal Medicine, University of Texas
Southwestern Medical School, Dallas, Texas 75235

INTRODUCTION

In the mammal, embryos of both sexes develop in an identical fashion for a portion of gestation, and only thereafter do anatomical and physiological development diverge to result in the formation of the male and female phenotypes. The gross anatomical features of this process are largely complete by the time of birth, but certain functional and structural aspects of sexual development, including maturation of the genital tract and gonads, are not finished until the postnatal period. The pioneering work of Jost (80–82) established that sexual differentiation is a sequential and ordered process; chromosomal (or genetic) sex, established at the time of conception, governs the development of gonadal sex; and gonadal sex, in turn, regulates the development of phenotypic sex. However, it is now clear that the processes by which gonadal and phenotypic sex are established also depend on the expression of specific genes at every stage. Thus, in a real sense, the entire process of sexual development depends on a sequential series of interactions between regulatory factors and the genetic machinery.

There is probably no aspect of embryological development in which the forces that regulate the process and the nature of the genes involved are as well understood as in the case of sexual differentiation. This fortunate circumstance is the result of two factors. First, most of the hormonal mechanisms by which the gonads dictate the development of phenotypic sex have been identified, and the molecular processes by which certain of these hormones act have been defined in considerable detail in the recent past. Second, aberrations at any stage of sexual development, whether due to environmental causes, multifactoral etiologies, chromosomal nondisjunction, or single gene mutations, produce profound consequences, each of which is expressed as a characteristic abnormality in the sexual phenotype.

279

0066-4278/78/0301-0279$01.00

The analysis of the single gene mutations that produce aberrations in sexual development in man and animals has been particularly informative in defining the molecular and genetic determinants that regulate the process in the normal. Identification of such a large number of genes involved in the process [a minimum of 19 in man (57, 165)] is probably not the result of greater complexity for sexual development than for other developmental processes. Rather, it is assumed to be the consequence of the fact that normal sexual development is essential only to the survival of the species and not to the life of individuals, whereas developmental defects in organ systems essential to life frequently cause lethal abnormalities that result in abortion. Thus, as a result of information obtained at endocrinological, molecular, genetic, and clinical levels, we now have considerable insight into the overall programming by which sexual differentiation takes place.

In this review, attention is directed first toward the anatomic events and then to the regulatory factors that control this sequence. It should be recognized that the formation of the final sexual phenotype involves functional as well as anatomical processes. The former, which include the development of gender identity, the regulation of hypothalamic-pituitary function, the imprinting of enzymatic development, and certain aspects of behavior, are not considered here. While the fundamental mechanisms of sexual differentiation are thought to be the same in all species, the time sequence and certain anatomical aspects of the process vary. The focus of this review is on the time sequence and events in the human, and information derived from other species is included only when appropriate.

ANATOMICAL EVENTS IN SEXUAL DIFFERENTIATION

Establishment of Genetic Sex

Chromosomal sex is established at the moment of fertilization of the ovum. In the mammal, the homogametic state in which the two sex chromosomes are identical (XX) is female, and the heterogametic state (XY) is male. The ovum, containing 22 autosomes and one X chromosome, is penetrated by one spermatozoon of the surrounding swarm, half of which contain 22 autosomes and a Y chromosome and half of which contain 22 autosomes and an X chromsome. If the fertilizing sperm contains an X chromosome, the zygote will have a 46,XX composition characteristic of the female; if the successful sperm carries a Y, the 46,XY karyotype characteristic of the male will result. It has been assumed generally that the Y chromosome contains determinants that are essential for the development of maleness and, in particular, for the development of a testis and that either the X chromosomes, the autosomes, or both, are female-determining (18, 48, 145).

Analysis of the clinical disorders that result from nondisjunctions of the X and Y chromosomes has substantiated the fundamental validity of this view. For example, no matter how many X chromosomes are present, if a Y chromosome is also present (as in 47,XXY or 48,XXXY individuals) a testis develops, and the fundamental phenotype is that of a male (albeit usually sterile) (41). Furthermore in man and in the mouse, the XO individual is a phenotypic female (42, 132, 157) whereas in species such as *Drosophila* both the XO and XY phenotypes are male (145). As a consequence, it has been concluded that during evolution critical information has been transferred from the autosomes to the Y so that in mammals the Y contains information essential for the determination of maleness (145).

However, it is now clear from analysis of other forms of abnormal sexual development in man and animals, particularly those resulting from single gene mutations, that genetic sex is more complicated than can be explained by such a simple mechanism. Indeed, genes essential for normal male development are also located on the X chromosome (96, 101), and genes essential to the development of both male and female phenotypes are located on the autosomes (57, 165). While certain of these genes play a role only in the terminal phases of sexual differentiation (for example, those that provide the essential machinery for steroid hormone synthesis and for hormone action within cells), others are essential for the differentiation of the gonads themselves. In the syndrome of pure gonadal dysgenesis of the familial 46,XX type, in which streak gonads develop despite the presence of a normal female karotype, at least seven sibships (three consanguineous) are suggestive of autosomal recessive inheritance, implying that at least one autosomal gene is essential for the development of a normal ovary (65, 79, 139). Furthermore, several pedigrees of familial pure gonadal dysgenesis of the 46,XY variety have been identified in which genetic men differentiate as women with streak gonads and in which the mutation involves an X-linked gene (29, 31, 38, 40, 146). Evidence for autosomal recessive inheritance has been assembled for the following disorders: (*a*) goats with the sex reversal syndrome, in which XX animals develop a testis and male phenotype (67, 142); (*b*) some cases of human familial true hermaphroditism of the 46,XX type, in which affected individuals develop both ovaries and testes in the absence of a Y chromosome (30, 103, 109, 131); (*c*) congenital anorchia in the mouse, in which the testicular development in XY males is incomplete because of failure of migration of the germ cells into the gonadal folds (104, 105); and (*d*) the vestigial-testis defect in the rat, in which the fetal interstitial cells fail to mature (11).

Thus, normal differentiation of the ovary and testis is controlled by specific autosomal genes as well as by genes on the sex chromosomes, and development of the normal testis requires genes on the X chromosome as well as those on the autosomes and the Y. Consequently, it is clear that genetic sex is complex and cannot be explained by the composition of the sex chromosomes alone. As noted above, a minimal estimate of nineteen genes involved in the process in man has been derived from analysis of single gene mutations, and the elucidation of the molecular biology by which their normal alleles act should eventually allow characterization of the entire complement of genetic determinants involved in the development of the completed male and female phenotypes.

Establishment of Gonadal Sex

The germ cells do not originate in the area of the embryo that corresponds to the gonad. Indeed, in the early embryo all germ cells are located in the endoderm of the yolk sac near the allantoic evagination, but by about the 1 mm stage of development of the human embryo, they have been transferred from the yolk sac to the mesoderm of the gut (124, 171). Shortly thereafter, the germ cells leave the gut and move through the mesentery to advance laterally by pseudopodal movement toward the genital ridges of the coelomic epithelium, which are located on the medial aspect of the mesonephros. The presence of pseudopods and the fact that the germ cells reach a specific location in the primitive gonads suggest that the course of the migration is oriented by some chemotactic substance elaborated by the prospective gonadal region. During the migration, the germ cells increase steadily in number by mitotic division. After the germ cells have reached their final destination, the primitive gonad of both sexes consists of three components—the primordial germ cells themselves, the coelomic epithelium, and the underlying mesenchyme of the mesonephric (or genital) ridge. Until later in embryogenesis (embryos of 15–20 mm length in man), the development of the gonads and the urogenital tracts is indistinguishable in the two sexes. Beginning at about the sixth week of development, the testis in the human male embryo undergoes rapid histological development, commencing with formation of seminiferous tubules and then the development of interstitial cells (51). During this period the potential ovaries grow but undergo little if any histologic differentiation (51, 58). Later the germ cells in the ovary become grouped and enter meiosis. Still later they become surrounded by follicular cells, and eventually a definitive ovary with follicles and stroma results. The factors that regulate the development of the indifferent gonad into the testis or ovary are poorly understood, although both sex chromosomes appear to be active in the embryonic germ cells of the ovary, in contrast to peripheral tissues in which random inactivation of one X chromosome occurs (95). Indeed, it is not certain whether the genetic determinants on the Y chromosome act directly to induce differentiation of the testis or whether they activate genes on other chromosomes. There has

been considerable recent interest in the H-Y antigen, a cell surface component that is present in males of all mammalian species. In a varity of types
of intersex the presence of the H-Y antigen correlates more closely with the
presence of a testis than with the presence of a Y chromosome (14, 55,
149–154), a relation that is in keeping with the possibility that the H-Y
antigen is coded by an autosomal or X-linked gene that is activated in the
normal by some gene product of the Y chromosome (37, 138). The suggestion has been made that the H-Y antigen itself acts as the hormone or
inducer responsible for differentiation of the indifferent gonad into a testis
(118, 119), but whether the antigen is causally linked to testicular differentiation or is instead a passive marker of the process is at present unclear.

Establishment of Phenotypic Sex

Although it is convenient to speak of an indifferent phase of sexual differentiation, in strict terms no such period can be delineated in embryonic
development. As indicated in Figure 1, the terminal portions of the urogenital tract undergo a final "identical" development in both sexes after clearcut
histological differentiation of the testis has already commenced. Thus, the
indifferent phase of phenotypic development does not correspond exactly to
the indifferent phase of gonadal development (51, 74, 144).

The anatomical events in the development of the definitive male and
female urogenital tracts have been summarized in considerable detail in a
number of reference works (5, 68, 91, 106, 123, 164). In brief, at the end
of the indifferent phase of phenotypic development, the urogenital tract
consists of two sets of components: (a) a dual duct system (wolffian and
müllerian) derived from the mesonephric kidney that constitutes the anlage
of the internal organs of accessory reproduction and the upper vagina; and
(b) the urogenital sinus and urogenital tubercle, which are the anlagen of
the external genitalia and, in the male, the terminal urethra. The mesonephric kidney system is not only the anlage of the internal organs of accessory
reproduction but a large portion of the definitive excretory system as well.
At the 7–8 mm stage in the human embryo the system consists of a mesonephros proper and a mesonephric or wolffian duct that connects the mesonephric kidney to the urogenital sinus. The wolffian duct is also a precursor
of the ureteral bud that will eventually develop into the renal collecting
tubules, the ureter, and a portion of the bladder for the final excretory
system in both sexes. At the 10–15 mm stage, the development of a second
(paramesonephric or müllerian) duct commences in both sexes. The origin
of the müllerian duct has been studied by Gruenwald (62, 63) and more
recently by Potemkina, Grebenshchikova & Korosteleva (127). The duct
itself has two components—the cephalic portion, derived from the coelomic
epithelium, which gives rise to the fallopian tubes, and a caudal end,

DEVELOPMENTAL PROCESS

Approximate Crown-Rump Length (mm)	After Fertilization (days)	Trimester	MALE	Indifferent	Female
1-3	19	First		Germ Cells Commence Migration From Yolk Sac Endoderm to Mesenchyme	
2-3	25-30			Wolffian Duct Appears as Pronephric Duct	
7-15	37-45			Genital Ridge Develops	
13-15	44-48			Mullerian Ducts Development Commences	
16-18	50			Formation of Urogenital Sinus Commences; Urogenital Tubercle and Swellings, and	
17-20	52			Urethral Fold and Groove Complete	
13-20	43-50		Testicular Cords Appear; Tunica Albuginea Develops; Sertoli Cells Apparent		
18-32	48-60		Regression of Mullerian Duct Begins		
30	60		Testis Begins to Move Anteriorly	Urogenital Sinus, Mullerian and Wolffian Ducts Complete Indifferent Development; Mullerian Ducts are Attached to the Mullerian Tubercle Without Penetrating; Wolffian Ducts Open Laterally Breaking the Epithelium.	
32-35	65		Leydig Cells Appear; Onset of Testosterone Synthesis		
40-50	60-75		Lengthening of Urogenital Distance; Fusion of Labioscrotal Swelling; Growth of Wolffian Ducts		Formation of Vagina Commences
46	72		Closure of Median Raphe		
50	75		Closure of Urethral Groove		
55	78				Regression of Wolffian Duct Commences; Germ Cells Enter Meiosis
70	80		Mullerian Regression Complete		Vaginal Node Starts to Proliferate to Form Vaginal Plate.
120	105	Second	Prepuce Formation Complete		Prepuce Formation Complete; Histological Development of Definitive Ovary Commences.
150	120		Testis Comes to Rest Against Anterior Abdominal Wall.		Uterus Complete
170	133		Tip of Gubernaculum Presses Into Scrotum		Canalization of Vaginal Plate Commences
300-550	160-260	Third	True Testicular Descent Into the Scrotum; Growth of External Genitalia		Formation of Vagina Complete

Figure 1   Approximate sequence development of the gonads and genital tract in the two sexes. [From [51, 74, 87]]

derived from the wolffian duct, that gives rise to the uterus and upper vagina. It is clear that müllerian duct development cannot take place in the absence of the wolffian duct. Furthermore, the fact that the syndrome of congenital absence of the vagina (associated with hypoplasia of the uterus) can apparently occur as the result of a single gene mutation implies that at least one gene product must be responsible for normal development of the duct system (59). It is of interest that the cranial group of mesonephric tubules actually connects to the gonad to provide ultimately a true excretory system for sperm and seminal fluid, in contrast to the müllerian duct, which never becomes continuous with the gonad.

The termination of the mesonephric ducts in the primitive urogenital sinus divides the urogenital sinus into an upper and a lower portion. The upper portion, the vesico-urethral canal, is involved in the development of the bladder and upper urethra, whereas the lower portion, the definitive urogenital sinus, is intimately involved in the developmental history of the external genitalia.

MALE DEVELOPMENT   Beginning shortly after the commencement of differentiation of the spermatogenic tubules of the testis, the initial event in development of the male urogenital tract is the onset of müllerian duct regression, which is evidenced by degenerative changes and loss of the lumen (74). The cranial extremity of each duct persists to form the appendix testis, and the remainder of the duct disappears, with the possible exception of the lower end, which may contribute to the prostatic utricle. The commencement of müllerian duct regression in the male is followed shortly by the virilization of the wolffian duct (51, 74, 144). The blind cranial end of the wolffian duct persists to form the appendix epididymis, and the remainder of the cranial portion of the wolffian duct becomes connected to the seminiferous tubules to form the rete testis. The portion immediately caudal becomes elongated and convoluted to form the epididymus, and the remainder of the duct eventually develops a thick muscular coat to become the vas deferens. Each vas deferens becomes dilated close to its junction with the primitive urogenital sinus to form an ampulla from which the seminal vesicle will eventually arise. The part of the original mesonephric duct between this vesicle and the urethra becomes the ejaculatory duct. Thus, the principal internal accessory organs of reproduction are derived from the wolffian duct system.

The lower portion of the urogenital sinus becomes the prostatic and membranous urethra (53, 75). The prostate gland arises from a series of endodermal buds that appear in the lining of the primitive urethra in fetuses of about 55 mm length (94). These buds grow into the dense surrounding mesenchyme which forms the muscular and connective tissue components.

The buds arise from all sides of the urethra, both above and below the region of the openings of the mesonephric ducts; most buds originally lie along two rows at the lateral angles of the posterior urethral wall. Although a subsequent lobar development of the prostate occurs in some species, there are no visible boundaries and no documented histological differences between these lobes in man, and it is unclear whether such lobes have any developmental or functional significance. It is of interest that whereas buds initially develop throughout most of the length of the urethra, the most extensive development and growth into the prostate is in the area surrounding the termination of the wolffian ducts (the ejaculatory ducts) and the müllerian ducts (the verumontanum) in the male urethra. It is possible that the interaction of these various components is critical for the future development (normal and abnormal) of the gland (43, 100). Growth and development of the prostate continue throughout embryonic life.

Development of the male external genitalia begins shortly after virilization of the wolffian duct and urogenital sinus. (5, 68, 91, 106, 123, 144, 164). The genital tubercle and genital fold elongate to form the penis; on the caudal surface, the urethral folds close over the groove to form the penile portion of the male urethra. The line of closure of the urethral groove remains marked by a scarlike vestige, the penile raphe. As the penis develops, it migrates anteriorly to become distant from the anus. At approximately 55 mm of development, when the urethra is almost completed, the prepuce starts to differentiate as a fold of skin that grows out to cover the glans penis completely by the 120 mm stage (36, 53, 71). At approximately the same time, the urogenital swellings on both sides of the urethral plate have migrated ventrally and anteriorally to form the scrotum. Thus, the formation of the male phenotype is accomplished largely between days 40 and 90 of gestation.

However, during the latter two thirds of gestation two other important events take place, namely the completion of descent of the testes, and the growth of the genitalia. The mechanism by which descent of the testes occurs has been the subject of scrutiny by several investigators (9, 10, 50, 130, 172) but is less well understood than other phases of male development, both in regard to the "forces" that result in movement and to the hormonal factors that regulate the movement. On anatomical grounds, the process can be separated into three phases: transabdominal movement, formation of the processus vaginalis and inguinal canal, and actual movement of the testis into its permanent site in the scrotum. The sequence in the human takes place over a seven-month period, commencing about the sixth week and not being completed in some instances until after birth. The importance of growth of the genitalia during the latter phases of embryogenesis is illustrated by the fact that at the time the male urethra is completed (around day 75), there has been so little differential growth of the male external genitalia that the size of the phallus does not differ significantly in male and female embryos. Subsequently, growth of the external genitalia, the prostate, and the structures of the wolffian duct commences and continues until shortly before birth.

FEMALE DEVELOPMENT   In the female embryo, the wolffian ducts either regress or remain only in remnant form as Gartner's ducts. As described above, the cephalic ends of the müllerian ducts (the portion derived from the coelomic epithelium) are the anlagen of the fallopian tubes, and the caudal portions fuse to form the uterus (62, 63). The fusion of the caudal portions is at first partial so that there is a temporary septum between the two lumina. This septum disappears, however, so that a single cavity lined by a cuboidal epithelium is formed. The future junction of the body and cervix of the uterus can be recognized by the 40 mm stage, but the uterus is not completely defined until the 150 mm stage. Throughout fetal and early postnatal life the cervical portion of the uterus is larger than its body. The musculature of the female genital tract is derived from the mesenchyme surrounding the müllerian ducts. The fusion of the müllerian ducts to form the uterus, the regression of the mesonephros, and descent of the uterus and ovaries result in the transformation of the urogenital mesentery into the broad ligament.

The embryogenesis of the vagina is not entirely clear. It is established that fusion of the caudal end of the müllerian duct with the urogenital sinus is followed by a major epithelial proliferation and elongation that results in the formation of an initially solid vaginal plate. The vaginal plate in turn canalizes, beginning at the 150 mm stage, to form the vagina proper (13, 87). Although Bulmer has concluded that the cellular origin of the vaginal plate is principally from the urogenital sinus, interaction of the müllerian duct with the urogenital sinus is essential for complete vaginal development (26). As the lower vagina canalizes, the hymen forms as a partition that persists to varying degrees between the lumen and the external layer of the urogenital sinus proper.

It is only after the embryo has reached the 50 mm Crown-Pump (CR) length that sex can be determined without error from external characteristics (51). Soon after this time in the female fetus, the genital tubercle becomes bent caudally and can be recognized as the clitoris. The genital or labial swellings fuse posteriorly to form the posterior forchette, and the lateral portions of the labial swellings enlarge to form the labia majora. The urethral folds flanking the urogenital orifice do not fuse but persist as the labia minora. Thus, the phallic portion and most of the pelvic portion of the urogenital sinus are exposed on the surface as a cleft into which the vagina and urethra open.

BREAST DEVELOPMENT   Although the embryogenesis of the human breast is fundamentally the same as in other species, in man the mammary line (well developed in the 7 mm embryo) shortens and condenses to give rise to only one functional mammary bud on each side, whereas in many species multiple glands develop. Between 20 and 30 mm the epithelial bud assumes a globular shape, and the breast is well differentiated by the end of the second month of intrauterine life. Little change occurs between the second and fifth month, but during the fifth month (120 to 150 mm) both the nipple and the secondary epithelial buds develop. During the remainder of embryonic life ductular proliferation continues so that by the time of birth 15–25 buds are present, each of which connects to the exterior (88). There is clear-cut sexual dimorphism in the embryogenesis of the breast in the two sexes in several species. In the male rodent the excretory duct tends to regress during the latter phases of embryogenesis, and as a consequence the breast proper is left as an isolated island in the subcutaneous tissue (88–90). However, such dimorphism has never been documented in the human embryo, and there does not appear to be any clear-cut histological difference between the breasts of male and female children prior to the onset of puberty (126).

ONSET OF ENDOCRINE FUNCTION OF THE TESTES AND OVARIES

The work of Jost (80–82) established that the translation of the indifferent urogenital tract and external genitalia into male and female phenotype is determined by secretions of the fetal gonads. According to this model, genetic sex determines gonadal sex, and it is gonadal sex that induces the development of phenotypic sex. The basic experiment upon which this thesis was based involved the demonstration that removal of the gonads from embryos of either sex prior to the onset of phenotypic differentiation results in the development of a female phenotype. As a consequence of this type of experiment and of studies involving either transplantation of embryonic gonads or hormone administration, it was concluded that the male is the induced phenotype, that is, testicular secretions cause the formation of the male urogenital tract. In contrast, development of the female urogenital tract is thought not to require secretions from the embryonic gonad since it occurs in the absence of ovaries and testes. It was also deduced that two substances from the fetal testis are essential for male development. The first is the androgenic steroid responsible for virilization of the wolffian duct system to form the epididymis, vas deferens, and seminal vesicle, and for virilization of the urogenital sinus and external genitalia as well. The second (müllerian regression factor) is a poorly understood and incompletely characterized testicular secretion, thought to be peptide in character, that acts ipsilaterally to cause the regression of the müllerian ducts in the male (76–78).

On the basis of careful time-sequence studies it is clear that in the human male embryo müllerian regression commences shortly after differentiation of the spermatogenic tubules; hence it is likely that the factor responsible for müllerian regression is probably formed by the tubules, and that its formation constitutes the first, and consequently the most fundamental, endocrine function of the embryonic testis (74). The concept that müllerian regression is an active process essential to normal male development has been substantiated by study of the persistant müllerian duct syndrome (49, 110, 115, 173). In this disorder, genetic phenotypic males (with cryptorchidism) have fundamentally male wolffian duct structures but in addition have fallopian tubes and a uterus. Sufficient numbers of family studies have been reported to support the concept that in some instances the disorder is inherited recessively (either autosomal or X-linked) (6, 23, 35, 64, 141). The exact nature of the defect is uncertain, but it must reside either in a failure to produce the müllerian-inhibiting substance, or a failure of the tissue to respond to the hormone.

The onset of the capacity of the fetal testis to synthesize testosterone from the C_{21} precursors pregnenolone and progesterone occurs after the commencement of differentiation of the spermatogenic tubules and correlates closely with the histological differentiation of the Leydig calls in both animal (2, 7, 17, 93, 116, 129, 141, 169) and human embryos (137) (Figure 2). On the basis of the recovery and quantification of all radioactive products following the incubation of fetal testes with radioactive pregnenolone and progesterone, it is clear that the only androgen synthesized in significant quantity by the fetal testis of man and rabbit at the time of male phenotypic development is testosterone itself (137, 169). Thus, it follows that testosterone is the major androgen of the fetal as well as of the adult male.

Testosterone formed by the fetal gonad plays two vital roles during embryogenesis. First, it is probably required in large amounts for the completion of maturation of the spermatogenic tubules and for spermatogenesis itself. Second, it is secreted as a hormone into the fetal circulation where it plays an equally vital role in extratesticular male development. Since gonadal sex, acting largely through the secretion of testosterone, causes virilization of the male fetus, it is clear that the elucidation of the factors that regulate the initiation of testicular testosterone synthesis within a spe-

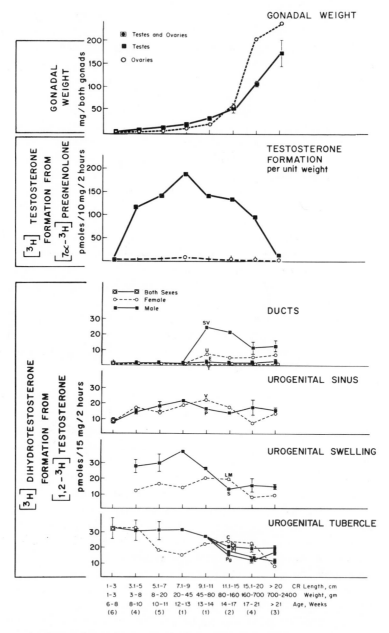

Figure 2 Onset of testosterone synthesis by the testis and conversion of testosterone to dihydrotestosterone by the tissues of the urogenital tract of the human embryo [After (137)]

cific time interval in embryogenesis is essential to an understanding of how genetic sex is translated into gonadal sex.

Perhaps the central unanswered question is whether the onset of testosterone synthesis is regulated by gonadotropic hormones. Consistent with gonadotropin control is the observation that histological differentiation of Rathke's Pouch, the anlage of the adenohypophysis, takes place at approximately the same time as differentiation of the Leydig cells (27, 34, 134). Moreover, in the male rabbit embryo it is possible to demonstrate the development of a specific gonadotropin receptor in the testis at approximately the same time as the onset of testosterone synthesis (28). These observations are compatible with the possibility that from its onset, testosterone synthesis is regulated by gonadotropin derived from the pituitary and/or the placenta. On the other hand, it has not been possible to demonstrate direct gonadotropic stimulation of testosterone synthesis by the fetal rabbit testis until later in embryogenesis (46). Moreover, the possibility exists that during the early phases of development the necessity for gonadotropin action in steroid hormone biosynthesis (presumed to be the side chain cleavage of cholesterol to pregnenolone) is circumvented by the presence of C_{21} steroids of placental origin in the circulation. If the latter formulation is correct (namely that during its initial phases, the availability of C_{21} steroids of placental origin is rate-limiting for testosterone biosynthesis), it would explain why in anencephaly (in which pituitary development is mostly rudimentary) male phenotypic development is generally unambiguous but terminal phenomena such as descent of the testes and growth of the genitalia are incomplete (175–177). The latter take place during the phase of embryogenesis in which gonadotropin control of the testes has been well documented (1, 3).

Although many questions are unresolved about the regulation of secretion of testosterone by the fetal testis, there is now ample genetic proof that its formation is essential to the development of the male phenotype as predicted by the Jost model (80–82). Five enzymatic defects have been described that result in inadequate testosterone synthesis and incomplete virilization of the male embryo during embryogenesis (16, 19, 20, 52, 54, 57, 86, 99, 114, 128, 133, 165, 170, 174, 178). Each of the enzymes (or enzyme complexes) involves a discrete biochemical step in the conversion of cholesterol to testosterone. Three of the reactions (20, 22-desmolase, 3 β-hydroxysteroid dehydrogenase, and 17-hydroxylase) are common to the synthesis of adrenal hormones as well as androgens, and consequently a deficiency results in defective glucocorticoid synthesis as well. The other two enzymes (17, 20-desmolase and 17β-hydroxysteroid dehydrogenase) are unique to the androgen pathway, and their deficiency results in pure male pseudohermaphroditism. The disorders in sexual differentiation that result from deficiency of these enzymes have a number of features in common (170). The clinical picture in 46,XY males is variable and can span the range from phenotypic men with mild hypospadias to phenotypic women. In 46,XY subjects no ovaries or fallopian tubes are present, indicating that the müllerian regression function of the testis has taken place normally during embryogenesis and that this function of the testis is independent of testosterone biosynthesis. However, the virilization of the wolffian ducts, urogenital sinus, and urogenital tubercle varies markedly, as does the degree of virilization and/or feminization that takes place at puberty. Plasma testosterone levels in affected individuals can also vary, depending on the severity of the enzymatic defect in question. Each of these disorders is rare, and many questions about the nature of the mutations involved are unsettled. The available data for the 17-hydroxylase and 3β-hydroxysteroid dehydrogenase deficiencies are compatible with autosomal recessive inheritance. Insufficient data are available for 20,22-desmolase deficiency to warrant any conclusions, and the limited family data for 17,20-desmolase deficiency and 17β-hydroxysteroid dehydrogenase deficiency mutations are compatible either with rare autosomal or X-linked recessive mutations (170).

Endocrine function in the fetal ovary is even less well understood. On the basis of histological evidence summarized above, it has been assumed generally that the ovary differentiates much later than the testis (51, 58) but it now appears that in terms of the acquisition of the capacity to synthesize estrogen or androgen, the enzymatic differentiation of the ovary and the testis takes place almost simultaneously (at least in the rabbit embryo) (102). The fact that acquisition of unique enzymic profiles occurs at the same time in the two tissues implies that the same or similar factors may be regulating the two processes. Whether ovarian synthesis of estrogen is important in the development of the female fetus is also unclear. Consequently, if ovarian estrogen does play a role in embryogenesis, it is likely to be exerted within the ovary itself rather than as a circulating hormone. Indeed, local estrogen formation may play a role in the differentiation of the ovary similar to the role that testosterone is assumed to play in the maturation of the testis.

MECHANISMS BY WHICH ANDROGENS VIRILIZE THE FETUS

If testosterone serves as the fetal androgen, are the molecular mechanisms for its action the same in the fetus as in the adult? In postnatal life testosterone is thought to have relatively few actions of its own, but instead serves principally as a prohormone for two other types of steroids formed in target tissues (163). Testosterone can undergo irreversible reduction to 5α-reduced steroids, principally dihydrotestosterone, which is thought to mediate many of the differentiative, growth-promoting, and functional actions of the hormone. In addition, circulating androgens are also converted in the peripheral tissues of both sexes to estrogens. The latter in some instances act in concert with androgens to influence physiological processes but also may exert independent effects on cellular function and, on occasion, have effects in opposition to those of androgens themselves. Thus, the physiological consequences of circulating testosterone in the postnatal state represent the sum total of the combined effects of testosterone itself and of its estrogenic and androgenic metabolites (163).

To determine whether testosterone acts directly in the cells of the developing embryo to induce virilization or whether it acts via conversion to dihydrotestosterone, dihydrotestosterone formation has been measured in embryonic tissues of man, rat, rabbit, and guinea pig varying in size from the phenotypically undifferentiated stage to late embryos (137, 160, 167) (Figure 2). At the earliest stages examined, the anlagen of the external genitalia and prostate (the urogenital tubercle and sinus) convert testosterone to dihydrotestosterone as actively as at any time in the life of the individual. Clearly, testosterone is converted to dihydrotestosterone in these tissues prior to the onset of phenotypic differentiation. The situation in the wolffian duct is distinctly different, however, since dihydrotestosterone formation cannot be demonstrated until after male differentiation is far advanced and the epididymis and seminal vesicles are formed. This difference between the wolffian duct system on the one hand and the urogenital sinus and urogenital swelling and tubercle on the other hand appears to be a consistent finding in all mammalian species examined.

The conversion of testosterone to estradiol by peripheral tissues of the developing embryo has not been studied in most species, but in the rabbit embryo aromatization has been demonstrated only in the ovary of the female and in the brain and placenta of both sexes (47, 102). Thus, the question of whether estradiol plays a role in mediating any androgen actions during embryogenesis has not been answered, although such a role in androgen-mediated virilization of the hypothalamus has been postulated (113).

To summarize, the action of three hormones must be invoked to explain the known events in male phenotypic differentiation. The regression of the müllerian duct is mediated by the müllerian regression factor. In addition, virilization requires at least two hormones. Testosterone, the androgen secreted by the fetal testis, itself causes virilization of the wolffian ducts prior to the onset of their ability to form dihydrotestosterone, whereas dihydrotestosterone appears to be the hormone that is responsible for virilization of the external genitalia and the male urethra.

The deduction that dihydrotestosterone formation is essential for normal virilization of the embryo was based originally on studies of androgen physiology in embryos and has also received genetic substantiation as the result of studies of another rare recessive form of male pseudohermaphroditism, pseudovaginal perineoscrotal hypospadias (117, 121, 140). In this disorder 46,XY males without any müllerian duct derivatives but with testes and male testosterone secretory rates have male wolffian duct structures (epididymis, vas deferens, seminal vesicles, and ejaculatory ducts). However, the ejaculatory ducts terminate in a blind-ending vagina, and the structures derived from the urogenital sinus and urogenital tubercle are predominantly female in character. The fact that defective virilization is limited to structures derived from the urogenital sinus and urogenital tubercle, where dihydrotestosterone rather than testosterone is believed to be the intracellular mediator of androgen action, suggested that defective dihydrotestosterone formation could explain the disorder (72, 125, 156). In confirmation of this deduction, dihydrotestosterone formation has been shown to be very low in slices of tissue removed from such patients (156), in fibroblast monolayers cultured from the foreskin of two patients (162), and in intact subjects from a large pedigree in the Dominican Republic (72, 125). Furthermore, direct assay of the 5α-reductase enzyme in extracts of fibroblasts indicates that the primary defect results from an abnormality of the enzyme itself (107, 108).

Due to the problems inherent in the small amounts of tissue available for study, the various binding proteins involved in the intracellular action of steroid hormones have not been characterized in detail in the embryonic tissues of the male urogenital tract (66, 161). However, as the result of studies in animals and human subjects with single gene mutations that cause resistance to androgen action and result in the development of male pseudohermaphroditism, it has been possible to deduce that the general process by which androgens are currently believed to act in the postnatal state is also operative during virilization of the embryo (Figure 3). Namely, dihydrotestosterone (D) is thought to combine with a specific cytosol binding protein (P) to form a hormone-protein complex (DP) which diffuses into the nucleus and combines with specific binding sites on the chromosomes. As a result of the latter interaction, messenger RNA (mRNA) is transcribed from previously dormant genes, and ultimately new proteins are synthesized in the cell.

At least three and possibly four separate single gene mutations have been demonstrated to involve the dihydrotestosterone binding protein of the

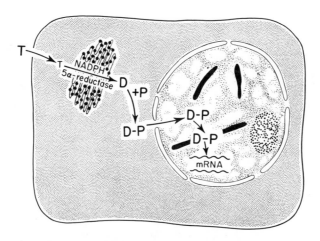

Figure 3   Postulated mechanism of action of testosterone in the cell of an androgen target tissue such as prostate. T, testosterone; D, dihydrotestosterone; P, dihydrostestosterone binding protein; mRNA, messenger RNA.

cytosol—the syndromes of complete and incomplete testicular feminization and the Reifenstein syndrome in man, and the *Tfm* mutation in the mouse. Both from the historical standpoint and because it has been best characterized in terms of genetics, endocrinology, and molecular biology, more is known about complete testicular feminization than the other disorders (69, 111, 112, 143, 168). In this disease, 46,XY males who have testes and normal (or high) male testosterone secretion differentiate as phenotypic females but without either wolffian or müllerian duct derivatives so that the vagina is blind-ending. At the time of expected puberty, breast development is feminine in character. Since the early study of Wilkins (158), ample evidence has accumulated to indicate that these individuals are profoundly resistant to exogenous as well as endogenous androgen. The nature of the molecular defect in the disorder has been identified. Kennan and coworkers showed that the dihydrotestosterone binding protein was almost undetectable in fibroblasts cultured from the skin of affected individuals (84, 85), a finding that has been confirmed in two other laboratories (60, 83). It was subsequently demonstrated by fibroblast cloning studies that the disorder is X-linked (101). Partial defects in the same binding protein (60, 61) result in less severe forms of male pseudohermaphroditism such as the Reifenstein syndrome, in which affected males have third degree hypospadias and sterility (22, 92, 155, 166) or in the syndrome of incomplete testicular feminization in which affected individuals resemble patients with the complete form except for minor virilization (98, 112). It is not clear, at present, whether these various mutations that appear to involve the same binding protein are allelic or whether more than one gene product is required to form the dihydrotestosterone binding protein.

The *Tfm* mutation in the mouse is an X-linked disorder in which the phenotype resembles that of complete testicular feminization in man (96, 120) and in which affected males are profoundly resistant to androgen both during embryogenesis and during postnatal life (56, 120). In this disorder, the uptake of dihydrotestosterone into the nucleus is deficient (25, 45, 56), and the 8s binding protein that is believed to be essential for transport of androgen from cytoplasm to nucleus is missing (8, 24, 44, 148). Smaller androgen-binding proteins appear to accumulate in excess (8, 44), raising the possibility that subunits of the 8s protein are present but are unable to function normally.

As the result of the study of these various mutations that influence the androgen binding protein, it is clear that a normal gene product of at least one X-linked locus must be responsible for formation of the dihydrotestosterone binding protein and, hence, differentiation of the normal male phenotype. Other forms of male pseudohermaphroditism due to androgen resistance have been identified in which both dihydrotestosterone formation and binding appear normal (4, 32). These disorders presumably involve steps in the intranuclear action of the hormone-protein complex. Indeed, on the basis of studies done in the mouse it is likely that multiple regulatory genes are influenced independently by the hormone-protein complex and that individual mutations in these genes result in a variety of selective abnormalities of androgen action (122, 147). Continued elucidation of the molecular defects in these various mutations should provide additional insight both into the mechanisms of sexual differentiation and into the pathway of androgen action in the normal.

The precise mechanisms by which the activation of genes by hormone-protein complexes during specific intervals results in differentiation are poorly understood. Recent studies by Cunha suggest that critical androgen action takes place within the mesenchyme of the indifferent urogenital tract and that differentiation of the various epithelial cells is secondary to hormone effects within the mesenchyme (33). This concept is in keeping with the previous observation that epithelial cells from whatever source, when transplanted to the vagina, assume the character of a normal vaginal epithelium (59). How the mesenchymal cells influence the various epithelia, or why a receptor-recognition machinery for individual steroid hormones is present only in certain mesenchymes is not known.

To summarize, virtually the entire process of differentiation and growth of the male urogenital tract is regulated by hormones formed by the fetal testis. One exception is the prepuce which achieves approximately the same degree of development in the two sexes (although in the female it does not fuse ventrally and as a consequence is hooded rather than cylindrical in shape). In addition, it should be emphasized that the forces involved (and, hence, the exact role of testicular hormones) in the three phases of testicular descent have never been defined clearly, although the studies in various single gene mutations in man have shown that androgen action must play some role in the process. Finally, little is known either about the character of the müllerian regression factor or the process by which müllerian regression is accomplished; as a consequence, we do not understand how development of fallopian tubes and uterus is prevented in the normal male.

ROLE OF HORMONES IN FEMALE PHENOTYPIC DEVELOPMENT

Embryogenesis normally takes place in a sea of hormones (steroid and nonsteroid) derived from the placenta, the maternal circulation, the fetal adrenal gland, the fetal testis, and possibly from the fetal ovary itself. It is not known, however, whether any of these substances influence female phenotypic development. This uncertainty arises because, by definition, the embryo develops in a female environment generated by the mother, and consequently it is not possible to remove female hormones. Thus, it is not possible to perform an experiment analogous to Jost's, in which male fetuses were deprived of male hormones by removal of the testis. The fact that the vagina contains a steroid receptor with distinctive and perhaps unique binding specificity (135) is compatible with the possibility that adrenal androgen may play a role in its development, and it is likely that estrogens and progestins are involved in the growth and maturation of the female organs of accessory reproduction during the latter phases of embryonic life even if not required for their differentiation (136).

Considerably more is known about the deleterious effects of androgen on female development. Whether from ingestion, from maternal tumors, or from overproduction within the fetus, such hormones may result in florid virilization of the female fetus (39). The commonest cause of this female pseudohermaphroditism is congenital adrenal hyperplasia due to the absence of either 21-hydroxylase or 11-hydroxylase enzymes as the result of an autosomal recessive defect (12, 21, 39, 73, 159). In either case, as the result of deficient glucocorticoid synthesis there is a compensatory increase in the synthesis of adrenal androgen late in gestation, and, as a consequence, a variable virilization of the external genitalia may be produced in affected females.

It is of interest that in contrast to the situation in regard to testosterone synthesis and action, in which many single gene mutations have been characterized, no mutations have been identified to date that result in either deficient estrogen synthesis or resistance to estrogen action. This raises the possibility that estrogen action might be essential to life itself [possibly for the survival or implantation of the blastocyst (15)] and that mutations interfering with either estrogen synthesis or estrogen action are lethal. In contrast, testosterone action is essential to the survival of the species but not of individuals.

ROLE OF HORMONES IN BREAST DEVELOPMENT

The differentiation of the embryonic mammary gland in rodents is regulated by testosterone. In these species, testosterone exerts a negative influence by producing a partial regression of the mammary bud. In the absence of testosterone, normal female differentiation takes place; whereas in the male fetus, testosterone induces a regression of the duct system that connects the breast proper to the nipple, resulting in incomplete development of the latter (88, 89). Furthermore, it is clear from studies in the *Tfm* mouse that the same molecular mechanisms that are responsible for positive induction of male differentiation of the genital tract are involved in the control of regression of the mammary bud in the male (90). In this regard, it has also been established, as the result of careful dissection and recombination experiments with embryonic tissues, that the mesenchyme of the mammary rudiment is the target tissue for testosterone and that all changes in the gland epithelium, including its necrosis, are caused secondarily by androgen-activated mesenchymal cells (90). However, in the human embryo histological dimorphism in the breasts of males and females has never been documented prior to puberty (126), and the equal frequency of transient milk secretion in the newborn male and female suggests that there is no functional difference between the two sexes until later in life. The subsequent endocrinologic control of breast development and milk formation is exceedingly complex; but it is clear that estrogen and progesterone exert key roles in the growth and maturation of the gland (97), and that the administration of estrogen (or the alteration of the normal male ratio of androgen to estrogen) can result in profound breast development in the human male at any phase in life (70).

SUMMARY

Genetic sex is established at the time of fertilization both by the composition of the sex chromosomes and by a variety of autosomal genes. The number and location of the various genetic determinants are multiple, and it is no longer appropriate to consider chromosomal sex as the sole (or even main) basis for sex determination. From the standpoint of embryogenesis, the initial manifestation of sexual dimorphism involves the formation of gonadal sex in which the indifferent gonadal primordia differentiate into either testis or ovary. The various factors involved in this complex differentiation are poorly understood, but it is clear that endocrine function of both types of gonad is an early manifestation of the process. Gonadal sex, in concert with a variety of genetic determinants, in turn determines phenotypic sex. The terminal phase of this process, namely the translation of gonadal sex into phenotypic sex, is now sufficiently well understood at genetic, endocrine, and molecular levels so that it is possible to describe the overall process in considerable detail. However, the fundamental issues in the embryonic development of the genital tract (as in all embryology) are still poorly understood, namely, the mechanisms by which genetic and developmental factors influence differentiation of tissues during the initial phases of embryogenesis so that, at the appropriate time, a hormonal stimulus can effect specific transformation of cell type and initiate specific anatomic developmental processes. Ultimately, these fundamental issues of embryogenesis will have to be clarified before it will be possible to understand the overall program by which the myriad of genetic determinants and regulatory factors interact to cause the development of phenotypic sex.

ACKNOWLEDGMENT

This work has been supported in part by Grant AM03892 from the National Institutes of Health.

Literature Cited

1. Abramovich, D. R., Baker, T. G., Neal, P. 1974. Effect of human chorionic gonadotrophin on testosterone secretion by the fetal human testis in organ culture. *J. Endocrinol.* 60:179–85
2. Acevedo, H. F., Axelrod, L. R., Ishikawa, E., Takaki, F. 1963. Studies in fetal metabolism. II. Metabolism of progesterone-4-C^{14} and pregnenolone-7α-H^3 in human fetal testes. *J. Clin. Endocrinol. Metab.* 23:885–90
3. Ahluwalia, B., Williams, J., Verma, P. 1974. *In vitro* testosterone biosynthesis in the human fetal testis. II. Stimulation by cyclic AMP and human chorionic gonadotropin (hCG). *Endocrinology* 95:1411–15
4. Amrhein, J. A., Meyer, W. J. III, Jones, H. W. Jr., Migeon, C. J. 1976. Androgen insensitivity in man: evidence for genetic heterogeneity. *Proc. Natl. Acad. Sci. USA* 73:891–94
5. Arey, L. B. 1965. The genital system. In *Developmental Anatomy. A Textbook and Laboratory Manual of Embryology*, pp. 315–41. Philadelphia: Saunders. 695 pp. 7th ed.
6. Armendares, S., Buentello, L., Frenk, S. 1973. Two male sibs with uterus and fallopian tubes. A rare, probably inherited disorder. *Clin. Genet.* 4:291–96
7. Attal, J. 1969. Levels of testosterone, androstenedione, estrone and estradiol-17β in the testes of fetal sheep. *Endocrinology* 85:280–89
8. Attardi, B., Ohno, S. 1974. Cytosol androgen receptor from kidney of normal and testicular feminized (*Tfm*) mice. *Cell* 2:205–12
9. Backhouse, K. M. 1964. The gubernaculum testis hunteri: testicular descent and maldescent. *Ann. Roy. Coll. Surg. Engl.* 35:15–33
10. Backhouse, K. M., Butler, H. 1960. The gubernaculum testis of the pig (*Sus scropha*). *J. Anat.* 94:107–20
11. Bardin, C. W., Bullock, L. P., Sherins, R. J., Mowszowisz, I., Blackburn, W.

R. 1973. Part II. Androgen metabolism and mechanism of action in male pseudohermaphroditism: a study of testicular feminization. *Recent Prog. Horm. Res.* 29:65–105

12. Bartter, F. C., Albright, F., Forbes, A. P., Leaf, A., Dempsey, E. Carroll, E. 1951. The effects of adrenocorticotropic hormone and cortisone in the adrenogenital syndrome associated with congenital adrenal hyperplasia: an attempt to explain and correct its disordered hormonal pattern. *J. Clin. Invest.* 30:237–51

13. Bengmark, S., Forsberg, J.-G. 1959. On the development of the rat vagina. *Acta Anat.* 37:106–25

14. Bennett, D., Boyse, E. A., Lyon, M. F., Mathieson, B. J., Scheid, M., Yanagisawa, K. 1975. Expression of H-Y (male) antigen in phenotypically female *Tfm/Y* mice. *Nature* 257:236–38

15. Bhatt, B. M., Bullock, D. W. 1974. Binding of oestradiol to rabbit blastocysts and its possible rôle in implantation. *J. Reprod. Fert.* 39:65–70

16. Biglieri, E. G., Herron, M. A., Brust, N. 1966. 17-hydroxylation deficiency in man. *J. Clin. Invest.* 45:1946–54

17. Bloch, E. 1964. Metabolism of 4-^{14}C-progesterone by human fetal testis and ovaries. *Endocrinology* 74:833–45

18. Boczkowski, K. 1971. Sex determination and gonadal differentiation in man. A unifying concept of normal and abnormal sex development. *Clin. Genet.* 2:379–86

19. Bongiovanni, A. M. 1962. The adrenogenital syndrome with deficiency of 3 β-hydroxysteroid dehydrogenase. *J. Clin. Invest.* 41:2086–92

20. Bongiovanni, A. M. 1972. Disorders of adrenocortical steroid biogenesis. In *The Metabolic Basis of Inherited Disease,* ed. J. B. Stanbury, J. B. Wyngaarden, D. S. Fredericksen, pp. 857–85. New York: McGraw-Hill. 3rd ed.

21. Bongiovanni, A. M., Root, A. W. 1963. The adrenogenital syndrome. *New Engl. J. Med.* 268:1283–89

22. Bowen, P., Lee, C. S. N., Migeon, C. J., Kaplan, N. M., Whalley, P. J., McKusick, V. A., Reifenstein, E. C. Jr. 1965. Hereditary male pseudohermaphroditism with hypogonadism, hypospadias, and gynecomastia (Reifenstein's syndrome). *Ann. Intern. Med.* 62: 252–70

23. Brook, C. G. D., Wagner, H., Zachmann, M., Prader, A., Armendares, S., Frenk, S., Alemán, P., Najjar, S. S., Slim, M. S., Genton, N., Bozic, C. 1973. Familial occurrence of persistent Müllerian structures in otherwise normal males. *Brit. Med. J.* 1:771–73

24. Bullock, L. P., Bardin, C. W. 1974. Androgen receptors in mouse kidney: a study of male, female and androgeninsensitive (tfm/y) mice. *Endocrinology* 94:746–56

25. Bullock, L. P., Bardin, C. W., Ohno, S. 1971. The androgen insensitive mouse: absence of intranuclear androgen retention in the kidney. *Biochem. Biophys. Res. Commun.* 44:1537–43

26. Bulmer, D. 1957. The development of the human vagina. *J. Anat.* 91:490–509

27. Campbell, H. J. 1966. The development of the primary portal plexus in the median eminence of the rabbit. *J. Anat.* 100:381–87

28. Catt, K. J., Dufau, M. L., Neaves, W. B., Walsh, P. C., Wilson, J. D. 1975. LH-hCG receptors and testosterone content during differentation of the testis in the rabbit embryo. *Endocrinology* 97:1157–65

29. Chemke, J., Carmichael, R., Stewart, J. M., Geer, R. H., Robinson, A. 1970. Familial XY gonadal dysgenesis. *J. Med. Genet.* 7:105–11

30. Clayton, G. W., Smith, J. D., Rosenberg, H. S. 1958. Familial true hermaphroditism in pre- and postpubertal females. Hormonal and morphologic studies. *J. Clin. Endocrinol. Metab.* 18:1349–58

31. Cohen, M. M., Shaw, M. W. 1965. Two XY siblings with gonadal dysgenesis and a female phenotype. *New Engl. J. Med.* 272:1083–88

32. Collier, M. E., Griffin, J. E., Wilson, J. D. 1977. Intranuclear binding of [^{3}H]-dihydrotestosterone by cultured human fibroblasts. In press

33. Cunha, G. R. 1972. Tissue interactions between epithelium and mesenchyme of urogenital and integumental origin. *Anat. Rec.* 172:529–42

34. Daikoku, S. 1958. Studies on the human foetal pituitary. 2. On the form and histological development, especially that of the anterior pituitary. *Tokushima J. Exp. Med.* 5:214–31

35. David, L., Saez, J. M., François, R. 1972. Male pseudohermaphroditism in two brothers. *Acta Pediat. Scand.* 61:249–250

36. Deibert, G. A. 1933. The separation of the prepuce in the human penis. *Anat. Rec.* 57:387–99

37. Erickson, R. P. 1971. Androgen-modified expression compared with Y linkage of male specific antigen. *Nature.* 265:59–61

38. Espiner, E. A., Veale, A. M. O., Sands, V. E., Fitzgerald, P. H. 1970. Familial syndrome of streak gonads and normal male karyotype in five phenotypic females. *New Engl. J. Med.* 203: 6–11

39. Federman, D. D. 1967. *Abnormal Sexual Development; A Genetic and Endocrine Approach to Differential Diagnosis.* Philadelphia: Saunders. 206 pp.

40. Federman, D. D. 1973. Genetic control of sexual difference. In *Progress in Medical Genetics,* ed. A. G. Steinberg, A. G. Bearn, 9:215–235. New York: Grune & Stratton

41. Ferguson-Smith, M. A. 1961. Chromosomes and human disease. In *Progress in Medical Genetics,* ed. A. G. Steinberg, 1:292–234. New York: Grune & Stratton

42. Ford, C. E., Jones, K. W., Polani, P. E., de Almeida, J. C., Briggs, J. H. 1959. A sex-chromosome anomaly in a case of gonadal dysgenesis (Turner's syndrome). *Lancet* 1:711–13

43. Frazer, J. E. 1935. The terminal part of the Wolffian duct. *J. Anat.* 69:455–68

44. Gehring, U., Tomkins, G. M. 1974. Characterization of a hormone receptor defect in the androgen-insensitivity mutant. *Cell* 3:59–64

45. Gehring, U., Tomkins, G. M., Ohno, S. 1971. Effect of the androgen-insensitivity mutation on a cytoplasmic receptor for dihydrotestosterone. *Nature New Biol.* 232:106–7

46. George, F. W., Catt, K. J., Neaves, W. B., Wilson, J. D. 1977. Studies on the regulation of testosterone synthesis in the fetal rabbit testis. In press

47. George, F. W., Tobleman, W. E., Milewich, L., Wilson, J. D. Aromatase activity in the developing rabbit brain. In press

48. Gerald, P. S. 1975. Y-linked genes and male-sex determination. *New Engl. J. Med.* 293:1095

49. Giacobine, J. W. 1946. Congenital hernia in a male containing a rudimentary uterus. *Am. J. Surg.* 72:604–7

50. Gier, H. T., Marion, G. B. 1969. Development of mammalian testes and genital ducts. *Biol. Reprod.* 1:1–23

51. Gillman, J. 1948. The development of the gonads in man, with a consideration of the role of fetal endocrines and the histogenesis of ovarian tumors. *Carnegie Contrib. Embryol., No. 210* 32:83–131

52. Givens, J. R., Wiser, W. L., Summitt, R. L., Kerber, I. J., Andersen, R. N., Pittaway, D. E., Fish, S. A. 1974. Familial male pseudohermaphroditism

53. Glenister, T. W. 1954. The origin and fate of the urethral plate in man. *J. Anat.* 88:413–25

54. Goebelsmann, U., Horton, R., Mestman, J. H., Arce, J. J., Nagata, Y., Nakamura, R. M., Thorneycroft, I. H., Mishell, D. R. Jr. 1973. Male pseudohermaphroditism due to testicular 17β-hydroxysteroid dehydrogenase deficiency. *J. Clin. Endocrinol. Metab.* 36:867–79

55. Goldberg, E. H., Boyse, E. A., Bennett, D., Scheid, M., Carswell, E. A. 1971. Serological demonstration of H-Y (male) antigen on mouse sperm. *Nature* 232:478–80

56. Goldstein, J. L., Wilson, J. D. 1972. Studies on the pathogenesis of the pseudohermaphroditism in the mouse with testicular feminization. *J. Clin. Invest.* 51:1647–58

57. Goldstein, J. L., Wilson, J. D. 1973. Hereditary disorders of sexual development in man. In *Birth Defects. Proceedings of the Fourth International Conference, Vienna, Austria,* ed. A. G. Motulsky, W. Lentz, pp. 165–73. Amsterdam: Excerpta Medica.

58. Gondos, B., Bhiraleus, P., Hobel, C. J. 1971. Ultrastructural observations on germ cells in human fetal ovaries. *Am. J. Obstet. Gynecol.* 110:644–52

59. Griffin, J. E., Edwards, C., Madden, J. D., Harrod, M. J., Wilson, J. D. 1976. Congenital absence of the vagina. The Mayer-Rokitansky-Kuster-Hauser syndrome. *Ann. Int. Med.* 85:224–36

60. Griffin, J. E., Punyashthiti, K., Wilson, J. D. 1976. Dihydrotestosterone binding by cultured human fibroblasts. Comparison of cells from control subjects and from patients with hereditary male pseudohermaphroditism due to androgen resistance. *J. Clin. Invest.* 57:1342–51

61. Griffin, J. E., Wilson, J. D. 1977. Studies on the pathogenesis of the incomplete forms of androgen resistance in man. *J. Clin. Endocrinol. Metab.* In press

62. Gruenwald, P. 1941. The relation of the growing Müllerian duct to the Wolffian duct and its importance for the genesis of malformations. *Anat. Rec.* 81:1–19

63. Gruenwald, P. 1959. Growth and development of the uterus: the relationship of epithelium to mesenchyme. *Ann. NY Acad. Sci.* 75:436–40

64. Güell-González, J. R., Paramio-Ruibal, A., Delgado-Morales, B. 1970. Male

pseudohermaphroditism with internal bisexual genitals (a report on two brothers). *Rev. Roum. Endocrinol.* 7:343–47

65. Guisti, G., Borghi, A., Salti, M., Bizozzi, V. 1966. "Disgenesia Gonadica para" con corietipo 44A + XX in sorelle figlie di cugini. *Acta Genet. Med. Gemellol.* 15:51

66. Gupta, C., Bloch, E. 1976. Testosterone-binding protein in reproductive tracts of fetal rats. *Endocrinology* 99:389–99

67. Hamerton, J. L., Dickson, J. M., Pollard, C. E., Grieves, S. A., Short, R. V. 1969. Genetic intersexuality in goats. *J. Reprod. Fert.* (Suppl. 7):25–51

68. Hamilton, W. J., Boyd, J. D., Mossman, H. W. 1962. *Human Embryology; Prenatal Development of Form and Function*, pp. 267–314. Baltimore: Williams & Wilkins.

69. Hauser, G. A. 1963. Testicular feminization. In *Intersexuality*, ed. C. Overzier, pp. 255–76. London: Academic

70. Hendrickson, D. A., Anderson, W. R. 1970. Diethylstilbestrol therapy. Gynecomastia. *J. Am. Med. Ass.* 213:468

71. Hunter, R. H. 1933. Notes on the development of the prepuce. *J. Anat.* 70:68–75

72. Imperato-McGinley, J., Guerrero, L., Gautier, T., Peterson, R. E. 1974. Steroid 5α-reductase deficiency in man: an inherited form of male pseudohermaphroditism. *Science* 186:1213–15

73. Jailer, J. W., Gold, J. J., Vande Wiele, R., Lieberman, S. 1955. 17α-Hydroxyprogesterone and 21-deoxyhydrocortisone: their metabolism and possible role in congenital adrenal virilism. *J. Clin. Invest.* 34:1639–46

74. Jirásek, J. E. 1971. Development of the genital system in human embryos and fetuses. In *Development of the Genital System and Male Pseudohermaphroditism*, ed. M. M. Cohen, Jr., p. 3–41. Baltimore: Johns Hopkins Press.

75. Johnson, F. P. 1920. The later development of the urethra in the male. *J. Urol.* 4:447–93

76. Josso, N. 1971. Interspecific character of the Müllerian-inhibiting substance: action of the human fetal testis, ovary and adrenal on the fetal rat Müllerian duct in organ culture. *J. Clin. Endocrinol. Metab.* 32:404–9

77. Josso, N. 1972. Evolution of the Müllerian-inhibiting activity of the human testis. Effect of fetal, perinatal and postnatal human testicular tissue on the Müllerian duct of the fetal rat in organ culture. *Biol. Neonate* 20:368–79

78. Josso, N. 1972. Permeability of membranes to the Müllerian-inhibiting substances synthesized by the human fetal testis *in vitro*: a clue to its biochemical nature. *J. Clin. Endocrinol.* 34:265–70

79. Josso, N., de Grouchy, J., Frézal, J., Lamy, M. 1963. Le syndrome de Turner familial, étude de deux familles avec caryotypes XO et XX. *Ann. Pediatr. Paris* 10:163–67

80. Jost, A. 1953. Problems of fetal endocrinology: the gonadal and hypophyseal hormones. *Recent Prog. Horm. Res.* 8:379–418

81. Jost, A. 1961. The role of fetal hormones in prenatal development. In *Harvey Lectures, Series 55,* pp. 201–226. New York: Academic

82. Jost, A. 1972. A new look at the mechanisms controlling sex differentiation in mammals. *Johns Hopkins Med. J.* 130:38–53

83. Kaufman, M., Straisfeld, C., Pinsky, L. 1976. Male pseudohermaphroditism presumably due to target organ unresponsiveness to androgens. Deficient 5α-dihydrotestosterone binding in cultured skin fibroblasts. *J. Clin. Invest.* 58:345–50

84. Keenan, B. S., Meyer, W. J. III, Hadjian, A. J., Jones, H. W., Migeon, C. J. 1974. Syndrome of androgen insensitivity in man: absence of 5 α-dihydrotestosterone binding protein in skin fibroblasts. *J. Clin. Endocrinol. Metab.* 38:1143–46

85. Keenan, B. S., Meyer, W. J. III, Hadjian, A. J., Migeon, C. J. 1975. Androgen receptor in human skin fibroblasts. Characterization of a specific 17β-hydroxy-5α-androstan-3-one-protein complex in cell sonicates and nuclei. *Steroids* 25:535–52

86. Kirkland, R. T., Kirkland, J. L., Johnson, C. M., Horning, M. G., Librik, L., Clayton, G. W. 1973. Congenital lipoid adrenal hyperplasia in an eight-year-old phenotypic female. *J. Clin. Endocrinol.* 36:488–96

87. Koff, A. K. 1933. Development of the vagina in the human fetus. *Carnegie Contrib. Embryol. No. 140* 24:61–90

88. Kon, S. K., Cowie, A. T., eds. 1961. *Milk: the Mammary Gland and Its Secretion,* 1:3–46. New York: Academic

89. Kratochwil, K. 1971. *In vitro* analysis of the hormonal basis for the sexual dimorphism in the embryonic development of the mouse mammary gland. *J. Embryol. Exp. Morph.* 25:141–53

90. Kratochwil, K., Schwartz, P. 1976. Tissue interaction in androgen response of embryonic mammary rudiment of mouse: identification of target tissue for testosterone. *Proc. Natl. Acad. Sci. USA* 73:4041–44

91. Langman, J. 1969. *Medical Embryology. Human Development - Normal and Abnormal,* pp. 160–200. Baltimore: Williams & Wilkins. 2nd ed.

92. Leonard, J. M., Bremner, W. J., Capell, P. T., Paulsen, C. A. 1975. Male hypogonadism: Klinefelter and Reifenstein syndromes. *Birth Defects Orig. Artic. Ser.* 11(4):17–22

93. Lipsett, M. B., Tullner, W. W. 1965. Testosterone synthesis by the fetal rabbit gonad. *Endocrinology* 77:273–77

94. Lowsley, O. S. 1912. The development of the human prostate gland with reference to the development of other structures at the neck of the urinary bladder. *Am. J. Anat.* 13:299–346

95. Lyon, M. F. 1974. Sex chromosome activity in germ cells. In *Physiology and Genetics of Reproduction, Part A,* ed. E. M. Coutinho, F. Fuchs, p. 63–71. New York: Plenum

96. Lyon, M. F., Hawkes, S. G. 1970. X-linked gene for testicular feminization in the mouse. *Nature* 227:1217–19

97. Lyons, W. R., Li, C. H., Johnson, R. E. 1958. The hormonal control of mammary growth and lactation. In *Recent Progress in Hormones Research,* ed. G. Pincus, 14:219–54. New York: Academic

98. Madden, J. D., Walsh, P. C., MacDonald, P. C., Wilson, J. D. 1975. Clinical and endocrinological characterization of a patient with the syndrome of incomplete testicular feminization. *J. Clin. Endocrinol. Metab.* 41:751–60

99. Mantero, F., Busnardo, B., Riondel, A., Veyrat, R., Austoni, M. 1971. Hypertension artérielle. Alcalose hypokaliémique et pseudohermaphroditisme mâle par déficit en 17α-hydroxylase. *Schweiz. Med. Wochenschr.* 101:38–43

100. McNeal, J. E. 1976. Developmental and comparative anatomy of the prostate. In *Benign Prostatic Hyperplasia,* ed. J. T. Grayhack, J. D. Wilson, M. J. Scherbenske, pp. 1–9. Bethesda, Md: NIH Workshop

101. Meyer, W. J. III, Migeon, B. R., Migeon, C. J. 1975. Locus on human X chromosome for dihydrotestosterone receptor and androgen insensitivity. *Proc. Natl. Acad. Sci. USA* 72:1469–72

102. Milewich, L., George, F. W., Wilson, J. D. 1977. Estrogen formation by the ovary of the rabbit embryo. *Endocrinology* 100:187–96

103. Milner, W. A., Garlick, W. B., Fink, A. J., Stein, A. A. 1958. True hermaphrodite siblings. *J. Urol.* 79:1003–9

104. Mintz, B. 1957. Embryological development of primordial germ-cells in the mouse: influence of a new mutation, *Wʲ J. Embryol. Exp. Morph.* 5:396–403

105. Mintz, B., Russell, E. S. 1957. Gene-induced embryological modifications of primordial germ cells in the mouse. *J. Exp. Zool.* 134:207–38

106. Moore, K. L. 1973. *The Developing Human. Clinically Oriented Embryology,* p. 198–238. Philadelphia: Saunders

107. Moore, R. J., Griffin, J. E., Wilson, J. D. 1975. Diminished 5α-reductase activity in extracts of fibroblasts cultured from patients with familial incomplete male pseudohermaphroditism, type 2. *J. Biol. Chem.* 250:7168–72

108. Moore, R. J., Wilson, J. D. 1976. Steroid 5α-reductase in cultured human fibroblasts. Biochemical and genetic evidence for two distinct enzyme activities. *J. Biol. Chem.* 251:5895–5900

109. Mori, Y., Mizutani, S. 1968. Familial true hermaphroditism in genetic females. *Jpn. J. Urol.* 59:857–64

110. Morillu-Gucci, G., German, J. 1971. Males with a uterus and fallopian tubes, a rare disorder of sexual development. *Birth Defects Orig. Artic. Ser.* 7(6): 229–31

111. Morris, J. M. 1953. The syndrome of testicular feminization in male pseudohermaphrodites *Am. J. Obstet. Gynecol.* 65:1192–1211

112. Morris, J. M., Mahesh, V. B. 1963. Further observations on the syndrome, "testicular feminization." *Am. J. Obstet. Gynecol.* 87:731–48

113. Naftolin, F., Ryan, K. J., Petro, Z. 1971. Aromatization of androstenedione by the diencephalon. *J. Clin. Endocrinol. Metab.* 33:368–70

114. New, M. I. 1970. Male pseudohermaphroditism due to 17α-hydroxylase deficiency. *J. Clin. Invest.* 49:1930–41

115. Nilson, O. 1939. Hernia uteri inguinalis beim Manne. *Acta Chir. Scand.* 83: 231–49

116. Noumura, T., Weisz, J., Lloyd, C. W. 1966. *In vitro* conversion of 7-³H-progesterone to androgens by the rat testis during the second half of fetal life. *Endocrinology* 78:245–53

117. Nowakowski, H., Lenz, W. 1961. Genetic aspects of male hypogonadism. *Recent Prog. Horm. Res.* 17:53–95

118. Ohno, S. 1976. Major regulatory genes for mammalian sexual development. *Cell* 7:315–21

119. Ohno, S., Christian, L. C., Wachtel, S. S., Koo, G. C. 1976. Hormone-like role of H-Y antigen in bovine freemartin gonad. *Nature* 261:579–99

120. Ohno, S., Lyon, M. F. 1970. X-linked testicular feminization in the mouse as a non-inducible regulatory mutation of the Jacob-Monod type. *Clin. Genet.* 1:121–27

121. Opitz, J. M., Simpson, J. L., Sarto, G. E., Summitt, R. L., New, M., German, J. 1972. Pseudovaginal perineoscrotal hypospadias. *Clin. Genet.* 3:1–26

122. Paigen, K., Swank, R. T., Tomino, S., Ganschow, R. E. 1975. The molecular genetics of mammalian glucuronidase. *J. Cell Physiol.* 85:379–92

123. Patten, B. M. 1953. *Human Embryology*, p. 549–607. New York: McGraw-Hill. 2nd ed.

124. Peters, H. 1970. Migration of gonocytes into the mammalian gonad and their differentiation. *Phil. Trans. Roy. Soc. London Ser. B* 259:91–101

125. Peterson, R. E., Imperato-McGinley, J., Gautier, T., Sturla, E. 1977. Male pseudohermaphroditism due to steroid 5α-reductase deficiency. *Am. J. Med.* 62:170–191

126. Pfaltz, C. R. 1949. Das embryonale und postnatale Verhalten der männlichen Brustdrüse beim Menschen. II. Das Mammarorgan im Kindes-, Jünglings-, Mannes- und Greisenalter. *Acta Anat.* 8:293–328

127. Potemkina, D. A., Grebenshchikova, V. I., Korosteleva, L. I. 1971. Interaction of cells of Wolffian duct and mesothelium during initial growth period of Müllerian ducts in the axolotl (*Ambystoma mexicanum*). *Sov. J. Dev. Biol.* 2:311–22

128. Prader, A., Gurtner, H. P. 1955. Das Syndrom des Pseudohermaphroditismus masculinus bei kongenitalen Nebennierenrinden-Hyperplasie ohne Androgenüberproduktion (adrenaler Pseudohermaphroditismus masculinus). *Helv. Paediat. Acta* 10:397–412

129. Price, D., Ortiz, E. 1965. The role of fetal androgen in sex differentiation in mammals. In *Organogenesis*, ed. R. L. DeHaan, H. Ursprung, pp. 629–52. New York: Holt, Rinehart & Winston

130. Rajfer, J., Walsh, P. C. 1977. Testicular descent. In press

131. Rosenberg, H. S., Clayton, G. W., Hsu, T. C. 1963. Familial true hermaphroditism. *J. Clin. Endocrinol. Metab.* 23:203–6

132. Russell, W. L., Russell, L. B., Gower, J. S. 1959. Exceptional inheritance of a sex-linked gene in the mouse explained on the basis that the X/O sex-chromosome constitution is female. *Proc. Natl. Acad. Sci. USA* 45:554–60

133. Saez, J. M., Morera, A. M., de Peretti, E., Bertrand, J. 1972. Further *in vivo* studies in male pseudohermaphroditism with gynecomastia due to testicular 17-ketosteroid reductase defect (compared to a case of testicular feminization). *J. Clin. Endocrinol. Metab.* 34:598–600

134. Schechter, J. 1970. A light and electron microscopic study of Rathke's pouch in fetal rabbits. *Gen. Comp. Endocrinol.* 14:53–67

135. Shao, T. -C., Castañeda, E., Rosenfield, R. L., Liao, S. 1975. Selective retention and formation of a Δ⁵-androstenediol-receptor complex in cell nuclei of the rat vagina. *J. Biol. Chem.* 250:3095–3100

136. Shapiro, B. H., Goldman, A. S., Bongiovanni, A. M., Marino, J. M. 1976. Neonatal progesterone and feminine sexual development. *Nature* 264:795–96

137. Siiteri, P. K., Wilson, J. D. 1974. Testosterone formation and metabolism during male sexual differentiation in the human embryo. *J. Clin. Endocrinol. Metab.* 38:113–25

138. Silvers, W. K., Billingham, R. E., Sanford, B. H. 1968. The H-Y transplantation antigen: a Y-linked or sex-influenced factor? *Nature* 220:401–3

139. Simpson, J. L., Christakos, A. C., Horwith, M., Silverman, F. S. 1971. Gonadal dysgenesis in individuals with apparently normal chromosomal complements: tabulation of cases and compilation of genetic data. *Birth Defects Orig. Artic. Ser.* 7(6):215–28

140. Simpson, J. L., New, M., Peterson, R. E., German, J. 1971. Pseudovaginal perineoscrotal hypospadias (PPSH) in sibs. *Birth Defects Orig. Artic. Ser.* 7:140–44

141. Sloan, W. R., Walsh, P. C. 1976. Familial persistent Müllerian duct syndrome. *J. Urol.* 115:459–61

142. Soller, M., Padeh, B., Wysoki, M., Ayalon, N. 1969. Cytogenetics of Saanen goats showing abnormal development of the reproductive tract associated with the dominant gene for polledness. *Cytogenetics* 8:51–67

143. Southren, A. L. 1965. The syndrome of testicular feminization. In *Advances in Metabolic Disorders*, ed. R. Levine, R.

Luft, 2:227–55. New York: Academic
144. Spaulding, M. H. 1921. The development of the external genitalia in the human embryo. *Carnegie Contrib. Embryol. No. 61* 13:67–88
145. Stern, C. 1961. The genetics of sex determination in man. In *2nd Int. Congr. Human Genet.*, 2:1121–1127. Amsterdam: Excerpta Medica
146. Sternberg, W. H., Barclay, D. L., Kloepfer, H. W. 1968. Familial XY gonadal dysgenesis. *New Engl. J. Med.* 278:695–700
147. Swank, R. T., Paigen, K., Ganschow, R. E. 1973. Genetic control of glucuronidase induction in mice. *J. Mol. Biol.* 81:225–43
148. Verhoeven, G., Wilson, J. D. 1976. Cytosol androgen binding in submandibular gland and kidney of the normal mouse and the mouse with testicular feminization. *Endocrinology* 98:79–92
149. Wachtel, S. S., Koo, G. C., Boyse, E. A. 1975. Evolutionary conservation of H-Y ("male") antigen. *Nature* 254:270–72
150. Wachtel, S. S., Koo, G. C., Breg, W. R., Elias, S., Boyse, E. A., Miller, O. J. 1975. Expression of H-Y antigen in human males with two Y chromosomes. *New Engl. J. Med.* 293:1070–72
151. Wachtel, S. S., Koo, G. C., Breg, W. R., Thaler, H. T., Dillard, G. M., Rosenthal, I. M., Dosik, H., Gerald, P. S., Saenger, P., New, M., Lieber, E., Miller, O. J. 1976. Serologic detection of a Y-linked gene in XX males and XX true hermaphrodites. *New Engl. J. Med.* 195:750–54
152. Wachtel, S. S., Koo, G. C., Ohno, S., Gropp, A., Dev, V. G., Tantravahi, R., Miller, D. A., Miller, O. J. 1976. H-Y antigen and the origin of XY female wood lemmings (*Myopus schisticolor*). *Nature* 264:638–39
153. Wachtel, S. S., Koo, G. C., Zuckerman, E. E., Hammerling, U., Scheid, M. P., Boyse, E. A. 1974. Serological cross-reactivity between H-Y (male) antigens of mouse and man. *Proc. Natl. Acad. Sci. USA* 71:1215–18
154. Wachtel, S. S., Ohno, S., Koo, G. C., Boyse, E. A. 1975. Possible role for H-Y antigen in the primary determination of sex. *Nature* 257:235–36
155. Walker, A. C., Stack, E. M., Horsfall, W. A. 1970. Familial male pseudohermaphroditism. *Med. J. Aust.* 1:156–160
156. Walsh, P. C., Madden, J. D., Harrod, M. J., Goldstein, J. L., MacDonald, P. C., Wilson, J. D. 1974. Familial incomplete male pseudohermaphroditism,

type 2. Decreased dihydrotestosterone formation in pseudovaginal perineoscrotal hypospadias. *New Engl. J. Med.* 291:944–49
157. Welshons, W. J., Russell, L. B. 1959. The Y-chromosome as the bearer of male determining factors in the mouse. *Proc. Natl. Acad. Sci. USA* 45:560–66
158. Wilkins, L. 1957. *The Diagnosis and Treatment of Endocrine Disorders in Childhood and Adolescence*, p. 276–78. Springfield, Ill: Thomas. 2nd. ed.
159. Wilkins, L., Lewis, R. A., Klein, R., Rosemberg, E. 1950. The suppression of androgen secretion by cortisone in a case of congenital adrenal hyperplasia. Preliminary report. *Bull. Johns Hopkins Hosp.* 86:249–52
160. Wilson, J. D. 1971. Testosterone metabolism in skin. *Symp. Deut. Ges. Endokrin.* 17:11–18
161. Wilson, J. D. 1973. Testosterone uptake by the urogenital tract of the rabbit embryo. *Endocrinology* 92:1192–99
162. Wilson, J. D. 1975. Dihydrotestosterone formation in cultured human fibroblasts. Comparison of cells from normal subjects and patients with familial incomplete male pseudohermaphroditism, type 2. *J. Biol. Chem.* 250:3498–504
163. Wilson, J. D. 1975. Metabolism of testicular androgens. In *Handbook of Physiology. Section 7: Endocrinology. Vol. V. Male reproductive system,* ed. D. W. Hamilton, R. O. Greep, pp. 491–508. Washington: Am. Physiol. Soc.
164. Wilson, J. D. 1977. Embryology of the genital tract. In press
165. Wilson, J. D. Goldstein, J. L. 1975. Classification of hereditary disorders of sexual development. *Birth Defects Orig. Artic. Ser.* 11(4):1–16
166. Wilson, J. D., Harrod, M. J., Goldstein, J. L., Hemsell, D. L., MacDonald, P. C. 1974. Familial incomplete male pseudohermaphroditism, type 1. Evidence for androgen resistance and variable clinical manifestations in a family with the Reifenstein syndrome. *New Engl. J. Med.* 290:1097–1103
167. Wilson, J. D., Lasnitzki, I. 1971. Dihydrotestosterone formation in fetal tissues of the rabbit and rat. *Endocrinology* 89:659–68
168. Wilson, J. D., MacDonald, P. C. 1977. Male pseudohermaphroditism due to androgen resistance: testicuar feminization and related syndromes. In *Metabolic Basis of Inherited Disease*, ed. J. B. Stanbury, J. Wyngaarden, D. S. Fredricksen. In press

169. Wilson, J. D., Siiteri, P. K. 1973. Developmental pattern of testosterone synthesis in the fetal gonad of the rabbit. *Endocrinology* 92:1182–91

170. Wilson, J. D., Walsh, P. C. 1977. Abnormalities of sexual development. In press

171. Witschi, E. 1948. Migration of the germ cells of human embryos from the yolk sac to the primitive gonadal folds. *Carnegie Contrib. Embryol. No. 209* 32:69–80

172. Wyndham, N. R. 1943. A morphological study of testicular descent. *J. Anat.* 77:179–88

173. Young, D. 1951. Hernia uteri inguinalis in the male. *J. Obstet. Gynaecol. Brit. Emp.* 58:830–31

174. Zachmann, M., Völlmin, J. A., Hamilton, W., Prader, A. 1972. Steroid 17, 20-desmolase deficiency: a new cause of male pseudohermaphroditism. *Clin. Endocrinol.* 1:369–85

175. Zondek, L. H., Zondek, T. 1965. Observations on the testis in anencephaly with special reference to the Leydig cells. *Biol. Neonatorum* 8:329–47

176. Zondek, L. H., Zondek, T. 1965. The secretory activity of the human epididymis in anencephaly. *Ann. Paediat.* 204:301–11

177. Zondek, L. H., Zondek, T. 1970. The human prostate in anencephaly. *Acta Endocrinol.* 64:548–56

178. Zurbrügg, R. P. 1974. Inborn errors in testosterone biosynthesis with special reference to 17-oxosteroid reductase deficiency. *Helv. Paediat. Acta Suppl.* 34:63–77

Ann. Rev. Physiol. 1978. 40:307–43
Copyright © 1978 by Annual Reviews Inc. All rights reserved

INSULIN, GLUCAGON, AND SOMATOSTATIN SECRETION IN THE REGULATION OF METABOLISM

❖1194

R. H. Unger and R. E. Dobbs

Veterans Administration Hospital and Department of Internal Medicine, University of Texas Southwestern Medical School, Dallas, Texas

L. Orci

Institute of Histology and Embryology, University of Geneva School of Medicine, Geneva, Switzerland

INTRODUCTION

Regulation of nutrient homeostasis constitutes one of the most important of all physiologic functions, determining the ability of organisms to perform optimally and thereby survive in an environment that imposes unpredictable changes in the supply of and the demand for fuels. A virtually foolproof system for the storage and subsequent redistribution of fuels is required to meet the competing needs of all of the tissues of the body. Charged with the formidable task of regulating nutrient homeostasis are the islets of Langerhans, microorgans that perform these functions through the secretion of three or more polypeptides. The biologic activities of two of these, insulin and glucagon, and their roles in regulating nutrient flux have been relatively well characterized; the roles of insular somatostatin in nutrient homeostasis are now under intensive study, while those of "pancreatic polypeptide" remain enigmatic.

It seems increasingly probable that the islets are anatomically constituted to operate as a functional unit, and that their secretory products exert metabolically interrelated effects on target tissues (reviewed in 159, 161). The physiologic roles of each islet hormone must, therefore, be considered in relation to the functions of the other islet hormones, inasmuch as pre-

307

0066-4278/78/0301-0307$01.00

cisely titrated hormonal mixtures of biological antagonists or synergists may determine net metabolic effects. Therefore, although glucagon is emphasized in this review, an attempt is made to integrate information in this area with new knowledge of the structure of the islets and the function of other of their secretory products, insulin and somatostatin.

FUNCTIONAL ROLE OF THE ISLETS OF LANGERHANS

The function of the regulator of nutrient homeostasis is to control both the rates at which various fuels enter and leave the extracellular space, and their concentrations as they pass through this space (152). In the case of glucose this task is particularly critical, because in contrast to other fuels, its concentration must be maintained within a narrow range (26). If the rate of glucose flux into the extracellular space were permitted to fall below the rate of glucose flux out of the space, hypoglycemia would ensue and the function of the glucose-dependent central nervous system would be compromised, imposing a clear and immediate threat to survival. Conversely, if the rate of glucose flux out of the extracellular space were permitted to lag behind the rate of glucose influx, hyperglycemia would develop. In poorly controlled diabetes, which is, of course, the ultimate expression of the latter circumstance, excretion by the kidney becomes a factor in the removal of circulating glucose, which creates new problems of fluid and acid-base balance. But even in "well controlled" diabetes, repeated daily periods of hyperglycemia may, in time, damage certain tissues; there are those who argue that thickening of capillary basement membranes may be the direct consequence of chronic hyperglycemia.

Such potentially deleterious perturbations of nutrient concentration are prevented by the normal islets of Langerhans. Their capacity to sense fuel needs and changes in fuel concentrations, and their ability to alter rates of nutrient influx and efflux through secretion of insulin, glucagon, and perhaps a third hormone, somatostatin, make it possible to maintain fuel concentrations within the ranges considered normal (152).

The Islets in Situations Demanding Production of Endogenous Fuels

The human brain requires approximately 6 g of glucose per hour (142) throughout life—during meals or in starvation, during violent exercise or at rest, and during severe stress. Inasmuch as glucose is the obligatory substrate for the central nervous system, glucose delivery to the brain has the highest priority—it is the most important single physiologic task of the islets of Langerhans. They maintain glycemia above 50 mg%, and, except during stress, below 170 mg%, and prevent the dangers of both hypo-glycemia and hyperglycemia through the appropriate secretion of the biological antagonists (74, 78), insulin and glucagon, and, possibly, of somatostatin. Glucagon prevents the hypoglycemia by maintaining glucose production at a rate sufficient to meet the needs of the central nervous system, plus other glucose needs, such as those generated by exercising muscle, as insulin levels decline reciprocally. A declining insulin:glucagon ratio promotes hepatic glycogenolysis (116). And, when hepatic glycogen is depleted, low insulin levels permit increased release of amino acids from muscle protein (82) and free fatty acids from triglycerides (84), thus provid-ing the liver with substrates for gluconeogenesis and ketogenesis; glucagon, in turn, promotes both gluconeogenesis and ketogenesis by the liver. Thus, this low insulin–high glucagon mixture achieves two vital changes: first, it provides the liver with the precursors, mobilized from muscle and fat, needed for glucose and ketone production; second, it enhances the gluconeogenic (37) and ketogenic capacities (86) of the liver. As the produc-tion of ketones rises, they are increasingly used by the central nervous system as an alternative fuel to glucose. This permits a reduction in gluconeogenesis and a sparing of proteins—perhaps a crucial adaptive mechanism that prolongs survival in starvation (26).

Similarly, during strenuous exercise the increase in utilization of glucose by muscle (167) will be matched by an increase in hepatic glucose produc-tion (164, 165), in large part glucagon-mediated (43, 44). This prevents hypoglycemia and provides another adjustment vital to survival in "flight or fight" situations.

Finally, during serious injury or shock (68, 69, 171, 172) a prompt rise in glucagon, together with a relatively low insulin level, brings about so-called "stress hyperglycemia," a means by which glucose delivery to an under-perfused brain can be maximized. In time of threatened or actual diminution of cerebral fuel delivery resulting from a decline in cerebral blood flow, an instant adrenergically mediated fall in the insulin:glucagon ratio (151) will raise glucose levels from the normal range to a range that would, under normal circumstances, be regarded as abnormally high; this is another valuable survival aid—an "endogenous glucose infusion" by which nature achieves what the physician provides when he administers glucose. But the persistence of a low insulin:glucagon ratio during serious stressful illness may be a contributing factor to many of the manifestations of the catabolic state (151).

Situations Demanding Increased Utilization of Nutrients

At the other extreme of the spectrum is the islet cell response to fuel abundance. Although this response is markedly influenced by the composition of the particular meal and by the antecedent diet (92), under normal circumstances a carbohydrate-containing meal elicits an outpouring of insulin that clears glucose from the extracellular fluid at a rate that will prevent hyperglycemia in excess of 150–170 mg%. The absorbed glucose is stored as glycogen in the liver and to a lesser extent in muscle, and is metabolized in adipocytes to triglycerides; the ingested amino acids are incorporated into body protein. If the meal should contain protein without much carbohydrate, as in a carnivorous diet, a substantial rise in glucagon will accompany the rise in insulin (157). This prevents hypoglycemia secondary to the protein-induced increase in insulin secretion by increasing hepatic glucose production (39, 157), while permitting sufficient insulin secretion to promote an anabolic disposition of the amino acids. Glucose turnover increases, but glucose concentration remains unchanged (28).

GLUCAGON AND THE A-CELL

Glucagon, a 29 amino acid polypeptide with a molecular weight of 3485 (23), has an identical primary structure in all mammalian species thus far studied with the exception of the guinea pig (146); the sequences of avian and piscine glucagons differ (146) from mammalian glucagon.

Immunocytochemical techniques employing relatively specific antisera to glucagon have identified A-cells of the islets of Langerhans as the glucagon-containing cells (10). At the ultrastructural level the typical α-granules of such cells (Figure 1) have been shown by immunocytochemical techniques to contain glucagon (36). Recently, however, the A-cells of the islets (and those of the gastric fundus) have been demonstrated by immunocytochemical techniques to contain, in addition to glucagon, a polypeptide known as "glucagon-like immunoreactivity" (GLI) (90). Hitherto, GLI had been identified only in so-called "A-like" cells (109), which are most prevalent in the postduodenal small bowel (123). The significance of the surprising presence in glucagon-containing cells of the pancreas of a polypeptide with physicochemical, biologic, and immunochemical properties which differ from those of glucagon (90, 140) remains to be determined.

Exocytosis has been demonstrated to occur in pancreatic A-cells (110) as it does in B-cells (63) and D-cells (60), and it is assumed that much, if not all, glucagon is secreted by this process.

Extrapancreatic Glucagon

Although extrapancreatic glucagon has been difficult to identify in adult humans, the fact that measurable levels of "immunoreactive glucagon" (IRG) are present in totally depancreatized patients (89, 114, 115) is evidence of its existence. A-cells have been found in the gastric fundus of

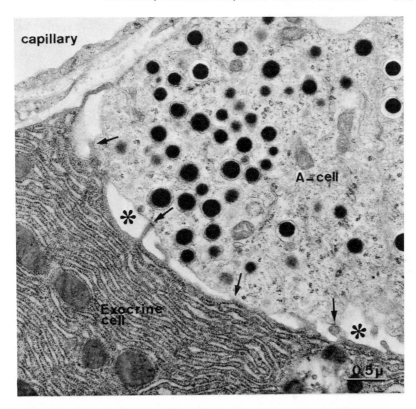

Figure 1   Adult rat pancreas. In this peripheral part of an islet, one sees that the intercellular space (*) between an A-cell and an exocrine cell seems obliterated in several places (arrows) suggesting the presence of junctional specialization between these two cell types.

human fetuses (L. Orci, unpublished observations); but in adults they have thus far been identified only in the duodenum (60), with the exception of one patient in whom glucagon-containing cells were identified in the fundus (96). According to Lawrence et al, glucagon is also present in the salivary gland of humans (67).

In contrast, glucagon-containing A-cells are abundant in the canine fundus (8, 65). In the normal dog measurable glucagon secretion by the stomach does not occur under physiologic conditions, although the infusion of pharmacologic amounts of arginine does stimulate modest release of gastric immunoreactive glucagon (95). However, in the insulin-deprived animal, whether totally depancreatized (13) or alloxan diabetic (12), the gastric fundus releases large amounts of IRG and is a substantial contributor to the high levels of circulating immunoreactive glucagon. The extrapancreatic A-cells are exquisitely sensitive to insulin, and small quantities instantly "turn off" the secretion of extrapancreatic glucagon (12, 13).

Immunoreactive Glucagon (IRG) in Tissues and Plasma

Immunoreactive glucagons (IRGs) of varying molecular size have been identified in the major glucagon-containing organs, the pancreas and the canine fundus, as well as in plasma. [IRG is used to designate immunoreactivity measurable with a "C-terminal reacting" antibody (130), believed to recognize the C-terminal segment of true glucagon and to react poorly with GLI (4, 52).] A small quantity of an IRG of approximately 2000 mol wt is present in extracts of pancreas and fundus (144) and in the plasma (162). It is regarded as a degradation product of glucagon. An IRG of ~3500 mol wt, believed to be glucagon is, of course, present in extracts of both pancreas and canine fundus (144) and in the plasma (162). It is this fraction that accounts both for the rapid rise in plasma IRG induced by arginine or alanine infusion, by insulin deficiency (166), or by hypoglycemia and for the decline in whole plasma IRG caused by somatostatin or insulin (162). It is likely that this represents the true glucagon fraction, and is the principal biologically active IRG moiety of plasma.

An IRG of about 9000 daltons has also been identified in pancreas and gastric tissue extracts (144), and in plasma (162). Pulse-chase experiments in islets by Noe & Bauer (98) have suggested that this is a glucagon precursor, a "proglucagon," which is probably cleaved to a polypeptide of about 4900 daltons which, in turn, is converted to true glucagon (97, 147). IRG^{9000} is devoid of biologic activity and, in fact, does not bind to glucagon receptors, activate adenylate cyclase (131, 140, 144), or stimulate glycogenolysis (131, 140).

Still larger IRGs have been identified (53). Tager reports a 50,000 dalton moiety in isolated islets (147), while Srikant et al have identified a 65,000 mol wt IRG in canine gastric fundus (144) and, more recently, have gathered preliminary evidence of a 65,000 mol wt IRG in both isolated rat islets and in plasma (C. B. Srikant, unpublished observations). The quantities in the latter sites are extremely small. The 65,000 mol wt IRG partially purified from dog stomach has biologic activity comparable to true glucagon, activating adenylate cyclase in isolated liver membranes and stimulating glucose production by the isolated perfused rat liver (144).

Another easily detected IRG component of plasma is so-called "big plasma glucagon" (BPG) (163), a moiety in excess of 160,000 daltons observed in the plasma of man and of all species thus far studied. There is evidence, as yet inconclusive, that this material may be biologically active (161). In man in the basal state it normally accounts for approximately half of the plasma IRG. In some individuals, particularly diabetics, abnormally high levels of BPG have been observed, and a family in which high levels of BPG and other large IRG moieties were present has been identified by Palmer et al (114). The family was otherwise normal and the trait appeared to be an autosomal dominant. The source and fate of BPG are unknown. Srikant believes he has recovered small amounts of BPG from isolated rat islets (unpublished observations). Tryptic digestion of BPG gives rise to smaller IRG moieties (163).

The relationships, if any, of the various IRG fractions to one another and to GLI, are not clear at the moment. The present status of these polypeptides is summarized in Table 2, page 332.

Apparent hyperglucagonemia may be the consequence of increased levels of any IRG fraction, BPG, IRG^{9000}, or true glucagon, and at times it may be clinically important to differentiate them. In patients with glucagonoma (33, 114, 129) and in renal failure (62), both IRG^{9000} levels and true glucagon levels are high (33, 62, 114, 129). It is important to recognize the heterogeneity of plasma IRG (162) and to distinguish between IRG fractions that differ from one another with respect to biologic activities and catabolic rates.

Physiologic Effects of Glucagon

The biologic activity of glucagon is believed to require the three C-terminally located residues of this 29 amino acid peptide (22). This portion of glucagon appears to be necessary for its binding to the receptor site, while the N-terminal and perhaps the central portion of the glucagon molecule are involved both in binding to the receptor and in activation of adenylate cyclase (54). Blundell et al have speculated that the glucagon-receptor complex arises from the hydrophobic side chains brought together in the helical conformer by means of its receptor through the two hydrophobic patches, the intermediate residues being initially flexible (16). As for the molecular basis of glucagon's actions, the reader is referred to a recent brief review by Rodbell & Londos (133).

Table 1 Number of insulin-, glucagon-, and somatostatin-immunofluorescent cells in the islets of chronic juvenile type diabetic subjects, and of nondiabetic subjects

	Insulin[a]	Glucagon[a]	Somatostatin[a]
Controls (N = 4)	61.2 ± 3.1	29.2 ± 3.0	9.7 ± 1.2
Diabetics (N = 2)	—	75.6 ± 2.7[b]	24.5 ± 2.7[c]

[a] Percent of total number of immunofluorescent cells
[b] $p < 0.0005$
[c] $p < 0.0025$

At the present time it is believed that the interaction of glucagon with its receptor initiates a cascade of reactions in which increased adenylate cyclase activity augments the production of cyclic AMP. The nucleotide binds to a regulatory subunit dimer of the cyclic AMP-dependent protein kinase (reviewed in 27), thereby causing it to dissociate from the two catalytic subunits of the enzyme to which it is bound and thus releasing them from its inhibition. This increases phosphorylase activity and glycogenolysis, and reduces glycogen synthase activity and glycogenesis.

Glucagon's site of action in gluconeogenesis remains unknown, but attention has been directed recently toward the enzyme pyruvate kinase which, if inhibited by glucagon, would reduce the amount of phosphoenol pyruvate converted to pyruvate and thus favor glucose formation (reviewed in 121). But whatever the mechanism, glucagon appears to increase net hepatic uptake of gluconeogenic precursors such as alanine and glutamine (21) and, in addition, increases intrahepatic shunting of alanine into gluconeogenic pathways within the liver (29). The gluconeogenic effect of glucagon, like the glycogenolytic effect, is inhibited by insulin (30), which, incidentally, increases pyruvate kinase activity (11).

A role for glucagon in ketogenesis is strongly supported by the studies of McGarry et al (84), who have proposed a bihormonal mechanism involving reduced levels of insulin and increased levels of glucagon. The low insulin levels increase lipolysis, and free fatty acid delivery to the liver is thereby increased. In the presence of glucagon, free fatty acids are preferentially directed towards ketogenesis by a mechanism that has now been worked out in detail (85). Suffice it to say that a high ketogenic capacity of the liver requires that hepatic glycogen be depleted, which, of course, is a consequence of a high glucagon–low insulin mixture. It is noteworthy that in ketosis, whether from starvation, alcohol, or severe diabetes, glucagon levels are high relative to insulin levels.

SOMATOSTATIN

It has been demonstrated recently that somatostatin, the tetradecapeptide discovered by Brazeau et al in the hypothalamus (20) and subsequently localized by Luft et al (71) and Dubois (34) in cells within the islets of Langerhans, is present in the pancreatic D-cells or A_1-cells (103, 120, 124). Arimura and coworkers report that the pancreatic islets have one of the highest levels of somatostatin-like immunoreactivity (3). While the endocrine role of the pancreatic D-cells, if any, remains to be elucidated, presently available evidence has suggested that pancreatic somatostatin may be a third islet hormone with a role in nutrient flux (149). The evidence for this premise is as follows:

1. Exocytotic figures have been identified at the capillary poles of the pancreatic D-cells, which, like A-cells, are generally arrayed in close proximity to afferent capillaries. This is evidence that secretory granules containing somatostatin enter the pericapillary spaces (L. Orci, unpublished observations).

2. Studies using the perfused canine pancreas have demonstrated that release of immunoreactive somatostatin into the pancreatic vein is stimulated by perfusion with high concentrations of glucose (55, 141, 170), arginine (118, 119), leucine (55), amino acid mixture (55), pancreozymin-cholecystokinin (55), and secretin (E. Ipp, unpublished observations). (This strongly suggests endocrine activity related in some manner to the concentrations of perfusing nutrients and alimentary hormones, the same substances that stimulate insulin secretion, and thereby implies a commonality of function.)

3. Pharmacologic quantities of somatostatin administered by peripheral vein are known to reduce a variety of digestive functions including gastric emptying (15); the secretion of HCl (14), pepsin (14) and gastrin (14); antral (17), duodenal (17), and gall bladder motility (32); pancreatic exocrine function (32); the secretion of secretin (19), motilin (15), and GLI (134) by the small bowel; splanchnic blood flow (168); and the absorption of xylose (168), glucose (168), and triglycerides (122, 134). The demonstration that somatostatin inhibits the release of acetylcholine by electrically stimulated parasympathetic nerves to the jejunum (50) may, in part, account for many of these inhibitory actions.

4. It has been reported recently that the intraportal infusion of somatostatin at the same physiologic rate at which it is released by the nutrient-stimulated pancreas retards the entry of ingested nutrients into the circulation (143).

5. MacGregor et al (72, 73) have observed that infusion of glucose, a stimulus of pancreatic somatostatin secretion, reduces gastric emptying, gastrin secretion, gall bladder contraction, and pancreatic exocrine function, thus mimicking the effects of somatostatin on the digestive organs.

On the basis of the foregoing it has been hypothesized that somatostatin may constitute an afferent limb of a gut-islet-gut axis and may give the islets of Langerhans a measure of control over the principal route of nutrient influx, the gastrointestinal tract (149). According to this hypothesis, the function of pancreatic somatostatin is to restrain the rate of nutrient entry by inhibiting various digestive events in response to signals from enteric hormones and rising nutrient concentrations. This would permit the endocrine pancreas to coordinate the influx of nutrients from the gut with their efflux from the extracellular space by coordinating the secretion of somatostatin and insulin, just as coordinated secretion of insulin and glucagon controls the influx and efflux of endogenous nutrients. Coordination may take effect, at least in part, through specialized junctions—gap junctions— between islet cells allowing exchange of metabolites from one cell to another; gap junctions have been found between A- and B-cells (107) and it is likely that such junctions also exist between the other cell types of the islet, for example between D-cells, as well as between D-cells and A- or B-cells (L. Orci, unpublished observations), thus making a functional syncytium of islet cells. Somatostatin may well be an extremely important component of the islet system with respect to control of nutrient flux. Its hypothesized role, together with those of insulin and glucagon, is schematized in Figure 2.

MORPHOFUNCTIONAL CORRELATIONS IN THE ISLETS OF LANGERHANS

The microorgans of Langerhans appear to be remarkably well adapted to subserve the functions just considered and in all probability many others that have not yet been as clearly defined. It becomes of considerable interest, in view of recent advances in our understanding of the topographical arrangements of the four major cell types of the islets of Langerhans and their recently identified membrane specializations, to attempt to draw morphofunctional correlations (161) that are admittedly highly speculative.

Anatomical Location

The first requirement for a system designed to meet the diverse fuel requirements of the far flung organ systems of the body is an appropriate location in which to perceive and respond to sudden changes in the extracellular

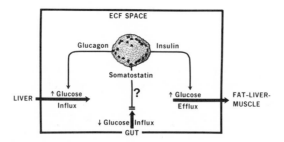

Figure 2 A hypothetical scheme depicting the functional role of the islets of Langerhans upon glucose flux. The box represents the extracellular fluid (ECF) space. [Reproduced by permission of *Life Sciences.*]

concentrations of nutrients. Clearly, such a system would have to be located at a distance from the gut, in which changes in luminal nutrient concentration resulting from food intake might render virtually impossible a realistic reading of nutrient concentrations in the extracellular fluid. Therefore, on teleologic grounds, the budding off of the primitive pancreatic anlage and its separation from the wall of the gut in the course of embryologic development would seem to be a prerequisite for its sensing function.

The deployment of these elements in separate clusters of cells embedded in a firm retroperitoneal environment may provide a unique measure of protection from trauma for such delicate, highly vascular microorgans, which, if gathered together into a single organ, might have been more vulnerable to trauma or disease. In addition to its theoretical protective value, the small size of the individual islet units may signify that a critical cluster size is required for certain intercellular functions and relationships (see below).

Neurovascular Input

A second prerequisite for the fulfillment of the function of sensing fuel needs would be the access to all relevant external information through afferent channels of communication, the blood vessels and nerves. The islets are highly vascular (Figure 3). They are also richly supplied with autonomic nerve endings that terminate with direct contacts with islet cells (108) (Figure 4). Afferent vessels and nerves enter in the heterocellular zone (42) in which the A-, B- and D-cells are contiguous. In man and in the rat this region is largely in the periphery of the islet.

Topographical Arrangements of Islet Cells

The composition and topographical arrangements of cells within the islets have recently been studied in a variety of species (111). In rodents approximately 60% of the islet cells have been identified by immunofluorescent staining techniques as insulin-containing B-cells; these form the great central mass of the microorgan (105). The most peripherally situated cells are glucagon-containing A-cells, forming a rim one to three cells in thickness, and comprising approximately 25% of the endocrine cells (105). In man rows of A-cells and D-cells project into the central mass of the islets along capillary axes, forming lobulations in which the A- and D-cells remain peripheral in relation to centrally assembled B-cells (Figure 5). In islets located in the paraduodenal area the peripheral glucagon-containing A-cells appear to be replaced by cells containing pancreatic polypeptide (66, 104) (Figure 6). Between the outer mantle of A-cells are the D-cells, demon-

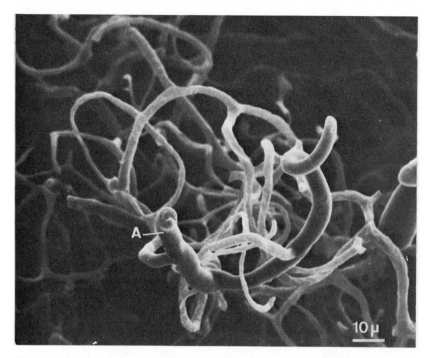

Figure 3   Scanning electron micrograph of the vascular cast of a rat pancreatic islet. The main branches of the vas afferens (A) run along the periphery of the islet before giving branches into the deeper regions. (Unpublished document of M. Fukuma and L. Orci.)

strated by immunofluorescent staining techniques to contain somatostatin or somatostatin-like immunoreactive material (105).

Specific topographical relationships appear to be relatively characteristic for each species studied. Although there are species differences with respect to the relative number of cells and to their distribution within the islets, in all species studied a heterocellular region in which A-cells (or pancreatic polypeptide-containing cells), somatostatin-containing D-cells, and insulin-containing B-cells are in close proximity has been identified (111).

The heterocellular region may have a special function inasmuch as afferent capillaries and nerves appear to enter this zone (42). In view of possible intercellular communications via intercellular (paracrine) (160) and intracellular (gap junction) (106, 107) routes (see the section below on membrane specializations), the heterocellular area could function as a "pacemaker" (88) for the entire islet, information received from outside the islet being transmitted from this zone to other cells through one or both of these mechanisms.

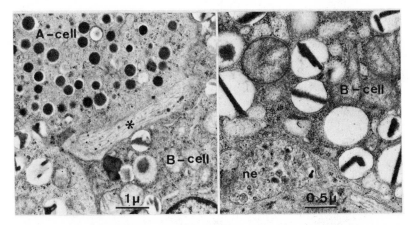

Figure 4 (*left panel*) Adult dog pancreatic islet. A nerve axon (*) is seen between an A-cell and a B-cell. (*right panel*) Adult dog pancreatic islet. A nerve ending (ne) of adrenergic type is seen in close relationship with a B-cell.

Membrane Specializations

A characteristic morphologic feature of the islet cells are membrane specializations that may be involved in intercellular relationships. These specializations, called intercellular junctions (145), consist of tight junctions (102, 112) [linear points of fusion between the outer leaflets of the plasma membranes of two adjacent cells (Figure 7)] and gap junctions [believed to be areas of intercellular communication, low resistance pathways through which molecules of less than 1,000 daltons can move from the cytosol of one cell to that of an adjacent cell without entering the intercellular space (Figure 8) (106, 107)]. In addition, islet cells share desmosomes, which are primarily involved in cell-to-cell adhesion. Although the precise function of tight and gap junctions in the islets of Langerhans remains to be determined, the fact that they are present in the islets of all species studied may have special functional significance. It is known that tight junctions are "plastic"—that is, are constantly changing and may form extensive networks during high levels of secretory activity (101). It is also known that they can form barriers to diffusion of secretory products (38) such as those of the islets of Langerhans (101, 102). They could, therefore, represent a means by which the islets of Langerhans compartmentalize the polypeptides they release (100, 160). Since the islets are the only endocrine organs that produce secretory products with profound influence upon the activity of their neighboring endocrine cells, tight junctions may constitute a vital method of separating the pericapillary intercellular space of islet cells (in which the concentrations of hormones intended for export must obviously

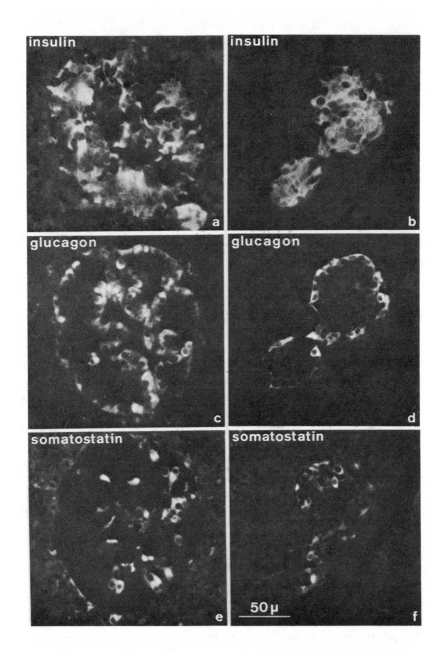

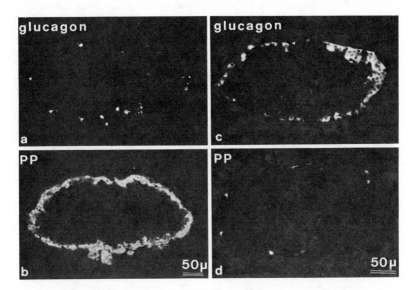

Figure 6   Rat pancreas: serial sections of an islet from the head (a,b) and an islet from the tail (c,d), after application of antiglucagon and antibovine pancreatic polypeptide (PP) sera. Notice the inverse relationship between PP and glucagon in the two islets.

be very high) from the remaining interstitium of the islet (in which much lower concentrations may be sufficient for local paracrine activities and/or endocrine effects of islet hormones). Inasmuch as the secretion of appropriate mixture of insulin, glucagon, and somatostatin may require a high degree of coordination between islet cells, these cell-to-cell communications, rendered possible by gap junctions and by paracrine and/or endocrine actions of islet cell hormones upon islet cells, could represent an important means of achieving this.

←————————————————————————————————————

Figure 5   Two sets of three consecutive serial sections of human islets treated by indirect immunofluorescence for revealing the populations of insulin- (a,b), glucagon- (c,d) and somatostatin- (e,f) containing cells. In the second set of sections (b,d,f) illustrating two islets of small size, one sees that insulin-containing cells occupy the center of the islet while glucagon- and somatostatin-containing cells are situated in a peripheral location. In the first set of sections (a,c,e), which involves an islet of large size, glucagon- and somatostatin-containing cells are no longer restricted at the islet periphery. The pattern suggests that the large islet is formed by several smaller units, each of which has the distribution of insulin-, glucagon-, and somatostatin-containing cells as described for small size islets (see b,d,f).

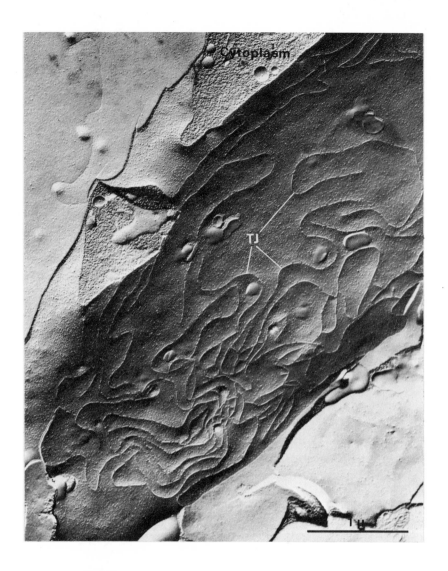

Figure 7 Freeze-fracture replica of an isolated islet incubated for 90 min with 4 μg × ml⁻¹ of pronase. An extensive network of tight junction elements (TJ) is present in the plasma membrane. The fibrils delimit the membrane face (and, of course, the corresponding intercellular space) in several labyrinthine compartments. The fact that such junctions can be modified experimentally clearly indicates that they are labile differentiations and probably reflects their ability constantly to modulate intercellular relationships. By controlling diffusion along the intercellular space, tight junctions may render specific areas of plasma membrane more or less accessible to substances moving in the intercellular fluid. Opening or closing certain membrane areas to the influence of the stimulatory or inhibitory substances would thus represent one of the possible regulatory mechanisms by which normal islet cells maintain glucose homeostasis.

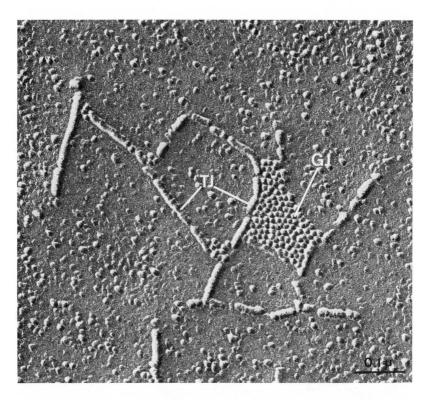

Figure 8   Freeze-fracture replicas of a rat pancreatic islet. On the exposed face of an islet cell membrane the aggregate of particles of regular size (GI) represents the gap junction, the fibrils (TJ) represent tight junction elements. The closely packed particles characterizing the gap junctions are believed to represent the morphological counterpart of channels that bridge the cytoplasms of the two cells sharing the junctions. The channels are assumed to let ions and molecules up to 1000 mol wt diffuse between the two cells, a process termed intercellular communication or coupling. At present it is not known what kind of molecules or ions are transferred between islet cells, nor is the significance of intercellular coupling for the integrated secretory behavior of the islet understood. The tight junctional elements correspond to focal regions where the outer leaflet of two adjacent plasma membranes are fused together. [Reprinted from *Dilemmas in Diabetes*, courtesy of Plenum Press.]

RESPONSES OF ISLETS TO SUBSTANCES IN THE CIRCULATION

Nutrients

GLUCOSE   Normally, a rise in glucose concentration suppresses glucagon secretion (99, 153, 158) and stimulates the release of both insulin and somatostatin, while a low glucose concentration stimulates glucagon secretion (155); this is probably a direct effect of hypoglycemia rather than a consequence of concomitant adrenergic effects (169). In vitro, glucose also stimulates pancreatic somatostatin release (55, 141, 170).

In view of the overriding importance of glucose as a cerebral fuel, it is hardly surprising that its influence on the response of A-cells and B-cells appears to be obligatory. By this is meant that islet cell responses to other stimuli or inhibitors are profoundly changed by the concentration of glucose. In circumstances of glucose need, such as starvation, substances that normally stimulate insulin secretion, e.g. amino acids and enteric hormones, have little or no effect on insulin secretion (2, 94). Conversely, substances that ordinarily stimulate the secretion of glucagon, such as amino acids and certain gut hormones, fail to elicit such a response when hyperglycemia is present (157).

AMINO ACIDS   Amino acids, with the exception of the branch chain amino acids, stimulate glucagon secretion to a varying degree (132). Alanine is a potent stimulus of glucagon secretion (93) and, since both its uptake by the liver (21) and its preferential disposition towards gluconeogenesis once it has entered the liver cell (29) appear to be increased by glucagon, alanine through glucagon plays a role in the regulation of its own concentration and disposition. Arginine, although not a gluconeogenic precursor, is also a potent stimulator of glucagon secretion (153) and is a commonly used test of A-cell function. Arginine also stimulates both insulin (40) and somatostatin secretion (118, 119).

FREE FATTY ACIDS   High concentrations of free fatty acids inhibit glucagon secretion and stimulate insulin secretion (77), effects that would tend to reduce the rate of lipolysis and ketogenesis in normal individuals. This negative feedback arrangement may serve to limit the rate at which these processes proceed, permitting them to meet fuel needs without danger of the massive ketogenesis that occurs when the islets are incapable of appropriate bihormonal responses, as in severe diabetes (75, 76).

HORMONES   A number of hormones modulate the secretory responses of the islets of Langerhans. In some instances, these effects appear to be permissive. In time of stress when cortisol levels are increased, the response of glucagon to stimulation is augmented (80, 174) and the sensitivity to glucagon of its major target organ, the liver, is also enhanced (116). Thus, it seems that hypercortisolemia, whether physiologic, iatrogenic, or pathologic in etiology, is associated with an exaggerated response of glucagon secretion to secretagogues, and that a given amount of glucagon will elicit a greater gluconeogenic response than under normal circumstances. It is possible that this potentiation of glucagon secretion and activity constitutes a factor in the catabolic state that characterizes hypercortisolemia.

Other hormones directly stimulate or inhibit secretion by the islets of Langerhans. The catecholamines inhibit both insulin (125) and somatostatin (141) secretion and stimulate glucagon secretion in the dog via β-adrenergic receptors (57). Norepinephrine release from nerve endings within the pancreas (59), as well as circulating catecholamines, constitutes an extremely important influence upon islet cell secretion (126).

Many of the gastrointestinal hormones released in the course of digestion stimulate secretion by the islet cells (148). Stimulation of insulin secretion by gut hormones enables the islets to coordinate the disposal rate of inflowing nutrients with their entry rate and thereby minimize the rise in the concentrations of such nutrients, keeping them within the ranges regarded as normal. Gastrin (156), pancreozymin-cholecystokinin (156), secretin (35), GIP (24), and perhaps other enteric hormones, may constitute afferent limbs of what has been referred to as an "enteroinsular axis" (154). These hormones are released during meals and are believed to enter the circulation before a substantial change in nutrient concentration has occurred. Since the responses of enteric hormones to various nutrients differ and since the magnitude of a hormonal response to a given nutrient may be related to the quantity of the nutrient consumed, quantitative and qualitative differences in the pattern of enteric hormone secretion may forewarn the islets of the amount and character of incoming nutrients. The islets may thus begin their secretory response at the very start of nutrient absorption, rather than react in an "after-the-fact", "catch-up" fashion to an undesirably high concentration of nutrients entering after a large meal. In the case of glucose, the early response of insulin preceding a rise in peripheral glycemia may prepare the liver to extract a higher fraction of ingested glucose entering the portal vein, thereby reducing the rise in glucose concentration in the post-hepatic circulation. Normally, the intraduodenal administration of a large glucose load does not cause proportionately greater hyperglycemia than a small glucose load because of the far greater insulin response elicited by the larger load; since this response begins before the entry of appreciable quantities of glucose into the circulation, it must be mediated by some signal—insulin-stimulating gut hormones such as GIP (24) and/or by cholinergic activity (175).

Autonomic Nervous System

As shown in Figure 4, the islets of Langerhans are richly endowed with autonomic nerve endings containing the usual load of "synaptic" vesicles (cholinergic or adrenergic). In addition, some endings share gap junctional contacts with islet cells (108). Stimulation of the ventromedial nucleus of the hypothalamus (41) or of a sympathetic nerve to the pancreas (83) elicits an outpouring of glucagon and restricts insulin secretion—much as does the administration of catecholamines. It seems likely that norepinephrine released from nerve endings within the pancreas (59) has a profound influence on the secretion of insulin and glucagon. Increased sympathetic discharge resulting from an acute stressful event will instantly raise glucagon secretion (68, 69, 171, 172) while inhibiting an increase in insulin release, much as does the electrical stimulation of the sympathetic nerves (83). The increase in hepatic glucose production thereby generates endogenous hyperglycemia; arterial glucose levels rise to concentrations which, in the absence of stress, would have been prevented by the release of insulin. This change in the insulin-glucagon mixture reduces glucose entry into liver, muscle, and fat (insulin-dependent tissues for which glucose is not an obligatory fuel), while sparing endogenously produced glucose for those tissues in which it is essential, such as the central nervous system. Thus, the central nervous system can regulate the insulin and glucagon response in such a way as to serve its own special fuel needs.

Acetylcholine also appears to influence the islets of Langerhans, increasing secretion of insulin and glucagon (56) while inhibiting somatostatin release (139). The possible role of the cholinergic system in islet cell response has not been elucidated however.

OTHER POSSIBLE CONTROLS OVER ISLET CELL FUNCTION

Intercellular or "Paracrine" Interactions

Islet cells may receive information from one another via the interstitial spaces of the islets, although the existence of a within-islet "paracrine" system has not yet been proven. It is, however, recognized that insulin, glucagon, and somatostatin, even in physiologic doses, each influences the secretion of at least one and probably at least two other pancreatic hormones: (a) Insulin clearly inhibits glucagon secretion (138) and may inhibit somatostatin secretion as well, although the latter has not been established. (b) Glucagon stimulates both insulin (135, 137) and somatostatin secretion (117, 118, 170). (c) Somatostatin inhibits both insulin and glucagon secretion (61, 91). A paracrine system, similar to the model depicted in Figure 9, could exist (160), but these same interactions between islet hormones and islet cells could occur via the bloodstream. It is of interest that anti-insulin serum causes hyperglucagonemia in vivo and that antisomatostatin serum increases glucagon but not insulin release in vitro (9, 93), but this does not help to distinguish between paracrine and endocrine routes of

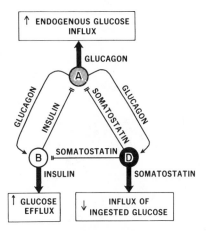

Figure 9 A hypothetical model depicting the endocrine and/or paracrine roles of insulin, glucagon, and somatostatin. The endocrine functions would apply not only to glucose but to certain other nutrients as well. The depicted effects of the hormones upon neighboring islet cells could be exerted via either paracrine or endocrine routes.

action. Nor does the fact that only very modest increments of insulin (128) and of somatostatin (136) are required to suppress glucagon secretion permit differentiation between an endocrine and a paracrine action; it had been tacitly assumed that because of the high concentrations of hormone that must be present at the capillary poles of islet cells for export to remotely situated target cells, paracrine actions within the islet must be mediated by similarly high hormone concentrations. But this assumption may well be wrong; the extensive network of tight junctions (Figure 7) provides a means of separating the afferent pericapillary spaces from other regions of the intercellular spaces of the islets. Compartmentalization of the intercellular spaces between islet cells could signify the existence of a specific interstitial paracrine system separate from the endocrine system. Sealing off of (Figure 10) the pericapillary secretory spaces of islet cells, where hormone concentrations are likely to be extremely high, from the interstitium between islet hormone receptor-containing areas of the islet cells by tight junctions would be analogous to exocrine cells in which a ring of well-developed tight junctions encircles the lumen to prevent back-diffusion of secretory product (101). In any case, it is necessary to postulate that islet cells have a secretory surface facing the afferent capillaries and a separate receptor surface capable of responding to other islet hormones carried there by paracrine and/or endocrine routes.

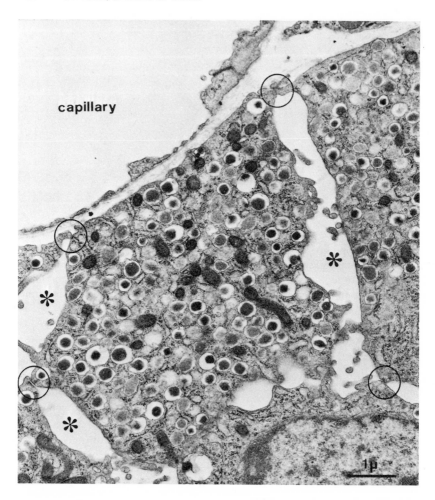

Figure 10 Electron micrograph of B-cells in an islet from rat pancreas perfused in situ with hypertonic phosphate buffer glutaraldehyde. The intercellular spaces (*) appear enlarged, except at the encircled areas where the adjacent islet cells approach or make focal contacts with each other. The exact nature of such contacts cannot be determined in this picture.

Intercellular Communications

The demonstration of gap junctions (Figure 8) between endocrine cells of the islets of Langerhans (100) indicates that it is, in the functional sense, a syncytium. One can envision a conduction system involving such elements and perhaps influencing or coordinating endocrine and/or paracrine secretory patterns. Conceivably, the small size of the islet cell clusters reflects the functional limits of such a conducting system and/or of a paracrine system involving diffusion of secretory products through intercellular channels.

DISEASES OF THE ISLETS OF LANGERHANS

Although a detailed clinical perspective of disordered islet cell function is beyond the scope of this review, the pathophysiology of the islets forms an important complement to our understanding of their physiology. We therefore consider here certain primary disorders of the islets of Langerhans and the metabolic malfunctions that are their consequence. As was the case in the normally functioning islets of Langerhans, the interrelationships of the secretory products of the various islet cells are so intimate and diverse that it is necessary to consider them once again as a multihormonal unit. However, it is possible to subclassify these disorders according to the lesion that, in the light of our present knowledge, appears to be primary.

Diabetes Mellitus

PRIMARY INSULIN DEFICIENCY   Experimental insulin deficiency states can be induced by destruction of B-cells with alloxan or streptozotocin. Additionally, insulin deficiency occurs spontaneously in certain strains of mice and in Chinese hamsters. In man, spontaneous loss of insulin secretion is observed in so-called juvenile type diabetics. It is now recognized that in addition to the loss of insulin-secreting cells, profound abnormalities in the structure (105) and function (153) of the remaining islet cells can be identified. Since 1969 it has been known that in juvenile type diabetics, as in other kinds of diabetics, excessive levels of glucagon relative to the prevailing glucose concentration are uniformly observed (2, 94, 153). Fasting glucagon levels are high relative to the fasting glucose concentrations and are not suppressed by further increments in glucose concentration (94, 128). Stimuli of A-cell secretion, such as arginine, elicit an exaggerated rise in plasma glucagon levels despite hyperglycemia. In nondiabetics such glycemia would reduce the A-cell response to these stimuli (1, 153). Hypoglycemia, which in nondiabetics elicits a rise in plasma glucagon levels (155), fails to do so in juvenile type diabetics (46). Thus, in diabetes it would appear that A-cell function is autonomous of glycemic control (150). An increase in free fatty acids, however, suppresses A-cell function in juvenile diabetics much as it does in nondiabetics, suggesting that the impairment of A-cell function is selective for glucose (47).

This A-cell defect in glucose-sensing may be directly related to the absence of the insulin-secreting cells within the islets of Langerhans. The exaggerated response to arginine stimulation can be restored to normal by prior insulinization (48, 127). Other manifestations of the abnormal function of A-cells are also greatly ameliorated by insulin (5, 6, 128), although even in very high concentrations (Figure 11) it appears impossible to restore the A-cell relationship with glycemia to that of the normal state (5, 6). While the lack of insulin is clearly a major factor in the abnormality of A-cell function, it would appear that, in addition to a defect involving insulin lack in the blood and/or the interstitial spaces, there is an abnormality not correctable by exogenous insulin administered in any quantity or pattern. It is possible that this defect is simply the consequence of the irreversible anatomical disruption that characterizes the islets in these forms of diabetes (105). Immunofluorescent staining techniques for insulin, glucagon, and somatostatin-like immunoreactivity reveal that, in addition to absence of insulin-containing cells, which in nondiabetics account for 60% of the islet cells, there is an increase in the percentage of glucagon-containing cells from 25% in nondiabetics to 75% in juvenile type diabetics and an increase in somatostatin-containing cells from 10% in nondiabetics to 25% in juvenile type diabetics (105) (Table 1, p. 313). Furthermore, the topographical relationships described previously are completely altered, the islets resembling a disorganized collection of A- and D-cells (Figure 12). Although careful comparisons have not as yet been made, it is not improbable that many, if not all, of the morphological relationships emphasized above, such as neurovascular relationships and cell-to-cell contacts via both interstitial and intercellular channels, are lacking or distorted. It is not implausible to consider, then, that while insulin lack plays a major role in the abnormal A-cell function, the restoration of insulin levels fails to correct A-cell behavior to normal because of the anatomical disruption.

Diabetes Without Insulin Deficiency

At the other extreme of the spectrum of hyperglycemic disorders is the form of hyperglycemia in which no evidence of absolute hypoinsulinemia is present. In man, this form of diabetes is often associated with obesity and, at least in the absolute sense, hyperinsulinemia. Such individuals are generally labeled as having the "adult type", "maturity onset type", or "ketoacidosis-resistant" form of diabetes. There is reason to suspect that its murine counterpart may be the ob/ob mouse, in which obesity and hyperglycemia are also associated with high insulin levels. Although pancreases of human adult type diabetics have not yet been scrutinized by the immunocytochemical techniques that have been applied to the juvenile type disorder, the islets of the ob/ob mouse have been extensively studied (7). They are characterized by an overall increase in the number of islet cells

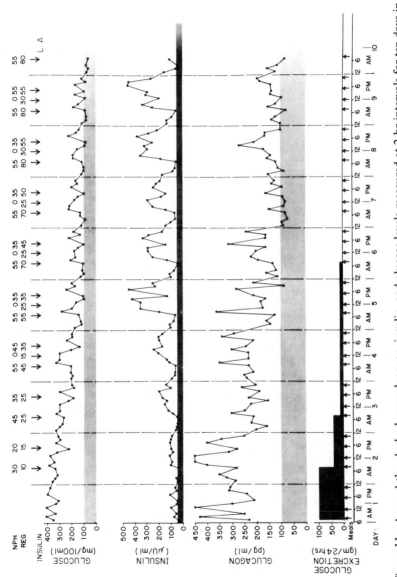

Figure 11 Around-the-clock plasma glucagon, insulin, and glucose levels measured at 2-hr intervals for ten days in an adult onset diabetic. At the top of the figure is indicated the dose of NPH and regular (REG) insulin, the arrows indicating the time of injection. On day nine, this patient received a total of 275 U of insulin, raising plasma insulin levels far above the normal range represented by the stippled stripes. Yet hyperglucagonemia persisted, as did hyperglycemia, as high as 200 mg%. (P. Raskin, unpublished study.)

Table 2 Characteristics of canine pancreatic and fundic IRGs

	Molecular size of IRG	pI	Percent of response to immunoequivalent concentration of glucagon		
			Glyco-genolytic activity	Displacement of ^{125}I glucagon	Activation of adenylate cyclase
Pancreatic IRGs	~2,000	—	—	—	—
	3,500	6.25	100	104	100
	~9,000	4.65	0	~10	0
	~50,000	—	—	—	—
	~65,000 (?)	—	—	—	—
Fundic IRGs	~2,000	—	—	—	—
	3,500	6.15	120	107	180
	~9,000	4.50	0	~10	0
	65,000	6.40	110	97.5	82.5
Plasma IRGs	~2,000	—	—	—	—
	~3,500	—	~100	—	—
	~9,000	—	—	—	—
	~65,000 (?)	—	—	—	—
	~180,000	—	~100	—	—

resulting from an increased number of insulin-containing cells, and a relative diminution in both glucagon-containing A-cells and somatostatin-containing D-cells. Yet, the same abnormalities in A-cell function that were identified in the case of juvenile type diabetics are also present in the adult form of the disease, i.e. an exaggerated response to stimuli such as arginine (153) and alanine (173), and relative hyperglucagonemia despite fasting hyperglycemia (153). Moreover, an increase in plasma glucose resulting from an oral glucose load fails to elicit the normal nondiabetic suppression of plasma IRG (25, 94); in fact a paradoxical rise may occur (25). The most striking difference between the A-cell abnormality of the adult type diabetic and that of the juvenile type diabetic lies in the ability of insulin to improve the dysfunction; in the latter form of the disease, normalization of insulin levels restores to normal the exaggerated response of glucagon to arginine; in adult type diabetics, insulin, even in pharmacologic doses, does not correct the abnormality (127). If, in the human form of this disorder, there is a paucity of D-cells coupled with an abundance of B-cells, as is the case in the ob/ob mouse (7), the ineffectiveness of insulin in restraining abnormal glucagon secretion would not be surprising. Perhaps normally restrained A-cell function requires the presence of both insulin and somatostatin in the immediate vicinity of A-cells. As schematized in Figure 13, in juvenile diabetics, the A-cells lack the restraining influence of insulin, and their hyperfunction is partially corrected by insulin replacement; in adult dia-

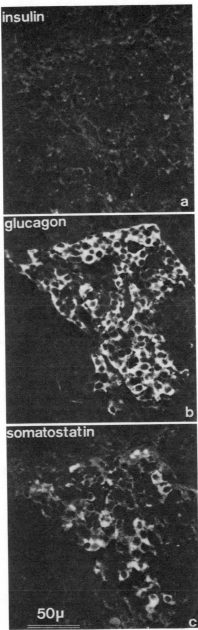

Figure 12 Islet of Langerhans in a chronic juvenile diabetic. Consecutive serial sections treated with indirect immunofluorescent technique against insulin (a), glucagon (b), and somatostatin (c). The only detectable immunofluorescent cells within the islet are the numerous glucagon- and somatostatin-containing cells. [Reprinted from *Insulin and Metabolism,* courtesy of Excerpta Medica, Amsterdam.]

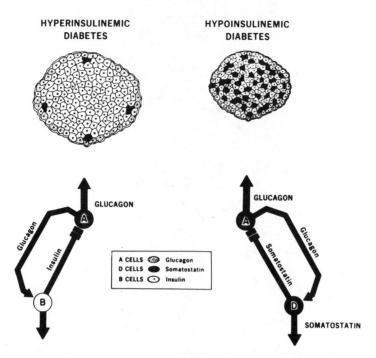

Figure 13 Hypothetical scheme depicting contrasting hormonal derangements in two forms of diabetes. In "hyperinsulinemic" diabetes, at least in the ob/ob mouse, the number of insulin-secreting B-cells is increased while a relative reduction in somatostatin-containing D-cells is observed (7). Hyperinsulinemia and probably hyperglucagonemia coexist, the hyperglucagonemia perhaps a consequence of the lack of nearby D-cells or adequate somatostatin secretion. In insulin-deficiency states, increased numbers of glucagon-secreting A-cells and somatostatin-containing D-cells are observed. Here the hyperglucagonemia may be attributed to the lack of restraining insulin secretion, and indeed, is greatly improved by insulin repletion. It cannot, however, be restored to normal, perhaps because of the anatomical disruption of the islet.

betes, however, it may be that the A-cells lack the restraining influence of somatostatin—not of insulin—and consequently even pharmacologic doses of insulin do not correct its abnormal secretory patterns.

ISLET CELL TUMORS

Insulinoma

Benign and malignant insulin-secreting tumors are characterized by relative or complete autonomy of insulin release with respect to glycemic control. Uncontrolled insulin release has also been reported in infants with islet cell hyperplasia of the pancreas, in which B-cell involvement is prominent (31). The consequence of insulin excess is, of course, hypoglycemia, which may vary from mild episodes, readily controlled by an increase in food intake, to severe and intractable hypoglycemia leading to convulsions and death. The latter is most common in malignant B-cell tumors and in instances of endocrine cell hyperplasia of the pancreas in infants. Although fasting plasma glucagon levels are at times increased in the hypoglycemia of insulinoma, not infrequently one finds a relative or absolute reduction in plasma glucagon (51). This is not surprising in view of the fact that during prolonged insulin-induced hypoglycemia in dogs the hyperglucagonemia of the first hour begins to wane after the second hour, despite continuing severe hypoglycemia (J. T. Braaten, R. E. Dobbs, and R. H. Unger, unpublished observations). This contrasts with the marked and sustained hyperglucagonemia that is associated with hypoglycemia with low insulin levels. Phloridzin-induced hypoglycemia (155), alcohol-induced hypoglycemia (113), and the hypoglycemia of adrenal insufficiency (R. E. Dobbs, unpublished observations) are examples.

Glucagonoma

The glucagonoma syndrome includes hyperglucagonemia, dermatitis and stomatitis, and metabolic abnormalities that vary with the ability of the patient to secrete insulin (18, 79, 87, 176). When insulin secretion is relatively unimpaired, as in the case reported by Boden et al (18), hyperglycemia may be minimal. Other manifestations of hyperglucagonemia, such as hypoaminoacidemia, hyperketonemia, and a catabolic state with weight loss, may be present (18). When the pancreatic tumor begins to encroach on the insulin-secreting capacity of the pancreas, however, then severe and relatively resistant diabetes may supervene (176). Somatostatin-containing cells have also been observed in some glucagonoma tumors (L. Orci, unpublished observations); hypersomatostatinemia may be present and perhaps contribute to the syndrome.

Somatostatinoma

Two patients with somatostatinoma have recently been described (45, 64). In the case of Larsson et al (64) the diagnosis was proven by immunofluorescent staining of the tumor and by the demonstration of marked hypersomatostatinemia in the patient's plasma. In both cases hypoinsulinemia and hypoglucagonemia were present. As might have been predicted, hypoinsulinemia resulted in impaired glucose tolerance with only modest fasting hyperglycemia, which in the patient of Ganda et al (45) was 169 mg% and was not recorded in the report of Larsson et al (64). When such hypoinsulinemic patients consume substantial amounts of carbohydrate, severe hyperglycemia and symptomatic diabetes may develop; this did, in fact, occur in the patient of Ganda et al. However, somatostatin has gastrointestinal (14, 15, 17, 19, 32, 122, 134, 168) and perhaps central (70) effects that may limit food intake; weight loss may be a manifestation of the disorder. In the patient of Larsson, steatorrhea was present, perhaps the result of somatostatin-induced inhibition of fat digestion. Both patients had gall bladder disease and in both the tumor was accidentally discovered in the course of gall bladder surgery; inasmuch as somatostatin in high doses is known to inhibit gall bladder contraction (32), it is conceivable that hypersomatostatinemia may increase the incidence of cholelithiasis by encouraging bile stasis (149).

Literature Cited

1. Aguilar-Parada, E., Eisentraut, A. M., Unger, R. H. 1969. Pancreatic glucagon secretion in normal and diabetic subjects. *Amer. J. Med. Sci.* 257:415–19
2. Aguilar-Parada, E., Eisentraut, A. M., Unger, R. H. 1969. Effects of starvation on plasma pancreatic glucagon in normal man. *Diabetes* 18:717–23
3. Arimura, A., Sato, H., Dupont, A., Nishi, N., Schally, A. V. 1975. Somatostatin: Abundance of immunoreactive hormone in rat stomach and pancreas. *Science* 189:1007–9
4. Assan, R., Slusher, N. 1972. Structure-function and structure-immunoreactivity relationships of the glucagon molecule and related synthetic peptides. *Diabetes* 21:843–55
5. Aydin, I., Raskin, P., Unger, R. H. 1977. The effect of insulin on the glucagon response to a carbohydrate meal in adult onset and juvenile type diabetes. *Diabetologia.* In press
6. Aydin, I., Yamamoto, T., Raskin, P. 1977. The role of insulin lack in A-cell dysfunction of human diabetes. *Diabetes* 26 (Suppl.):382
7. Baetens, D., Coleman, D. L., Orci, L. 1976. Islet cell population in ob/ob and db/db mice. *Diabetes* 25 (Suppl.):344
8. Baetens, D., Rufener, C., Srikant, C. B., Dobbs, R. E., Unger, R. H., Orci, L. 1976. Identification of glucagon-producing cells (A-cells) in dog gastric mucosa. *J. Cell Biol.* 69:455–64
9. Barden, N., Lavoie, M., Alvarado-Urbina, G., Cote, J. P., Dupont, A. 1977. A physiologic role of somatostatin in the control of insulin and glucagon secretion. *Fed. Proc.* 36:298
10. Baum, J., Simons, B. E., Unger, R. H., Madison, L. L. 1962. Localization of glucagon in the alpha cells in the pancreatic islet by immunofluorescent technics. *Diabetes* 11:371–74
11. Blair, J. B., Cimbala, M. A., Foster, J. L., Morgan, R. A. 1976. Hepatic pyruvate kinase. Regulation by glucagon, cyclic adenosine 3'5'-monophosphate, and insulin in the perfused rat liver. *J. Biol. Chem.* 251:3756–62
12. Blazquez, E., Munoz-Barragan, L., Patton, G. S., Dobbs, R. E., Unger, R. H. 1977. Demonstration of gastric glucagon hypersecretion in insulin-deprived alloxan diabetic dogs. *J. Lab. Clin. Med.* 89:971–77
13. Blazquez, E., Munoz-Barragan, L., Patton, G. S., Orci, L., Dobbs, R. E., Unger, R. H. 1976. Gastric A-cell function in insulin-deprived depancreatized dogs. *Endocrinology* 99:1182–88
14. Bloom, S. R., Mortimer, C. H., Thorner, M. O., Besser, G. M., Hall, R., Gomez-Pan, A., Roy, V. M., Russell, R. C. G., Coy, D. H., Kastin, A. J., Schally, A. V. 1974. Inhibition of gastrin and gastric-acid secretion by growth-hormone release-inhibiting hormone. *Lancet* 2:1106–9
15. Bloom, S. R., Ralphs, D. N., Besser, G. M., Hall, R., Coy, D. H., Kastin, A. J., Schally, A. V. 1975. Effect of somatostatin on motilin levels and gastric emptying. *Gut* 16:834
16. Blundell, T. L., Dockerill, S., Sasaki, K., Tickle, I. J., Wood, S. P. 1976. The relation of structure to storage and receptor binding of glucagon. *Metabolism* 25 (Suppl.):1131–39
17. Boden, G., Jacoby, H. I., Staus, A. 1976. Somatostatin interacts with basal and carbachol stimulated antral and duodenal motility. *Gastroenterology* 70:961
18. Boden, G., Owen, O. E., Rezvani, I., Elfenbein, B. I., Quickel, K. E. 1977.

An islet cell carcinoma containing glucagon and insulin. *Diabetes* 26: 128–37

19. Boden, G., Sivitz, M. C., Owen, O. E., Essa-Koumar, N., Landor, J. H. 1975. Somatostatin suppresses secretin and pancreatic exocrine secretion. *Science* 190:163–65

20. Brazeau, P., Vale, W., Burgus, R., Ling, N., Butcher, M., Rivier, J., Guillemin, R. 1973. Hypothalamic polypeptide that inhibits the secretion of immunoreactive growth hormone. *Science* 179:77–79

21. Brockman, R. P., Bergman, E. N., Joo, P. K., Manns, J. G. 1975. Effects of glucagon and insulin on net hepatic metabolism of glucose precursors in sheep. *Am. J. Physiol.* 229:1344–49

22. Bromer, W. W. 1976. Studies with glucagon analogs. *Metabolism* 25 (Suppl.):1315–16

23. Bromer, W. W., Sinn, L. G., Staub, A., Behrens, O. K., Diller, E. R., Bird, H. L. 1957. The amino acid sequence of glucagon. V. Localization of amide groups, acid degradation studies, and summary of sequential evidence. *J. Am. Chem. Soc.* 79:2807–10

24. Brown, J. C., Dryburgh, J. R., Ross, S. A., Dupre, J. 1975. Identification and actions of gastric inhibitory polypeptide. *Rec. Prog. Horm. Res.* 31:487–526

25. Buchanan, K. D., McCarroll, A. M. 1972. Abnormalities of glucagon metabolism in untreated diabetes mellitus. *Lancet* 2:1394–95

26. Cahill, G. F. Jr. 1971. Physiology of insulin in man (Banting Memorial Lecture). *Diabetes* 20:785–99

27. Cherrington, A. D., Exton, J. H. 1976. Studies on the role of cAMP-dependent protein kinase in the actions of glucagon and catecholamines on liver glycogen metabolism. *Metabolism* 25 (Suppl.): 1351–54

28. Cherrington, A. D., Kawamori, R., Pek, S., Vranic, M. 1974. Arginine infusion in dogs: Model for the roles of insulin and glucagon in regulating glucose turnover and free fatty acid levels. *Diabetes* 23:805-15

29. Chiasson, J. L., Liljenquist, J. E., Sinclair-Smith, B. C., Lacy, W. W. 1975. Gluconeogenesis from alanine in normal postabsorptive man. Intrahepatic stimulatory effect of glucagon. *Diabetes* 24:574–84

30. Claus, T. H., Pilkis, S. J. 1976. Regulation by insulin of gluconeogenesis in iso-lated rat hepatocytes. *Biochim. Biophys. Acta* 421:246–62

31. Cornblath, M., Schwartz, R. 1976. Specific hypoglycemic syndromes. In *Disorders of Carbohydrate Metabolism in Infancy,* ed. A. J. Schaffer, M. Markowitz, pp. 378–439. Philadelphia: Saunders.

32. Creutzfeldt, W., Lankisch, P. G., Folsch, U. R. 1975. Hemmung der Sekretin und cholezystokinin-pankreozymin-induzierten Saft-und-Enzymsekretion des Pankreas und der Gallenblasen Kontraktion beim Menschen durch Somatostatin. *Dtsch. Med. Wochenschr.* 100:1135–38

33. Danforth, D. N. Jr., Triche, T., Doppman, J. L., Beazley, R. M., Perrino, P. V., Recant, L. 1976. Elevated plasma proglucagon-like component with a glucagon-secreting tumor. Effect of streptozotocin. *N. Engl. J. Med.* 295: 242–45

34. Dubois, M. P. 1975. Immunoreactive somatostatin is present in discrete cells of the endocrine pancreas. *Proc. Natl. Acad. Sci. USA* 72:1340–43

35. Dupre, J., Rojas, L., White, J. J., Unger, R. H., Beck, J. C. 1966. Effects of secretin on insulin and glucagon in portal and peripheral blood in man. *Lancet* 2:26–27

36. Erlandsen, S. L., Parsons, J. A., Burke, J. P., Redick, J. A., Van Orden, D. E., Van Orden, L. S. 1975. A modification of the unlabeled antibody enzyme method using heterologous antisera for the light microscopic and ultrastructural localization of insulin, glucagon and growth hormone. *J. Histochem. Cytochem.* 23:666–77

37. Exton, J. H., Park, C. R. 1969. Control of gluconeogenesis in liver. 3. Effects of L-lactate, pyruvate, fructose, glucagon, epinephrine, and adenosine 3',5'-monophosphate on gluconeogenic intermediates in the perfused rat liver. *J. Biol. Chem.* 244:1424–33

38. Farquhar, M. G., Palade, G. E. 1963. Junctional complexes in various epithelia. *J. Cell Biol.* 17:375–412

39. Felig, P., Wahren, J., Hendler, R. 1976. Influence of physiologic hyperglucagonemia on basal and insulin-inhibited splanchnic glucose output in normal man. *J. Clin. Invest.* 58:761–65

40. Floyd, J. C. Jr., Fajans, S., Conn, J. W., Knopf, R. F., Rull, J. 1966. Stimulation of insulin secretion by amino acids. *J. Clin. Invest.* 45:1487–1502

41. Frohman, L. A., Bernardis, L. L., Stachura, M. E. 1974. Factors modifying

plasma insulin and glucose responses to ventromedial hypothalamic stimulation. *Metabolism* 23:1047–57

42. Fujita, T., Yanatori, Y., Murakami, T. 1976. Insulo-acinar axis, its vascular basis and its functional and morphological changes caused by CCK-PZ and caerulein. In *Endocrine, Gut and Pancreas,* ed. T. Fujita, pp. 347–57. Amsterdam: Elsevier

43. Galbo, H., Holst, J. J. 1976. The influence of glucagon on hepatic glycogen mobilization in exercising rats. *Pfluegers Arch.* 363:49–53

44. Galbo, H., Holst, J. J., Christensen, N. J. 1975. Glucagon and plasma catecholamine responses to graded and prolonged exercise in man. *J. Appl. Physiol.* 38:70–76

45. Ganda, O. P., Weir, G. C., Soeldner, J. S., Legg, M. A., Chick, W. L., Patel, Y. C., Ebeid, A. M., Gabbay, K. H., Reichlin, S. 1977. "Somatostatinoma": A somatostatin-containing tumor of the endocrine pancreas. *N. Engl. J. Med.* 296:963–67

46. Gerich, J. E., Langlois, M., Noacco, C., Karam, J. H., Forsham, P. H. 1973. Lack of glucagon response to hypoglycemia in diabetes: Evidence for an intrinsic pancreatic alpha cell defect. *Science* 182:171–73

47. Gerich, J. E., Langlois, M., Noacco, C., Lorenzi, M., Karam, J. H., Forsham, P. H. 1976. Comparison of the suppressive effects of elevated plasma glucose and free fatty acid levels on glucagon secretion in normal and insulin-dependent diabetic subjects. Evidence for selective alpha cell insensitivity to glucose in diabetes mellitus. *J. Clin. Invest.* 58:320–25

48. Gerich, J. E., Tsalikian, E., Lorenzi, M., Karam, J. H., Schneider, V., Gustafson, G., Bohannon, N. V. 1975 Normalization of fasting hyperglucagonemia and excessive glucagon responses to intravenous arginine in human diabetes mellitus by prolonged perfusion of insulin. *J. Clin. Endocrinol. Metab.* 41:1178–80

49. Goodner, C. J., Walike, B. C., Koerker, D. J., Brown, A. C., Ensinck, J. W., Chideckel, E. W., Palmer, J., Kalnasy, L. W. 1976. Insulin, glucagon, and glucose exhibit synchronous stable oscillations in the Rhesus monkey. *Diabetes* 25 (Suppl.):340

50. Guillemin, R. 1976. Somatostatin inhibits the release of acetylcholine induced electrically in the mesenteric plexus. *Endocrinology* 99:1653–54

51. Hayashi, M., Floyd, J. C. Jr., Pek, S., Fajans, S. S. 1977. Insulin, proinsulin, glucagon and gastrin in pancreatic tumors and in plasma of patients with organic hyperinsulinemia. *J. Clin. Endocrinol. Metab.* 44:681–94

52. Heding, L. G., Frandsen, E. K., Jacobsen, H. 1976. Structure-function relationship: Immunologic. *Metabolism* 25 (Suppl.):1327–29

53. Hellerstrom, C., Howell, S. L., Edwards, J. C., Andersson, A., Ostenson, G. C. 1974. Biosynthesis of glucagon in isolated pancreatic islets of guinea pigs. *Biochem. J.* 140:13–23

54. Hruby, V. J., Wright, D. E., Lin, M. C., Rodbell, M. 1976. Semisynthetic glucagon derivatives for structure-function studies. *Metabolism* 25 (Suppl.): 1323–25

55. Ipp, E., Arimura, A., Vale, W., Harris, V., Unger, R. H. 1977. Release of immunoreactive somatostatin from the pancreas in response to glucose, amino acids, pancreozymin-cholecystokinin, and tolbutamide. *J. Clin. Invest.* 60:760–65

56. Iversen, J. 1973. Effect of acetylcholine on the secretion of glucagon and insulin from the isolated perfused canine pancreas. *Diabetes* 22:381–87

57. Iversen, J. 1973. Adrenergic receptors and the secretion of glucagon and insulin from the isolated, perfused canine pancreas. *J. Clin. Invest.* 52:2102–16

58. Jaspan, J. B., Huen, A., Morley, C., Rubenstein, A. H. 1977. Hepatic metabolism of glucagon. *Clin. Res.* 25:496A

59. Johnson, D. G., Ensinck, J. W. 1976. Stimulation of glucagon secretion by scorpion toxin in the perfused rat pancreas. *Diabetes* 25:645–49

60. Kobayashi, S., Fujita, T. Sasagawa, T. 1970. The endocrine cells of human duodenal mucosa. *Arch. Histol. Jap.* 31:477–94

61. Koerker, D. J., Ruch, W., Chideckel, E., Palmer, J., Goodner, C. J., Ensinck, J., Gale, C. C. 1974. Somatostatin: Hypothalamic inhibitor of the endocrine pancreas. *Science* 184:482–84

62. Kuku, S. F., Jaspan, J. B., Emmanouel, D. S., Zeidler, A., Katz, A. I., Rubenstein, A. H. 1976. Heterogeneity of plasma glucagon. Circulating components in normal subjects and patients with chronic renal failure. *J. Clin. Invest.* 58:742–50

63. Lacy, P. E. 1970. Beta cell function from the standpoint of a pathologist (Banting Memorial Lecture). *Diabetes* 19:895–905

64. Larsson, L.-I., Hirsch, M. A., Holst, J. J., Ingemansson, S., Kuhl, C., Lindka-er-Jensen, S., Lundqvist, G., Rehfeld, J. F., Schwartz, T. W. 1977. Pancreatic somatostatinoma. *Lancet* 1:666–68

65. Larsson, L.-I., Holst, J., Hakanson, R., Sundler, F. 1975. Distribution and properties of glucagon immunoreactivity in the digestive tract of various mammals: An immunohistochemical and immunochemical study. *Histochemistry* 44:281–90

66. Larsson, L.-I., Sundler, F., Hakanson, R. 1975. Immunohistochemical localization of human pancreatic polypeptide (HPP) to a population of islet cells. *Cell Tiss. Res.* 156:167–71

67. Lawrence, A. M., Tan, S., Hojvat, S., Kirsteins, L., Mitton, J. 1976. Salivary gland glucagon in man and animals. *Metabolism* 25 (Suppl.):1405–8

68. Lindsey, C. A., Faloona, G. R., Unger, R. H. 1975. Plasma glucagon levels during rapid exsanguination with and without adrenergic blockade. *Diabetes* 24:313–16

69. Lindsey, C. A., Santeusanio, F., Braaten, J., Faloona, G. R., Unger, R. H. 1974. Pancreatic alpha cell function in trauma. *J. Am. Med. Ass.* 227:757–61

70. Lotter, E. C., Woods, S. C. 1977. Somatostatin decreases food intake. *Diabetes* 26 (Suppl.):358

71. Luft, R., Efendic, S., Hokfelt, T., Johansson, O., Arimura, A. 1974. Immunohistochemical evidence for the localization of somatostatin-like immunoreactivity in a cell population of the pancreatic islets. *Med. Biol.* 52: 428–30

72. MacGregor, I. L., Deveney, C., Way, L. W., Meyer, J. H. 1976. The effect of acute hyperglycemia on meal-stimulated gastric, biliary, and pancreatic secretion and serum gastrin. *Gastroenterology* 70:197–202

73. MacGregor, I. L., Gueller, R., Watts, H. D., Meyer, J. H. 1976. The effect of acute hyperglycemia on gastric emptying in man. *Gastroenterology* 70:190–96

74. Mackrell, D. J., Sokal, J. E. 1969. Antagonism between the effects of insulin and glucagon on the isolated liver. *Diabetes* 18:724–32

75. Madison, L. L., Mebane, D., Unger, R. H., Lochner, A. 1963. Evidence for and physiologic significance of a stimulatory feedback of ketone bodies on the B-cells. In *The Structure and Metabolism of Pancreatic Islets. Proc. 3rd. Int. Symp., Stockholm, 1963,* Vol. 3, pp. 457–68

76. Madison, L. L., Mebane, D., Unger, R. H., Lochner, A. 1964. The hypoglycemic action of ketones. II. Evidence for a stimulatory feedback of ketones on the pancreatic beta cells. *J. Clin. Invest.* 43:408–15

77. Madison, L. L., Seyffert, W. A. Jr., Unger, R. H., Baker, B. 1968. Effect of plasma free fatty acids on plasma glucagon and serum insulin concentrations. *Metabolism* 17:301–4

78. Mallette, L. E., Exton, J. H., Park, C. R. 1969. Control of gluconeogenesis from amino acids in the perfused rat liver. *J. Biol. Chem.* 244:5713–23

79. Mallinson, C. N., Bloom, S. R., Warin, A. P., Salmon, P. R., Cox, B. 1974. A glucagonoma syndrome. *Lancet* 2:1–5

80. Marco, J., Calle, C., Roman, D., Diaz-Fierros, M., Villanueva, M. L., Valverde, I. 1973. Hyperglucagonism induced by glucocorticoid treatment in man. *N. Engl. J. Med.* 288:128–31

81. Marliss, E. B., Aoki, T. T., Cahill, G. F. Jr. 1972. Glucagon and amino-acid metabolism. In *Glucagon. Molecular Physiology, Clinical and Therapeutic Implications,* ed. P. J. Lefebvre, R. H. Unger, pp. 123–50. Oxford: Pergamon

82. Marliss, E. B., Aoki, T. T., Pozefsky, T., Most, A. S., Cahill, G. F. Jr. 1971. Muscle and splanchnic glutamine and glutamate metabolism in post-absorptive and prolonged-starved man. *J. Clin. Invest.* 50:814–17

83. Marliss, E. B., Girardier, L., Seydoux, J., Wollheim, C. B., Kanazawa, Y., Orci, L., Renold, A. E., Porte, D. Jr. 1977. Glucagon release induced by pancreatic nerve stimulation in the dog. *J. Clin. Invest.* 52:1246–59

84. McGarry, J. D., Foster, D. W. 1977. Hormonal control of ketogenesis. *Arch. Int. Med.* 137:495–501

85. McGarry, J. D., Mannaerts, G. P., Foster, D. W. 1977. A possible role for malonyl-CoA in the regulation of hepatic fatty acid oxidation and ketogenesis. *J. Clin. Invest.* 60:265–70

86. McGarry, J. D., Wright, P., Foster, D. W. 1975. Hormonal control of ketogenesis: Rapid activation of hepatic ketogenic capacity in fed rats by anti-insulin serum and glucagon. *J. Clin. Invest.* 55:1202–9

87. McGavran, M. H., Unger, R. H., Recant, L., Polk, H. C., Kilo, C., Levin, M. E. 1966. A glucagon-secreting alpha cell carcinoma of the pancreas. *N. Engl. J. Med.* 274:1408–13

88. Meissner, H. P. 1976. Electrophysiologic evidence for coupling between B-

cells of pancreatic islets. *Nature* 262: 502–4

89. Miyata, M., Yamamoyo, T., Yamaguchi, M., Nakao, K., Yoshida, T. 1976. Plasma glucagon after total resection of the pancreas in man. *Proc. Soc. Exp. Biol. Med.* 152:540–43

90. Moody, A. J., Frandsen, E. K., Jacobsen, H., Sundby, F., Orci, L. 1976. Discussion. *Metabolism* 25 (Suppl.): 1336–38

91. Mortimore, C. H., Turnbridge, W. M. G., Carr, D., Yeomans, L., Lind, T., Coy, D. H., Bloom, S. R., Kastin, A., Mallinson, C. N., Besser, G. M., Schally, A. V., Hall, R. 1974. Effects of growth hormone release-inhibiting hormone on circulating glucagon, insulin and growth hormone in normal, diabetic, acromegalic, and hypopituitary patients. *Lancet* 1:697–701

92. Müller, W. A., Faloona, G. R., Unger, R. H. 1971. The influence of antecedent diet upon glucagon and insulin secretion. *N. Engl. J. Med.* 285:1450–54

93. Müller, W. A., Faloona, G. R., Unger, R. H. 1971. The effect of experimental insulin deficiency on glucagon secretion. *J. Clin. Invest.* 50:1992–99

94. Müller, W. A., Faloona, G. R., Unger, R. H., Aguilar-Parada, E. 1970. Abnormal alpha cell function in diabetes. Response to carbohydrate and protein ingestion. *N. Engl. J. Med.* 283:109–15

95. Munoz-Barragan, L., Blazquez, E., Patton, G. S., Dobbs, R. E., Unger, R. H. 1976. Gastric A-cell function in normal dogs. *Am. J. Physiol.* 231:1057–61

96. Munoz-Barragan, L., Rufener, C., Srikant, C. B., Dobbs, R. E., Shannon, W. A. Jr., Baetens, D., Unger, R. H. 1977. Immunocytochemical evidence for glucagon-containing cells in the human stomach. *Horm. Metab. Res.* 9:37–39

97. Noe, B. D. 1976. Biosynthesis of glucagon. *Metabolism* 25 (Suppl.):1339–41

98. Noe, B. D., Bauer, G. E., Steffes, M. W., Sutherland, D. E., Najarian, J. S. 1975. Glucagon biosynthesis in human pancreatic islets: Preliminary evidence for a biosynthetic intermediate. *Horm. Metab. Res.* 7:314–22

99. Ohneda, A., Aguilar-Parada, E., Eisentraut, A. M., Unger, R. H. 1969. Control of pancreatic glucagon secretion by glucose. *Diabetes* 18:1–10

100. Orci, L. 1976. A fresh look at the interrelationships within the islets of Langerhans. In *Diabetes Research Today*. pp. 135–151

101. Orci, L. 1976. The microanatomy of the islets of Langerhans. *Metabolism* 25 (Suppl.):1303–13

102. Orci, L., Amherdt, M., Henquin, J. C., Lambert, A. E., Unger, R. H., Renold, A. E. 1973. Pronase effect on pancreatic beta cell secretion and morphology. *Science* 180:647–49

103. Orci, L., Baetens, D., Dubois, M. P., Rufener, C. 1975. Evidence for the D-cell of the pancreas secreting somatostatin. *Horm. Metab. Res.* 7:400–402

104. Orci, L., Baetens, D., Ravazzola, M., Stefan, Y., Malaisse-Lagae, F. 1976. Pancreatic polypeptide and glucagon: Non-random distribution in pancreatic islets. *Life Sci.* 19:1811–16

105. Orci, L., Baetens, D., Rufener, C., Amherdt, M., Ravazzola, M., Studer, P., Malaisse-Lagae, F., Unger, R. H. 1976. Hypertrophy and hyperplasia of somatostatin containing D-cells in diabetes. *Proc. Natl. Acad. Sci. USA* 73:1338–42

106. Orci, L., Malaisse-Lagae, F., Amherdt, M., Ravazzola, M., Weisswange, A., Dobbs, R. E., Perrelet, A., Unger, R. H. 1975. Cell contacts in human islets of Langerhans. *J. Clin. Endocrinol. Metab.* 41:841–44

107. Orci, L., Malaisse-Lagae, F., Ravazzola, M., Rouiller, C., Renold, A. E., Perrelet, A., Unger, R. H. 1975. A morphological basis for intercellular communication between A- and B-cells in the endocrine pancreas. *J. Clin. Invest.* 56:1066–70

108. Orci, L., Perrelet, A., Ravazzola, M., Malaisse-Lagae, F., Renold, A. E. 1973. A specialized membrane junction between nerve endings and B-cells in islets of Langerhans. *Eur. J. Clin. Invest.* 3:443–45

109. Orci, L., Pictet, R., Forssmann, W. G., Renold, A. E., Rouiller, C. 1968. Structural evidence for glucagon producing cells in the intestinal mucosa of the rat. *Diabetologia* 4:56–67

110. Orci, L., Stauffacher, W., Renold, A. E., Rouiller, C. 1970. The ultrastructural aspect of A-cells of nonketotic and ketotic diabetic animals: Indications for stimulation and inhibition of glucagon production. *Acta Isot.* 10:171–86

111. Orci, L., Unger, R. H. 1975. Hypothesis: Functional subdivisions of the islets of Langerhans and the possible role of the insular D-cells. *Lancet* 2:1243–44

112. Orci, L., Unger, R. H., Renold, A. E. 1973. Structural coupling between pancreatic islet cells. *Experientia* 29: 1015–18

113. Palmer, J. P., Ensinck, J. W. 1975. Stimulation of glucagon secretion by ethanol-induced hypoglycemia in man. *Diabetes* 24:295–300

114. Palmer, J. P., Werner, P. L., Benson, J. W., Ensinck, J. W. 1976. Dominant inheritance of large molecular weight immunoreactive glucagon (IRG). *Diabetes* 25 (Suppl.):326

115. Palmer, J. P., Werner, P. L., Benson, J. W., Ensinck, J. W. 1976. Immunoreactive glucagon responses to arginine in three pancreatectomized humans. *Metabolism* 25 (Suppl.):1483–86

116. Park, C. R., Exton, J. H. 1972. Glucagon and the metabolism of glucose. See Ref. 81, pp. 77–108

117. Patton, G. S., Dobbs, R. E., Orci, L., Vale, W., Unger, R. H. 1976. Stimulation of pancreatic immunoreactive somatostatin (IRS) release by glucagon. *Metabolism* 25 (Suppl.):1499–1500

118. Patton, G. S., Ipp, E., Dobbs, R. E., Orci, L., Vale, W., Unger, R. H. 1977. Studies of pancreatic immunoreactive somatostatin (IRS) release. *Proc. Natl. Acad. Sci. USA* 74:2140–43

119. Patton, G. S., Ipp, E., Dobbs, R. E., Vale, W., Orci, L., Unger, R. H. 1976. Response of pancreatic immunoreactive somatostatin to arginine. *Life Sci.* 19:1957–60

120. Pelletier, G., Leclerc, R., Arimura, A., Schally, A. V. 1975. Immunohistochemical localization of somatostatin in the rat pancreas. *J. Histochem. Cytochem.* 23:699–701

121. Pilkis, S. J., Claus, T. H., Riou, J. P., Park, C. R. 1976. Possible role of pyruvate kinase in the hormonal control of dihydroxyacetone gluconeogenesis in isolated hepatocytes. *Metabolism* 25 (Suppl.):1355–60

122. Pointner, H., Hengle, G., Bayer, P. M., Flegel, U. 1976. Somatostatin inhibits the increase of serum triglyceride concentration following a test meal. *Scand. J. Gastroenterol.* 11 (Suppl.):51

123. Polak, J. M., Bloom, S. R., Coulling, I., Pearse, A. G. E. 1971. Immunofluorescent localization of enteroglucagon cells in the gastrointestinal tract of the dog. *Gut* 12:311–18

124. Polak, J. M., Pearse, A. G. E., Grimelius, L., Bloom, S. R., Arimura, A. 1975. Growth hormone release inhibiting hormone in gastrointestinal and pancreatic D-cells. *Lancet* 1:1220–22

125. Porte, D. Jr., Graber, A. L., Kuzuyma, T., Williams, R. H. 1966. The effect of epinephrine on immunoreactive insulin levels in man. *J. Clin. Invest.* 42:228–36

126. Porte, D. Jr., Robertson, R. P., Halter, J. B., Kulkosky, P. J., Makous, W. L., Woods, S. C. 1977. Neuroendocrine recognition of glucose: The glucoreceptor hypothesis and the diabetic syndrome. In *Proc. Int. Symp. Food Intake Chemical Senses,* Tokyo: Univ. Tokyo Press, pp. 000 In press

127. Raskin, P., Aydin, I., Unger, R. H. 1976. The effect of insulin on the exaggerated glucagon response to arginine stimulation in diabetes mellitus. *Diabetes* 25:227–29

128. Raskin, P., Fujita, Y., Unger, R. H. 1975. Effect of insulin-glucose infusions on plasma glucagon levels in fasting diabetics and nondiabetics. *J. Clin. Invest.* 56:1132–38

129. Recant, L., Perrino, P. V., Bhathena, S. J., Danforth, D. N. Jr., Lavine, R. L. 1976. Plasma immunoreactive glucagon fractions in four cases of glucagonoma: Increased "large glucagon-immunoreactivity". *Diabetologia* 12:319–26

130. Report of the Nomenclature Committee of the International Glucagon Symposium. 1976. *Metabolism* 25 (Suppl.): ix

131. Rigopoulou, D., Valverde, I., Marco, J., Faloona, G., Unger, R. H. 1970. Large glucagon immunoreactivity in extracts of pancreas. *J. Biol. Chem.* 245:496–501

132. Rocha, D. M., Faloona, G. R., Unger, R. H. 1972. Glucagon-stimulating activity of twenty amino acids in dogs. *J. Clin. Invest.* 51:2346–51

133. Rodbell, M., Londos, C. 1976. Regulation of hepatic adenylate cyclase by glucagon, GTP, divalent cations, and adenosine. *Metabolism* 25 (Suppl.): 1347–49

134. Sakurai, H., Dobbs, R. E., Unger, R. H. 1975. The effect of somatostatin on the response of GLI to the intraduodenal administration of glucose, protein, and fat. *Diabetologia* 11:427–30

135. Samols, E., Harrison, J., 1976. Intraislet negative insulin-glucagon feedback. *Metabolism* 25 (Suppl.):1443–48

136. Samols, E., Harrison, J. 1976. Remarkable potency of somatostatin as a glucagon suppressant. *Metabolism* 25 (Suppl.):1495–97

137. Samols, E., Marris, G., Marks, V. 1965. Promotion of insulin secretion by glucagon. *Lancet* 2:415–17

138. Samols, E., Tyler, J. M., Marks, V. 1972. Glucagon-insulin interrelationships. See Ref. 81, pp. 151–73

139. Samols, E., Weir, G. C., Patel, Y. C., Loo, S. W., Gabbay, K. H. 1977. Autonomic control of somatostatin and pancreatic peptide secretion by the isolated perfused canine pancreas. *Clin. Res.* 25:499A

140. Sasaki, H., Rubalcava, B., Baetens, D., Blazquez, E., Srikant, C. B., Orci, L., Unger, R. H. 1975. Identification of glucagon in the gastrointestinal tract. *J. Clin. Invest.* 56:135–45

141. Schauder, P., McIntosh, C., Arends, J., Arnold, R., Frerichs, H., Creutzfeldt, W. 1976. Somatostatin and insulin release from isolated rat pancreatic islets stimulated by glucose. *FEBS Lett.* 68:225–27

142. Scheinberg, P. 1965. Observations on cerebral carbohydrate metabolism in man. *Ann. Intern. Med.* 62:367–71

143. Schusdziarra, V., Ipp, E., Unger, R. H. 1977. Somatostatin, a physiologic regulator of nutrient influx. *Diabetes* 26 (Suppl.):359

144. Srikant, C. B., McCorkle, K., Unger, R. H. 1977. Properties of immunoreactive glucagon (IRG) fractions of canine stomach and pancreas. *J. Biol. Chem.* 252:1847–51

145. Staehelin, L. A. 1974. Structure and function of intercellular junctions. *Int. Rev. Cytol.* 39:191–283

146. Sundby, F. 1976. Species variations in the primary structure of glucagon. *Metabolism* 25 (Suppl.):1319–21

147. Tager, H. S., Markese, J. 1976. Glucagon-like immunoreactivity in pancreatic islets. *Metabolism* 25 (Suppl.): 1343–46

148. Unger, R. H. 1970. The gastrointestinal hormones as modifiers of islet cell hormone secretion. *Proc. Nobel Symp. Stockholm 1970*, pp. 259–69

149. Unger, R. H. 1977. Somatostatinoma. *N. Engl. J. Med.* 296:998–1000

150. Unger, R. H. 1971. Glucagon physiology and pathophysiology: Abnormal alpha cell function as a characteristic of human diabetes mellitus. *N. Engl. J. Med.* 285:443–49

151. Unger, R. H. 1971. Glucagon and the insulin/glucagon ratio in diabetes and other catabolic illnesses. *Diabetes* 20: 834–38

152. Unger, R. H. 1976. Diabetes and the alpha cell (Banting Memorial Lecture). *Diabetes* 25:136–51

153. Unger, R. H., Aguilar-Parada, E., Müller, W. A., Eisentraut, A. M. 1970. Studies of pancreatic alpha cell function in normal and diabetic subjects. *J. Clin. Invest.* 49:837–48

154. Unger, R. H., Eisentraut, A. M. 1969. Entero-insular axis. *Arch. Intern. Med.* 123:261–66

155. Unger, R. H., Eisentraut, A. M., McCall, M. S., Madison, L. L. 1962. Measurements of endogenous glucagon in plasma and the influence of blood glucose concentration upon its secretion. *J. Clin. Invest.* 41:682–89

156. Unger, R. H., Ketterer, H., Dupre, J., Eisentraut, A. M. 1967. The effects of secretin, pancreozymin, and gastrin upon insulin and glucagon secretion in anesthetized dogs. *J. Clin. Invest.* 46:630–45

157. Unger, R. H., Ohneda, A., Aguilar-Parada, E., Eisentraut, A. M. 1969. The role of aminogenic glucagon secretion in blood glucose homeostasis. *J. Clin. Invest.* 48:810–22

158. Unger, R. H., Ohneda, A., Valverde, I., Eisentraut, A. M., Exton, J. 1968. Characterization of the responses of circulating glucagon-like immunoreactivity to intraduodenal and intravenous administration of glucose. *J. Clin. Invest.* 47:48–65

159. Unger, R. H., Orci, L. 1976. Physiology and pathophysiology of glucagon. *Physiol. Rev.* 56:778–826

160. Unger, R. H., Orci, L. 1977. Hypothesis: The possible role of the pancreatic D-cell in the normal and diabetic states. *Diabetes* 26:241–44

161. Unger, R. H., Raskin, P., Srikant, C. B., Orci, L. 1977. Glucagon and the A-cells. *Rec. Prog. Horm. Res.* 33:477–517

162. Valverde, I., Villanueva, M. L. 1976. Heterogeneity of plasma immunoreactive glucagon. *Metabolism* 25 (Suppl.): 1393–96

163. Valverde, I., Villanueva, M. L., Lozano, I., Marco, J. 1974. Presence of glucagon immunoreactivity in the globulin fraction of human plasma ("big plasma glucagon"). *J. Clin. Endocrinol. Metab.* 39:1020–28

164. Vranic, M., Kawamori, R., Pek, S., Kovacevic, N., Wrenshall, G. A. 1976. The essentiality of insulin and the role of glucagon in regulating glucose utilization and production during strenuous exercise in dogs. *J. Clin. Invest.* 57: 245–55

165. Vranic, M., Kawamori, R., Wrenshall, G. A. 1974. Mechanism of exercise-induced hypoglycemia in depancreatized insulin-treated dogs. *Diabetes* 23 (Suppl.):353

166. Vranic, M., Pek, S., Kawamori, R. 1974. Increased "glucagon immunoreactivity" (IRG) in plasma of totally

depancreatized dogs. *Diabetes* 23: 905–12

167. Vranic, M., Wrenshall, G. A. 1969. Exercise, insulin, and glucose turnover in dogs. *Endocrinology* 85:165–71

168. Wahren, J. 1976. Influence of somatostatin on carbohydrate disposal and absorption in diabetes mellitus. *Lancet* 2:1213–16

169. Walter, R. M., Dudl, R. J., Palmer, J. P., Ensinck, J. W. 1974. The effect of adrenergic blockade on the glucagon responses to starvation and hypoglycemia in man. *J. Clin. Invest.* 54:1214–20

170. Weir, G. C., Samols, E., Ramseur, R., Day, J. A. Jr., Patel, Y. C. 1977. Influence of glucose and glucagon upon somatostatin secretion from the isolated perfused canine pancreas. *Clin. Res.* 25:403A

171. Willerson, J. T., Hutcheson, D., Leshin, S. J., Faloona, G. R., Unger, R. H. 1974. Serum glucagon and insulin levels and their relationship to blood glucose values in patients with acute myocardial infarction and acute coronary insufficiency. *Am. J. Med.* 27:747–53

172. Willmore, D. W., Lindsey, C. A., Faloona, G. R., Moylan, J., Pruitt, B., Unger, R. H. 1974. Hyperglucagonemia after burns. *Lancet* 1:73–75

173. Wise, J. K., Hendler, R., Felig, P. 1973. Evidence of alpha cell function by infusion of alanine in normal, diabetic and obese subjects. *N. Engl. J. Med.* 288:487–90

174. Wise, J. K., Hendler, R., Felig, P. 1973. Influence of glucocorticoids on glucagon secretion and plasma amino acid concentrations in man. *J. Clin. Invest.* 52:2774–82

175. Woods, S. C., Porte, D. Jr. 1974. Neural control of the endocrine pancreas. *Physiol. Rev.* 54:596–619

176. Yoshinaga, T., Okuno, G., Shinji, Y., Tsujii, T., Nishikama, M. 1966. Pancreatic A-cell tumor associated with severe diabetes mellitus. *Diabetes* 15:709–13

Ann. Rev. Physiol. 1978. 40:345–76
Copyright © 1978 by Annual Reviews Inc. All rights reserved

LOCALIZATION AND RELEASE OF NEUROPHYSINS

❖1195

Said M. Seif and Alan G. Robinson

Department of Medicine, University of Pittsburgh School of Medicine,
Pittsburgh, Pennsylvania 15261

INTRODUCTION

The theory of neurosecretion put forward by Bargmann & Scharrer (6) was based on the concept that the peptide hormones, oxytocin and vasopressin, were synthesized in hypothalamic nuclei, packaged into neurosecretory vesicles, and conveyed by axonal transport to nerve terminals in the neural lobe of the pituitary gland whence they were released into the circulation by appropriate physiologic stimuli. The theory was developed from anatomic studies using the technique of Gomori (38) to demonstrate that the central nervous system combined neural and endocrine functions. Bargmann (4, 5) observed that the acid-permanganate chrom-alum-haematoxylin (CAH) staining technique, which was developed to stain the beta cells of the pancreas, also gave intense staining of the neural cell bodies in the supraoptic nuclei (SON) and paraventricular nuclei (PVN) of the hypothalamus. This neurosecretory material was also traced along the nerve fibers in the neurohypophysial tract and appeared as dense aggregations in the neural lobe of the pituitary gland. Such dense staining was attributed to a protein-bound cysteine (95). The histochemical reaction of cysteine might be due to oxytocin, vasopressin, or to a carrier protein packed in the neurosecretory granules, since all these substances are cysteine rich and gave the appropriate histochemical reaction in vitro (39, 41, 85, 98). The carrier proteins of oxytocin and vasopressin were identified as "neurophysine" (1, 43). Neurophysine was defined as a polypeptide with a molecular weight of 10,000, capable of binding to oxytocin and vasopressin to form a nondialyzable molecule at an optimum pH.

345

0066-4278/78/0301-0345$01.00

Bargmann & Scharrer (6) and Scharrer & Scharrer (91) identified the hypothalamo-neurohypophysial tract, which they illustrated as having three projections of secretion: first, to the posterior pituitary, where the terminals of the long axons of these neurons reach the systemic circulation rather than synapse with other neurons; second, to the anterior pituitary portal vessels via the zona externa of the median eminence (67, 82, 112); and finally, to the cerebrospinal fluid via the third ventricle. The latter two alternate pathways for neurohypophysial secretion were largely ignored until the system was reexamined with the more sensitive immuno-histo-chemical technique using neurophysin as the tissue fixed antigen (Figure 1; 56, 67, 68, 82, 113). Quantitatively the major site of release of posterior pituitary hormones and their neurophysins into the general circulation is the neurohypophysis, but the alternate minor pathways may subserve major physiologic functions that are as yet poorly understood.

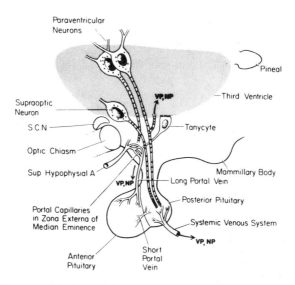

Figure 1   Diagram of the hypothalamus and pituitary gland in sagittal view depicting pathways of neurophysin (NP) and vasopressin (VP) secretion. The neurohypophysial peptides are synthesized in magnocellular perikarya of the supraoptic and paraventricular nuclei, transported in neurosecretory granules along the axons of these neurons, and secreted at three sites: (*a*) posterior pituitary into systemic circulation; (*b*) zona externa of the median eminence into hypophysial portal circulation; and (*c*) third ventricle into cerebrospinal fluid. Inconsistent staining of neurophysin in tanycytes and the suprachiasmatic nucleus is discussed in the text. [Reprinted with permission from (114).]

NEUROPHYSIN LOCALIZATION

Neural Neurophysins

Neurophysins have been localized in significant amounts in the large cells of the supraoptic (SON) and paraventricular (PVN) nuclei. In the SON, most or all of the cells contained neurophysin. Accessory portions of SON, including cells of the retrochiasmatic portions along the lateral base of the brain near the median eminence also stain for neurophysins (113). The axons of the supraoptic neurons were found to run most often in a ventromedial direction to join those coming from the PVN and to form the supraoptico-hypophysial tract in the median eminence. Some of the beaded axons branched near the cell bodies. Stained axons could occasionally be followed for long distances from the PVN to the SON, and cell processes occasionally ran toward the third ventricle (82). In contrast to SON, not all the large PVN cells contained neurophysins, and the reactive cells never exceeded 75% of the total (113). Neurophysins were also found in many large neurons that lay along the heavy axonal tract of the PVN, which courses laterally around and through the fornix and swings ventromedially into the SON to join the supraoptico-hypophysial tract. The neurophysin-containing cells scattered along the tract of the PVN were often clustered in groups lining both sides of blood vessels.

In both the rat and mouse, neurophysin was found in neurons of the suprachiasmatic nucleus of the anterior hypothalamus. In man and monkey this nucleus is poorly developed.

Neurophysin staining was heavy in the supraoptico-hypophysial tract in the reticular layer of the median eminence where the fibers of the PVN, the SON and of the internuclear group transport neurophysins to the posterior pituitary. In some animals a heavy neurophysin staining was observed in the zona externa of the median eminence in close proximity to the anterior pituitary portal vessels; in the monkey neurophysin staining clearly outlines the palisading pattern of this region (82, 99). The actual secretion of neurophysins and vasopressin into the portal system was established in the monkey by Zimmerman et al (112) and in the rat by Porter et al (71).

Early studies of monkey and rat brain fixed in Bouin's solution also demonstrated neurophysin staining in the specialized ependymal cells of the lower third ventricle. These "stretch cells," called tanycytes, have been postulated to have a transport function for transfer of peptides from the third ventricle to the portal vessels (82). The heavy staining in tanycytes and the presence of neurophysin in cerebrospinal fluid led to the suggestion that tanycytes might be a source of neurophysin in the external zone. However, tanycyte staining has not occurred in some animals where there was obvious staining in the external zone (114). Furthermore, the studies of Antunes et al (2) demonstrated that interruption of the paraventricular tract decreased the staining of neurophysin in the external zone, which indicated a supraoptico-hypophysial tract origin for the fibers that contain neurophysin in the external zone.

Finally, intense staining of neurophysin can be followed through the pituitary stalk to the posterior pituitary gland. Here, Herring bodies filled with neurophysin are numerous, and large collections of neurophysins are found around capillaries.

Extra-neural Neurophysins

Neurophysins have been found in extra-neural tissues. The studies of Fawcett et al (30) demonstrated that a neurophysin-like material was secreted into the blood stream. This finding stimulated the development of assays for neurophysin. Distribution of neurophysin in tissues was studied using precipitation of antigen antibody in gel diffusion and immunoelectrophoretic tests (35, 36) and by specific radioimmunoassay techniques. Ginsburg & Jayasena (35, 36) studied the distribution of proteins that bind neurohypophysial hormones (i. e. neurophysins) in porcine tissue extracts. They used antibody produced against porcine pituitary neurophysins. An antigen that reacted with anti-neurophysin serum was demonstrated in acetic acid extracts of porcine kidney but not of liver or spleen prepared in the same way. A specific protein fraction, "N-fraction," from kidney, uterus, mammary gland, and serum reacted positively to neurophysin antibody, whereas fractions from liver, spleen, and skeletal muscle did not react.

The "N-fractions" extracted from uterus or mammary gland formed nondialyzable complexes with oxytocin but not with LVP, while the protein extracted from kidney bound LVP but not oxytocin. Proteins from serum bound both hormones. Thus, with the exception of those from serum, the reactive protein fractions were obtained from organs where the neurohypophysial hormones exert their physiologic action, i.e. oxytocin on the uterus or mammary gland and vasopressin on the kidney. No other investigator, however, has reported similar binding results. Instead, all other extracted neurophysins have bound both oxytocin and vasopressin.

Using radioimmunoassay techniques, Ciarochi et al (20) detected neurophysin in tissue extracts in the rat. They found negligible neurophysin in all rat tissues except kidney (290 ng g^{-1} of tissue), uterus (185 ng g^{-1}), anterior pituitary (greater than 1500 ng g^{-1}), and posterior pituitary (greater than 11 X 10^6 ng g^{-1} tissue). The rat neurophysin assay used in this study was developed by Seif et al (92) and measures total rat neurophysins, i.e. vasopressin-neurophysin and oxytocin-neurophysin. Robinson et al (76) presented data suggesting possible local synthesis of a neurophysin-like molecule in the uterus of the rat and localized the material in the endometrial layer in intracellular granules. Such granules stain with immunohistochemical techniques and cross-react fully with rat neurophysin from the posterior pituitary. The significance of the "uterine neurophysin" and other extra-neural neurophysins is not understood and is being further investigated. At this point, neurophysins do not appear to be important in hormone binding at the target tissue (46, 97).

Elevated levels of neurophysin have been found in the plasma of patients with the syndrome of inappropriate antidiuretic hormone secretion where vasopressin was produced ectopically by a carcinoma. Hamilton et al (40) and Legros (50) have studied extracts of carcinoma of the lung and demonstrated that some tumors that contained vasopressin also contained a human neurophysin. Presumably the neurophysin was made by the tumor. In this case, the extra-neural neurophysin would appear to be linked to ectopic hormone production, and such observations have been quoted to prove that neurophysin synthesis is necessary for vasopressin synthesis. There is no evidence that hypothalamic neurons ever synthesize hormone without neurophysin. The mouse hypothalamic cells maintained in tissue culture by De Vitry et al (26) synthesize both vasopressin and neurophysin. On the other hand, Pettingill et al (69) have grown an oat cell tumor of the lung in tissue culture and have demonstrated that the tumor produced vasopressin in the absence of any synthesis of neurophysin. Some tumor cells must have the ability to synthesize vasopressin alone.

NEUROPHYSIN CLASSIFICATION

Ideally, individual neurophysins in any species would be classified by specific biologic function, i.e. the binding of oxytocin or the binding of vasopressin. Unfortunately, the hormone binding is not specific; once isolated, all neurophysins bind both hormones (8, 43). Therefore, neurophysins have been classified according to their differing electrophoretic mobility (44, 45), their amino acid sequence (15, 16), or according to their response to physiological maneuvers (74).

Electrophoretic Mobility

With the original sulfuric acid extraction of Du Vigneaud (28), numerous neurophysins were isolated from bovine and porcine posterior pituitaries. As many as seven hormone-binding fractions were identified based on electrophoretic mobility (42). It was subsequently shown that degradative enzymes in neurohypophysial extracts were active after sulfuric acid extraction but inactive in 0.1 N HCl (43). Extraction of the posterior pituitary of bovine species with 0.1 N HCl yielded predominantly two major peptide bands by electrophoresis, bovine neurophysin I and bovine neurophysin II (Figure 2). It was believed that any other neurophysins present in extracts of the posterior lobe were due to catabolic degradation of the two natural neurophysins. The concept of two neurophysins was appealing because of the presence of two hormones in the posterior lobe. Isolation of neurosecretory granules indicated the association of bovine neurophysin I with oxytocin and bovine neurophysin II with vasopressin (23). However, by electrophoresis some workers identified only a single neurophysin in sheep and guinea pig and a third neurophysin in cow and pig. By using a variety of extraction techniques and electrophoretic identification, more than two neurophysins have been isolated in humans (18, 19, 74, 110).

Amino Acid Composition

Neurophysins have also been grouped into two main classes based on their amino acid composition (15). The amino acid sequences of neurophysins show a large area of homology among the various neurophysins from individual species and the neurophysins from various species (Figure 3). The central amino acid sequence of the neurophysins appears to be most stable in comparing neurophysins from various species (13, 15, 108). Alanine is consistently the N-terminal amino acid in all neurophysins so far

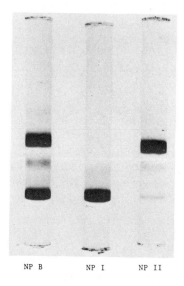

NP B   NP I   NP II

Figure 2   Disc gel electrophoresis of bovine neurophysins. Crude bovine neurophysins (NP B) is shown on the left and contains two major bands of neurophysin, which were subsequently separated into bovine neurophysin I (NP I), center, and bovine neurophysin II (NP II), right. [Reprinted with permission from (83).]

sequenced (which suggests that the N-terminus forms the peptide bond with any putative precursor molecule). The more variable portions of the neurophysin molecule are the nine N-terminal residues and the approximately 20 C-terminal residues (13). Within the central core of the neurophysin molecule is the only tyrosine in the molecule, and this highly charged area may be important in binding. Chauvet et al (16) have proposed that the amino acid positions 2, 3, 6, and 7 from the N-terminus can be used to divide neurophysins into two groups of neurophysins called MSEL (Met, Ser, Glu, Leu) and VLDV (Val, Leu, Asp, Val) based on the amino acids present in these positions. This grouping was appealing because bovine neurophysin I was grouped with porcine neurophysin II, and these are both thought to be oxytocin neurophysins. Likewise the vasopressin neurophysins, bovine neurophysin II and porcine neurophysin I, were grouped together. However, the human neurophysin isolated by Foss et al (33) and the work of Capra et al (12) with the human neurophysin I isolated by Cheng & Friesen (18) have both shown that the N-terminus contains an alanine-alanine sequence that does not fit into either of the groups proposed by Chauvet et al (16). The dog neurophysin isolated by Walter et al (109) also contains an alanine-alanine sequence.

Response to Pharmacologic Stimuli

Neurophysins have been characterized by the biologic response to pharmacologic stimuli. Robinson (74) developed radioimmunoassays for two human neurophysins and demonstrated that the four electrophoretically distinct human neurophysins could be accounted for by only two antigeni-

	1			5				10					15					20
Ovine	Ala–Met–Ser–Asp–Leu–Glu–Leu–Arg–Gln–Cys–Leu–Pro–Cys–Gly–Pro–Gly–Gly–Lys–Gly–Arg
Bovine	————————————————————————————
Porcine	————————————————————————————

	21				25				30					35					40
Ovine	Cys–Phe–Gly–Pro–Ser–Ile–Cys–Cys–Gly–Asp–Glu–Leu–Gly–Cys–Phe–Val–Gly–Thr–Ala–Glu
Bovine	————————————————————————————
Porcine	————————————————————————————

	41			45			48		50					55				60
Ovine	Ala–Leu–Arg–Cys–Gln–Glu–Glu–Ile–Tyr–Leu–Pro–Ser–Pro–Cys–Gln–Ser–Gly–Gln–Lys–Pro
Bovine	————————————— –Asn– ————————————
Porcine	————————————— –Asn– ————————————

	61		65				70				75				80
Ovine	Cys–Gly–Ser–Gly–Gly–Arg–Cys–Ala–Ala–Ala–Gly–Ile–Cys–Cys–Asn–Asp–Glu–Ser–Cys–Val
Bovine	————————————————————————————
Porcine	————————————————————————————

	81		85				89	90		92			95
Ovine	Thr–Glu–Pro–Glu–Cys–Arg–Glu–Gly–Ile–Gly–Phe–Pro–Arg–Arg–Val
Bovine	———————————————— –Val– ————————
Porcine	————————————— –Ala–Ser– —— –Leu– ——— – Ala

Figure 3 Complete amino acid sequence of ovine, bovine, and porcine MSEL-neurophysins. For VLDV-neurophysins, see text. [Reprinted with permission from (16).]

cally distinct neurophysins. It was then demonstrated that one of these radioimmunoassays measured a neurophysin that increased in plasma in response to estrogen administration: estrogen-stimulated neurophysin (Figure 4); the other radioimmunoassay measured a neurophysin that increased in plasma in response to cigarette smoking: nicotine-stimulated neurophysin (Figure 5). As described below, nicotine-stimulated neurophysin is thought to be associated with vasopressin and estrogen-stimulated neurophysin with oxytocin.

Unclassified Neurophysins

Considerable confusion exists in the nomenclature of neurophysins. It is anticipated that in every species there will eventually be identified an oxytocin-neurophysin and a vasopressin-neurophysin, but one must explain why more than two neurophysins have been found in the cow (25), pig (17, 105, 111), rat (92), and in man (74). The extra neurophysins might be explained as artifacts of the separation technique—in vitro degradation products of one of the two major neurophysins thought to be present in most species. Indeed, radioimmunoassay studies have indicated that the extra neurophysins in cow (25) and man (74) react in exactly the same manner as one of the two major neurophysins. By amino acid analysis the third porcine neurophysin has been shown to be just three amino acids longer than porcine neurophysin I (111), and therefore porcine neurophysin I may have been derived from porcine neurophysin II by proteolysis. Furthermore, the work of North et al has demonstrated that there are enzymes present in hypothalamic extracts that will convert one neurophysin to a different neurophysin by proteolysis (66). Thus, there is considerable evidence that extracted neurophysins can be further broken down in vitro by proteolytic enzymes. Nevertheless, even rapid extraction from the freshest tissue has identified more than two neurophysins in the cow and the dog (108, 109). In studies of in vivo synthesis of three rat neurophysins, called A, B, and C, Burford & Pickering (11) determined that A and B were synthesized first and that C was derived from B through enzymatic conversion by a proteinase "within the granule." Enzymes that can cause the catabolic proteolysis of neurophysins may then exist within neurosecretory granules, and neurophysins that do not fit any classification may be formed in vivo. It is reasonable to assume that catabolic enzymes present in the neurosecretory granules have some biologic function. Since we have no evidence that it is biologically important to degrade the neurophysins from two major components to minor derivatives, it might be assumed that the enzymes are present to cleave neurophysins from some larger precursor molecule. There is evidence for a precursor molecule in the synthesis of neurophysin and hormone.

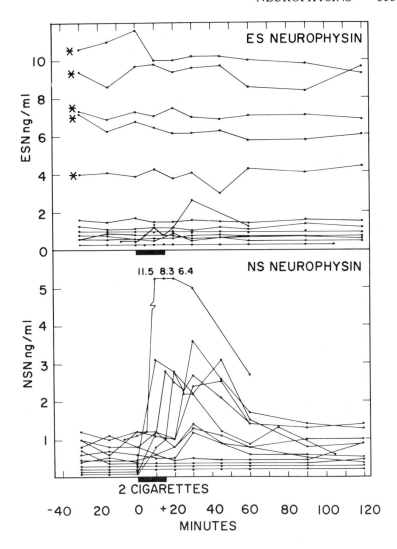

Figure 4 Changes in plasma estrogen-stimulated neurophysin, top, and nicotine-stimulated neurophysin, bottom, in 13 normal subjects who smoked two cigarettes in the interval from 0 to 12 minutes. Women on oral contraceptives (*) maintained elevated estrogen-stimulated neurophysin. Not all subjects respond with a rise of nicotine-stimulated neurophysin, but the increase of NSN is independent of any increase in ESN. The subject exhibiting a small increase of ESN at 30 minutes was the same subject whose NSN rose to 11.5 ng ml^{-1}. [Reprinted with permission from (74).]

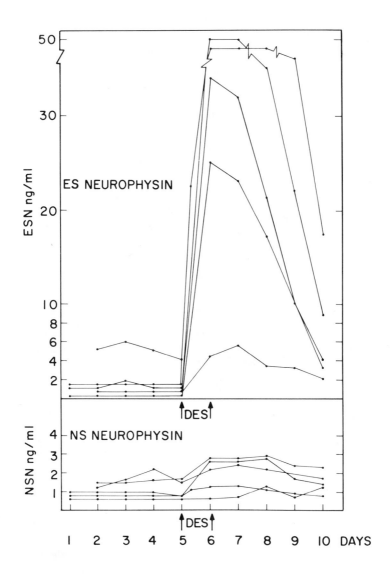

Figure 5   Changes in plasma estrogen-stimulated neurophysin, top, and nicotine-stimulated neurophysin, bottom, in five normal men given 5 mg diethylstilbestrol on days 5 and 6. [Reprinted with permission from (74).]

NEUROPHYSIN SYNTHESIS

When oxytocin and vasopressin are synthesized in the perikarya of the neurons of the supraoptic and paraventricular nuclei, there is believed to be concurrent synthesis of neurophysins (88). Whether synthesis of neurophysin is obligatory for synthesis of hormone has not been established, but evidence to date does not support the suggestion that neurophysin is a vasopressin pro-hormone; rather the data of Sachs et al (88) indicate there might be a common pro-hormone for both neurophysin and vasopressin or oxytocin. The concept of a parent molecule for neurophysin and its companion hormones, oxytocin and vasopressin, was postulated by Sachs et al (89). Sachs and co-workers reported that 35_S-cysteine injected into the third ventricle was incorporated into vasopressin and neurophysin; inhibition of protein synthesis stopped simultaneously the incorporation of cysteine into neurophysin and vasopressin. If the label was introduced into CSF as a pulse for 1.5–3 hr in vivo and then incubated in vitro under conditions in which further protein synthesis was blocked by the presence of puromycin and a large pool of unlabeled amino acid, there was still further production of radioactive vasopressin and neurophysin in vitro (90). Because de novo protein synthesis was blocked, the data were interpreted to indicate formation of some labeled precursor in vivo during the initial infusion period and subsequent formation of vasopressin and neurophysin from the prelabeled precursor during in vitro incubation (90). Gainer et al (34) used a similar technique in the rat. One to six hours after pulse labeling with cysteine, a sulfhydryl-labeled peptide of about 20,000 mol wt, which was thought to represent a precursor for neurophysin, was isolated from the supraoptic nucleus. By 24 hr after injection, all of the label in the SON resided in the 10,000 mol wt neurophysin fraction. The putative precursor was also present in the neurohypophysial axons in the median eminence 2 hr after injection, but absent 24 hr after injection of label. Because all the neurophysin in axons of the median eminence is within granules, the presence of precursor in axons in the median eminence indicates that the precursor is likewise present in the neurosecretory granules. This finding would indicate that separation of neurophysin and hormone from precursor may not occur until after packaging. Packaging of precursor into neurosecretory granules provides a logical explanation for the presence of proteolytic enzymes within the granules. The enzymes may be necessary to split neurophysin (and hormone?) from the precursor molecule. The proteolytic enzymes may explain the further degradation of neurophysins into the various minor neurophysins that have been isolated from the posterior lobe.

TURNOVER OF NEUROPHYSIN

Norstrom & Sjostrand (64) studied the turnover of neurosecretory material in hypothalamic nuclei and demonstrated that part of the material had a short half-life during the first 1–2 days followed by a slower disappearance rate from 7.5 days onward. This slow turnover was confirmed by the work of Sachs (87), who observed that some radioactive vasopressin and neurophysin could still be released from the neural lobe as late as three weeks after intraventricular injection of 35_S-cysteine. Burford & Pickering (10) estimated intraneural half-lifes of 13.3 and 19.8 days for oxytocin-neurophysin and vasopressin-neurophysin, respectively.

In a series of experiments on rats, Norstrom & Sjostrand (64) studied the effect of hemorrhage on the synthesis and transport of the neurosecretory material. They reported that after injection with 35_S-cysteine the neural lobe radioactivity remained low for two hours in the bled rats as well as in controls. This finding was taken as evidence that hemorrhage did not appreciably influence the rate at which neurohypophysial proteins were transported. When the rats were bled two hours after the isotope injection or later, the total neural lobe radioactivity that occurred during a 15-minute period was higher in bled animals than in controls. The results suggested that synthesis and perikarya packaging of neurosecretory material took approximately 1.5 hr, consistent with the observation of Takabatake & Sachs (102). Following an acute stimulation with hemorrhage the amount of neurosecretory material transported per unit time was increased, but the transport rate was unaffected. In addition, Norstrom & Sjostrand (64) found that the incorporation of 35_S-cysteine into proteins of SON neurons was increased following bleeding. With severe osmotic stimulation by water deprivation or 2% NaCl solution for seven days there occurred an initial steep increase of neurophysin-bound radioactivity and then a return to a low level within three days, indicating a much enhanced turnover of neurosecretory material (65). These studies that use cysteine to track the neurosecretory material are studies of both neurophysin and hormone, but similar results have been obtained with pure hormone.

Using methods for the preparation of pure radioactive oxytocin and vasopressin from groups of four or five rats, Jones & Pickering (48, 49) were able to show that radioactive hormones began to arrive in the gland between one and two hours after intracisternal injection of ^3H-tyrosine; this suggested a minimum transport rate of 2–3 mm hr^{-1}, which was similar to the transport of purified neurophysin studied in the rat by Norstrom & Sjostrand (64).

POSSIBLE BIOLOGIC ROLES OF NEUROPHYSIN

Neurohypophysial Hormone Release

There is some evidence that precursor neurophysin may be membrane-bound. In the studies of Swann & Pickering (101) most of the 35_S-labeled neurophysin that was synthesized in the rat and packaged in neurosecretory granules could be released by treatment of the rat with 2% saline, but a small portion of the neurophysin could be sedimented with the granule membrane after exhaustion of the neurosecretory contents. This was thought to represent membrane-bound neurophysin. A similar finding was obtained by Norstrom & Hansson (63) and Norstrom (61). It is uncertain whether the membrane-bound neurophysin is part of a lipid-neurophysin complex (59) and whether membrane-bound neurophysin plays a role in release of neurosecretory granules. McKelvy (57) has summarized the evidence for a possible role of cyclic AMP–stimulated protein kinase in the release of neurohypophysial peptides and has suggested that neurosecretory granule membranes can be phosphorylated by activated cAMP. However, bovine neurophysin was not found to possess any protein kinase activity, nor to serve as a substrate for the protein kinase activity in neurosecretory granules. The results would indicate that a membrane-associated neurophysin was not involved in phosphorylation or (if cAMP plays any role) in extrusion of the neurosecretory contents into the perivascular space.

Similarly, the methanol-forming enzyme described by Axelrod & Daily (3) and by Edgar & Hope (29) has been postulated to play some role in regulating release of posterior pituitary hormones, in part because neurophysins are a particularly active substrate for the protein-carboxyl methyltransferase enzyme. However, as with the studies of membrane-bound neurophysin, subcellular fractionation of fresh bovine posterior pituitary glands found that the methyltransferase activity was not associated with the particulate fractions that contained neurosecretory granules (29). The enzyme was compartmentalized away from neurophysins and the neurophysins are unlikely to serve as a natural substrate in the intact neuron. There are no data at the present time to indicate that neurophysins play an active role in the process of neurosecretion.

Physiological Activity

As mentioned earlier, several investigations have tended to support the association of one neurophysin with oxytocin and another with vasopressin. The factors that cause changes in the release or turnover of neurophysins are mainly those associated with changes in vasopressin and oxytocin (78). In certain situations, however, such as during renal failure and during estrogen administration, plasma neurophysin may be elevated while the levels of oxytocin and vasopressin are not known to be increased (78). This suggests a dissociation in response between the different neurohypophysial peptides, and might suggest an independent function for neurophysins.

Neurophysin as a natriuretic factor was studied by Robinson et al (80) and Cort et al (21). Earlier results had shown that there was an increase in plasma neurophysin in response to hypertonic saline. Gitleman & Blythe (37) had isolated a natriuretic factor from the posterior pituitary, and Dewardener (27) had suggested the neurohypophysis as a possible site of origin of the third factor. Robinson et al (81) reported some effect of bovine neurophysin I (BNp I) on Na^+ excretion in dogs. They showed that Na^+ excretion in dogs given BNp I increased by a factor between 3 and 25. The circulating plasma levels of neurophysin reached 23–27 ng ml^{-1}. These plasma neurophysin levels are not superpharmacologic since in human pregnancy plasma neurophysin levels may be as high as 49 ng ml^{-1} (78). However, the natriuretic effect of neurophysin needs further investigation since possible contaminants of small peptides may introduce a natriuretic effect as suggested by Cort et al (21), and in any case the natriuretic effect observed was rather small.

Neurophysin as a lipolytic factor was suggested by the work of Trygstad et al (104) and Rudman et al (86). The lipid-mobilizing activity was the first in vivo metabolic effect observed for neurophysins, and they were regarded as novel pituitary adipokinetic factors (33). Human neurophysin I (HNp I) in near physiologic concentrations (10–25 ng ml^{-1}) in vitro and in vivo had lipolytic effect in the rabbit, but in man injection of 45 μg human neurophysin per kg body weight gave no lipolytic effect. It was not certain whether neurophysin itself had a lipolytic effect or whether the observed response might be attributed to contamination with the pituitary lipid-mobilizing activity described by Trygstad (103). Neurophysin was also suggested to have serum amino-acid-lowering effects (104). Injection of human neurophysin II in a dose of 30 μg kg^{-1} decreased serum amino acids.

The mechanism by which neurophysins might exert these various effects is not understood. Mediators that could have accounted for the responses but that were ruled out include epinephrine, growth hormone, insulin, glucocorticoids, and ACTH (104). While it seems possible that some may possess biologic activity, no physiologic function has been established for neurophysins after secretion from the posterior lobe.

ONE NEURON:ONE HORMONE:ONE NEUROPHYSIN

The association of one neurophysin with one neurohypophysine hormone was demonstrated anatomically when Dean et al (23) performed differential centrifugation of intact neurosecretory granules from the posterior pituitary of the cow. Some granules were relatively enriched in vasopressin and contained a greater amount of bovine neurophysin II, while other granules were relatively enriched with oxytocin and contained a greater amount of bovine neurophysin I. A similar association was found by Pickup et al (70) with neurosecretory granules from porcine posterior lobe. Similarly, Zimmerman et al (115) isolated and extracted peptides from the SON and PVN of the cow and found a strong relationship between the content of bovine neurophysin II and vasopressin and of bovine neurophysin I and oxytocin in the two nuclei. The overall ratio of vasopressin to oxytocin and of bovine neurophysin II to bovine neurophysin I showed significant correlation, with a $p<0.01$. The data quantitatively associate a specific neurophysin with a specific hormone in the hypothalamus but do not locate the hormone and neurophysin qualitatively within single cells. Recognition of single cell content of hormone and neurophysin requires either the isolation of a single neuron, the study of an animal that lacks one hormone, or identification of hormone and neurophysin in single cells by specific immunologic techniques. The first of these three possibilities is not technically feasible; the second has been pursued in the vasopressin-deficient Brattleboro rat; the third has been investigated by the application of an immunohistochemical technique utilizing specific antisera to locate hormones and neurophysins within hypothalamic neurons.

The Brattleboro rat has provided a model of a vasopressin-deficient animal. In fact, histologic study of the neurons of this animal provided a major boost to the one neuron : one hormone hypothesis. In the rat, axons within the posterior pituitary are grouped according to hormone content and there is clustering of hormone-producing neurons within the supraoptic and paraventricular nuclei. When the Brattleboro rat was treated with exogenous vasopressin to allow reaccumulation of neurosecretory material, it was noted that neurosecretory material appeared in some of the clusters of axon terminals in the posterior pituitary and in some of the neurons within the nuclei of hormone synthesis (106). Because the cells that remained devoid of neurosecretory material were clustered anatomically, it was possible to identify these groups of neurons in all animals and to determine that some cells were permanently devoid of neurosecretory material (i.e. they were not otherwise active hormone-producing cells in a resting phase). Absence of neurosecretory material would indicate that the neurons lack not only vasopressin, but also neurophysin. Lack of neurophysin was subsequently proven by Sokol et al (96) in a study of neurophysin-producing neurons in normal and Brattleboro rats. Tissue sections from normal and Brattleboro rats were stained with the immunoperoxidase technique utilizing antisera to oxytocin, vasopressin, and neurophysin. The clusters of cells in the

Brattleboro rat that contained oxytocin also contained immunoreactive neurophysin, and the clusters of neurons in the Brattleboro rat that were unstained by either oxytocin or vasopressin were devoid of any neurophysins. These anatomic findings, coupled with the work of Burford et al (9) and of Sunde & Sokol (100), which demonstrated by biochemical techniques the absence of one neurophysin in the Brattleboro rat, seem to confirm the hypothesis of one neuron : one hormone : one neurophysin. Unfortunately, data in the normal rat were less conclusive in support of this hypothesis. In the normal rat, the vasopressin-containing neurons never contained oxytocin, but some cells that were strongly positive for oxytocin also contained vasopressin. Exhaustive attempts at differential absorption were unable to exclude the possibility that some cells in the normal rat might synthesize both hormones.

In the cow where the association of bovine neurophysin I with oxytocin and bovine neurophysin II with vasopressin is established, Vandesande et al (107) using highly purified antisera have reported an absolute distinction between neurons that contain neurophysin I and oxytocin and those that contain neurophysin II and vasopressin. In the human hypothalamus, using somewhat less specific antisera, Defendini & Zimmerman (24) described a geographic association of neurons that contain oxytocin and estrogen-stimulated neurophysin and neurons that contain vasopressin and nicotine-stimulated neurophysin.

The concept of one neuron : one hormone : one neurophysin remains a reasonable hypothesis but it has not been proven in all animals.

NEUROPHYSIN SECRETION

If hormone release is by exocytosis and hormone and neurophysin are stored within neurosecretory granules in equimolar concentrations, then hormone and neurophysin in plasma should also be in molar equivalents. However, most investigators have found a relative molar excess of neurophysin in plasma when compared to vasopressin (114). Differences in basal concentrations of hormone and neurophysin have been explained by the longer half-life of neurophysin. Half-life of vasopressin is usually reported to be under 6 min (7), whereas the half-life of neurophysin may be as long as 18 min (83). With a brisk stimulus to release of vasopressin and neurophysin, it would be expected that plasma concentrations would approach a 1:1 ratio. Such a 1:1 relationship was reported in the goat (58) and in the rat (32), but in our studies in humans, there was a seven-fold molar excess of neurophysin after nicotine stimulation even at the time of peak vasopressin concentration (47). While differences in molar ratios in plasma may be due to differences in degradation after release, one cannot be certain that all neurophysin and all vasopressin in the posterior pituitary exist in equimolar concentrations within granules. Norstrom (62) found free neurophysin in his preparation of neurosecretory granules from the posterior lobe, and Silver & Zimmerman (94) have anatomical evidence to support the possibility that hormones and neurophysin may exist outside granules. If this is so, then the possibility exists that extragranular vasopressin could diffuse into the circulation without the concurrent appearance of neurophysin in plasma; when the gland was subsequently stimulated, there might be released a molar excess of neurophysin.

Nonetheless, it may be expected that measurement of neurophysins will provide a measure of release of vasopressin and oxytocin. The development of radioimmunoassay techniques for different neurophysins marked the beginning of a new spectrum of investigation to determine whether, in fact, neurophysin release was a measure of hormone release. We review the data for each hormone.

Vasopressin-related Events

BOVINE AND PORCINE   The cow was the first species in which the two major neurophysins, neurophysin I and neurophysin II, could be separately measured by specific radioimmunoassays (83, 84). With these assays it was found that the two major neurophysins were independently secreted in the cow, consistent with bioassay data suggesting independent secretion of vasopressin and oxytocin. Subsequently, other specific bovine neurophysin assays (55) showed an increase in bovine neurophysin II with hemorrhage. Basal values of less than 1 ng ml^{-1} plasma increased to peak values of greater than 30 ng ml^{-1} during graded hemorrhage in cows, while neurophysin I showed only a slight increase in some animals (55). Likewise in the pig, Dax et al (22) showed an increase of neurophysin I (the "vasopressin-neurophysin" of the pig) to 2–25 times basal levels during graded hemorrhage, with little or no change in neurophysin II.

RAT   Seif et al (92) have recently developed a homologous radioimmunoassay for rat neurophysin. Unfortunately the assay does not distinguish among the various neurophysins of the rat. Basal neurophysin values were somewhat higher in the rat than in other animals—3.7 ± 0.2 ng ml^{-1} in unrestrained and unanesthetized rats on *ad libitum* water and food. The assay appears to be especially good for measurement of vasopressin-related neurophysin (Figure 6) because plasma neurophysin was suppressed to 2.8 ± 0.1 ng ml^{-1} after water loading and stimulated to 10.4 ± 2.1 ng ml^{-1} after hypertonic saline injection intraperitoneally. A brisk response of neurophysin to hemorrhage was noted in five rats that had 1 ml of blood removed from a carotid cannula every 5 min for 40 min. Plasma levels increased from a baseline of 3 ng ml^{-1} to 8 ng in the 25 min sample, and to 49 ng ml^{-1} in the 40 min sample. When the red cells resuspended in saline were injected there was a fall in neurophysin to near baseline level, 6 ng ml^{-1}. Neurophysin was not exhausted from the pituitaries of these rats since a second and massive hemorrhage at 155 min (at the end of a 60 min rest period) resulted in prompt increase in neurophysin concentration to greater than 400 ng ml^{1}. Another group of rats underwent serial blood withdrawal with immediate replacement with resuspended red blood cells in 0.9 g per 100 ml NaCl solution. No changes were observed in plasma neurophysin levels.

The rat was used as a model to study neurophysin response to simulated clinical disorders. Seif et al studied the effect of adrenalectomy on plasma and pituitary neurophysin and vasopressin (93) as measured by radioimmunoassay, and Stillman et al studied the hypothalamic content of neurophysin and vasopressin in the same groups of rats by immunohistology (99). Five days following adrenalectomy, the adrenalectomized rats showed elevated plasma neurophysin (4.5 ng ml^{-1}) compared to control (3.0 ng ml^{-1}), consistent with elevated plasma vasopressin (2.3 μU ml^{-1} in adrenalectomized rats and 0.7 μU ml^{-1} in control rats). After complete volume replacement and intragastric water loading, the adrenalectomized rats persisted with elevated plasma neurophysin and vasopressin as compared with controls. The enhanced release of both neurophysin and vasopressin was accompanied by a depletion of the posterior pituitary content of the neurosecretory peptides to less than 60% of the content in control rats. The immunohistochemical studies of the hypothalamus demonstrated intense staining of neurophysin (and vasopressin) in the zona externa of the median eminence in the adrenalectomized rats compared to normal rats (Figure 7).

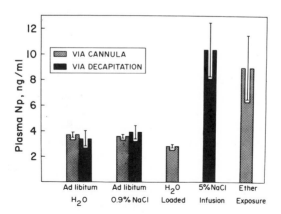

Figure 6 Neurophysin response to various physiologic stimuli in normal rats. [From the data in (92).]

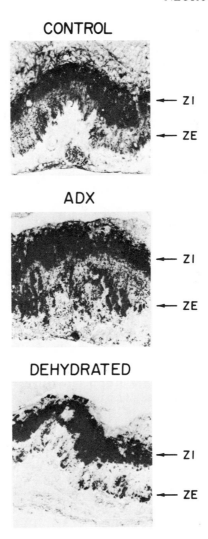

Figure 7   Neurophysin in the median eminence of the rat demonstrated by immunohistochemical stain as the dark reaction products. In the normal rat, top, neurophysin is localized in the heavily stained tract of the zona interna (ZI) and in a number of axons in the zona externa (ZE). Adrenalectomized rats, center, show a marked increase in the neurophysin fibers in the zona externa of the median eminence. Bottom: Dehydration, which depletes posterior pituitary neurophysin, produces no increase in staining in the zona externa.

The specificity of the increased staining of neurophysin after adrenalectomy was demonstrated by the lack of an increase in staining in the external zone in normal rats dehydrated for five days (Figure 7). Also there was no staining in the external zone of the Brattleboro rat and no increase in the small amount of oxytocin staining present in the external zone of rats (not shown). Neurophysin in this location is presumed to represent secretion of neurophysin and vasopressin into the long portal vessels, because extraordinary levels of neurophysin and vasopressin have been measured in pituitary portal blood (71, 112). The studies indicate that in adrenal-insufficient rats the release of neurohypophysial peptides into the anterior pituitary portal vessels via the zona externa of the median eminence was increased. The studies have been interpreted to indicate that vasopressin may (at some times) serve as one of the corticotropin releasing factors.

HUMAN   Maneuvers known to stimulate vasopressin release can be shown to stimulate a human neurophysin designated as nicotine-stimulated neurophysin (NSN) (79). Nicotine inhalation is an accepted stimulus of vasopressin release in man and is a potent stimulus for release of NSN. Husain et al (47) assayed NSN and vasopressin in plasma samples collected after smoking and noted a simultaneous rise in NSN and vasopressin with a close correlation between peak vasopressin and peak neurophysin. Hypotension, which is a potent stimulus for vasopressin release, was studied in patients subjected to tilt-table testing. Plasma NSN rose from 0.5 ng ml^{-1} to between 1.5 and 6 ng ml^{-1} after tilting (79). Surgery is another situation where vasopressin release may be greatly stimulated, with vasopressin values as high as 200 pg ml^{-1} (60). Nicotine-stimulated neurophysin level was elevated at the time of peak surgical stress in all patients undergoing abdominal surgery (79), while in patients undergoing thyroidectomy or inguinal herniorrhaphy there was little change in plasma neurophysins.

Lesser stimuli for vasopressin release cause little or no change in circulating plasma neurophysins in man. Plasma neurophysin levels were measured in human subjects after overnight dehydration, at which time all subjects showed urinary concentration with osmolalities above 900 mOsmol kg^{-1}. No significant increase in NSN was observed in any individual. The same subjects were given an infusion of hypertonic saline by the standard Hickey-Hare protocol, a test known to stimulate vasopressin release. In spite of a prompt reduction in urine flow from 15 ml min^{-1} to 3 ml min^{-1}, a rise in plasma osmolality from 280 to 297, and a rise in urinary osmolality from 106 to 602 mOsmol kg^{-1}, no changes in NSN occurred in two subjects and only a minimum elevation was observed in two other subjects (79).

In clinical disorders related to the defective release of antidiuretic hormone, nicotine-stimulated neurophysin levels correlated with those of vasopressin. In 13 patients with the syndrome of inappropriate secretion of ADH (SIADH), 8 patients had elevated NSN values. In patients with severe central diabetes insipidus where vasopressin secretion is thought to be absent, NSN was always less than 1 ng ml^{-1} (79).

MONKEY   The radioimmunoassay for human nicotine-stimulated neurophysin measures a similar neurophysin in the monkey. While the monkey seems somewhat less responsive to nicotine administration than the human (79), four monkeys subjected to hemorrhage of 60–100 ml of blood had a marked increase in plasma NSN to values as high as 28 ng ml^{-1} (Figure 8). In every animal there was a significant rise in NSN without a significant rise in ESN, and in every animal NSN decreased promptly after reinfusion of the blood that had been removed. The NSN measured in monkey plasma gave a dilution parallel with human pituitary NSN.

SUMMARY   In all species studied there has been a measurable increase in the putative vasopressin-neurophysin with potent stimuli for vasopressin release, and no increase in the alternate (oxytocin) neurophysin. However, molar equivalents of neurophysin and vasopressin are not always found in plasma, and under certain circumstances urinary concentration may be demonstrated without a measurable increase in the plasma neurophysin thought to be related to vasopressin. The latter problem is probably explained by the fact that the present assays for neurophysin are not sufficiently sensitive to detect picogram fluctuations in neurophysin secretion. If a maximum urine concentration can be produced by as little as 5 pg ml^{-1} vasopressin (72), an equimolar plasma concentration of neurophysin would be 0.05 ng ml^{-1}, approximately 10 times more dilute than the lowest level of neurophysin that can be detected with the present assays. Therefore, it is quite possible that physiologically significant fluctuations of neurophysin occur below the detectable level. Alternatively, as discussed above, the possibility that some release of vasopressin may occur without a simultaneous release of neurophysin has not been conclusively excluded.

Oxytocin-related Events

BOVINE AND PORCINE   No assay data have been reported that correlate plasma levels of oxytocin with those of a putative oxytocin-neurophysin. As with vasopressin, the first demonstration that a specific "oxytocin-neurophysin" could be separately assayed in plasma was obtained in the cow (83, 84). Legros et al (54) demonstrated a clear-cut increase in bovine neurophysin I after milking; values lay in the range 1.8–2.7 ng ml^{-1} before milking and in the range 2.2–6.1 ng ml^{-1} after milking (Figure 9). Bovine neurophysin II values were unchanged by milking. Dax et al (22) found that porcine

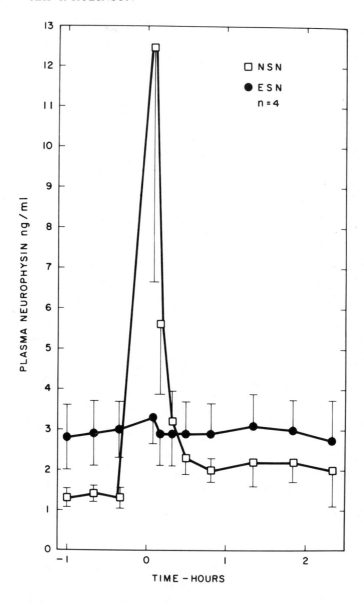

Figure 8 Plasma NSN and ESN in four monkeys during hemorrhage of 60–100 ml blood at time zero. A blood sample was taken five minutes after the onset of hemorrhage and the removed blood was immediately reinfused after the five minute blood samples. [Reprinted with permission from (77).]

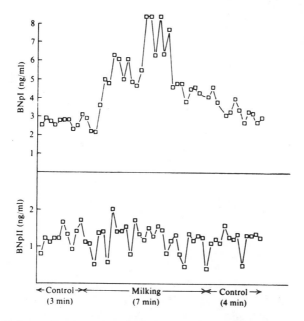

Figure 9   Release of bovine neurophysin I during hand milking. Continuous samples were obtained from the jugular vein and assayed for bovine neurophysin I and bovine neurophysin II. [Reprinted with permission from (54).]

neurophysin II (the "oxytocin-neurophysin" of the pig) was released during parturition and suckling in a pattern similar to that reported for oxytocin release (i.e. an increase at the end of parturition and spurt releases during suckling), while porcine neurophysin I was unchanged.

RAT   The rat plasma neurophysin assay described by Seif et al (92) is the only assay of rat neurophysin that has reported elevation of neurophysin in the rat at a time that might be related to oxytocin. Periodic plasma samples in ten pregnant rats throughout gestation showed a statistically significant increase in neurophysin by day 14; the level rose steadily to greater than 13 ng ml^{-1} by day 21, and fell dramatically toward normal by two days postpartum (Figure 10). Sixteen blood samples collected from four rats during parturition showed significantly higher values than before parturition, with a mean of 40 ± 5.3 ng ml^{-1} (92). This homologous assay, then, must measure vasopressin-neurophysin (see above) and oxytocin-neurophysin in the rat.

HUMAN AND MONKEY   Neurophysin in plasma was first measured in pregnant women using a radioimmunoassay for bovine neurophysin (52).

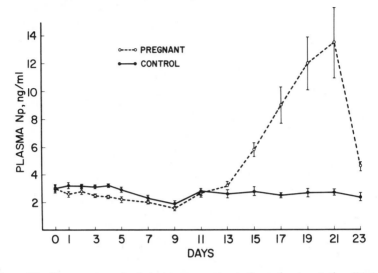

Figure 10   Plasma neurophysin in ten pregnant rats throughout gestation (21 days) and 2 days postpartum (day 23). Eight matched normal female rats were used as control. None of the samples were obtained during parturition (see text). [Reprinted with permission from (92).]

All investigators have found elevated neurophysin levels in pregnant women with heterologous neurophysin assays (78). Robinson (73) found that women on oral contraceptives maintained high levels of plasma neurophysin. It was demonstrated that the neurophysin elevation in women taking oral contraceptives was due to their estrogenic components, and it is now recognized that the neurophysin that is elevated in pregnant women is a specific neurophysin: estrogen-stimulated neurophysin (ESN) (74). While it is most consistent with previous animal data to conclude that this second human neurophysin is associated with oxytocin, that association has been difficult to confirm. The ESN level was elevated throughout pregnancy from the end of the first trimester (19), but no acute elevation of ESN at the time of parturition has been observed. Robinson et al (79) were unable to demonstrate an elevation of ESN in women during nursing, although Legros et al (53) reported some increase in total plasma neurophysin in women 30 min after the onset of nursing. Oxytocin and vasopressin are thought to be secreted by the infant at the time of parturition (14, 31), and it has been reported that human and bovine cord blood have elevated neurophysin levels consistent with an elevation of the oxytocin-related neurophysin and vasopressin-related neurophysin levels (79, 84).

The most consistent stimuli for estrogen-stimulated neurophysin release have been changes in plasma estrogen concentration. This was seen in response to pharmacologic doses of estrogen in humans and monkeys, with physiologic changes in estrogen (pregnancy in women and mid-cycle in monkeys), and with pathologic states of presumed estrogen excess (cirrhosis with feminization) (79). The constant ESN response to estrogen administration has prompted consideration that ESN might have a role in reproductive endocrinology. In the rhesus monkey, Robinson et al (77) found a close chronologic correlation among the mid-cycle elevation of estrogen, the mid-cycle surge of LH, and a mid-cycle increase in ESN (Figure 11). In women, neurophysin levels were increased at the time of mid-cycle; in some of these women the neurophysin remained elevated throughout the luteal phase (51). The finding of a mid-cycle rise of estrogen-stimulated neurophysin, the knowledge that neurophysin is present in the external zone of the

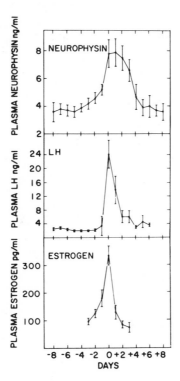

Figure 11 Correlation of plasma ESN, LH, and estrogen in 19 monkeys at mid-cycle. Day zero is the day of peak plasma estrogen. [Reprinted with permission from (77).]

median eminence, and the measurement of ESN values of greater than 200 ng ml⁻¹ in long portal vessels of monkeys raised the possibility that neurophysin might be related to the positive feedback effect of estrogen on LH secretion. There has been no convincing evidence that neurophysin is associated with any gonadotropin releasing or inhibiting factor that might be released by estrogen administration, and preliminary attempts to stimulate or inhibit gonadotropin secretion by neurophysin administration have been inconclusive (M. Ferin, personal communication). As ESN is postulated to be associated with oxytocin, the effect of estrogen on oxytocin secretion warrants careful investigation. However, even definitive proof that the ESN level is a reflection of oxytocin secretion would not explain the positive response of ESN to estrogen administration.

A striking new observation in humans has been the persistence of the release of ESN in response to estrogen administration in patients with diabetes insipidus (75). In these patients NSN was usually absent. Ten patients with central diabetes insipidus and absent NSN responded to 100 μg ethinyl estradiol with a marked elevation of plasma ESN level indistinguishable from a group of normal subjects (Figure 12). The patients with

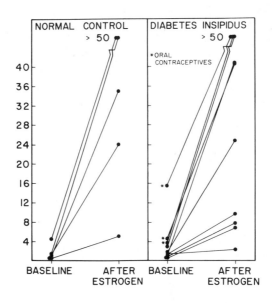

Figure 12   ESN response to oral estrogen administration in normal subjects, left, and patients with diabetes insipidus, right. Zero time is shown as baseline and peak value at 12, 24, or 36 hours is shown as the response. [Reprinted with permission from (75).]

diabetes insipidus (DI) included those with idiopathic DI, DI due to space-occupying lesions, and DI produced by head trauma. In two patients the peak plasma ESN was greater than 50 ng ml^{-1} in spite of complete inability to secrete vasopressin, with maximum urine osmolality of 90 mOsmol kg^{-1} after severe dehydration. Thus, the ESN system remains intact when the neurohypophysis is damaged. The anatomic explanation of this persistence has not been determined. One wonders whether the short axons of the neurohypophysis that appear to terminate near blood vessels in the hypothalamus as described by Zimmerman et al (113) might allow the secretion of ESN above the level of the stalk.

CONCLUSIONS

Neurophysins are proteins synthesized in association with the known hormones of the posterior pituitary, oxytocin and vasopressin. After synthesis (and possibly while still in a precursor form) the neurophysins and hormones are packaged in neurosecretory granules and transferred along the axons to the sites of secretion. Neurophysin staining by specific immunohistochemistry has demonstrated three projections of the hypothalamo-neurohypophysial system: (a) to the posterior pituitary and systemic circulation; (b) to the zona externa of the median eminence and the long portal vessels to the anterior pituitary; and (c) to the third ventricle and the cerebrospinal fluid. It is postulated that there is a specific neurophysin for vasopressin and a different neurophysin for oxytocin in most species; but because the neurophysins are so closely related biochemically, separation and classification of hormone-specific neurophysins has been difficult. Study of neurophysins has been enhanced by development of specific and sensitive radioimmunoassays in several species. In the cow a vasopressin-neurophysin and an oxytocin-neurophysin have been identified; when the hormone is released into the circulation there is the simultaneous release of the appropriate neurophysin. In the human, two specific neurophysins have been identified by their response to pharmacologic stimuli: nicotine-stimulated neurophysin (NSN) and estrogen-stimulated neurophysin (ESN). NSN is secreted at times when one would expect vasopressin secretion and ESN is postulated to mimic oxytocin secretion. The newest observation based on assay of neurophysins in plasma is the release of ESN in response to changes in circulating estrogen in humans and monkeys. Variations in plasma ESN do not correlate with the current knowledge of the physiology of neurohypophysial secretion, and further study of the secretory patterns of neurophysins in various experimental and physiological circumstances may yield new insights regarding the functioning of this neuroendocrine system.

ACKNOWLEDGMENTS

We would like to acknowledge the professional collaboration of Fred F. Ciarochi, Richard Defendini, Michel Ferin, Alan B. Huellmantel, Barry Markovitz, Christiane Sinding, and Earl A. Zimmerman and the technical assistance of Ms. Catherine Haluszczak and Ms. Julie Wilkins. Secretarial assistance was provided by Ms. Karen Bodnar.

These studies were supported by grants from the National Institutes of Health, AM16166; the Health and Research Services Foundation, T-61; and the Clinical Research Unit of the University of Pittsburgh, RR-00056. Dr. Robinson is the recipient of an NIH Research Career Development Award, AM00093.

Literature Cited

1. Acher, R., Manoussos, G., Olivry, G. 1955. Sur les relations entre l'ocytocine et la vasopressine d'une part et la proteine de van Dyke d'autre part. *Biochim. Biophys. Acta* 16:155–56
2. Antunes, J. L., Carmel, P. W., Ferin, M., Zimmerman, E. A. 1977. Paraventricular nucleus: The origin of vasopressin secreting terminals on hypophysial portal vessels in the monkey. (Abstr.) *Endocrinology.* In press
3. Axelrod, J., Daly, J. 1965. Pituitary gland: Enzymic formation of methanol from S-adenosylmethionine. *Science* 150:892–93
4. Bargmann, W. 1949. Über die neurosekretorische Verknupfung von Hypothalamus und Neurohypophyse. *Z. Zellforsch.* 34:610–34
5. Bargmann, W. 1951. Zwischenhirn und Neurohypophyse; eine neue Vorstellung über die functionelle Bedeutung des Hinterlappens. *Med. Monatsschr.* 5:466–70
6. Bargmann, W., Scharrer, E. 1951. The site of origin of the hormones of the posterior pituitary. *Am. Sci.* 39:255–59
7. Biro, G. P., Forsling, M. L., Martin, M. J., Wilmott, R. W. 1972. Relative rates of release and clearance of neurophysin and vasopressin in the dog. *J. Endocrinol.* 53:lvi–lvii
8. Breslow, E., Abrash, L. 1966. The binding of oxytocin and oxytocin analogues by purified bovine neurophysins. *Proc. Natl. Acad. Sci. USA* 56:640–46
9. Burford, G. D., Jones, C. W., Pickering, B. T. 1971. Tentative identification of a vasopressin-neurophysin and an oxytocin-neurophysin in the rat. *Biochem. J.* 124:809–13

10. Burford, G. D., Pickering, B. T. 1972. The number of neurophysins in the rat. Influence of the concentration of bromophenol blue, used as a tracking dye, on the resolution of protein by polyacrylamide gel electrophoresis. *Biochem. J.* 128:941–44
11. Burford, G. D., Pickering, B. T. 1973. Intra-axonal transport and turnover of neurophysin in the rat: A proposal for a possible origin of the minor neurophysin component. *Biochem. J.* 136:1047–52
12. Capra, J. D., Cheng, K. W., Friesen, H. G., North, W. G., Walter, R. 1974. Evolution of neurophysin proteins: The partial sequence of human neurophysin-I. *FEBS Lett.* 46:71–75
13. Capra, J. D., Walter, R. 1975. Primary structure and evolution of neurophysins. *Ann. NY Acad. Sci.* 248:397–407
14. Chard, T., Boyd, N. R. H., Forsling, M. L., McNeilly, A. S., Landon, J. 1970. The development of a radioimmunoassay for oxytocin: The extraction of oxytocin from plasma, and its measurement during parturition in human and goat blood. *J. Endocrinol.* 48:223
15. Chauvet, M. T., Chauvet, J., Acher, R. 1975. Phylogeny of neurophysins: Partial amino acid sequence of a sheep neurophysin. *FEBS Lett.* 52:212–15
16. Chauvet, M. T., Chauvet, J., Acher, R. 1976. The neurohypophyseal hormone-binding proteins: Complete amino-acid sequence of ovine and bovine MSEL-neurophysins. *Eur. J. Biochem.* 69:475–85
17. Cheng, K. W., Friesen, H. G. 1971. Isolation and characterization of a third component of porcine neurophysin. *J. Biol. Chem.* 246:7656–7665

18. Cheng, K. W., Friesen, H. G. 1972. The isolation and characterization of human neurophysin. *J. Clin. Endocrinol. Metab.* 34:165–76
19. Cheng, K. W., Friesen, H. G. 1973. Studies of human neurophysin by radioimmunoassay. *J. Clin. Endocrinol. Metab.* 36:553–60
20. Ciarochi, F. F., Haluszczak, C., Robinson, A. G. 1976. Neurophysin activity and dynamics in the rat. *The Endocrine Society, 58th, San Francisco,* p. 234 (Abstr.)
21. Cort, J. H., Sedlakova, E., Kluh, I. 1975. Neurophysin binding and natriuretic peptides from the posterior pituitary. *Ann. NY Acad. Sci.* 248:336–44
22. Dax, E. M., Cumming, I. A., Lawson, R. A. S., Johnston, C. I. 1977. The physiological release of specific individual neurophysins into the circulation in pigs. *Endocrinology* 100:635–41
23. Dean, C. R., Hope, D. B., Kazic, T. 1968. Evidence for a storage of oxytocin with neurophysin-I and of vasopressin with neurophysin-II in separate neurosecretory granules. *Brit. J. Pharmacol.* 34:192P–193P
24. Defendini, R., Zimmerman, E. A. 1977. Hypothalamic pathways containing oxytocin, vasopressin and associated neurophysins. *Conf. Neurohypophysis, Key Biscayne, 1976.* In press
25. De Mey, J., Vandesande, F. 1976. Bovine neurophysin I, II and C: New methods for their purification and for the production of specific antibodies. *Eur. J. Biochem.* 69:153–62
26. De Vitry, F., Camier, M., Czernichow, P., Benda, P., Cohen, P., Tixier-Vidal, A. 1974. Establishment of a clone of mouse hypothalamic neurosecretory cells synthesizing neurophysin and vasopressin. *Proc. Natl. Acad. Sci. USA* 71:3575–79
27. Dewardener, H. E. 1973. The natriuretic hormone. *Proc. Eur. Dial. Transplant Assoc.* 10:3–19
28. Du Vigneaud, V. 1956. Hormones of the posterior pituitary gland: Oxytocin and vasopressin. *Harvey Lect., Ser. L*:1–26
29. Edgar, D. H., Hope, D. B. 1976. Protein-carboxyl methyltransferase of the bovine posterior pituitary gland: Neurophysin as a potential endogenous substrate. *J. Neurochem.* 27:949–55
30. Fawcett, C. P., Powell, A. E., Sachs, H. 1968. Biosynthesis and release of neurophysin. *Endocrinology* 83:1299–1310
31. Fitzpatrick, R. J., Walmsley, C. F. 1965. The release of oxytocin during

parturition. In *Advances in Oxytocin Research,* ed. J. H. M. Pinkerton, p. 51. Oxford: Pergamon
32. Forsling, M. L., Martin, M. J., Sturdy, J. C., Burton, A. M. 1973. Observations on the release and clearance of neurophysin and the neurohypophysial hormones in the rat. *J. Endocrinol.* 57:307–15
33. Foss, I., Sletten, K. Trygstad, O. 1973. Studies on the primary structure and biological activity of a human neurophysin. *FEBS Lett.* 30:151–56
34. Gainer, H., Sarne, Y., Brownstein, M. J. 1977. Neurophysin biosynthesis: Conversion of a putative precursor during axonal transport. *Science* 195:1354–56
35. Ginsburg, M., Jayasena, K. 1968. The occurrence of antigen reacting to antibody to porcine neurophysin. *J. Physiol. London* 197:53–63
36. Ginsburg, M., Jayasena, K. 1968. The distribution of proteins that bind neurohypophyseal hormones. *J. Physiol. London* 197:65–76
37. Gitleman, H. J., Blythe, W. B. 1972. Isolation of a natriuretic factor from the posterior pituitary. *Clin. Res.* 20:594
38. Gomori, G. 1940. Observation with different stains on human islet of Langerhans. *Am. J. Pathol.* 17:395–406
39. Gutierrez, M., Sloper, J. C. 1969. Reaction in vitro of synthetic oxytocin and lysine-vasopressin with the pseudoisocyanin-chloride technique used for the demonstration of neurohypophyseal neurosecretory material. *Histochemie* 17:73–77
40. Hamilton, B. P. M., Upton, G. V., Amatruda, T. T. Jr. 1972. Evidence for the presence of neurophysin in tumors producing the syndrome of inappropriate antidiuresis. *J. Clin. Endocrinol. Metab.* 35:764–67
41. Hild, W., Zetler, G. 1953. Über die Funktion des Neurosekrets im Zwischenhirn-neurohypophysensystem als Tragersubstanz für Vasopressin, Adiuretin und Oxytocin. *Z. Gesampte Exp. Med.* 120:236–43
42. Hollenberg, M. D., Hope, D. B. 1967. Fractionation of neurophysin by molecular-sieve and ion-exchange chromatography. *Biochem. J.* 104:122–27
43. Hollenberg, M. D., Hope, D. B. 1968. The isolation of the native hormone-binding proteins from bovine pituitary posterior lobes. *Biochem. J.* 106:557–64
44. Hope, D. B. 1975. The neurophysin proteins: historical aspects. *Ann. NY Acad. Sci.* 248:6–14

45. Hope, D. B., Pickup, J. C. 1974. Neurophysins. In *Handbook of Physiology*, ed. E. Knobil, W. H. Sawyer, 4:173–89. Washington DC: Amer. Physiol. Soc.

46. Hope, D. B., Walti, M. 1971. [1-(L-2-Hydroxy-3-mercaptopropanoic acid)]-oxytocin, a highly potent analogue of oxytocin not bound by neurophysin. *Biochem. J.* 125:909–11

47. Husain, M. K., Frantz, A. G., Ciarochi, F. F., Robinson, A. G. 1975. Nicotine stimulated release of neurophysin and vasopressin in humans. *J. Clin. Endocrinol. Metab.* 41:1113–17

48. Jones, C. W., Pickering, B. T. 1970. Rapid transport of neurohypophysial hormones in the hypothalamo-neurohypophysial tract. *J. Physiol.* 208:73P–74P

49. Jones, C. W., Pickering, B. T. 1972. Intra-axonal transport and turnover of neurohypophysial hormones in the rat. *J. Physiol. London* 227:553–61

50. Legros, J. J. 1975. The radioimmunoassay of human neurophysins: Contribution to the understanding of the physiopathology of neurohypophysial function. *Ann. NY Acad. Sci.* 248:281–303

51. Legros, J. J., Franchimont, P., Burger, H. 1975. Variations of neurohypophyseal function in normally cycling women. *J. Clin. Endocrinol. Metab.* 41:54–59

52. Legros, J. J., Franchimont, P., Hendrick, J. C. 1969. Dosage radioimmunologique de la neurophysine dans le serum des femmes normales et des femmes enceintes. *C. R. Soc. Biol. Paris* 163:2773

53. Legros, J. J., Remacle, P., Van Cauwenberge, J. R., Gaspard, U., Franchimont, P., Lambotte, R. 1975. Liberation des neurophysines lors de la tétée chez la femme allaitante. *C. R. Soc. Biol. Paris* 169:1648–1650

54. Legros, J. J., Reynaert, R., Peeters, G. 1974. Specific release of bovine neurophysin I during milking and suckling in the cow. *J. Endocrinol.* 60:327–32

55. Legros, J. J., Reynaert, R., Peeters, G. 1975. Specific release of bovine neurophysin II during arterial or venous haemorrhage in the cow. *J. Endocrinol.* 67:297–302

56. Livett, B. G., Uttenthal, L. O., Hope, D. B. 1971. Localization of neurophysin-II in the hypothalamo-neurohypophysial system of the pig by immunofluorescence histochemistry. *Phil. Trans. R. Soc. London (Biol. Sci.)* 261:371–78

57. McKelvy, J. F. 1975. Phosphorylation of neurosecretory granules by cAMP-stimulated protein kinase and its implication for transport and release of neurophysin proteins. *Ann. NY Acad. Sci.* 248:80–91

58. McNeilly, A. S., Legros, J. J., Forsling, M. L. 1972. Release of oxytocin, vasopressin and neurophysin in the goat. *J. Endocrinol.* 52:209–10

59. Meyer-Grass, M., Pliska, V. 1974. Properties of neurophysin from neurosecretory granules ('native' neurophysin). *Experientia* 30:689–94

60. Moran, W. H. Jr., Miltenberger, F. W., Shuayb, W. A., Zimmerman, B. 1964. The relationship of antidiuretic hormone secretion to surgical stress. *Surgery* 56:99–108

61. Norström, A. 1974. Biosynthesis of neurohypophysial proteins in rats with hereditary hypothalamic diabetes insipidus (Brattleboro strain). *Brain Res.* 68:309–17

62. Norström, A. 1975. Axonal transport and turnover of neurohypophysial peptides in the rat. *Ann. NY Acad. Sci.* 248:46–63

63. Norström, A., Hansson, H. A. 1972. Isolation and characterization of neurosecretory granules of the rat posterior pituitary gland. *Z. Zellforsch.* 129:92–113

64. Norström, A., Sjöstrand, J. 1971. Axonal transport of proteins in the hypothalamo-neurohypophysial system of the rat. *J. Neurochem.* 18:29–39

65. Norström, A., Sjöstrand, J. 1972. Effect of salt-loading thirst and water-loading on transport and turnover of neurohypophysial proteins of the rat. *J. Endocrinol.* 52:87–105

66. North, W. G., Valtin, H., Morris, J. F., La Rochelle, F. T. Jr. 1977. Evidence for metabolic conversions of rat neurophysins within neurosecretory granules of the hypothalamo-neurohypophysial system. *Endocrinology* 101:110–18

67. Parry, H. B., Livett, B. G. 1973. A new hypothalamic pathway to the median eminence containing neurophysin and its hypertrophy in sheep with natural scrapie. *Nature* 242:63–65

68. Pelletier, G., Leclerc, R., Labrie, F., Puviani, R. 1974. Electron microscope immunohistochemical localization of neurophysin in the rat hypothalamus and pituitary. *Mol. Cell. Endocrinol.* 1:157–66

69. Pettengill, O. S., Faulkner, C. S., Wurster-Hill, D. H., Maurer, L. H., Sorenson, G. D., Robinson, A. G., Zim-

merman, E. A. 1977. Isolation and characterization of a hormone producing cell line from human small cell anaplastic carcinoma of the lung. *J. Natl. Cancer Inst.* 58:511–18

70. Pickup, J. C., Johnston, C. I., Nakamura, S., Uttenthal, L. O., Hope, D. B. 1973. Subcellular organization of neurophysins, oxytocin, [8-lysine]-vasopressin and adenosine triphosphate in porcine posterior pituitary lobes. *Biochem. J.* 132:361–71

71. Porter, J. C., Oliver, C., Mical, R. S. 1977. Hypothalamic-pituitary vasculature: Evidence for retrograde blood flow. *The Endocrine Society, 59th, Chicago,* p. 96 (Abstr.)

72. Robertson, G. L., Mahr, E. A., Athar, S., Sinha, T. 1973. Development and clinical application of a new method for the radioimmunoassay of arginine vasopressin in human plasma. *J. Clin. Invest.* 52:2340–52

73. Robinson, A. G. 1974. Evaluation of plasma neurophysin in women on oral contraceptives. *J. Clin. Invest.* 54:209–12

74. Robinson, A. G. 1975. Isolation, assay and secretion of individual human neurophysins. *J. Clin. Invest.* 55:360–67

75. Robinson, A. G. 1977. The neurophysins—health and disease. In *Clinics in Endocrinology and Metabolism,* ed. G. M. Besser, 6:261–75. London: Saunders

76. Robinson, A. G., Ciarochi, F. F., Markovitz, B., Sinding, C., Zimmerman, E. A. 1977. Rat uterus neurophysin—product of local synthesis? *The Endocrine Society, 59th, Chicago,* p. 240 (Abstr.)

77. Robinson, A. G., Ferin, M., Zimmerman, E. A. 1976. Neurophysin secretion in monkeys: Emphasis on the hypothalamic response to estrogen and ovarian events. *Endocrinology* 98:468–75

78. Robinson, A. G., Frantz, A. G. 1973. Radioimmunoassay of posterior pituitary peptides—a review. *Metabolism* 22:1047–57

79. Robinson, A. G., Haluszczak, C., Wilkins, J. A., Huellmantel, A. B., Watson, C. G. 1977. Physiologic control of two neurophysins in humans. *J. Clin. Endocrinol. Metab.* 44:330–39

80. Robinson, A. G., Michelis, M. F., Warms, P. C., Davis, B. B. 1974. Natriuretic effect of posterior pituitary neurophysin. *J. Clin. Endocrinol. Metab.* 39:913–18

81. Robinson, A. G., Michelis, M. F., Warms, P. C., Davis, B. B. 1975. Biologic activity of neurophysin: natriuresis. *Ann. NY Acad. Sci.* 248:317–23

82. Robinson, A. G., Zimmerman, E. A. 1973. Cerebrospinal fluid and ependymal neurophysin. *J. Clin. Invest.* 52:1260–67

83. Robinson, A. G., Zimmerman, E. A., Engleman, E. G., Frantz, A. G. 1971. Radioimmunoassay of bovine neurophysin: Specificity of neurophysin I and II. *Metabolism* 20:1138–47

84. Robinson, A. G., Zimmerman, E. A., Frantz, A. G. 1971. Physiologic investigation of the posterior pituitary binding proteins neurophysin I and neurophysin II. *Metabolism* 20:1148–55

85. Rodeck, H. 1959. Zusammenhänge zwischen Neurosekret und den sogenannten Hypophysenhinterlappenhormenen. III. Untersuchungen zur farberischen Darstellung von synthetischem Oxytocin. *Z. Gesamte Exp. Med.* 132:122–35

86. Rudman, D., Chawla, R. K., Khatra, B. S., Yodaiken, R. E. 1975. Observations on the lipolytic and melanotropic properties of neurophysin proteins. *Ann. NY Acad. Sci.* 248:324–35

87. Sachs, H. 1967. Biosynthesis and release of vasopressin. *Am. J. Med.* 42:687–700

88. Sachs, H., Fawcett, C.P., Takabatake, Y., Portanova, R. 1969. Biosynthesis and release of vasopressin and neurophysin. *Rec. Prog. Horm. Res.* 25:447–91

89. Sachs, H., Pearson, D., Nureddin, A. 1975. Guinea pig neurophysin: Isolation, developmental aspects, biosynthesis in organ culture. *Ann. NY Acad. Sci.* 248:36–45

90. Sachs, H., Pearson, D., Shainberg, A., Shin, S., Bryce, G., Malamed, S., Mowles, T. 1974. Studies on the hypothalamo-neurohypophysial complex in organ culture. In *Recent Studies of Hypothalamic Function International Symposium, Calgary, 1973,* pp. 50–66. Basel: Karger

91. Scharrer, E., Scharrer, B. 1954. Hormones produced by neurosecretory cells. *Rec. Prog. Horm. Res.* 10:183–240

92. Seif, S. M., Huellmantel, A. B., Platia, M. P., Haluszczak, C., Robinson, A. G. 1977. Isolation, radioimmunoassay and physiologic secretion of rat neurophysins. *Endocrinology* 100:1317–26

93. Seif, S. M., Robinson, A. G., Zimmerman, E. A., Wilkins, J. 1977. Plasma neurophysin and vasopressin in the rat: Response to adrenalectomy and steroid replacement. *Endocrinology.* In press

94. Silverman, A. J., Zimmerman, E. A. 1975. Ultrastructural immunocytochemical localization of neurophysin and vasopressin in the median eminence and posterior pituitary of the guinea pig. *Cell Tissue Res.* 159:291–301

95. Sloper, J. C. 1966. The experimental and cytopathological investigation of neurosecretion in the hypothalamus and pituitary. In *The Pituitary Gland,* ed. G. W. Harris, B. T. Donovan, 3:131. Berkeley: Univ. Calif. Press

96. Sokol, H. W., Zimmerman, E. A., Sawyer, W. H., Robinson, A. G. 1976. The hypothalamo-neurohypophysial system of the rat: Localization and quantification of neurophysin by light microscopic immunocytochemistry in normal rats and in Brattleboro rats deficient in vasopressin and a neurophysin. *Endocrinology* 98:1176–88

97. Soloff, M. S., Swartz, T. L. 1973. Characterization of a proposed oxytocin receptor in rat mammary gland. *J. Biol. Chem.* 248:6471–78

98. Sterba, G. 1964. Grundlagen des histochemischen und biochemischen Nachweises von Neuroseckret mit Pseudoisorzyaninen. *Acta Histochem.* 17:268–92

99. Stillman, M. A., Recht, L. D., Rosario, S. L., Seif, S. M., Robinson, A. G., Zimmerman, E. A. 1977. The effects of adrenalectomy and glucocorticoid replacement of vasopressin and vasopressin-neurophysin in the zona externa of the median eminence of the rat. *Endocrinology* 101:42–49

100. Sunde, D. A., Sokol, H. W. 1975. Quantification of rat neurophysin by polyacrylamide gel electrophoresis (PAGE): Application to the rat with hereditary hypothalamic diabetes insipidus. *Ann. NY Acad. Sci.* 248:345–64

101. Swann, R. W., Pickering, B. T. 1976. Incorporation of radioactive precursors into the membrane and contents of the neurosecretory granules of the rat neurohypophysis as a method of studying their fate. *J. Endocrinol.* 68:95–108

102. Takabatake, Y., Sachs, H. 1964. Vasopressin biosynthesis. III. In vitro studies. *Endocrinology* 75:934–42

103. Trygstad, O. 1968. The lipid-mobilizing effect of some pituitary gland preparations. *Acta Endocrinol.* 58:277–94

104. Trygstad, O., Foss, I., Sletten, K. 1975. Metabolic activities of human neurophysins. *Ann NY Acad. Sci.* 248:304–16

105. Uttenthal, L. O., Hope, D. B. 1970. The isolation of three neurophysins from porcine posterior pituitary lobes. *Biochem. J.* 116:899–909

106. Valtin, H. 1967. Hereditary hypothalamic diabetes insipidus in rats (Brattleboro strain). *Am. J. Med.* 42:814–27

107. Vandesande, F., Dierickx, K., De Mey, J. 1975. Identification of the vasopressin-neurophysin II and the oxytocin-neurophysin I producing neurons in the bovine hypothalamus. *Cell Tissue Res.* 156:289–300

108. Vilhardt, H., Robinson, I. C. A. F. 1975. Polyacrylamide gel electrophoresis of bovine neurophysins. *J. Neurochem.* 24:1275–76

109. Walter, R., Audhya, T. K., Schlesinger, D. H., Shin, S., Saito, S., Sachs, H. 1977. Biosynthesis of neurophysin proteins in the dog and their isolation. *Endocrinology* 100:162–74

110. Watkins, W. B. 1971. Neurophysins of the human pituitary gland. *J. Endocrinol.* 51:595–96

111. Wuu, T., Crumm, S. E. 1976. Characterization of porcine neurophysin III. Its resemblance and possible relationship to porcine neurophysin I. *J. Biol. Chem.* 251:2735–39

112. Zimmerman, E. A., Carmel, P. W., Husain, M. K., Ferin, M., Tannenbaum, M., Frantz, A. G., Robinson, A. G. 1973. Vasopressin and neurophysin: High concentrations in monkey hypophyseal portal blood. *Science* 182:925–27

113. Zimmerman, E. A., Defendini, R., Sokol, H. W., Robinson, A. G. 1975. The distribution of neurophysin-secreting pathways in the mammalian brain: Light microscopic studies using the immunoperoxidase technique. *Ann. NY Acad. Sci.* 248:92–111

114. Zimmerman, E. A., Robinson, A. G. 1976. Hypothalamic neurons secreting vasopressin and neurophysin. *Kidney Intl.* 10:12–24

115. Zimmerman, E. A., Robinson, A. G., Husain, M. K., Acosta, M., Frantz, A. G., Sawyer, W. H. 1974. Neurohypophysial peptides in the bovine hypothalamus: The relationship of neurophysin I to oxytocin, and neurophysin II to vasopressin in supraoptic and paraventricular regions. *Endocrinology* 95:931–936

Ann. Rev. Physiol. 1978. 40:377–410
Copyright © 1978 by Annual Reviews Inc. All rights reserved

THE RENIN-ANGIOTENSIN SYSTEM

♦1196

Ian A. Reid, Brian J. Morris, and William F. Ganong

Department of Physiology, University of California,
San Francisco, California 94143

INTRODUCTION

Since the discovery of renin 80 years ago, there have been remarkable advances in our understanding of the renin-angiotensin system. The system as it is known today is summarized in Figure 1. Angiotensin II[1], the active component of the system, has several important physiological actions. The first of these to be identified was its pressor action, and for many years it was felt that the sole function of the renin-angiotensin system was regulation of blood pressure. A new dimension was added in 1960 with the discovery that angiotensin II stimulates the secretion of aldosterone and is therefore in a position to exert important effects on salt and water balance. Several additional actions of angiotensin II were then discovered. It was found that the peptide can increase the secretion of catecholamines from the adrenal and facilitate adrenergic transmission. It also acts directly on the brain to increase blood pressure via sympathetic and parasympathetic pathways, to produce thirst, and to stimulate the secretion of vasopressin and ACTH. Through these actions, the renin-angiotensin system plays an important role in the regulation of blood pressure and of the volume and composition of the extracellular fluid.

Major advances have also been made in our understanding of other aspects of the renin-angiotensin system. It has become clear that the heptapeptide metabolite of angiotensin II, [des-Asp¹] angiotensin II ("angio-

[1]The IUPAC-IUB Commission on Biochemical Nomenclature Recommendations (*J. Biol. Chem.* 250:3215) has suggested that the peptide hormones referred to in this review—angiotensin I, angiotensin II, ACTH, and growth hormone—be termed proangiotensin, angiotensin, corticotropin, and somatotropin, respectively.

377

0066-4278/78/0301-0377$01.00

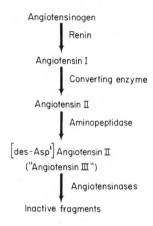

Figure 1   The renin-angiotensin system.

tensin III"), is biologically active and may mediate some of the actions of angiotensin II. There appear to be multiple interactions between the renin-angiotensin system and the ubiquitous thromboxane-prostaglandin system. Information concerning angiotensin receptors has become available, and antagonists of angiotensin II, as well as agents that block the formation of angiotensin II, have been developed. Renin has been purified. Inactive forms of renin have been discovered; in addition, enzymes with renin activity have been found in several extrarenal tissues including the uterus, salivary glands, and brain. Converting enzyme has been purified. Our knowledge of the neural mechanisms regulating the secretion of renin has been the subject of intensive research. Finally, angiotensinogen (renin substrate) has been almost completely purified and we are beginning to understand how the production of this glycoprotein is controlled.

Space does not permit us to review all of the new information that has become available during recent years. Fortunately, this has, to a large extent, been done by others. Areas that have been reviewed recently include the following: regulation of renin secretion (44, 230); converting enzyme (56, 198); angiotensin receptors (51); the role of the renin-angiotensin system in the control of aldosterone secretion (43); actions of angiotensin II on the central nervous system (187, 188); the "brain renin-angiotensin system" (70, 165); actions of "angiotensin III" (60); antagonists of angiotensin (211); interactions between prostaglandins and the renin-angiotensin system (153).

We limit this review to a consideration of three very topical areas in which we have been personally involved: (*a*) inactive renin; (*b*) the role of the central nervous system in the control of renin secretion; (*c*) regulation of the production of angiotensinogen. These topics are of particular significance since the levels of renin and angiotensinogen in the circulation determine the rate of formation of angiotensin and therefore the activity of the renin-angiotensin system.

INACTIVE RENIN

Discovery

Renin (EC 3 · 4 · 99 · 19) is a glycoprotein and a very specific carboxyl protease that cleaves the Leu^{10}-Leu^{11} bond in angiotensinogen to release angiotensin I. Until 1970, renin was thought to be an acid-stable enzyme of mol wt 37,000–43,000; forms differing slightly in isoelectric point were the only variants seen (191). Therefore, the discovery by Lumbers (118, 119) of an inactive form of renin which could be activated by acidification was of major interest. Inactive renin has now been found in plasma, amniotic fluid, and kidney extracts, and may be a biosynthetic precursor of renin. It has also been called "big renin" and "prorenin."

Activation

AMNIOTIC FLUID Observations of renin measurements in human plasma caused Lumbers to study the effect of pH on renin. Human amniotic fluid was used since it is a technically good model system, having a high concentration of renin without much angiotensinogen or angiotensinase activity (29, 117, 192). It also turned out to contain a large amount of inactive renin. Acidification to pH 3.3–3.6 (24 hr, 4°C) before assay at pH 7.4 caused a three- to nine-fold increase in the level of renin compared with that in samples treated to pH 4.0–7.5 (119). The increase did not appear to have resulted from the removal of a dissociable inhibitor and the activity was neutralized by antibody to partially purified renal renin (119, 133). The existence of a precursor or protein-bound form was therefore proposed.

Next, Morris & Lumbers (132, 133) showed that activation of renin at pH 3.3 was dependent on time and temperature, as is an enzyme reaction. They separated the activating principle which, unlike renin, was stable to pH 1.5 and could activate inactive renin at pH 4.5 but not at pH 7.5. Pepsin, which is stable at pH 1.5, could also activate inactive renin at pH 4.5, but not at pH 7.5. It was therefore proposed that the activation of inactive renin during acidification resulted from hydrolysis by pepsin subsequent to the autocatalytic activation of pepsinogen as H^+ concentration increased. Trypsin was able to activate renin at pH 7.5 indicating that H^+ itself was not a prerequisite. On the other hand, carboxypeptidase was ineffective, indicating that cleavage of internal peptide bonds was required for activation. The affinity of renin for angiotensinogen (i.e. the K_m) before and after activation by pepsin was similar, indicating that activation was not due to selective destruction of a competitive inhibitor. The intracellular pepsin-like enzyme, cathepsin D, can also activate inactive renin (128a). Gel filtration has shown that renin in human amniotic fluid has a mol wt of 59,000. Treatment of eluates with pepsin at pH 5 results in a large increase in renin in this region of elution. When activated by pepsin before chromatography the mol wt is similar (57,000) (B. J. Morris, unpublished results). Furthermore, when acidification is used to activate this so-called "big renin" in human amniotic fluid there is also no noticeable change in mol wt (47).

KIDNEY Day & Luetscher (45–48) found that plasma and extracts of kidney of some patients with Wilms' tumor and plasma of some patients with renal cell carcinoma, diabetes mellitus with proteinuria, renovascular hypertension with proteinuria, chronic renal failure, chronic pyelonephritis (47), and diabetes with hypoaldosteronism (49) also contain "big renin" (mol wt $\simeq$ 60,000) and that this replaces the normal form of renin (mol wt $\simeq$ 40,000). Day & Luetscher could find no big renin in extracts of normal kidneys, in the plasma of normal subjects, or in the plasma of patients with diabetes or renovascular hypertension who did not have proteinuria. In contrast, Slater & Haber (196) found big renin of mol wt near 60,000 in normal human kidney; this can be activated six-fold by acidification, but only in the less pure of the preparations used. Antibodies to the big renin inhibited both this and normal renin. A big renin (mol wt 58,000) was earlier reported by Overturf et al (154) in human kidney. However, it is not clear to what extent this result is due to the presence of other enzymes, since the synthetic tetradecapeptide renin substrate rather than the native substrate was used in the renin assay. Levine et al (113) found that approximately 20% of the renin in fractions of hog kidney had a high mol wt (57,000–59,000), but they were unable to increase its activity by acidification, pepsin, or trypsin. Perhaps it was already activated. Misono et al (124) reported the release of normal and big renin from slices of kidneys from rabbits (mol wt 60,000) and rats (mol wt 69,000). Most recently, Inagami & Murakami (94) have found in hog kidney forms of renin of mol wt 140,000, 61,000, and 42,000. Care was taken to avoid exposure to acid pH and to inhibit much of the endogenous protease activity. After purification, the specific enzymatic activity of the 140,000 and 61,000 forms were respectively 0.03% and 9% that of the 42,000 form.

The above studies of inactive renin indicate that it is big and does not change in size appreciably after activation. In contrast, several studies have demonstrated a change in mol wt from $\simeq$ 60,000 to $\simeq$ 40,000 upon activation by acid. Rubin (181) showed that treatment of an acetone-water extract of pig kidneys to pH 3.5 or 4.0 resulted in a 200–400% increase in activity of renin. Acidification after centrifugation was ineffective and she therefore suggested that an insoluble protein may be responsible for activation. If this activator was an enzyme, it was not inhibited by metal-chelating, reducing, or alkylating agents. Analytical ultracentrifugation of the extract after acidification showed a single 40,000 mol wt peak, but four forms differing in pI were observed on isoelectric focusing. Activation was not demonstrable in extracts of rat kidney (107).

Extracts of pig kidneys have been reported by Boyd (23–25) to contain two forms of renin. These were separated on DEAE cellulose and identified by their pressor response as normal renin (mol wt 40,000) and a slow acting renin, which was thought to be a renin-protein complex of mol wt 58,000. The complex could be dissociated by either low pH (less than 4.5) or high pH (greater than 10), exposure to a high concentration of NaCl, and by several other reagents. The nature of the inhibitory mechanism was not competitive because Boyd found no difference in K_m of the bound and normal forms. The mol wt of the binding protein inconsistently appeared high (55,000). Isoproterenol was capable of releasing the bound form from pig kidneys.

Leckie found that acidification of crude extracts of rabbit kidneys to pH 2.5 increased the renin-like pressor response almost three-fold (108). Gel filtration indicated a change in mol wt from 54,000 (inactive) to 37,000 (active) during acidification. Although she stated that this indicated a zymogen, later studies supported Boyd's concept of a protein-bound form of renin; a model analogous to "pepsinogen → pepsin + inhibitor peptide" was proposed (109). The activation at pH 2.5 took 10 hr at 4°C. The inhibitor protein could be separated at pH > 6 on DEAE cellulose. It had an apparent mol wt of 13,000, could elicit dose-dependent inhibition of renin, became dissociated from bound renin and was destroyed during acidification, resulting in irreversible activation. Preliminary studies with human kidneys produced less convincing results (110).

Evidence for the presence of inactive renin within renin storage granules isolated from rat kidney cortex by isopycnic gradient centrifugation was provided by Morris & Johnston (131). Acidification after gel filtration suggested that inactive renin had a mol wt 7,000 greater than normal renin present and had an electrophoretic mobility similar to normal renin. In experiments with a rabbit kidney pellet, Hiwada et al (88) claimed that a nondialysable, heat-labile principle, probably a soluble enzyme, could activate inactive renin; pH 3.5 treatment did not cause activation in their experiments. Evidence for activation by a sulfhydryl protease was provided by Hirose et al (87); this result does not fit with the findings of Rubin (181), who found that N-ethylmaleimide did not prevent activation.

PLASMA   Day & Luetscher found that acidification or incubation with pepsin or trypsin caused a ten-fold increase in the activity of big renin in

Wilms' tumor plasma. Pepsin did not alter renin activity in normal human plasma (46). Day & Luetscher did find a change in K_m upon activation, but this was too small to account for the large increase in activity seen. The mol wt did not change, but an increase in electrophoretic mobility after activation suggested a marked structural change.

Apparent cryoactivation in human plasma has recently been reported by Sealey & Laragh. It was first suggested that this occurred on exposure to −20°C for periods greater than 1 yr (185), but subsequent investigation revealed that activation occurred only in unfrozen plasma (186). At −2°C a 420% increase in plasma renin activity occurred after four days, whereas at +4°C the activation was more erratic and took four weeks. Activation at −5°C for four days appeared most effective at or above pH 7. However, it must be noted that acid pH can denature human renin substrate (160) prior to measurement of plasma renin activity. Patients with low renin hypertension had a greater proportion of inactive renin. Since activation did not appear to be a result of changes in the concentration of activators or inhibitors, Sealey & Laragh called the inactive renin "prorenin." Activation of renin in human amniotic fluid kept at 4°C for 50 days was earlier observed by Gibson (71). Since cold can rupture membranes, the possibility that the activation is due to a protease released from cellular contaminant rather than cold *per se* should be examined.

Factors Affecting Inactive Renin Levels In Vivo

Observations by Lumbers (117) suggested that natriuretic agents increase the proportion of active vs inactive renin secreted by the human kidney. James & Hall (95), in the same laboratory, later reported that administration of furosemide to dogs increased the release of active renin, whereas hemorrhage increased both active and inactive renin. They proposed that sodium ions at the macula densa initiate a mechanism (possibly enzymatic) that leads to activation of inactive renin prior to secretion. Earlier, Thurau et al (209) observed that increasing the concentration of NaCl from 20 to 140 mM in fluid perfused retrogradely past the macula densa caused a three-fold increase in the content of renin in single microdissected juxtaglomerular apparatuses (JGA) of the rat. Other chloride salts and mannitol were ineffective, suggesting that sodium ions were responsible, possibly by triggering a mechanism in the macula densa. The rapidity of the increase (20 min) was thought to indicate activation of inactive renin molecules. Later Weber et al (222) found that the K_m of renin (with homologous angiotensinogen) from single microdissected JGA of rabbits was 2.5 times that of plasma renin or purified renal renin, and that total renal ischemia or hemorrhage significantly decreased the K_m of JGA renin. They suggested that activation involved a decrease in inhibitory factors or an increase in activating factors in the JG cell.

Skinner et al (192) reported that inactive renin in normal human plasma constitutes 62% of the total amount of renin present. In the first trimester of pregnancy it constitutes 78% but decreases to 65% at term. Similar proportions (60% in normal and 70% in pregnancy plasma) were also reported by Leckie & McConnell (111). The concentration of angiotensin II in plasma correlated with active, but not with inactive renin; administration of the antagonist [Sar^1, Ala^8] angiotensin II to patients with renal hypertension increased active, but not inactive renin. Derkx et al (50) also used acidification to unmask inactive renin. Chronic stimuli to renin secretion released active and inactive renin into plasma, suggesting increased synthesis of both, whereas acute stimuli (such as isoproterenol, tilting, or diazoxide) increased active, but decreased inactive, suggesting conversion of inactive to active renin by these maneuvers. Conversely, acute inhibition of release by propranolol (50) or metoprolol (4) decreased active, but increased inactive renin. The K_ms of both were identical. Boyd (26) recently reported that 50% of the renin in human plasma is in the inactive form, but that in patients with low renin hypertension the proportion of inactive renin is much greater, so that acidification brings renin into the normal range. The mol wt of inactive renin appeared to be 2,000 greater than active renin (mol wt 41,000). Inactive renin eluted from DEAE-sepharose at 0.1 M NaCl compared with 0.2 M for active renin, suggesting that inactive renin is more positively charged. After activation by acidification, the apparent mol wt increased to 46,000 and Boyd suggested that activated renin in human plasma is a higher mol wt molecule rather than renin combined with a binding protein.

Morris and associates (130–133) proposed the existence of a renin precursor that is cleaved by selective intracellular proteolysis subsequent to biosynthesis. The ability of cathepsin D to activate inactive renin is of interest, as juxtaglomerular cells probably contain this enzyme. Furthermore, controlled proteolysis produces the active form of many precursor proteins, zymogens, and prohormones (202, 226). The proportion of active renin may be regulated by the extent of reaction of inactive renin with intracellular protease. The extent of fusion of renin granules with lysosome has been proposed as one way this could be achieved (131). Further support for an inactive precursor of renin is suggested by studies of renin replenishment of renin depleted kidneys of rats, in which secretory granules appear in the JGA before an increase in tissue renin (175). Acidification of extracts of kidneys of rats has been reported to increase renin more when there are numerous specific granules with paracrystalline structures and the rough endoplasmic reticulum is less well developed (7).

Summary

Our knowledge of inactive renin is still very limited. However, several positive statements can be made. The evidence for a species of mol wt near 60,000 appears unequivocal. Those who have found that this big form can be activated have found either that activation results in no change in size or else a marked reduction to yield active renin of normal size (mol wt near 40,000). The unaltered K_m and the role of proteolytic enzymes in the activation suggest that activation is not a result of the removal of a competitive inhibitor and that hydrolysis of peptide bonds is important. Hydrolysis of peptide bonds may cause a marked structural change in the molecule. A polypeptide cleaved from the big renin may remain loosely attached or be removed completely, depending on factors in the reaction mixture. The inhibitory protein that has been reported by some investigators may act noncompetitively. It must be realized that the structure of renin is still unknown. Most studies have used crude preparations. Results by direct bioassay have not excluded other pressor substances. Much of the work, particularly with plasma, has not included sufficient controls. Plasma contains low concentrations of renin, but high concentrations of renin substrate, so that angiotensin I formed during acid treatment must be taken into account. It must also be noted that human angiotensinogen is readily denatured below pH 4 (160) so that only measurements of plasma renin made using exogenous angiotensinogen have any relevance. Acidification may also denature enzymes that destroy renin. An action of still other enzymes on angiotensinogen during experimental manipulations and during the assay of renin must also be tested. Separation procedures may alter the distribution of an activating enzyme relative to inactive renin so that acidification of the fractions obtained may skew the activation produced. Thus the finding of inactive renin has presented an important challenge; however, much more information is required in order to gain a precise picture of its nature and role.

ROLE OF THE CENTRAL NERVOUS SYSTEM IN THE CONTROL OF RENIN SECRETION

Mechanisms Regulating Renin Secretion

It is now generally agreed that the secretion of renin is controlled by at least four mechanisms: (a) a renal vascular receptor that apparently responds to changes in wall tension in the afferent arteriole; (b) a macula densa receptor that appears to detect changes in the rate of delivery of sodium and/or chloride to the distal tubule; (c) a negative feedback effect of circulating angiotensin on renin secretion; (d) the central nervous system, which influences renin secretion via the renal nerves, the adrenal medulla, and the posterior pituitary. This section reviews our current knowledge of the role of the central nervous system in the control of renin secretion with emphasis on the mechanisms involved and their physiological significance.

Effects of Stimulation of the Central Nervous System on Renin Secretion

ELECTRICAL STIMULATION OF THE BRAIN   The secretion of renin is increased by stimulation of several areas of the brain; these include the mesencephalon (213), pons (174), medulla oblongata (156), and hypothalamus (229). The increases in secretion occur together with an increase in arterial pressure and, whenever measured, a decrease in renal blood flow. Renin secretion may also be decreased by stimulation of selected areas of the hypothalamus (231). The increases and decreases in renin secretion produced by electrical stimulation of the brain are abolished by renal denervation, indicating that they are mediated via the renal nerves.

CENTRALLY ACTING PHARMACOLOGICAL AGENTS   Several centrally acting drugs have marked effects on the secretion of renin. The level of renin in plasma is increased by most, if not all, general anesthetics including pentobarbital, ketamine, morphine, urethane, and a number of inhalation anesthetics (63, 158). It seems likely that these increases are mediated centrally, but direct evidence is not available. The rises in plasma renin caused by urethane and ketamine are reduced, but not abolished, by β-adrenergic blockade with propranolol (158). On the other hand, the responses to pentobarbital and morphine do not appear to be blocked by propranolol (63, 158).

Other agents can act on the brain to inhibit renin secretion. Clonidine, a centrally acting antihypertensive agent, inhibits renin secretion when administered centrally in doses that are ineffective when administered intravenously (149, 168). Most evidence indicates that this central effect is responsible for the inhibition of renin secretion by larger, systemically administered doses of clonidine. For example, the inhibition produced by intravenous clonidine is blocked by transection of the spinal cord (69), by ganglionic blockade (144), and by renal denervation (168).

Catecholamines can also act centrally to inhibit the secretion of renin. Blair et al (19) observed that when the catecholamine precursor L-dopa was administered intravenously in dogs in which extracerebral dopa decarboxylase was inhibited by intravenous carbidopa, there was a prompt fall in plasma renin activity. When central as well as peripheral dopa decarboxylase was inhibited by benserazide, the inhibitory effect of L-dopa was abolished (65). The inhibition was also blocked by renal denervation (19). These findings suggest that catecholamines formed from L-dopa within the central nervous system inhibit the secretion of renin and that this effect is mediated via the renal nerves.

PSYCHOLOGICAL STIMULI   Renin secretion can be altered by psychological stimuli. Blair et al (18) observed a two-fold increase in plasma renin activity in baboons during a 3 hr Sidman avoidance schedule in which the animals were required to press a lever in order to avoid an electric shock. Young et al (227) observed that the cardioacceleration produced during operant conditioning of heart rate in a human subject was associated with elevation of plasma renin activity. Clamage et al (39) studied the effects of two types of psychological stimuli on the secretion of renin in rats. They observed that exposure to a novel environment or the presence of a hungry cat resulted in significant increases in plasma renin activity. The renin response to exposure to a novel environment was reduced, but not abolished, by pretreatment with propranolol.

BRAIN SODIUM OR OSMORECEPTORS   Mouw et al (135) reported that plasma renin concentration increased in sheep when the concentration of NaCl in cerebrospinal fluid (CSF) was reduced by perfusing the cerebral ventricles with artificial CSF that contained NaCl at a concentration 25 mEq 1^{-1} less than normal. The increase in plasma renin was associated with a decrease in urinary sodium excretion. Similar observations were made earlier in the dog (136). On the basis of these results, it was suggested that the brain contains receptors sensitive to low concentrations of NaCl or low osmolality, activation of which results in increased secretion of renin and decreased excretion of sodium. The efferent pathway mediating the renin response was not identified. One possibility is that the response was mediated via a decrease in the concentration of vasopressin in plasma since it is known that vasopressin inhibits renin secretion (see below). Whatever the pathway, the data provide another example of a situation in which the secretion of renin may be influenced by the brain.

In summary, experiments involving electrical stimulation of the brain, centrally acting pharmacological agents, psychological stimuli, and alterations in the concentrations of electrolytes in CSF show that the brain can alter the secretion of renin.

Role of the Sympathetic Nervous System in the Control of Renin Secretion

The major efferent pathway by which the brain influences renin secretion is the sympathetic nervous system. The level of renin in plasma is increased in several situations in which sympathetic activity is increased. These include, in addition to those mentioned above, carotid occlusion (31, 91, 122, 167); nonhypotensive hemorrhage (31, 204); exercise (27); standing or tilting (126, 150, 210); hypoglycemia (152); intermittent electric shock (112); administration of 2-deoxyglucose (159), vasodilators (148, 157), or physostigmine (1); cervical vagotomy or vagal cooling (90, 120); and hyperthyroidism (83). Conversely, renin secretion is suppressed when sympathetic activity is decreased in response to distension of the left atrium (232).

Several investigators have reported that renin secretion is increased by administration of catecholamines, either systemically or directly into the renal artery (6, 99, 170, 212, 214, 220). Renin secretion is also increased by electrical stimulation of the renal nerves (41, 105, 115, 203) and decreased by renal denervation (12, 147, 170). Thus the changes in renin secretion listed above could be due to alterations in the activity of renal sympathetic nerves or to changes in the levels of catecholamines in the circulation. Both mechanisms appear to play a role. As mentioned earlier, the changes in renin secretion produced by electrical stimulation of the brain or administration of centrally acting drugs are reduced or abolished by renal denervation. In addition, the responses to hemorrhage (31, 204), vagal cooling (120), upright posture (229), and distension of the left atrium (232) are abolished by renal denervation or local anesthesia of the renal nerves. On the other hand, the response to hypoglycemia is associated with an increase in the rate of secretion and plasma concentration of epinephrine, and is abolished by adrenalectomy but not by renal denervation (152). Similarly, the increase in renin secretion produced by administration of 2-deoxyglucose in humans is accompanied by an increase in the secretion of epinephrine and is absent in patients with Addison's disease (159). The responses to hypoglycemia and administration of 2-deoxyglucose are therefore examples of stimuli to renin secretion mediated via circulating catecholamines.

Mechanisms by which the Renal Nerves and Catecholamines Increase Renin Secretion

There are several mechanisms by which catecholamines, either circulating in the blood or released locally from the renal sympathetic nerve endings, could increase renin secretion. These are summarized in Figure 2. (a) Catecholamines could exert a direct action on the renin-secreting cells of the juxtaglomerular apparatus. (b) By constricting the afferent arteriole, catecholamines could activate the renal vascular receptor with a resultant increase in renin secretion. (c) By constricting the afferent arteriole, catecholamines would reduce glomerular filtration rate and therefore reduce the filtered load of sodium and chloride; this would be reflected in decreased

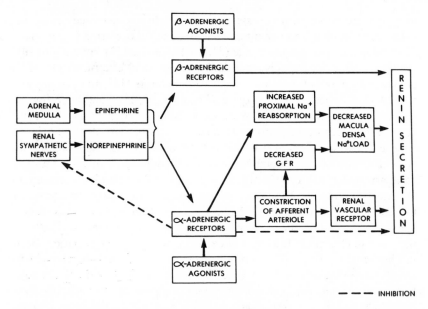

Figure 2 Summary of known and postulated effects of α- and β-adrenergic stimulation on the secretion of renin.

delivery of sodium and chloride to the distal tubule, which would increase renin secretion by the macula densa receptor mechanism. (*d*) Catecholamines could also decrease the delivery of sodium and chloride to the distal tubule by increasing the reabsorption of sodium and chloride in the proximal tubule.

DIRECT EFFECTS OF CATECHOLAMINES ON RENIN SECRETION   The juxtaglomerular cells are sympathetically innervated (8, 219); therefore it is likely that catecholamines stimulate the renin-secreting cells directly. This likelihood is supported by experiments involving electrical stimulation of the renal nerves or infusion of catecholamines into the renal artery. Interpretation of the results of some of these experiments has been complicated by associated changes in hemodynamics. However, Johnson et al (99) showed that stimulation of the renal nerves or infusion of norepinephrine in nonfiltering kidneys treated with papaverine resulted in an increased secretion of renin. In such a preparation, the renal vascular and macula densa mechanisms are presumed to be inoperative so that the stimulation of renin secretion probably resulted from a direct action of norepinephrine on the juxtaglomerular cells. Moreover, it has been reported that stimula-

tion of the renal nerves increases renin secretion when hemodynamic alterations are minimized by α-adrenergic blockade (115). Indeed, it has been
shown that when the appropriate stimulation parameters are used, stimulation of the renal nerves can increase renin secretion with no change in renal
blood flow, glomerular filtration rate, or electrolyte excretion (203).

Studies in vitro have provided further evidence for a direct action of
catecholamines on the renin-secreting cells. Several investigators have
shown that catecholamines increase the rate at which renin is released by
renal cortical slices or isolated renal cell preparations (96, 123, 146, 224).
Recently, Morris et al (134) reported that isoproterenol stimulates the
release of renin from isolated glomeruli with attached juxtaglomerular cells.
In preparations such as these, hemodynamic influences are reduced or
eliminated and, although several types of cells are present, it is likely that
changes in the release of renin result from direct actions of the catecholamines on the juxtaglomerular cells.

ROLE OF β-ADRENERGIC RECEPTORS   It is now generally accepted
that the direct effect of catecholamines on renin secretion is mediated, at
least in part, via β-adrenergic receptors. For example, the increases in renin
secretion produced by several stimuli are reduced or abolished by β-adren-
ergic blockade. These stimuli include electrical stimulation of the brain
(155, 174); standing (210); hypoglycemia (5); electric shock (112); stimulation of the renal nerves (41, 98, 115, 203); and administration of physostigmine (1), vasodilators (148, 157), or catecholamines (5, 212). Most of these
responses are not reduced by α-adrenergic blockade; indeed, the responses
to some of these stimuli are actually potentiated by α-blockade (5, 112). The
increase in the rate of renin release produced by norepinephrine in vitro is
also abolished by β-adrenergic blockade with propranolol and is potentiated by α-adrenergic blockade with phenoxybenzamine or phentolamine
(146).

Beta-adrenergic receptors have been subdivided into two types: β_1, which
includes receptors mediating cardiac stimulation and lipolysis; and β_2,
which includes receptors situated in the peripheral vasculature and in the
bronchi (106). There is now evidence that the β-receptors involved in the
control of renin secretion are of the β_2 type. In hypertensive humans, ICI
66082 (3) and practolol (57), β-blockers with predominantly β_1 receptor
affinity, appear to have little effect on plasma renin levels; on the other hand,
propranolol, which blocks both β_1 and β_2 receptors, decreases plasma renin
levels (30, 127). Similarly, ICI 66082 is much less potent than propranolol
in blocking the increase in renin secretion produced by stimulation of the
renal nerves of cats (97). In rabbits, H 35/25, a β_2-specific antagonist,

blocks the increase in renin secretion produced by isoproterenol (221). Conversely, metoprolol and practolol, blockers with predominantly β_1-receptor affinity, fail to block the renin response to this β-adrenergic agonist.

In many tissues, β-adrenergic effects are mediated via the activation of adenylate cyclase and the formation of adenosine 3',5'-monophosphate (cyclic AMP) (177). Evidence is accumulating that this mechanism is also involved in the adrenergic control of renin secretion. The dibutyryl derivative of cyclic AMP (2), but not cyclic AMP (201), stimulate renin stimulates when infused into the renal artery in dogs; cyclic AMP increases net renin production when added to renal cortical tissue of dogs in vitro (123). In addition, glucagon, which is known to increase cyclic AMP levels in several tissues including the kidney (176), has been reported to increase renin secretion (58, 218). Similarly, the phosphodiesterase inhibitor theophylline, which inhibits the degradation of cyclic AMP, increases plasma renin activity in the dog (172). This response is not blocked by α- or β-adrenergic blockade. Theophylline also potentiates the increase in renin release produced by norepinephrine in vitro (146). Finally, the renin response to norepinephrine in vitro is accompanied by an increase in the cyclic AMP content of the incubated tissue (67). These observations are not conclusive but do strongly suggest that the stimulation of renin secretion by catecholamines is mediated via cyclic AMP.

From the foregoing discussion it is clear that many sympathetic effects on renin secretion are mediated via intrarenal β-adrenergic receptors. However, it should be noted that there is evidence that the secretion of renin may also be influenced by extrarenal β-receptors. For example, Reid et al (170) observed that administration of low doses of isoproterenol stimulate renin secretion when administered intravenously but not when infused directly into the kidney, an organ that efficiently removes isoproterenol from the blood (114). Other investigators have been unable to demonstrate an intrarenal action of isoproterenol on renin secretion in vivo (31, 216). The location of the extrarenal β-adrenergic receptors has not been established. However, Privitera et al (162) recently reported that propranolol decreases plasma renin activity when administered intracisternally in doses that fail to alter plasma renin activity when injected intravenously. On the other hand, we failed to observe decreases in plasma renin activity when propranolol was injected into the third ventricle of anesthetized dogs (68). Thus additional studies are required to determine the location and role of the extrarenal β-adrenergic receptors that affect renin secretion.

ROLE OF α-ADRENERGIC RECEPTORS   Although it appears that catecholamines can increase renin secretion by a direct, β-mediated action on the juxtaglomerular cells, there is evidence that additional mechanisms are involved. For example, Johnson and associates (99) reported that the renin response to epinephrine in the nonfiltering kidney is blocked by the vasodilator drug papaverine. They therefore suggested that the response was due to an action of epinephrine on the renal arterioles. Comparison of the effects on renin secretion of administration of propranolol and of surgical renal denervation also point to the existence of receptors other than β-receptors. Most investigators agree that basal renin secretion is markedly reduced after renal denervation (12, 147, 170). On the other hand, administration of propranolol in doses known to block the renin responses to a variety of stimuli causes little or no decrease in renin secretion (93, 116).

It appears likely that α-adrenergic receptors also play a role in the neural regulation of renin secretion. Alpha-adrenergic stimulation could increase renin secretion by constricting the afferent arteriole with resulting activation of the renal vascular receptor (Figure 2). One would also expect α-stimulation to reduce the delivery of sodium and chloride to the macula densa, both by decreasing glomerular filtration rate and by increasing proximal tubular sodium and chloride reabsorption (11, 72, 228). Participation of α-receptors might explain the apparent effectiveness of dibenamine and phentolamine in blocking the increases in renin secretion produced by hemorrhage and stimulation of the renal nerves (16, 41).

The picture is even more complex than this, however, because stimulation of α-adrenergic receptors may in some circumstances inhibit the secretion of renin. This was first suggested by the finding that drugs that block α-adrenergic receptors frequently increase renin secretion. At first it seemed likely that this effect was simply due to the fall in blood pressure produced by the α-blocking drugs. However, in more recent studies in vitro, phenoxybenzamine and phentolamine potentiated the increase in renin release produced by norepinephrine (146). This observation suggested that the action of norepinephrine contains an inhibitory component that is mediated via the stimulation of intrarenal α-receptors. Support for this proposal was provided by Lopez and associates (67) and by Capponi & Vallotton (36), who observed that high doses of norepinephrine actually inhibit the release of renin in vitro and that this inhibition is converted into stimulation by the addition of α-blocking drugs.

It has been known for some time that the α-adrenergic agonist clonidine inhibits the secretion of renin (149, 168). Although the inhibition results primarily from an action of the drug in the central nervous system (see above), there have been reports that clonidine decreases the secretion of renin when infused into the renal artery of dogs (42) or into perfused rat kidneys (217). We recently observed that oxymetazoline, an α-agonist that is closely related to clonidine but that does not cross the blood-brain barrier, suppressed plasma renin activity in dogs when infused intravenously in a dose of 1.0 μg kg^{-1} (145). The inhibitory effect of oxymetazoline was blocked by phentolamine, indicating that it resulted from stimulation of α-adrenergic receptors. However, the location of the α-receptors was not established.

The inhibitory effect of α-agonists on the secretion of renin could be due to a direct action of catecholamines on the juxtaglomerular cells. The finding that norepinephrine inhibits the release of renin in vitro is consistent with this possibility. However, another possible mechanism exists. There is evidence that norepinephrine can reduce the release of norepinephrine from sympathetic nerve endings by stimulating α-adrenergic receptors located at these endings (199). Thus, in the intact animal, norepinephrine might stimulate α-receptors at the endings of the neurons that innervate the juxtaglomerular cells. This would reduce the release of norepinephrine and thus decrease β-mediated stimulation of renin secretion (Figure 2). Conversely, α-blockade would increase the release of norepinephrine and thus increase renin release by stimulating the β-receptor mechanism. The finding that the increase in renin secretion produced by α-blockade in vivo is blocked by propranolol (115) is consistent with this proposal.

It has been known for several years that the widely used antihypertensive drug α-methyldopa inhibits renin secretion (125). However, the mechanism of this inhibition has not been established. One possibility is that the drug is converted to α-methylnorepinephrine and that this compound activates the presynaptic α-receptor mechanism just described. Several observations are consistent with this proposal: (a) It is known that the inhibition of renin secretion produced by α-methyldopa is prevented in the dog when peripheral decarboxylation of the drug is blocked by carbidopa (59); (b) alphamethyldopa reduces the stimulation of renin secretion produced by electrical stimulation of the renal nerves (161); (c) the inhibition of renin secretion by α-methyldopa is blocked by renal denervation (78); (d) alphamethylnorepinephrine has a greater affinity for presynaptic α-receptors than for postsynaptic α-receptors (199). Further studies are required to evaluate the possible role of intrarenal α-adrenergic receptors in the control of renin secretion.

Role of Vasopressin, ACTH, and Growth Hormone in the Control of Renin Secretion

The sympathetic nervous system is not the only efferent pathway by which the brain can influence the secretion of renin. Several investigators have observed that administration of vasopressin inhibits renin secretion (32, 215). There is also evidence that renin secretion may be inhibited by endogenous vasopressin. For example, stimulation of vasopressin secretion by bilateral vagotomy in dogs undergoing a water diuresis decreases renin secretion (184). Furthermore, the increase in renin secretion produced by intravenous isoproterenol is greater in hypophysectomized dogs than in intact animals (170, 171). This difference may result from an increase in plasma vasopressin concentration since it is known that isoproterenol is a potent stimulus to the secretion of vasopressin (183). Further evidence that endogenous vasopressin suppresses renin secretion is provided by the observation that renin concentrations in plasma or kidneys of rats with hereditary diabetes insipidus are higher than in normal animals (77). However, the elevated levels of renin may be due, at least in part, to hypovolemia.

The exact mechanism by which vasopressin inhibits the secretion of renin is not known. It is possible that the inhibition results from a direct action of the peptide on the renin-secreting cells, since vasopressin inhibits renin secretion when infused into the nonfiltering kidney in doses that do not affect blood flow or arterial pressure (189). On the other hand, there is one report that vasopressin fails to alter the rate of renin release by kidney slices in vitro (180).

The decreases in the levels of renin in plasma produced by intravenous infusion of vasopressin are directly related to the concentration of vasopressin in plasma (S. A. Malayan, L. C. Keil, D. J. Ramsay, and I. A. Reid, unpublished observations). Furthermore, the plasma levels of vasopressin that inhibit renin secretion are within the range observed during water deprivation; thus it is likely that vasopressin blunts the increase in renin secretion observed in this situation (21, 40). However, the exact role that vasopressin plays in the physiological regulation of renin secretion remains to be determined.

There have been reports that renin secretion may be altered by administration of ACTH or growth hormone. Administration of ACTH has been reported to increase plasma renin levels in the rat and human (28, 82). In addition, Bozovic et al (28) observed that the rate of release of renin by slices of the renal cortex of rats pretreated with ACTH was greater than by slices from control rats. We have not observed stimulation of renin secretion by ACTH in the dog in vivo (64). Indeed, chronic treatment with ACTH actually results in suppression of the secretion of renin, both in the dog (64) and in man (13). This effect appears to be secondary to expansion of extracellular fluid volume (64). Growth hormone has also been reported to increase plasma renin levels in hypophysectomized rats (86). However, it does not appear to increase plasma renin activity in hypophysectomized dogs (66). Furthermore, patients with acromegaly have normal plasma renin levels and show normal increases in renin secretion in response to sodium restriction (33). Thus it seems unlikely that either ACTH or growth hormone plays an important role in the physiological regulation of renin secretion.

Summary

The central nervous system plays an important role in the control of renin secretion. The major efferent pathway from the brain to the kidney is the sympathetic nervous system. Vasopressin may also play an important role by virtue of its inhibitory effect on renin secretion, but there is little convincing evidence for the participation of ACTH or growth hormone.

The sympathetic nervous system affects the secretion of renin via the renal nerves and via circulating catecholamines. Sympathetic effects on renin secretion appear to be mediated via both α- and β-adrenergic receptors. Stimulation of β-receptors causes increased renin secretion, possibly by increasing the formation of cyclic AMP. The effects of α-adrenergic stimulation are less well understood. In some situations, α-stimulation increases renin secretion, presumably by activating the renal baroreceptor and macula densa mechanisms. In other situations, α-stimulation inhibits renin secretion, possibly by inhibiting the release of norepinephrine from renal sympathetic nerve endings and thereby decreasing β-stimulation of renin secretion. There is also evidence for direct α-adrenergic inhibition of renin secretion. Elucidation of the exact roles of these different receptor mechanisms in the physiological regulation of renin secretion awaits further investigation.

ANGIOTENSINOGEN (RENIN SUBSTRATE)

Sources and Properties

Angiotensinogen is the protein substrate from which renin enzymatically cleaves angiotensin I. Most evidence indicates that the angiotensinogen in the circulation is produced by the liver. For example, it has been shown that angiotensinogen is released by perfused livers (138), by liver slices (61), and by isolated heptocytes (223). In addition, the concentration of angiotensinogen in plasma decreases markedly after hepatectomy (205). However, the liver may not be the only site of angiotensinogen synthesis. In recent cell fractionation experiments, Morris & Johnston (130) separated angiotensinogen-containing granules from the renal cortex of rats. Angiotensinogen has also been found in cerebrospinal fluid (169), lymph (92), and human amniotic fluid (117, 192), but its origin is unknown. The function of the angiotensinogen in these tissues is also unknown; it may be utilized for local generation of angiotensin.

Angiotensinogen has been purified to varying degrees from human (54, 160, 182, 193, 208), hog (190), sheep (193), and dog (B. J. Morris, B. Moffat, and I. A. Reid, unpublished) plasma. The mol wt of these substrates has been estimated; the following are some of the reported values: human,

66,000–110,000 (54, 160, 193); hog, 57,000 (190); sheep, 52,000 (193); rat, 61,000 (130). Multiple forms of angiotensinogen have been observed by some investigators (160, 190) but not by others (54). It has been shown that hog, human, and rabbit angiotensinogens are glycoproteins (160, 190). Antibodies against human angiotensinogen have been prepared (53, 208) and have been used in a direct radioimmunoassay for plasma angiotensinogen concentration (53). A radiochemical assay that utilizes ^{125}I-labeled sheep angiotensinogen to measure human plasma renin concentration has also been developed (34).

Regulation of Angiotensinogen Production

Several factors regulate the production of angiotensinogen. The concentration of angiotensinogen in plasma is increased by administration of adrenocortical steroids, estrogens, and angiotensin II, and by nephrectomy, ureteral ligation, hemodilution, and hypoxia.

ADRENOCORTICAL STEROIDS   It is now well established that the adrenal cortex plays an important role in regulating the production of angiotensinogen. The concentration of angiotensinogen in plasma decreases after hypophysectomy (73, 85), adrenalectomy (38, 85, 137, 173), or adrenal enucleation (128), and increases after administration of ACTH or adrenocortical steroids (38, 84, 137, 173). On the basis of earlier studies (137) it was suggested that these changes were a function of mineralocorticoid activity rather than glucocorticoid activity but it now appears that the converse is true. For example, dexamethasone but not aldosterone increases the concentration of angiotensinogen in the plasma of adrenalectomized dogs (173), and cortisol but not deoxycorticosterone increases the rate of formation of angiotensinogen when added to the medium perfusing rat livers (79). In addition, plasma angiotensinogen levels are increased in patients with Cushing's syndrome but not in patients with primary aldosteronism (104).

ESTROGENS   Administration of estrogens is known to increase the plasma concentration of angiotensinogen (89, 141, 142, 194) as well as several other proteins including thyroxine-binding globulin and corticosteroid-binding globulin (9, 101). The increase in plasma angiotensinogen apparently results from a direct action of estrogens on the liver, since stilbestrol increases the formation of angiotensinogen when added to the medium perfusing rat livers (139). Eisenfeld et al (55) reported that administration of estradiol does not increase the concentration of angiotensinogen in the plasma of immature animals. These investigators also observed that the ability of estradiol to increase plasma angiotensinogen concentration correlated with the development of an hepatic estradiol-binding protein. It was suggested that the binding protein may be an estrogen receptor involved in modulating the synthesis of specific proteins. In contrast, the response in angiotensinogen to administration of glucocorticoid is not related to age (55). Plasma angiotensinogen concentration increases during pregnancy and this is presumably due to the concomitant increase in plasma estrogen levels (195, 225).

ANGIOTENSIN II   Administration of angiotensin II increases the concentration of angiotensinogen in the plasma of dogs (22) and rats (102, 140). The increase is not due to hemoconcentration since it is not accompanied by an increase in total plasma protein concentration or hematocrit (22, 102). It does not appear to result from decreased metabolism of angiotensinogen due to suppression of renin secretion by angiotensin since it can also be produced by administration of renin (37).

In the dog, the increase in plasma angiotensinogen concentration produced by angiotensin is accompanied by an increase in the concentration of corticosteroids in plasma and is abolished by adrenalectomy, indicating that adrenal steroids play an important role in the response (22). These observations raised the possibility that the angiotensinogen response is mediated via increased adrenocortical secretion. Such a mechanism seems unlikely, however, since angiotensin increases the concentration of angiotensinogen in the plasma of hypophysectomized dogs receiving a cortisol infusion (164). Under these conditions, angiotensin produces only a minor increase in plasma corticosteroid concentration. Furthermore, the latency of the angiotensinogen response to administration of angiotensin is less than the latency of the response to steroid administration (164). It therefore appears that the adrenocortical steroids play a permissive role for a direct action of angiotensin on angiotensinogen production. Such a direct action has been demonstrated in the rat by Nasjletti & Masson (140); they showed that addition of angiotensin to the medium perfusing an isolated liver preparation produced an increase in the rate of angiotensinogen production. Nevertheless, the possibility still remains that in some circumstances angiotensin II may exert an effect on the production of angiotensinogen via stimulation of adrenocortical secretion. It is known that angiotensin II can stimulate glucocorticoid secretion, both by a direct action on the adrenal cortex (100) and indirectly via stimulation of ACTH secretion (62, 121, 163), and that glucocorticoids increase angiotensinogen production (see above). Further investigation is required to determine whether angiotensin II can stimulate angiotensinogen production by increasing glucocorticoid secretion.

What is the significance of the stimulatory effect of angiotensin II on the production of angiotensinogen? One possibility is that it is a positive feedback mechanism to prevent plasma angiotensinogen concentration from falling when utilization of angiotensinogen is increased during periods of elevated renin secretion. Recent experiments by Beaty et al (10) have provided evidence consistent with this proposal. These investigators observed that plasma angiotensinogen concentration did not decrease when renin secretion was stimulated in dogs by hemorrhagic hypotension. However, when the experiment was repeated during administration of an antagonist of angiotensin II, a marked decrease in plasma angiotensinogen concentration occurred. It was therefore concluded that the maintenance of plasma angiotensinogen concentration during hemorrhagic hypotension results from stimulation of the production of angiotensinogen by angiotensin II.

Angiotensin II may also stimulate the production of angiotensinogen in other states of hyperreninemia. For example, plasma angiotensinogen concentration is within the normal range in sheep severely depleted of sodium, despite an estimated ten-fold increase in the rate of utilization of angiotensinogen (20). Moreover, the concentration of angiotensinogen in plasma is increased in renal and malignant hypertension (75, 76, 179). Studies with angiotensin antagonists should reveal the contribution of angiotensin II to the increased production of angiotensinogen in these situations.

NEPHRECTOMY   The concentration of angiotensinogen in plasma increases after nephrectomy (15, 38, 89). The increase is not simply a consequence of decreased consumption of angiotensinogen since it is not prevented by administration of renin (206). Furthermore, similar increases are seen after ureteral ligation (15, 206) and ureteral ligation with renal ischemia (17), situations in which renin secretion is increased. A common factor in these situations is uremia, but it seems unlikely that this is the cause of the increase in plasma angiotensinogen concentration since very little increase occurs following uretero–vena caval shunting (17). Another common feature is diminished glomerular filtration. However, it seems unlikely that the increase in plasma angiotensinogen is simply due to a failure of the kidneys to remove angiotensinogen since the mol wt (see above) is such that it would not be filtered.

Hasegawa and associates (80, 81) reported that blood from nephrectomized rats contains a factor that stimulates the release of angiotensinogen from slices of liver incubated in vitro; they suggested that this may be responsible for the increase in plasma angiotensinogen concentration after nephrectomy. The active material appeared to be a protein associated with both the γ_2-globulin and albumin fractions of the plasma. Beyond this, the identity of the factor was not established.

A possibility that should be considered is that the factor responsible for the increase in plasma angiotensinogen concentration after nephrectomy is an adrenal steroid. Surgical stress stimulates the secretion of adrenocortical steroids and the concentration of angiotensinogen in plasma increases for several days after sham operations in rabbits (35, 129, 178). A large proportion of the circulating corticosteroids is bound to plasma proteins including a globulin (corticosteroid-binding globulin) and albumin. Hasegawa et al (80) reported that the factor stimulating the production of angiotensinogen in their experiments was destroyed upon incubation with renin; however, the incubation mixture was dialyzed before its activity was tested and this procedure may have removed any steroids that were present.

Freeman & Rostorfer (61) presented evidence for the participation of the adrenals in the increase in the concentration of angiotensinogen in plasma after nephrectomy. They observed that the increased rate of release of angiotensinogen produced in rat liver slices by prior nephrectomy was reduced 70% by adrenalectomy. They also observed that the response could be mimicked by injecting the rats with cortisol and that both responses were abolished by treatment of the animals with actinomycin D. Carretero & Gross (37) also observed that the increase in plasma angiotensinogen after nephrectomy in adrenalectomized rats is smaller than in intact animals. On the other hand, Tateishi et al (206) observed normal increases in angiotensinogen after nephrectomy of adrenalectomized rats. Further investigation is required to resolve these differences. In the meantime, it seems reasonable to suggest that increased adrenocortical secretion does participate in the increase in plasma angiotensinogen concentration after nephrectomy but that another circulating factor(s) may also play a role.

OTHER FACTORS   Acute reduction of the concentration of angiotensinogen in the plasma of dogs by isovolemic, isoncotic hemodilution stimulates the release of angiotensinogen and this rapidly restores the concentration of angiotensinogen in plasma to control values within 5 hr (166). This response is reasonably specific for angiotensinogen since only a small increase in the total concentration of proteins in plasma occurs during the same period. The response is accompanied by an increase in the concentration of corticosteroids in plasma, and this may be a causative factor.

Plasma angiotensinogen concentration is also increased by hypoxia (15, 74). The mechanism underlying this response has not been elucidated; it may be due to increased secretion of adrenocortical steroids since it is known that hypoxia stimulates the secretion of ACTH (207).

SUMMARY   The regulation of the production of angiotensinogen is summarized in Figure 3. Angiotensinogen production is increased by glucocorticoids, angiotensin II, and estrogens. Glucocorticoids and angiotensin II are probably the most important physiological regulators, although estrogens are presumably responsible for the increase in plasma angiotensinogen

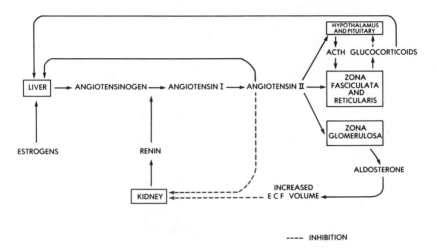

Figure 3   Summary of the known factors affecting the production of angiotensinogen and their possible interactions.

levels that occurs during pregnancy. The mechanisms responsible for the increases in plasma angiotensinogen concentration after nephrectomy, ureteral ligation, hemodilution, and hypoxia have not been elucidated. It has been proposed that an as yet unidentified factor increases the production of angiotensinogen after nephrectomy, but it seems likely that increased secretion of adrenocortical steroids plays an important role. Adrenocortical steroids may also mediate the increase in plasma angiotensinogen produced by ureteral ligation, hemodilution, and hypoxia.

Influence of Angiotensinogen Concentration on the Renin-Angiotensinogen Reaction

Several investigators have studied the effect of alterations in the concentration of angiotensinogen on the velocity of the renin-angiotensinogen reaction in vitro. Estimates of K_m are now available in a number of species. The values vary considerably within species as well as between species. This variation presumably reflects differences in methodology as well as the impurity of the renin and angiotensinogen preparations used. There is also some evidence for the existence of modifiers of the renin-angiotensinogen reaction (103, 197), and these would lead to erroneous estimates of the K_m. Some of the published values for K_m are summarized in Table 1. The normal concentrations of angiotensinogen in the plasma of these species are also shown in Table 1. These values are either approximately equal to or less than the corresponding K_m values and are therefore much less than the concentration required to produce the maximum reaction velocity. Thus the

Table 1 Concentrations of angiotensinogen in plasma and Michaelis constants (K_m) for the renin-angiotensinogen reaction of several species

Species	Plasma angiotensinogen concentration (μM)	$K_m{}^a$ (μM)	Reference
Human	1.0	3–8	193
	—	7.5–12.0	160
	—	2.8–4.1	182
	0.8	0.9	75
Sheep	0.4	2.0	193
Rat	0.3–0.5	—	38, 89, 137
	—	2.4	151
Rabbit	0.5–0.7	2.3	35

[a] For reaction with homologous angiotensinogen

increases in plasma angiotensinogen concentration that occur in Cushing's syndrome or pregnancy or with administration of glucocorticoids, estrogens, or oral contraceptives would be expected to significantly elevate the rate of formation of angiotensin. Conversely, the decreases in plasma angiotensinogen concentration that occur during adrenal insufficiency and in other situations would result in a slowing of the reaction. Indeed, Skinner et al (193) have suggested that the concentration of angiotensinogen may be as important as the concentration of renin in determining renin activity in plasma in vivo.

Little information is available concerning the physiological or pathological effects of alterations in plasma angiotensinogen concentration. It has been proposed that the normal response to an elevation in plasma angiotensinogen is suppression of renin secretion, so that the tendency for plasma renin activity to increase is minimized (143, 194). This appears to be the case in women taking oral contraceptives where plasma angiotensinogen concentration and plasma renin activity are elevated but plasma renin concentration is actually decreased (194). The exact mechanism responsible for the suppression of renin secretion is not known, but it could be due to the direct inhibitory action of angiotensin II on renin secretion or could be secondary to expansion of extracellular fluid volume (Figure 3). Failure to suppress renin secretion adequately would result in large increases in plasma renin activity; this may be an important factor in the hypertension occasionally associated with the use of oral contraceptives (143, 194). A recent report (200) that the antagonist [Sar^1, Ala^8] angiotensin II reduced blood pressure in rats made hypertensive by administration of estrogen-containing oral contraceptives is consistent with this proposal.

It seems reasonable to propose that when the normal feedback mechanisms controlling renin secretion become defective, a positive feedback loop between plasma angiotensin II and angiotensinogen production is initiated (see Figure 3). In such situations, the high plasma angiotensin II levels resulting from the increased renin secretion would stimulate the production of angiotensinogen; the high levels of angiotensinogen in plasma would lead to further increases in angiotensin II formation and so on. It is conceivable that such a mechanism contributes to the high levels of angiotensinogen in plasma in various high renin states including malignant and renal hypertension (75, 76, 179).

Less information is available concerning the effects of decreases in the concentration of angiotensinogen in plasma. Angiotensinogen levels are low in patients with cirrhosis of the liver (76) and following loss of liver weight after portacaval anastomosis (52). Blood pressure is decreased in these situations and it has been suggested that this is a consequence of decreased formation of angiotensin subsequent to the decrease in the concentration of angiotensinogen in plasma (52). Indeed, it has been hypothesized that the low angiotensinogen levels in cirrhotic patients are ultimately responsible for the development of the hepatorenal syndrome (14, 233). Few data are available to support or deny these speculations, and further investigation is required. However, it does seem safe to conclude that the concentration of angiotensinogen in plasma is a very important determinant of the activity of the renin-angiotensin system.

CONCLUSION

Our understanding of the physiology of the renin-angiotensin system has increased greatly during recent years. It is clear that the system is more complex than was originally envisioned, and that much additional investigation is required. We feel confident that the renin-angiotensin system will continue to be a fruitful area of research in years to come.

ACKNOWLEDGMENTS

Dr. Reid is the recipient of Research Career Development Award HL 00104. Dr. Morris is the recipient of a C. J. Martin Research Fellowship from the National Health and Medical Research Council of Australia.

Literature Cited

1. Alexandre, J. M., Menard, J., Chevillard, C., Schmitt, H. 1970. Increased plasma renin activity induced in rats by physostigmine and effects of alpha- and beta-receptor blocking drugs thereon. *Eur. J. Pharmacol.* 12:127–31
2. Allison, D. J., Tanigawa, H., Assaykeen, T. A. 1972. The effect of cyclic nucleotides on plasma renin activity and renal function in dogs. In *Control of Renin Secretion,* ed. T. A. Assaykeen, pp. 33–47. New York: Plenum. 290 pp.
3. Amery, A., Billiet, L., Fagard, R. 1974. Beta receptors and renin release. *N. Engl. J. Med.* 290:284
4. Amery, A., Lijnen, P., Fagard, R., Reybrouck, T. 1976. Plasma renin activity vs. concentration. *N. Engl. J. Med.* 295:1198–99
5. Assaykeen, T. A., Clayton, P. L., Goldfien, A., Ganong, W. F. 1970. Effect of alpha- and beta-adrenergic blocking agents on the renin response to hypoglycemia and epinephrine in dogs. *Endocrinology* 87:1318–22
6. Ayers, C. R., Harris, R. H., Lefer, L. G. 1969. Control of renin release in experimental hypertension. *Circ. Res.* 24–25 (Suppl. II):103–12
7. Banichahi, F., Capponi, A., Pricam, C., de Senardens, C. D., Vallotton, M. B. 1976. Control of renin secretion *in vivo* and *in vitro* in rats—arguments in favour of a precursor form of renin and of a role of microtubular system. *Clin. Sci. Mol. Med.* 51:93s–96s
8. Barajas, L., Müller, J. 1973. The innervation of the juxtaglomerular apparatus and surrounding tubules: A quantitative analysis by serial section electron microscopy. *J. Ultrastruct. Res.* 43: 107–32
9. Barbosa, J., Seal, U. S., Doe, R. P. 1973. Anti-estrogens and plasma proteins. II. Contraceptive drugs and gestagens. *J. Clin. Endocrinol. Metab.* 36:706–14
10. Beaty, O., Sloop, C. H., Schmid, H. E., Buckalew, V. M. 1976. Renin response and angiotensinogen control during graded hemorrhage and shock in the dog. *Am. J. Physiol.* 231:1300–1307
11. Bello-Reuss, E., Colindres, R. E., Pastoriza-Muñoz, E., Mueller, R. A., Gottschalk, C. W. 1975. Effects of acute unilateral renal denervation in the rat. *J. Clin. Invest.* 56:208–17
12. Bencsáth, P., Szalay, L., Debreczeni, L. A., Vajda, L., Takács, L., Fischer, A. 1972. Denervation diuresis and renin secretion in the anaesthetized dog. *Eur. J. Clin. Invest.* 2:422–25

13. Benraad, T. J., Kloppenborg, P. W. C. 1970. Plasma renin activity and aldosterone secretory rate in man during chronic ACTH administration. *J. Clin. Endocrinol. Metab.* 31:581–83
14. Berkowitz, H. D., Galvin, C., Miller, L. D. 1972. Significance of altered renin substrate in the hepatorenal syndrome. *Surg. Forum* 23:342–43
15. Bing, J., Poulsen, K. 1969. Experimentally induced changes in plasma angiotensinogen and plasma renin. *Acta Pathol. Microbiol. Scand.* 77:389–98
16. Birbari, A. 1971. Effect of sympathetic nervous system on renin release. *Am. J. Physiol.* 220:16–18
17. Blaine, E. H., Davis, J. O., Baumber, J. S. 1971. Plasma renin substrate changes in experimental uremia. *Proc. Soc. Exp. Biol. Med.* 136:21–24
18. Blair, M. L., Feigl, E. O., Smith, O. A. 1976. Elevation of plasma renin activity during avoidance performance in baboons. *Am. J. Physiol.* 231:772–76
19. Blair, M. L., Reid, I. A., Ganong, W. F. 1977. Effect of L-dopa on plasma renin activity with and without inhibition of extracerebral dopa decarboxylase in dogs. *J. Pharmacol. Exp. Ther.* 202: 209–15
20. Blair-West, J. R., Brook, A. H., Coghlan, J. P., Denton, D. A., Scoggins, B. A. 1974. Renin secretion and sodium metabolism. *Proc. Int. Congr. Nephrol., 5th, Mexico, 1972.* 2:193–98
21. Blair-West, J. R., Brook, A. H., Simpson, P. A. 1972. Renin responses to water restriction and rehydration. *J. Physiol. London* 226:1–13
22. Blair-West, J. R., Reid, I. A., Ganong, W. F. 1974. Stimulation of angiotensinogen release by raised blood angiotensin concentration in the dog. *Clin. Sci. Mol. Med.* 46:665–69
23. Boyd, G. W. 1972. The nature of renal renin. In *Hypertension 1972,* ed. J. Genest, E. Koiw, pp. 161–69. Berlin, Heidelberg, New York: Springer. 617 pp.
24. Boyd, G. W. 1973. Isolation of a binding protein for pig renin. *J. Physiol.* 232:22P–23P
25. Boyd, G. W. 1974. A protein-bound form of porcine renal renin. *Circ. Res.* 35:426–38
26. Boyd, G. W. 1977. An inactive higher-molecular-weight renin in normal subjects and hypertensive patients. *Lancet* i:215–18
27. Bozovic, L., Castenfors, J. 1967. Effect of dihydralazine on plasma renin activity and renal function during supine ex-

ercise in normal subjects. *Acta Physiol. Scand.* 70:281–89

28. Bozovic, L., Efendic, S., Rosenquist, U. 1969. The effect of ACTH on plasma renin activity. *Acta Endocrinol.* 138:123 (Abstr.)

29. Brown, J. J., Davies, D. L., Doak, P. B., Lever, A. F., Robertson, J. I. S., Tree, M. 1964. The presence of renin in human amniotic fluid. *Lancet* ii:64–66

30. Bühler, F. R., Laragh, J. H., Baer, L., Vaughan, E. D., Brunner, H. R. 1972. Propranolol inhibition of renin secretion. *N. Engl. J. Med.* 287:1209–14

31. Bunag, R. D., Page, I. H., McCubbin, J. W. 1966. Neural stimulation of release of renin. *Circ. Res.* 19:851–58

32. Bunag, R. D., Page, I. H., McCubbin, J. W. 1967. Inhibition of renin release by vasopressin and angiotensin. *Cardiovasc. Res.* 1:67–73

33. Cain, J. P., Williams, G. H., Dluhy, R. G. 1972. Plasma renin activity and aldosterone secretion in patients with acromegaly. *J. Clin. Endocrinol. Metab.* 34:73–81

34. Campbell, D. J., Skinner, S. L. 1975. Measurement of renin concentration in human plasma using ^{125}I-labelled sheep renin substrate. *Clin. Chim. Acta* 65:361–70

35. Campbell, D. J., Skinner, S. L., Day, A. J. 1973. Cellophane perinephritis hypertension and its reversal in rabbits. *Circ. Res.* 33:105–12

36. Capponi, A. M., Vallotton, M. B. 1976. Renin release by rat kidney slices incubated *in vitro.* Role of sodium and of α- and β-adrenergic receptors, and effect of vincristine. *Circ. Res.* 39:200–3

37. Carretero, O., Gross, F. 1967. Evidence for humoral factors participating in the renin-substrate reaction. *Circ. Res.* 20-21 (Suppl. II):115–26

38. Carretero, O., Gross, F. 1967. Renin substrate in plasma under various experimental conditions in the rat. *Am. J. Physiol.* 213:695–700

39. Clamage, D. M., Sanford, C. S., Vander, A. J., Mouw, D. R. 1976. Effects of psychosocial stimuli on plasma renin activity in rats. *Am. J. Physiol.* 231:1290–94

40. Claybaugh, J. R. 1976. Effect of dehydration on stimulation of ADH release by heterologous renin infusions in conscious dogs. *Am. J. Physiol.* 231:655–60

41. Coote, J. H., Johns, E. J., Macleod, V. H., Singer, B. 1972. Effect of renal nerve stimulation, renal blood flow and adrenergic blockade on plasma renin activity in the cat. *J. Physiol. London* 226:15–36

42. Crayton, S., Keeton, T. K., Pettinger, W. A. 1976. Clonidine suppression of renin release in the conscious dog. *Pharmacologist* 18:138 (Abstr.)

43. Davis, J. O. 1974. The renin-angiotensin system in the control of aldosterone secretion. In *Angiotensin*, ed. I. H. Page, F. M. Bumpus, pp. 322–36. Berlin, Heidelberg: Springer. 591 pp.

44. Davis, J. O., Freeman, R. H. 1976. Mechanisms regulating renin release. *Physiol. Rev.* 56:1–56

45. Day, R. P., Luetscher, J. A. 1974. Big renin: a possible prohormone in kidney and plasma of a patient with Wilms' tumor. *J. Clin. Endocrinol. Metab.* 38:923–26

46. Day, R. P., Luetscher, J. A. 1975. Biochemical properties of big renin extracted from human plasma. *J. Clin. Endocrinol. Metab.* 40:1085–93

47. Day, R. P., Luetscher, J. A., Gonzales, C. M. 1975. Occurrence of big renin in human plasma, amniotic fluid and kidney extracts. *J. Clin. Endocrinol. Metab.* 40:1078–84

48. Day, R. P., Luetscher, J. A., Zager, P. G. 1976. Big renin: identification, chemical properties and clinical implications. *Am. J. Cardiol.* 37:667–74

49. de Leiva, A., Christlieb, A. R., Melby, J. C., Graham, C. A., Day, R. P., Luetscher, J. A., Zager, P. G. 1976. Big renin and biosynthetic defect of aldosterone in diabetes mellitus. *N. Engl. J. Med.* 295:639–43

50. Derkx, F. H. M., van Gool, J. M. G., Wenting, G. J., Verhoeven, R. P., Man in t'Veld, A. J., Schalekamp, M. A. D. H. 1976. Inactive renin in human plasma. *Lancet* ii:496–99

51. Devynck, M.-A., Meyer, P. 1976. Angiotensin receptors in vascular tissue. *Am. J. Med.* 61:758–67

52. Edwards, K. D. G. 1976. Plasma renin substrate and blood pressure after portacaval anastomosis. *Med. J. Aust.* 2:581

53. Eggena, P., Barrett, J. D., Hidaka, H., Chu, C. L., Thananopavarn, C., Golub, M. S., Sambhi, M. P. 1977. A direct radioimmunoassay for human renin substrate and identification of multiple substrate types in plasma. *Circ. Res.* In press

54. Eggena, P., Chu, C. L., Barrett, J. D., Sambhi, M. P. 1976. Purification and partial characterization of human angiotensinogen. *Biochim. Biophys. Acta* 427:208–17

55. Eisenfeld, A. J., Aten, R., Weinberger, M., Haselbacher, G., Halpern, K., Krakoff, L. 1976. Estrogen receptor

in the mammalian liver. *Science* 191: 862–65

56. Erdos, E. G. 1977. The angiotensin I converting enzyme. *Fed. Proc.* 36: 1760–65

57. Esler, M. D., Nestel, P. J. 1973. Evaluation of practolol in hypertension. Effects on sympathetic nervous system and renin responsiveness. *Br. Heart J.* 35:469–74

58. Fernandez-Cruz, A., Noth, R. H., Heldler, R. G., Mulrow, P. J. 1975. Glucagon stimulation of plasma renin activity in humans. *J. Clin. Endocrinol. Metab.* 41:183–85

59. Frankel, R. J., Reid, I. A., Ganong, W. F. 1977. Role of central and peripheral mechanisms in the action of α-methyldopa on blood pressure and renin secretion. *J. Pharmacol. Exp. Ther.* 201: 400–5

60. Freeman, R. H., Davis, J. O., Lohmeier, T. E., Spielman, W. S. 1977. [Des-Asp¹] angiotensin II: mediator of the renin-angiotensin system? *Fed. Proc.* 36:1766–70

61. Freeman, R. H., Rostorfer, H. H. 1972. Hepatic changes in renin substrate biosynthesis and alkaline phosphatase activity in the rat. *Am. J. Physiol.* 223:364–70

62. Gann, D. S. 1969. Parameters of the stimulus initiating the adrenocortical response to hemorrhage. *Ann. NY Acad. Sci.* 156:740–55

63. Ganong, W. F. 1972. Sympathetic effects on renin secretion: mechanism and physiological role. See Ref. 2, pp. 17–32

64. Ganong, W. F. 1972. Effects of sympathetic activity and ACTH on renin and aldosterone secretion. See Ref. 23, pp. 4–14

65. Ganong, W. F. 1977. Neurotransmitters involved in ACTH secretion. *Ann. NY Acad. Sci.* In press

66. Ganong, W. F., Henderson, I. W., Otsuka, K., Assaykeen, T. A., Shackelford, R., Boryczka, A. T. 1974. Role of growth hormone in the regulation of adrenocortical responsiveness and aldosterone secretion in the dog. *Endocrinology* 94:A239 (Abstr.)

67. Ganong, W. F., Lopez, G. A. 1977. Control of the juxtaglomerular apparatus. *Excerpta Med. Sect.* In press

68. Ganong, W. F., Reid, I. A. 1976. Role of the sympathetic nervous system and central α- and β-adrenergic receptors in regulation of renin secretion. In *Regulation of Blood Pressure by the Central Nervous System*, ed. G. Onesti, M. Fer-

nandes, K. E. Kim, pp. 261–73. New York: Grune & Stratton. 484 pp.

69. Ganong, W. F., Wise, B. L., Reid, I. A., Holland, J., Kaplan, S., Shackelford, R., Boryczka, A. T. 1977. Effect of spinal cord transection on the endocrine and blood pressure responses to intravenous clonidine. *Neuroendocrinology.* In press

70. Ganten, D., Hutchinson, J. S., Schelling, P., Ganten, U., Fischer, H. 1976. The iso-renin angiotensin systems in extrarenal tissue. *Clin. Exp. Pharmacol. Physiol.* 3:103–26

71. Gibson, R. 1973. *Properties of renin in human amniotic fluid and foetal membranes.* M.Sc. Thesis. Univ. Melbourne, Australia.

72. Gill, J. R., Casper, A. G. T. 1972. Effect of renal alpha-adrenergic stimulation on proximal tubular sodium reabsorption. *Am. J. Physiol.* 223:1201–05

73. Goodwin, F. J., Kirshman, J. D., Sealey, J. E., Laragh, J. H. 1970. Influence of the pituitary gland on sodium conservation, plasma renin and renin substrate concentrations in the rat. *Endocrinology* 86:824–34

74. Gould, A. B., Goodman, S. A. 1970. The effect of hypoxia on the renin-angiotensinogen system. *Lab. Invest.* 22: 443–47

75. Gould, A. B., Green, D. 1971. Kinetics of the human renin and human substrate reaction. *Cardiovasc. Res.* 5:86–89

76. Gould, A. B., Skeggs, L. T., Kahn, J. R. 1966. Measurement of renin and substrate concentrations in human serum. *Lab. Invest.* 15:1802–13

77. Gutman, Y., Benzakein, F. 1974. Antidiuretic hormone and renin in rats with diabetes insipidus. *Eur. J. Pharmacol.* 28:114–18

78. Halushka, P. V., Keiser, H. R. 1974. Acute effects of alpha-methyldopa on mean blood pressure and plasma renin activity. *Circ. Res.* 35:458–63

79. Hasegawa, H., Nasjletti, A., Rice, K., Masson, G. M. C. 1973. Role of pituitary and adrenals in the regulation of plasma angiotensinogen. *Am. J. Physiol.* 225:1–6

80. Hasegawa, H., Shainoff, J. R., Lewis, L. A., Masson, G. M. C. 1976. Further evidence for the existence of angiotensinogen stimulating activity (ASA) after nephrectomy. *Proc. Soc. Exp. Biol. Med.* 153:37–43

81. Hasegawa, H., Tateishi, H., Masson, G. M. C. 1973. Evidence for an angiotensinogen-stimulating factor after ne-

phrectomy. *Can. J. Physiol. Pharmacol.* 51:563–66

82. Hauger-Klevene, J. H., Brown, H. 1970. Effect of pentolinium on ACTH stimulation of renin release. *Endocrinology* 87:430–31

83. Hauger-Klevene, J. H., Brown, H., Zavaleta, J. 1972. Plasma renin activity in hyper- and hypothyroidism: Effect of adrenergic blocking agents. *J. Clin. Endocrinol. Metab.* 34:625–29

84. Haynes, F. W., Forsham, P. H., Hume, D. M. 1953. Effects of ACTH, cortisone, desoxycorticosterone and epinephrine on the plasma hypertensinogen and renin concentration of dogs. *Am. J. Physiol.* 172:265–75

85. Helmer, O. M., Griffith, R. S. 1951. Biological activity of steroids as determined by assay of renin-substrate (hypertensinogen). *Endocrinology* 49:154–61

86. Henderson, I. W., Balment, R. J. 1975. Renal responses of the hypophysectomized rat to infusions of bovine growth hormone. *J. Endocrinol.* 67:60P (Abstr.)

87. Hirose, S., Matoba, T., Ingami, T. 1976. Enzymatic conversion of high molecular weight precursors of renin to the low molecular weight renin. *Circulation* 53–54 (Suppl. II):142 (Abstr.)

88. Hiwada, K., Kokubu, T., Yamamura, Y. 1976. Possible existence of prorenin in rabbit renal cortex. *Jpn. Circ. J.* 40:119–22

89. Hiwada, K., Tanaka, H., Kokubu, T. 1976. The influence of nephrectomy, ureteral ligation, and of estradiol on plasma renin substrate in unilaterally nephrectomized rats. *Pfluegers Arch.* 365:177–82

90. Hodge, R. L., Lowe, R. D., Ng, K. K. F., Vane, J. R. 1969. Role of the vagus nerve in the control of the concentration of angiotensin II in the circulation. *Nature* 221:177–79

91. Hodge, R. L., Lowe, R. D., Vane, J. R. 1966. Increased angiotensin formation in response to carotid occlusion in the dog. *Nature* 211:491–93

92. Horky, K., Rojo-Ortega, J. M., Rodriguez, J., Boucher, R., Genest, J. 1971. Renin, renin substrate, and angiotensin I—converting enzyme in the lymph of rats. *Am. J. Physiol.* 220:307–11

93. Imbs, J. L., Kraetz, J., Schmidt, M., Desaulles, E., Schwartz, J. 1975. Beta-blocking drugs and renin secretion in the anaesthetized dog. *Clin. Sci. Mol. Med.* 48:105S–107S

94. Inagami, T., Murakami, K. 1977. Purification of high molecular weight forms of renin from hog kidney. *Circ. Res.* In press

95. James, S. K., Hall, R. C. 1974. The nature of renin released in the dog following haemorrhage and frusemide. *Pfluegers Arch.* 347:323–28

96. Johns, E. J., Richards, H. K., Singer, B. 1975. Effects of adrenaline, noradrenaline, isoprenaline and salbutamol on the production and release of renin by isolated renal cortical cells of the cat. *Br. J. Pharmacol.* 53:67–73

97. Johns, E. J., Singer, B. 1974. Comparison of the effects of propranolol and ICI 66082 in blocking the renin releasing effect of renal nerve stimulation in the cat. *Br. J. Pharmacol.* 52:315–18

98. Johns, E. J., Singer, B. 1974. Specificity of blockade of renal renin release by propranolol in the cat. *Clin. Sci. Mol. Med.* 47:331–43

99. Johnson, J. A., Davis, J. O., Witty, R. T. 1971. Effects of catecholamines and renal nerve stimulation on renin release in the nonfiltering kidney. *Circ. Res.* 29:646–53

100. Kaplan, N. M. 1965. The biosynthesis of adrenal steroids: Effects of angiotensin II, adrenocorticotropin, and potassium. *J. Clin. Invest.* 44:2029–39

101. Katz, F. H., Kappas, A. 1967. The effects of estradiol and estriol on plasma levels of cortisol and thyroid hormone-binding globulins and on aldosterone and cortisol secretion rates in man. *J. Clin. Invest.* 46:1768–77

102. Khayyall, M., MacGregor, J., Brown, J. J., Lever, A. F., Robertson, J. I. S. 1973. Increase of plasma renin-substrate concentration after infusion of angiotensin in the rat. *Clin. Sci.* 44:87–90

103. Kotchen, T. A., Rice, T. W., Walters, D. R. 1972. Renin reactivity in normal, hypertensive, and uremic plasma. *J. Clin. Endocrinol. Metab.* 34:928–37

104. Krakoff, L. R. 1973. Measurement of plasma renin substrate by radioimmunoassay of angiotensin I: Concentration in syndromes associated with steroid excess. *J. Clin. Endocrinol. Metab.* 37:110–17

105. La Grange, R. G., Sloop, C. H., Schmid, H. E. 1973. Selective stimulation of renal nerves in the anesthetized dog. *Circ. Res.* 33:704–12

106. Lands, A. M., Arnold, A., McAuliff, J. P., Luduena, F. P., Brown, T. G. 1967. Differentiation of receptor systems activated by sympathomimetic amines. *Nature* 214:597–98

107. Lauritzen, M., Damsgaard, J. J., Rubin, I., Lauritzen, E. 1976. A comparison of the properties of renin isolated from pig and rat kidney. *Biochem. J.* 155:317–23

108. Leckie, B. 1973. The activation of a possible zymogen of renin in rabbit kidney. *Clin. Sci.* 44:301–4

109. Leckie, B. J., McConnell, A. 1975. A renin inhibitor from rabbit kidney. Conversion of a large inactive renin to a smaller active enzyme. *Circ. Res.* 36:513–19

110. Leckie, B., McConnell, A. 1975. Acid-activation of renin in human kidney extracts and plasma. *Acta Endocrinol.* 199 (Suppl.):280 (Abstr.)

111. Leckie, B., McConnell, A. 1976. Active and inactive renin in normal subjects, anephric patients and pregnant women. *J. Endocrinol.* 71:75P (Abstr.)

112. Leenen, F. H., Shapiro, A. P. 1974. Effect of intermittent electric shock on plasma renin activity in rats. *Proc. Soc. Exp. Biol. Med.* 146:534–38

113. Levine, M., Lentz, K. E., Kahn, J. R., Dorer, F. E., Skeggs, L. T. 1976. Partial purification of a high molecular weight renin from hog kidney. *Circ. Res.* 38 (Suppl. II):90–94

114. Lifschitz, M. D., Keller, D., Goldfien, A., Schrier, R. W. 1973. Mechanism of renal clearance of isoproterenol. *Am. J. Physiol.* 224:733–36

115. Loeffler, J. R., Stockigt, J. R., Ganong, W. F. 1972. Effect of alpha- and beta-adrenergic blocking agents on the increase in renin secretion produced by stimulation of the renal nerves. *Neuroendocrinology* 10:129–38

116. Lokhandwala, M. F., Asaad, M. M., Buckley, J. P. 1976. Effect of propranolol on vascular responses to sympathetic nerve stimulation and plasma renin activity in mongrel dogs. *Eur. J. Pharmacol.* 38:141–47

117. Lumbers, E. R. 1969. *The quantitation and significance of renin in biological fluids.* M.D. thesis. Univ. of Adelaide, Australia.

118. Lumbers, E. R. 1970. Activation of renin in amniotic fluid by low pH treatment. *Proc. Aust. Physiol. Pharmacol. Soc.* 1:25 (Abstr.)

119. Lumbers, E. R. 1971. Activation of renin in human amniotic fluid by low pH. *Enzymologia* 40:329–36

120. Mancia, G., Romero, J. C., Shepherd, J. T. 1975. Continuous inhibition of renin release in dogs by vagally innervated receptors in the cardiopulmonary region. *Circ. Res.* 36:529–35

121. Maran, J. W., Yates, F. E. 1974. Locus of ACTH-releasing action of angiotensin II. *Endocrinology* 94:A118 (Abstr.)

122. McPhee, M. S., Lakey, W. H. 1971. Neurologic release of renin in mongrel dogs. *Can. J. Surg.* 14:142–47

123. Michelakis, A. M., Caudle, J., Liddle, G. W. 1969. *In vitro* stimulation of renin production by epinephrine, norepinephrine, and cyclic AMP. *Proc. Soc. Exp. Biol. Med.* 130:748–53

124. Misono, K., Whorton, R. A., Inagami, T., Hollifield, J. W. 1976. Renin release (RR) from renal cortical slices: effect of isoproterenol (IP), angiotensin II (AII) and molecular characterization of renin released. *Endocrinology* 98:A345 (Abstr.)

125. Mohammed, S., Fasola, A. F., Priviter a, P. J., Lipicky, R. J., Martz, B. L., Gaffney, T. E. 1969. Effect of methyldopa on plasma renin activity in man. *Circ. Res.* 25:543–48

126. Molzahn, M., Dissmann, T. H., Halim, S., Lohmann, F. W., Oelkers, W. 1972. Orthostatic changes of haemodynamics, renal function, plasma catecholamines and plasma renin concentration in normal and hypertensive man. *Clin. Sci.* 42:209–22

127. Morgan, T. O., Roberts, R., Carney, S. L., Louis, W. J., Doyle, A. E. 1975. Beta-adrenergic receptor blocking drugs, hypertension and plasma renin. *Br. J. Clin. Pharmacol.* 2:159–64

128. Morimoto, S., Hasatani, K., Uchida, K., Takeda, R. 1975. Influence of adrenal enucleation on plasma renin substrate concentration in saline loaded and unilaterally nephroadrenalectomized rats. *Endocrinology* 96:1314–19

128a. Morris, B. J. 1978. Activation of human inactive ('pro-')renin by cathepsin D and pepsin. *J. Clin. Endocrinol. Metab.* In press

129. Morris, B. J., Davis, J. O., Zatzman, M. L., Williams, G. M. 1977. The renin-angiotensin-aldosterone system in rabbits with congestive heart failure produced by aortic constriction. *Circ. Res.* 40:275–82

130. Morris, B. J., Johnston, C. I. 1976. Renin substrate in granules from rat kidney cortex. *Biochem. J.* 154:625–37

131. Morris, B. J., Johnston, C. I. 1976. Isolation of renin granules from rat kidney cortex and evidence for an inactive form of renin (prorenin) in granules and plasma. *Endocrinology* 98:1466–74

132. Morris, B. J., Lumbers, E. R. 1971. The mechanism of activation of renin in hu-

man amniotic fluid. *Proc. Aust. Physiol. Pharmacol. Soc.* 2:65–66

133. Morris, B. J., Lumbers, E. R. 1972. The activation of renin in human amniotic fluid by proteolytic enzymes. *Biochim. Biophys. Acta* 289:385–91

134. Morris, B. J., Nixon, R. L., Johnston, C. I. 1976. Release of renin from glomeruli isolated from rat kidney. *Clin. Exp. Pharmacol. Physiol.* 3:37–47

135. Mouw, D. R., Abraham, S. F., Blair-West, J. R., Coghlan, J. P., Denton, D. A., McKenzie, J. S., McKinley, M. J., Scoggins, B. A. 1974. Brain receptors, renin secretion, and renal sodium retention in conscious sheep. *Am. J. Physiol.* 226:56–62

136. Mouw, D. R., Vander, A. J. 1970. Evidence for brain Na receptors controlling renal Na excretion and plasma renin activity. *Am. J. Physiol.* 219:822–32

137. Nasjletti, A., Masson, G. M. C. 1969. Effects of corticosteroids on plasma angiotensinogen and renin activity. *Am. J. Physiol.* 217:1396–1400

138. Nasjletti, A., Masson, G. M. C. 1971. Hepatic origin of renin substrate. *Can. J. Physiol. Pharmacol.* 49:931–32

139. Nasjletti, A., Masson, G. M. C. 1972. Studies on angiotensinogen formation in a liver perfusion system. *Circ. Res.* 30-31 (Suppl. II):187–202

140. Nasjletti, A., Masson, G. M. C. 1973. Stimulation of angiotensinogen formation by renin and angiotensin. *Proc. Soc. Exp. Biol. Med.* 142:307–10

141. Nasjletti, A., Matsunaga, M., Masson, G. M. C. 1971. Effects of sex hormones on the renal pressor system. *Can. J. Physiol. Pharmacol.* 49:292–301

142. Nasjletti, A., Matsunaga, M., Tateishi, H., Masson, G. M. C. 1971. Effects of stilbestrol on the renal pressor system as modified by adrenalectomy and secondary aldosteronism. *J. Lab. Clin. Med.* 78:30–38

143. Newton, M. A., Sealey, J. E., Ledingham, J. G. G., Laragh, J. H. 1968. High blood pressure and oral contraceptives. *Am. J. Obstet. Gynecol.* 101:1037–45

144. Nolan, P. L., Reid, I. A. 1977. Mechanism of suppression of renin secretion by clonidine. *Fed. Proc.* 36:459 (Abstr.)

145. Nolan, P. L., Reid, I. A. 1977. Inhibition of renin release by α-adrenergic stimulation. *Ann. Meet. Soc. for Neurosci., 7th.* In press (Abstr.)

146. Nolly, H. L., Reid, I. A., Ganong, W. F. 1974. Effect of theophylline and adrenergic blocking drugs on the renin response to norepinephrine *in vitro. Circ. Res.* 35:575–79

147. Nomura, G., Kurosaki, M., Takabatake, T., Kibe, Y., Takeuchi, J. 1972. Reinnervation and renin release after unilateral renal denervation in the dog. *J. Appl. Physiol.* 33:649–55

148. O'Malley, K., Velasco, M., Wells, J., McNay, J. L. 1975. Control plasma renin activity and changes in sympathetic tone as determinants of minoxidil-induced increase in plasma renin activity. *J. Clin. Invest.* 55:230–35

149. Onesti, G., Schwartz, A. B., Kim, K. E., Paz-Martinez, V., Swartz, C. 1971. Antihypertensive effect of clonidine. *Circ. Res.* 28–29 (Suppl. II):53–69

150. Oparil, S., Vassaux, C., Sanders, C. A., Haber, E. 1970. Role of renin in acute postural homeostasis. *Circulation* 41:89–95

151. Orth, H., Krahe, P., Steigelmann, C., Gross, F. 1971. An improved method for the determination of renin in rat kidneys. *Pfluegers Arch.* 329:125–35

152. Otsuka, K., Assaykeen, T. A., Goldfien, A., Ganong, W. F. 1970. Effect of hypoglycemia on plasma renin activity in dogs. *Endocrinology* 87:1306–17

153. Overturf, M. L., Kirkendall, W. M. Renin-angiotensin-aldosterone system. In *Prostaglandins and Cardiovascular Function,* ed. S. Greenburg, P. S. Kadowitz, T. A. Burk. New York: Dekker. In press

154. Overturf, M., Leonard, M., Kirkendall, W. M. 1974. Purification of human renin and inhibition of its activity by pepstatin. *Biochem. Pharmacol.* 23:671–83

155. Passo, S. S., Assaykeen, T. A., Goldfien, A., Ganong, W. F. 1971. Effect of α- and β-adrenergic blocking agents on the increase in renin secretion produced by stimulation of the medulla oblongata in dogs. *Neuroendocrinology* 7:97–104

156. Passo, S. S., Assaykeen, T. A., Otsuka, K., Wise, B. L., Goldfien, A., Ganong, W. F. 1971. Effect of stimulation of the medulla oblongata on renin secretion in dogs. *Neuroendocrinology* 7:1–10

157. Pettinger, W. A., Keeton, K. 1975. Altered renin release and propranolol potentiation of vasodilatory drug hypotension. *J. Clin. Invest.* 55:236–43

158. Pettinger, W. A., Tanaka, K., Keeton, K., Campbell, W. B., Brooks, S. N. 1975. Renin release, an artifact of anesthesia and its implications in rats. *Proc. Soc. Exp. Biol. Med.* 148:625–30

159. Peytremann, A., Favre, L., Vallotton, M. B. 1972. Effect of cold pressure test and 2-deoxy-D-glucose infusion on plasma renin activity in man. *Eur. J. Clin. Invest.* 2:432–38

160. Printz, M. P., Printz, J. M., Dworschack, R. T. 1977. Human angiotensinogen. Purification, partial characterization, and a comparison with animal prohormones. *J. Biol. Chem.* 252: 1654–62

161. Privitera, P. J., Mohammed, S. 1972. Studies on the mechanism of renin suppression by alpha methyldopa. See Ref. 2, pp. 93–101

162. Privitera, P. J., Walle, T., Knapp, D. R., Gaffney, T. E. 1976. Central renin suppressing action of propranolol. See Ref. 68, pp. 443–50

163. Rayyis, S. S., Horton, R. 1971. Effect of angiotensin II on adrenal and pituitary function in man. *J. Clin. Endocrinol. Metab.* 32:539–46

164. Reid, I. A. 1977. Effect of angiotensin II and glucocorticoids on plasma angiotensinogen concentration in the dog. *Am. J. Physiol.* 232:E234–E236

165. Reid, I. A. 1977. Is there a brain renin-angiotensin system? *Circ. Res.* 41: 147–53

166. Reid, I. A., Blair-West, J. R., Ganong, W. F. 1974. Stimulation of angiotensinogen release by hemodilution in the dog. *Endocrinology* 95:1482–85

167. Reid, I. A., Jones, A. 1976. Effects of carotid occlusion and clonidine on renin secretion in anaesthetized dogs. *Clin. Sci. Mol. Med.* 51:109s–111s

168. Reid, I. A., MacDonald, D. M., Pachnis, B., Ganong, W. F. 1975. Studies concerning the mechanism of suppression of renin secretion by clonidine. *J. Pharmacol. Exp. Ther.* 192:713–21

169. Reid, I. A., Ramsay, D. J. 1975. The effects of intracerebroventricular administration of renin on drinking and blood pressure. *Endocrinology* 97: 536–42

170. Reid, I. A., Schrier, R. W., Earley, L. E. 1972. An effect of extrarenal beta-adrenergic stimulation on the release of renin. *J. Clin. Invest.* 51:1861–69

171. Reid, I. A., Schrier, R. W., Earley, L. E. 1972. Effect of beta-adrenergic stimulation on renin release. See Ref. 2, pp. 49–64

172. Reid, I. A., Stockigt, J. R., Goldfien, A., Ganong, W. F. 1972. Stimulation of renin secretion in dogs by theophylline. *Eur. J. Pharmacol.* 17:325–32

173. Reid, I. A., Tu, W. H., Otsuka, K., Assaykeen, T. A., Ganong, W. F. 1973. Studies concerning the regulation and importance of plasma angiotensinogen concentration in the dog. *Endocrinology* 93:107–14

174. Richardson, D., Stella, A., Leonetti, G.,

Bartorelli, A., Zanchetti, A. 1974. Mechanisms of renal release of renin by electrical stimulation of the brain stem in the cat. *Circ. Res.* 34:425–34

175. Riedel, B., Bucher, O., Peters-Haefeli, L., Baechtold-Fowler, N., Peters, G. 1974. The replenishment of the juxtaglomerular renin store after temporary renin depletion. An electron-microscopic and functional study. *Pfluegers Arch.* 347:125–35

176. Robison, G. A., Butcher, R. W., Sutherland, E. W. 1971. *Cyclic AMP,* p. 232. New York: Academic. 531 pp.

177. Robison, G. A., Sutherland, E. W. 1970. Sympathin E, sympathin I, and the intracellular level of cyclic AMP. *Circ. Res.* 26–27 (Suppl. I):147–61

178. Romero, J. C., Lazar, J. D., Hoobler, S. W. 1970. Effects of renal artery constriction and subsequent contralateral nephrectomy on the blood pressure, plasma renin activity, and plasma renin substrate concentration in rabbits. *Lab. Invest.* 22:581–87

179. Rosset, E., Scherrer, J. R., Veyrat, R. 1973. Increased plasma renin substrate concentrations in human malignant hypertension. *Clin. Sci. Mol. Med.* 45: 291s–294s

180. Rosset, E., Veyrat, R. 1971. Effect of vasopressin (ADH), aldosterone, norepinephrine (NE), angiotensin I (AI) and II (AII) on renin release (RR) by human kidney (HK) slices *in vitro. Acta Endocrinol.* 155:179 (Abstr.)

181. Rubin, I. 1972. Purification of hog renin. Properties of purified hog renin. *Scand. J. Clin. Lab. Invest.* 29:51–58

182. Schioler, V., Nielsen, M. D., Kappelgaard, A. M., Giese, J. 1976. Partial purification of human renin substrate. *Eur. J. Clin. Invest.* 6:229–40

183. Schrier, R. W., Lieberman, R., Ufferman, R. C. 1972. Mechanism of antidiuretic effect of beta adrenergic stimulation. *J. Clin. Invest.* 51:219–27

184. Schrier, R. W., Reid, I. A., Berl, T., Earley, L. E. 1975. Mechanism of suppression of renin secretion by cervical vagotomy. *Clin. Sci. Mol. Med.* 48: 83–89

185. Sealey, J. E., Laragh, J. H. 1975. "Prorenin" in human plasma? Methodological and physiological implications. *Circ. Res.* 36–37 (Suppl. I):10–16

186. Sealey, J. E., Moon, C., Laragh, J. H., Alderman, M. 1976. Plasma prorenin: cryoactivation and relationship to renin substrate in normal subjects. *Am. J. Med.* 61:731–38

187. Severs, W. B., Daniels-Severs, A. E.

1973. Effects of angiotensin on the central nervous system. *Pharmacol. Rev.* 25:415–49
188. Severs, W. B., Summy-Long, J. 1975. The role of angiotensin in thirst. *Life Sci.* 17:1513–26
189. Shade, R. E., Davis, J. O., Johnson, J. A., Gotshall, R. W., Spielman, W. S. 1973. Mechanism of action of angiotensin II and antidiuretic hormone on renin secretion. *Am. J. Physio.* 224:926–29
190. Skeggs, L. T., Lentz, K. E., Hochstrasser, H., Kahn, J. R. 1963. The purification and partial characterization of several forms of hog renin substrate. *J. Exp. Med.* 118:73–98
191. Skeggs, L. T., Lentz, K. E., Kahn, J. R., Hochstrasser, H. 1967. Studies on the preparation and properties of renin. *Circ. Res.* 20–21 (Suppl. II):91–100
192. Skinner, S. L., Cran, E. J., Gibson, R., Taylor, R., Walters, W. A. W., Catt, K. J. 1975. Angiotensins I and II, active and inactive renin, renin substrate, renin activity, and angiotensinase in human liquor amnii and plasma. *Am. J. Obstet. Gynecol.* 121:626–30
193. Skinner, S. L., Dunn, J. R., Mazzetti, J., Campbell, D. J., Fidge, N. H. 1975. Purification, properties and kinetics of sheep and human renin substrates. *Aust. J. Exp. Biol. Med. Sci.* 53:77–88
194. Skinner, S. L., Lumbers, E. R., Symonds, E. M. 1969. Alteration by oral contraceptives of normal menstrual changes in plasma renin activity, concentration and substrate. *Clin. Sci.* 36:67–76
195. Skinner, S. L., Lumbers, E. R., Symonds, E. M. 1972. Analysis of changes in the renin-angiotensin system during pregnancy. *Clin. Sci.* 42:479–88
196. Slater, E. E., Haber, E. 1976. A large form of renin from normal human kidney. *Circulation* 53–54 (Suppl. II):143 (Abstr.)
197. Smeby, R. R., Bumpus, F. M. 1971. In *Kidney Hormones*, ed. J. W. Fisher, pp. 207–16. London: Academic. 665 pp.
198. Soffer, R. L. 1976. Angiotensin-converting enzyme and the regulation of vasoactive peptides. *Ann. Rev. Biochem.* 45:73–94
199. Starke, K., Endo, T. 1976. Presynaptic α-adrenoceptors. *Gen. Pharmacol.* 7:307–12
200. Stubbs, D. H., Johnson, J. A., Keitzer, W. F. 1976. Effect of 1-sarcosine-8-alanine angiotensin II on arterial pressure in oral contraceptive–induced hypertension in rats. *Fed. Proc.* 35:398 (Abstr.)
201. Tagawa, H., Vander, A. J. 1970. Effects of adenosine compounds on renal function and renin secretion in dogs. *Circ. Res.* 26:327–38
202. Tager, H. S., Steiner, D. F. 1974. Peptide hormones. *Ann. Rev. Biochem.* 43:509–38
203. Taher, M. S., McLain, L. G., McDonald, K. M., Schrier, R. W. 1976. Effect of beta-adrenergic blockade on renin response to renal nerve stimulation. *J. Clin. Invest.* 57:459–65
204. Tanigawa, H., Dua, S. L., Assaykeen, T. A. 1974. Effect of renal and adrenal denervation on the renin response to slow haemorrhage in dogs. *Clin. Exp. Pharmacol. Physiol.* 1:325–32
205. Tateishi, H., Masson, G. M. C. 1972. Role of the liver in the regulation of plasma angiotensinogen and renin levels. *Proc. Soc. Exp. Biol. Med.* 139:304–9
206. Tateishi, H., Nasjletti, A., Masson, G. M. C. 1971. Role of renin in the regulation of angiotensinogen levels in plasma. *Proc. Soc. Exp. Biol. Med.* 137:1424–28
207. Tepperman, J. 1973. *Metabolic and Endocrine Physiology*, p. 139. Chicago: Yearb. Med. 246 pp. 3rd ed.
208. Tewksbury, D. A., Premeau, M. R., Dumas, M. L. 1976. Isolation of human angiotensinogen. *Biochim. Biophys. Acta* 446:87–95
209. Thurau, K. W. C., Dahlheim, H., Gruner, A., Mason, J., Granger, P. 1972. Activation of renin in the single juxtaglomerular apparatus by sodium chloride in the tubular fluid at the macula densa. *Circ. Res.* 30–31 (Suppl. II):182–86
210. Tobert, J. A., Slater, J. D. H., Fogelman, F., Lightman, S. L., Kurtz, A. B., Payne, N. N. 1973. The effect in man of (+)-propranolol and racemic propranolol on renin secretion stimulated by orthostatic stress. *Clin. Sci.* 44:291–95
211. Türker, R. K., Page, I. H., Bumpus, F. M. 1974. Antagonists of angiotensin II. See Ref. 43 pp. 162–69
212. Ueda, H., Yasuda, H., Takabatake, Y., Iizuka, M., Iizuka, T., and Ihori, M., Sakamoto, Y. 1970. Observations on the mechanism of renin release by catecholamines. *Circ. Res.* 26–27 (Suppl. II):195–200
213. Ueda, H., Yasuda, H., Takabatake, Y., Iizuka, M., Iizuka, T., Ihori, M.,

Yamamoto, M., Sakamoto, Y. 1967. Increased renin release evoked by mesencephalic stimulation in the dog. *Jpn. Heart J.* 8:498–506

214. Vander, A. J. 1965. Effect of catecholamines and the renal nerves on renin secretion in anesthetized dogs. *Am. J. Physiol.* 209:659–62

215. Vander, A. J. 1968. Inhibition of renin release in the dog by vasopressin and vasotocin. *Circ. Res.* 23:605–9

216. Vander, A. J. 1976. Discussion. In *The Nervous System in Arterial Hypertension,* ed. S. Julius, M. D. Esler, pp. 201–2. Springfield, Ill: Thomas. 476 pp.

217. Vandongen, R., Greenwood, D. M. 1975. The inhibition of renin secretion in the isolated rat kidney by clonidine hydrochloride (Catapres). *Clin. Exp. Pharmacol. Physiol.* 2:583–88

218. Vandongen, R., Peart, W. S., Boyd, G. W. 1973. Adrenergic stimulation of renin secretion in the isolated perfused rat kidney. *Circ. Res.* 32:290–96

219. Wagermark, J., Ungerstedt, U., Ljungqvist, A. 1968. Sympathetic innervation of the juxtaglomerular cells of the kidney. *Circ. Res.* 22:149–53

220. Wathen, R. L., Kingsbury, W. S., Stouder, D. A., Schneider, E. G., Rostorfer, H. H. 1965. Effects of infusion of catecholamines and angiotensin II on renin release in anesthetized dogs. *Am. J. Physiol.* 209:1012–24

221. Weber, M. A., Stokes, G. S., Gain, J. M. 1974. Comparison of the effects on renin release of beta-adrenergic antagonists with differing properties. *J. Clin. Invest.* 54:1413–19

222. Weber, P., Held, E., Uhlich, E., Eigler, J. O. C. 1975. Reaction constants of renin in juxtaglomerular apparatus and plasma renin activity after renal ischemia and hemorrhage. *Kidney Int.* 7:331–41

223. Weigand, K., Wernze, H., Falge, C. 1977. Synthesis of angiotensinogen by isolated rat liver cells and its regulation in comparison to serum albumin. *Biochem. Biophys. Res. Commun.* 75:102–10

224. Weinberger, M. H., Aoi, W., Henry, D. P. 1975. Direct effect of beta-adrenergic stimulation on renin release by the rat kidney slice *in vitro. Circ. Res.* 37:318–24

225. Weir, R. J., Brown, J. J., Fraser, R., Lever, A. F., Logan, R. W., McIlwaine, G. M., Morton, J. J., Robertson, J. I. S., Tree, M. 1975. Relationship between plasma renin, renin-substrate, angiotensin II, aldosterone and electrolytes in normal pregnancy. *J. Clin. Endocrinol. Metab.* 40:108–15

226. Yalow, R. S. 1974. Heterogeneity of peptide hormones. *Rec. Prog. Horm. Res.* 30:597–633

227. Young, L. D., Langford, H. G., Blanchard, E. G. 1976. Effect of operant conditioning of heart rate on plasma renin activity. *Psychosom. Med.* 38:278–81

228. Zambraski, E. J., Dibona, G. F., Kaloyanides, G. J. 1976. Effect of sympathetic blocking agents on the antinatriuresis of reflex renal nerve stimulation. *J. Pharmacol. Exp. Ther.* 198:464–72

229. Zanchetti, A., Stella, A. 1975. Neural control of renin release. *Clin. Sci. Mol. Med.* 48:215s–223s

230. Zanchetti, A., Stella, A., Leonetti, G., Morganti, A., Terzoli, L. 1976. Control of renin release: A review of experimental evidence and clinical implications. *Am. J. Cardiol.* 37:675–91

231. Zehr, J. E., Feigl, E. O. 1973. Suppression of renin activity by hypothalamic stimulation. *Circ. Res.* 32–33 (Suppl. I):17–26

232. Zehr, J. E., Hasbargen, J. A., Kurz, K. D. 1976. Reflex suppression of renin secretion during distention of cardiopulmonary receptors in dogs. *Circ. Res.* 38:232–39

233. Zeigler, T. W. 1976. Hepatorenal syndrome: A disease mediated by the intrarenal action of renin. *Med. Hypotheses* 2:15–21

Ann. Rev. Physiol. 1978. 40:411–45
Copyright © 1978 by Annual Reviews Inc. All rights reserved

ENDOCRINE MECHANISMS OF PARTURITION

❖1197

Peter W. Nathanielsz

Physiological Laboratory, Cambridge University,
Cambridge, England, CB2 3EG

INTRODUCTION

Intrauterine growth and development follow an orderly sequence of critical phases that influence the several organ systems of the fetus differently at various times. Thus, placental growth and differentiation precede major growth of the fetus. The fetus develops in utero until capable of an independent existence outside the uterus. In some mammals, for example the goat, cow, rat, and rabbit, progesterone production by the corpus luteum (CL) of pregnancy continues throughout gestation (51, 61, 82–84, 193, 194, 195, 196). In other species, the placenta gradually takes over this role (12, 25, 37, 83, 84, 118, 119, 127, 152, 208). Estrogens are also produced by the ovary and placenta during gestation (4, 11, 25, 31, 38, 53, 84, 119, 120, 136, 156, 169). In the primate species the fetal and maternal adrenals provide precursors for placental estrogen synthesis (87, 164, 169, 175). Other hormones, such as placental lactogen (PL) (chorionic somatomammotrophin) and chorionic gonadotrophin are necessary for normal maternal, placental, and fetal metabolism (51, 88, 90, 120, 201). PL is produced by the syncytiotrophoblast of the placenta and is a hormone of fetal origin. Thus, both fetal and maternal endocrine factors are of importance in the mechanisms that maintain the pregnant state. The process of parturiton also involves fetal and maternal factors whose role is to remove or supplant these maintenance mechanisms.

Variations in the Degree of Fetal Maturation at Birth

Although the mammalian neonate is capable of an independent extrauterine existence, the degree of competence of neonatal physiological systems

411

0066-4278/78/0301-0411$01.00

differs considerably among species. Many of the endocrine homeostatic mechanisms required in the immediate postnatal period develop in utero and are capable of homeostatic function. For example, the fetal sheep's pituitary-adrenal axis responds to both hypoxia and hemorrhage (6, 22). Species differences in the degree of endocrine development at birth suggest that fetal endocrine involvement at the time of delivery may also differ. The general development and competence of fetal endocrine systems have been reviewed in detail elsewhere (37, 147).

Mean litter size varies considerably among species. Species that usually produce one fetus are termed monotocous. Other species have several fetuses in each litter and are termed polytocous. In general, the young of polytocous species are delivered in an immature state after a relatively short gestation. There are exceptions; in the sow, gestation lasts 114 days. The endocrine mechanisms involved in both the maintenance of pregnancy and parturition differ in polytocous and monotocous species. However, progesterone and estrogen, as well as placental protein hormones, are involved in the maintenance of pregnancy and normal fetal growth and development in both monotocous and polytocous species. There are examples of both polytocous species (the rat and rabbit) and monotocous species (the goat and cow) in which the CL survives and is functional throughout gestation (27, 83, 84). In some monotocous species (sheep and primates) and some polytocous species (guinea pig), the placenta takes over the role of progesterone production as gestation proceeds (25, 83, 84, 119, 120). From the endocrinological viewpoint, polytocous and monotocous species are clearly not completely separate groups. This review examines both fetal and maternal endocrine mechanisms that terminate the pregnant state; it emphasizes both the significant physiological differences among species and the mechanisms they have in common.

SOURCES OF EXPERIMENTAL OBSERVATIONS

Investigation of the endocrinology of parturition requires a detailed study of both mother and fetus. In vitro studies of tissue removed from maternal endocrine organs, the placenta, and fetal endocrine glands have yielded much useful information. However, in vitro systems can only suggest what may happen in utero. They need confirmation from in vivo techniques. The availability of essential precursors may be a limiting factor in vitro but not in vivo. Tissues generally lose some of their responsiveness when studied in vitro. Therefore, in vitro investigations suffer from the need to use hormone concentrations in the medium that are often several orders of magnitude greater than those that exist in utero (134). In vitro investigations are susceptible to many other possible pitfalls. For example, they cannot reproduce the results of changes in blood flow or vascular and tissue permeability that occur during pregnancy and at parturition (81, 184, 204). Detailed electron microscopy of the sheep placenta at delivery has demonstrated a disintegration of the feto-maternal villous junction that certainly affects permeability (184). These ultrastructural changes in the placenta may be under fetal endocrine control (14, 15). In vivo, fetal tissues are exposed to blood gas tensions considerably different from those present in the adult. The fetal vascular shunts (the ductus arteriosus, foramen ovale, and ductus venosus) produce different pH and blood gas tensions in various regions of the fetal circulation. It has been demonstrated that the in vitro activity of certain important enzyme systems [for example, tyrosine hydroxylase (54)] is dependent on P_{O_2}; more attention should be paid to the conditions prevailing in fetal organ perfusion and tissue homogenate systems. The usual practice of using 95% O_2:5% CO_2 (134) produces a P_{O_2} far in excess of that found in regions of the fetus perfused with the best oxygenated fetal blood, umbilical vein blood [$P_{O_2} \approx 35$ mm Hg, P_{CO_2} 42 mm Hg, pH 7.4 (46, 147)]. Fetal adrenal arterial blood is equivalent to umbilical arterial blood [P_{O_2} 23 mm Hg, P_{CO_2} 46 mm Hg, pH 7.35 (46)]. This should be borne in mind in studies of fetal adrenal function in vitro.

In vivo studies of fetal material are of two types. Tissues may be taken for single point analysis after death or under anesthesia, or serial samples can be taken from the same animal over a period of time. Attempts to maintain isolated fetuses in the latter part of gestation have not been rewarding (162). In many small polytocous species, the first source is the only one available. Much human material is obtained at cesarian section (cs) or following abortion, either spontaneous or induced. In these situations, maternal starvation and any other preoperative preparation, including pharmacological premedication, anesthesia, and surgical trauma, may all complicate the experiment. In none of these situations can the material be considered as exactly representative of fetal tissues. Too often, neonatal umbilical cord plasma concentrations are referred to as fetal plasma concentrations. Neonatal plasma samples may not be representative of the values in the undisturbed fetus in utero prior to delivery, since they will also reflect changes induced by delivery, whether vaginal or by cs.

Sequential studies of maternal and fetal endocrine changes at the time of parturition have been carried out in primates and ruminants. Gestation in the sheep lasts approximately 148 days. After 80–90 days, vascular catheters can be placed in various fetal blood vessels while the ewe is under general or local anesthesia (46, 55, 138, 139, 147). The catheters are then exteriorized to the ewe's flank. After the animal recovers from anesthesia, fetal blood is withdrawn as required for hormone and chemical analysis. Hormones or other metabolically active physiological or pharmacological agents can be infused and their effects on the fetus assessed. At the time of catheter placement the fetal endocrine glands, such as the pituitary (51, 126) or adrenals (57, 58, 67), can be removed or destroyed. Function of the fetus can be monitored by placing electroencephalographic (EEG) leads on the fetal skull (55, 151), by implanting electromagnetic flow meters in the fetal trachea to assess movements of tracheal fluid (55), and by inserting pressure-sensitive balloons in the uterus to monitor uterine activity (87, 149). Vascular catheters can also be placed in the maternal utero-ovarian vein (if blood draining from the uterus is to be sampled), in the maternal inferior vena cava, and in the aorta. Similar preparations can be established in the fetal calf and goat (45, 51, 62). The recent advances in our understanding of the endocrinology of pregnancy and parturition have resulted from the combination of these surgical and experimental techniques with specific and sensitive methods of hormone estimation (principally radioimmunoassay and competitive protein binding used in conjunction with various chromatographic separation methods).

The ease with which the fetal sheep preparation with indwelling vascular catheters can be prepared obscures the problems involved in the maintenance of stable preparations for the long term investigations necessary to obtain sound information on fetal endocrinology. Surgical procedures on the pregnant ewe and fetus affect fetal function, and time should be given for adequate recovery (138, 139, 147). Various methods are available for monitoring the condition of the fetus. Small blood samples should be taken frequently to analyze fetal blood gas tensions and fetal blood pH. Although such data cannot prove stability of the fetus, they can exclude certain gross abnormalities of fetal function. Experiments with chronically catheterized fetal preparations should always give the following data: preoperative preparation, gestational age at operation, details of the surgery, drugs and antibiotics administered; blood gas tensions and pH values, preferably individually with each sample; the time interval between surgery and the commencement of sampling; uterine contraction records; the ultimate fate of the lamb. Too often, reports of fetal endocrine work include no reference to these factors.

There are several problems in producing a similar primate preparation. The rhesus monkey (*Macaca mulatta*) is the subhuman primate most commonly used (154). The fetus is smaller than the sheep fetus; in addition, the myometrium of the pregnant monkey is extremely irritable. This difference in myometrial irritability may be related to the lack of metabolism of prostaglandins (PG) by the primate myometrium when compared with the ovine myometrium (105). Uterine surgery during pregnancy requires the administration of uterine muscle relaxants at the time of surgery and for six days postoperatively (154). In view of this uterine irritability, factors that might cause an increased length of gestation can only be demonstrated when compared with an adequate set of sham-operated controls. This has not usually been done.

Experimental design is complicated by the fact that parturition is a multifactorial process containing several interconnected systems, many of which involve positive-feedback loops. In this situation the analytical experimental method of isolating individual variables encounters certain difficulties. Experimentally introduced perturbations may produce an abnormal progression of events. This critical interrelationship of various events creates problems when the administration of different agents is investigated at different stages of gestation against varying hormonal backgrounds in maternal, placental, and fetal tissues. One such example has been described following the administration of 20 mg stilbestrol to 12 pregnant ewes, five at 85–105 days gestation and seven at 132–142 days gestation (87). In the older group, uterine activity increased after 24 hr. Although the older group went into labor, three of the ewes developed cervical dystocia and two required delivery by cs. When they eventually went into labor at 143–146 days, four of the five ewes in the earlier group required manual dilatation of the cervix. A similar failure of coordination of the normal sequence of mechanical and endocrinological events has been demonstrated following the infusion of adrenocorticotrophin (ACTH) into the hypophysectomized sheep fetus at 125 days gestation (98, 108). Apparently in certain situations uterine contraction can be initiated without correctly stimulating the necessary supportive mechanisms. When premature induction of labor is attempted and fails, it may be because other parturitional systems are not mature. In addition, even when the systems are mature it is likely that the endocrine and mechanical events in both mother and fetus must occur in a particular, ordered sequence. Normal pregnancy lasts 114 days in the sow. Administration of $PGF2\alpha$ at 112 days gestation results in a rapid elevation of maternal peripheral plasma relaxin concentrations. Following this premature stimulation of relaxin secretion, the normal increase in plasma relaxin in the last 24 hr of gestation is not seen (174).

It has already been noted that fetal and maternal endocrine changes interact in delivery. We may subdivide the endocrine phenomena into those considered as playing an *initiatory* role and those with a *supportive* and augmenting role once the process of parturition has begun.

EVIDENCE IN FAVOR OF A FETAL ROLE IN THE INITIATION OF PARTURITION

A role for the human fetus in the initiation of parturition has been suggested by reports that various forms of anencephaly and other cranial abnormalities are associated with postmaturity (20, 44, 114, 118, 127). Recent endocrine studies on human neonatal umbilical cord blood concentrations of various pituitary hormones have shown that pituitary hormones are present in varying amounts in different anencephalic neonates. In two anencephalics of unstated gestational age, neonatal umbilical cord plasma concentrations of ACTH were within the normal range in one study (210). In a second study of two anencephalics, low neonatal plasma ACTH concentrations were measured, but again it was not stated whether these infants were postmature (7, 8). Some newborn anencephalics respond to the administration of thyrotropin releasing hormone (TRH) by secreting thyrotropin (TSH) and prolactin (PRL) (100). Data are not available to compare these observations with the response of normal neonates. Clearly, anencephalics are a heterogeneous group in their endocrinological function. In one study, fetal adrenal weight at birth was related inversely to the degree of prolongation of pregnancy in anencephaly (10). In addition, varying degrees of polyhydramnios are present in anencephalic pregnancies. Stretching of human myometrium in vitro increases the release of prostaglandin E (PGE) (113). Therefore, hydramnios may stimulate myometrial contraction. In a recent retrospective study, a control group of 49,996 normal deliveries has been compared with 147 anencephalics (188, 189). The anencephalics were divided into pregnancies without polyhydramnios and pregnancies with clinically demonstrable hydramnios. A further complication was the presence of macerated still births and twinning, factors that may alter both the length of gestation and the course of labor. The gestation length in patients with hydramnios differed significantly from the group of patients with anencephalic fetuses but no hydramnios. Although the mean gestational length was almost the same in the anencephalic group without hydramnios (39.7 weeks) as in the controls (39.6 weeks), the distribution of delivery was very different. Thus in this group of anencephalics, delivery occurred before 38 weeks in 41.4% (12.6% in the control group) and 34.5% of deliveries occurred after 42 weeks (6.2% of the control group). Histological examination of fetal adrenals from five prematurely delivered, five term, and five postmature infants demonstrated hypoplasia in each group. This observation conflicts with another report based on eight anencephalic fetuses (199). Adrenal hypoplasia was present in the five fetuses in which the onset of labor was delayed by at least 14 days, while two anencephalic fetuses delivered after spontaneous labor at 275 and 289 days of gestation had almost normal adrenals. Thus, data from the human suggest that anencephaly is accompanied by loss of the precise timing of delivery and indicates that in anencephalics some important contribution to the initiation of delivery is lacking. Evidence discussed below suggests that parturient endocrine mechanisms in experimental animals possess a large safety factor. Functional assessment based solely on histology is inadequate. A more detailed understanding of the various types of anencephalic pregnancy and their relationship to the timing of delivery requires data on maternal and amniotic fluid hormone concentrations at least, and preferably neonatal hormone concentrations as well.

In experimental animals, various genetic abnormalities are associated with prolonged gestation. Unfortunately no endocrinological data are available in these studies. In Holstein-Friesian cattle, fetal adrenal hypofunction is associated with prolonged gestation and continued growth in utero until the fetus outgrows the ability of the placenta to provide essential nutrients, whereupon fetal death occurs (92). In contrast, failure of development of the fetal pituitary in Guernsey cattle results in prolonged gestation without continued growth (109). Both these abnormalities affect the fetal hypothalamo-adenohypophyseal-adrenal axis and amount to a spectacular experiment in teratogenesis conducted by nature. Pregnant ewes that eat the skunk cabbage *Veratrum californicum* on day 14 of gestation are affected by an alkaloid in the plant that produces several gross fetal deformities, including cyclopia, a grossly enlarged tongue, and varying degrees of malformation of the central nervous system, particularly in the region of the hypothalamus and pituitary. Pregnancy continues indefinitely until cs is performed or the lamb dies in utero (20, 124).

Experimental Observations

RUMINANTS Providing at least 70% of the fetal pituitary is destroyed, hypophysectomy of the fetal lamb before 136 days of gestation results in prolongation of gestation well past normal term (up to 187 days) (128–130). Following successful hypophysectomy, the circulating fetal plasma concentrations of ACTH and PRL fall to undetectable levels [< 10 pg ml^{-1} for ACTH and 1.5 ng ml^{-1} for PRL (151)]. No data are available for plasma concentrations of fetal pituitary hormone concentrations following incomplete hypophysectomy that does not delay the onset of delivery. Such observations would aid assessment of the extent of the "safety factor" available in terms of the fetal pituitary contribution to the onset of delivery.

Permanent interruption of the pituitary portal system before 116 days gestation also leads to prolongation of pregnancy (126). The pituitary-stalk-sectioned fetus is similar to the deformed fetus produced by the alkaloid from *Veratrum californicum;* in both, although the pituitary is present, it is dislocated from its normal relationship to the hypothalamus. Pituitary stalk section carried out after 116 days stimulates fetal adrenal growth and induces premature delivery, probably due to stimulation of pituitary ACTH secretion (126). Following pituitary stalk section at about 110 days gestation, fetal plasma growth hormone concentrations fall to 50% of preoperative values. ACTH can still be detected in fetal plasma, and fetal plasma

PRL concentration is relatively little changed (151). Pituitary stalk section in the adult rat causes increased PRL secretion (207). Continued ACTH secretion has been reported following stalk section in the adult monkey (107).

The recent demonstration of the reversal of flow in the pituitary-portal system introduces the possibility that effects of fetal pituitary stalk section may involve interruption of pituitary influences on the hypothalamus (19, 158). Complete bilateral fetal adrenalectomy delays parturition in the ewe. If remnants of fetal adrenal remain in situ, delivery occurs at term (58). Infusion of ACTH, dexamethasone (a synthetic glucocorticoid) or cortisol (the naturally occurring glucocorticoid in this species) at physiological rates all precipitate premature delivery accompanied by relatively normal maternal endocrine changes (123, 126, 185, 195). ACTH or glucocorticoid administration to the pituitary-stalk-sectioned, hypophysectomized or adrenalectomized fetus will initiate delivery (67, 98, 151). All of these lines of evidence suggest participation of the hypothalamo-pituitary-adrenal axis in the mechanism of parturition in this species.

Similar experiments implicating the fetal adrenal axis have been performed in other ruminant species. The administration of ACTH, dexamethasone, or cortisol to the fetal calf at 250–260 days gestation initiates premature delivery (45). Hypophysectomy of the fetal goat delays parturition, and infusions of ACTH or glucocorticoids will initiate premature parturition with normal maternal endocrine changes (51, 195). In summary, the timing of parturition can be delayed or brought forward by the experimental manipulation of the fetal hypothalamo-pituitary-adrenal axis in several ruminant species.

PRIMATES   Ablation of fetal endocrine glands has been performed in fetal subhuman primates, particularly the rhesus monkey (42, 142, 154). Following destruction of the fetal pituitary by implantation of radioactive crystals of yttrium 90 at approximately 123 days gestation, three rhesus monkey fetuses continued to grow and were delivered postmaturely (42). Two were liveborn and showed no histological evidence of residual pituitary tissue; adrenal, thyroid, and gonadal weights were reduced. Microscopic examination of the adrenals from these two liveborn hypophysectomized fetuses showed well-developed adult cortical zones. The fetal zone had regressed considerably in comparison with the controls in which it comprised 80% of the gland. In a second study in the rhesus monkey, functional hypophysectomy of 18 fetuses (73–78 days of gestation) was performed by removal of the head cranial to the plane formed by the occipito-cervical and mandibulo-maxillary junctions. In two of these pregnancies the fetus died several weeks after surgery, yet they were not delivered until after 200 days (normal gestation 167 ± 0.4 days, mean ± SEM for 320 normal pregnancies) (154). Fetectomy was performed in 11 pregnant rhesus monkeys at 70–157 days gestation and was followed by expulsion of the placenta at 114–184 days (203). In a more recent study, in 5 of 8 pregnant rhesus monkeys fetectomized at 80–140 days, delivery of the placenta was delayed (120). Maternal plasma progesterone concentration was maintained following fetectomy. However, when ovariectomy was performed after fetectomy, the placenta was delivered 3–8 days later. In the pregnant rhesus monkey, ovariectomy by itself did not induce delivery and these observations suggest that following fetectomy, the ovary is required to maintain the placental pregnancy, probably as an additional source of progesterone to compensate for decreased placental progesterone production following fetectomy (205). This interpretation is borne out by the observation that when ovariectomy was performed first, followed by fetectomy 20 days or more later, maternal plasma progesterone concentration fell slowly and delivery of the placenta occurred after about 30 days. Thus the placenta alone was incapable of maintaining maternal plasma progesterone concentrations without some influence from the fetus. In this type of experiment, uterine activity should be monitored in order to assess the influence of the procedure on both the onset and the time course of delivery. Placental conversion of Δ^5-pregnenolone to progesterone is decreased when the placenta of the hypophysectomized rhesus fetus is examined in vitro (79), suggesting a role of the fetal pituitary in the control of placental endocrine function.

Umbilical cord ligation at 101–114 days gestation in four pregnant rhesus monkeys was followed by abortion after three days in one monkey and after 16–21 days in the other three (25). Plasma progesterone concentration fell in all cases. These results are very different from the observations following fetectomy and demonstrate the problems associated with the assessment of the role of different fetal endocrine systems in the initiation of parturition in the subhuman primate. In all ablation experiments including fetectomy and fetal death, in addition to the deficit produced following removal of tissue, it is necessary to consider both the normal and the experimentally modified activity of the remaining tissues. Umbilical cord ligation and fetectomy constitute very different experimental situations. The autolysing fetus is a potential source of such active molecules as PG.

In a separate study, following surgery and fetal death in two pregnant rhesus monkeys, maternal plasma progesterone concentration was unchanged and plasma estrogens fell (confirming the partial fetal source of estrogen precursors). PG and PG metabolites in maternal peripheral plasma and amniotic fluid increased just before delivery (37). The source of these PGs is not clear but they may have been released following tissue breakdown since degenerative changes have been demonstrated histologically in the placenta and fetal membranes when fetal death was caused by intra-amniotic saline injection in the rhesus monkey (146). Bilateral fetal adrenalectomy at 105–120 days of gestation has been performed in eight rhesus monkeys (142). Six monkeys delivered slightly before or at the normal date of delivery. In five of these six, fetal adrenal tissue was observed at autopsy; the sixth was not investigated. Two monkeys delivered 12 and 49 days late. No fetal adrenal tissue was observed in the monkey delivering at 12 days past term. The other post-term fetus was not autopsied. Clearly, although the experimental evidence in the primate is less comprehensive than that available in the ruminant, there is a body of evidence to suggest a role for the fetal hypothalamo-pituitary-adrenal axis in the timing of the onset of labor in the primate.

POLYTOCOUS SPECIES   Decapitation of all the fetuses in the litter leads to prolongation of gestation in the sow (186). If all but one fetus are decapitated, gestation is still prolonged, but when more than one intact fetus is present, parturition occurs at the expected time. Crushing all embryos at day 30 does not affect maternal plasma progesterone concentrations up to 60 days (206). These observations suggest that mechanisms similar to those discussed in monotocous species are operating in the pregnant sow. The additional complication is that more than one intact fetus is required for the normal initiatory signal(s) to produce parturition. In twin pregnancy in the ewe it is necessary to hypophysectomize both fetuses to delay delivery; the presence of one intact fetus will result in delivery at the normal time (130).

The interpretation of fetectomy experiments in the common laboratory polytocous species of short gestation length is complicated. In one investigation on a colony of mice in which unoperated animals delivered between 19–23 days, fetectomy was performed in 20 animals, five on each of days 12, 13, 14, and 15. Delivery occurred on day 16–23 (153). It is unfortunate that surgery was performed over such a wide range of gestational ages, constituting 20% of the length of gestation. Critical signals during development occur at specific, discrete times and such a varied experimental protocol makes analysis difficult. The timing of experimental surgery is of especially critical importance when the duration of gestation is short. Surgery at 15 days or so of gestation may have taken place after the fundamental signal for the initiation of delivery has already occurred. In addition, the surgery–delivery interval was not itemized for the different gestational ages. Mechanisms must exist to evacuate the uterus following fetal death, and since there is a wide variability in the timing of both normal and experimental delivery, few conclusions of substance can be drawn in short-gestation-length species from experiments in which no endocrinological data are available and which involve fetectomy at such different stages of pregnancy.

In summary, there is overwhelming evidence from the sheep, goat, and cow that the fetus plays an important role in the timing of delivery. In the sheep, the fetal adrenal may be assigned a central role in the initiation of parturition (Figure 1). We may consider the events that bring about the increased secretion of cortisol from the fetal adrenal as the INPUT side; the mechanisms whereby the increased secretion of cortisol produces the endocrine changes that bring about delivery may be considered the OUTPUT side. We must also assess the relevance of such a flow path to other species, such as the primates. The evidence from human anencephalics, a heterogeneous group both endocrinologically and in relation to other existing abnormalities, is best interpreted as showing that in the presence of abnormalities of the fetal hypothalamo-hypophyseal-adrenal axis the precise timing of delivery is lost. Experimental manipulation of the subhuman primate fetus suggests a similar conclusion. Certainly there are many species differences, which have their basis in such diversities as the different location of key enzymes in hormone synthesis and placental cytoarchitecture, that may affect both hormone synthesis and placental transport.

Fetal Adrenal Activity

EXPERIMENTAL OBSERVATIONS IN THE SHEEP, GOAT, AND COW
In these three species the rate of growth of the fetal adrenal, measurements of fetal plasma corticosteroids, and assessments of fetal adrenal responsiveness to ACTH demonstrate increased adrenal activity towards the end of gestation (45, 51, 62, 91, 125, 126, 134, 147, 150). In the sheep, fetal plasma corticosteroid concentrations increase over the last 10 days or so of gestation (16, 59, 150, 185). Investigations with radioactive cortisol infused on both the maternal and fetal sides of the placenta show that the ovine placenta has a considerable diffusion resistance to cortisol (18, 126). The maternal–fetal transfer of cortisol 19 days before delivery was 0.16 mg per day (126). It has been calculated that at the time fetal plasma cortisol concentration begins to rise, a transplacental gradient of 175:1 (ewe:fetus) would be required to initiate delivery. To achieve this, maternal plasma cortisol concentration would need to increase to 500 ng ml^{-1} (maximum concentrations under the stress of surgery are about 100 ng ml^{-1}). The calculation of fetal blood production rates (BPR) for cortisol of 10 mg per day on the day before delivery (150) is in agreement with the ranges of cortisol infusion into the fetus required to initiate labor at 130 days gestation, and is equivalent to adequate doses of dexamethasone infused intraperitoneally or intravascularly into the fetus (2, 147). When 1–10 μg ACTH hr^{-1} is infused into the fetal sheep, parturition occurs after 4–8 days. At the time of delivery, fetal plasma cortisol concentrations have risen from pre-infusion concentrations to concentrations similar to those observed at

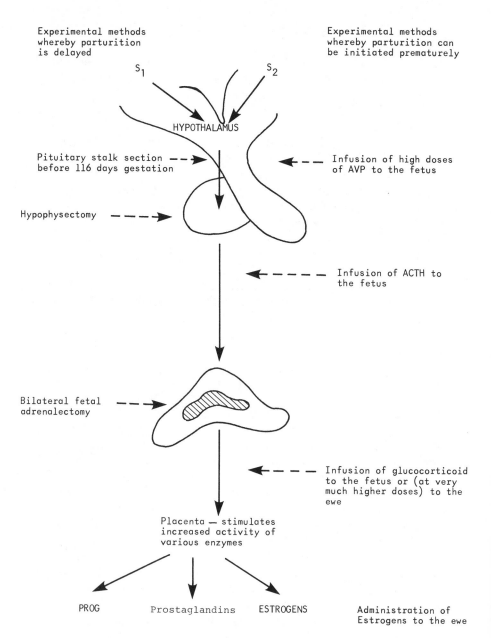

Experimental methods
whereby parturition
is delayed

Experimental methods
whereby parturition can
be initiated prematurely

S_1

S_2

HYPOTHALAMUS

Pituitary stalk section
before 116 days gestation

Infusion of high doses
of AVP to the fetus

Hypophysectomy

Infusion of ACTH to
the fetus

Bilateral fetal
adrenalectomy

Infusion of glucocorticoid
to the fetus or (at very
much higher doses) to the
ewe

Placenta — stimulates
increased activity of
various enzymes

PROG   Prostaglandins   ESTROGENS

Administration of
Estrogens to the ewe

Figure 1 The various levels of the fetal hypothalamo-hypophyseal-adrenal-placental axis at which important events may occur prior to parturition. On the left are shown experimental techniques whereby parturition can be delayed. On the right are methods of initiating parturition prematurely. S_1 and S_2 represent the various stimuli that may act on the hypothalamus. Modified and reproduced with permission from (147).

the time of normal delivery at term (98, 108, 151). It should be noted that the infusions of ACTH used experimentally have been constant, whereas fetal ACTH secretion is phasic (151). Lambs delivered prematurely following ACTH or glucocorticoid infusion are not affected by respiratory distress (123). Thus in addition to playing a role in the initiation of delivery, cortisol has a function in the preparation of the lung and other organ systems for extrauterine life (35). Many of these changes involve the stimulation of key enzyme systems. The action in the lung represents an increase in choline phosphotransferase activity (63).

EXPERIMENTAL OBSERVATIONS IN THE PRIMATE   Sequential sampling of fetal plasma is not possible in the human, and the practical problems of chronic vascular catheterization have prevented sequential sampling from the rhesus monkey fetus up to the time of delivery. Available data are derived from amniotic fluid samples and neonatal umbilical cord plasma concentrations. Amniotic fluid cortisol concentration, as measured by radioimmunoassay, increases over the last 60 days of gestation in the fetal rhesus monkey, with an indication of a more rapid increase over the last 10–20 days (37, 160). In the human, amniotic fluid cortisol is 2.4 times as high between 35 and 40 weeks as it is before 34 weeks; after 40 weeks, it is 1.8 times higher than at 35–40 weeks. Amniotic fluid cortisol concentrations correlate better with umbilical cord plasma cortisol concentrations than with maternal plasma cortisol (64, 145). The levels of umbilical arterial total plasma cortisol and of the physiologically active cortisol fraction (free, diffusible cortisol) were higher after delivery following spontaneous labor than after induced labor, even when there was no significant difference in the duration of the induced and spontaneous labors studied (29, 143). It should be noted that the higher neonatal cord blood concentration of cortisol following spontaneous delivery, compared with induced delivery, may simply reflect a greater responsiveness of the fetal adrenal to stress when labor occurs spontaneously than when it is induced, even when the two groups are controlled for gestational age. Changes that have occurred to bring about spontaneous labor may very well involve alteration in the sensitivity of the adrenal produced by such factors as PG (see below). In addition, the physical and endocrine changes of spontaneous and induced labor may differ considerably. The use of different methods of hormone estimation and the different sources of plasma (mixed cord blood or blood withdrawn by puncture of a vein or artery) are additional complications in any interpretation of the literature comparing fetal steroids in umbilical circulation following different methods of delivery. In one study, mixed cord blood estimated for cortisol by a competitive protein binding technique without any chromatographic separation showed slightly higher concentrations (though not significantly higher) in infants following spontaneous labor (191). In another laboratory the use of a fluorometric method showed no difference related to mode of delivery (178), whereas competitive protein binding without chromatography did demonstrate a difference (173).

The administration of adequate doses of glucocorticoid to the fetal lamb or pregnant ewe invariably results in the initiation of delivery; much larger doses are required in the ewe (73). The situation is more complicated in the primate. Administration of 8 mg dexamethasone per day intramuscularly to pregnant rhesus monkeys from 146–156 days gestation did not initiate premature delivery. Delivery occurred at normal term (166–176 days) (32, 33, 37). Any interpretation of this observation in terms of the role of glucocorticoids in the initiation of parturition must account for the marked depression of both maternal and fetal adrenal function produced by these injections. Maternal plasma estrogen concentration fell to 15–40% of initial concentration due to the decrease in C-19 estrogen precursors of adrenal origin. This fall provides an adequate explanation for the failure of these doses of glucocorticoid to elicit delivery. Despite failure by several groups to induce delivery in the human with glucocorticoids, in one study on postmature human females, administration of dexamethasone did result in earlier delivery than with controls (137). The successful response in the postmature situation could result from the presence of adequate precursor and substrate concentrations. The primate and the ruminant also differ in regard to placental permeability to glucocorticoids. Unlike the ovine placenta, which is relatively impermeable to glucocorticoids, the primate placenta is permeable to cortisol. However, since it contains a potent 11-dehydrogenase enzyme, 85% of cortisol is converted to cortisone as it crosses the placenta (144). Since cortisone is inactive and the fetus lacks the amount of 11-reductase enzyme needed to reconvert cortisone to cortisol, the primate fetus is effectively protected from fluctuations in circulating maternal plasma cortisol concentration. The similarity of metabolism of labelled cortisol in pregnant and post-partum baboons suggests that the fetus does not play an important role in the metabolism of maternal cortisol (161).

In summary, activity of the fetal adrenal increases before delivery in ruminants, subhuman primates, and in man. Placental permeability to cortisol is effectively low, thereby permitting fetal autonomy. The time scale of increase in fetal adrenal glucocorticoid production apparently differs between primates and nonprimates. In addition, the biosynthetic pathways in the adrenal are different. For example, the primate adrenal lacks the 3β-ol dehydrogenase, Δ^5-isomerase complex and cannot synthesize progesterone. However, the fetal adrenal can obtain adequate amounts of progesterone for glucocorticoid and androgen synthesis from the placenta. In contrast, the ovine adrenal can synthesize its own progesterone. A further difference, discussed in detail below, is in the interrelationship of the adrenal and placenta in ruminants and primate. The ovine placenta is capable of using progesterone as a substrate for estrogen biosynthesis, whereas the primate placenta lacks the 17-hydroxylase and 17,20 lyase enzymes necessary to convert C-21 steroids to C-19 estrogen precursors. C-19 precursors are supplied to the placenta by the maternal and fetal adrenals.

Control of the Fetal Adrenal

The mechanism responsible for the increased activity of the fetal sheep adrenal prior to normal delivery is uncertain. It has so far not been possible on the basis of daily fetal blood sampling to demonstrate an increase in fetal plasma ACTH concentration prior to the rise in fetal plasma cortisol. A marked increase has been demonstrated only in the last few hours of fetal life (167). This increase is probably secondary to the stress of labor and serves to augment the fetal plasma cortisol concentration. Since it occurs at a time when the maternal plasma progesterone concentration has begun to fall and estrogen to rise, it is not an initiatory event. A phasic release of ACTH has been demonstrated in the sheep fetus (151). Frequent blood sampling may be necessary to demonstrate any rise in fetal plasma ACTH that occurs before fetal plasma cortisol concentration rises. This problem raises difficulties, both practical and interpretational. Too frequent sampling may produce hemorrhagic stress, which has been shown to be a stimulus to the release of fetal ACTH and activation of several other fetal endocrine systems (6). The rate of infusion of ACTH into the fetal lamb (10 μg hr^{-1}) used to precipitate delivery is probably considerably in excess of the fetal blood production rate (BPR) for ACTH. Metabolic clearance rate (MCR) for ACTH calculated following single injection of labelled isotope was 55 ml min^{-1} kg^{-1} with a BPR of 1245 pg min^{-1} kg^{-1} (99). Following continuous infusion of ACTH at 10 μg hr^{-1} into hypophysectomized lamb fetuses, MCR of up to 550 ml min^{-1} kg^{-1} can be obtained (98, 108, 147). Data from other continuous infusion studies give values for BPR of around 800 pg min^{-1} at fetal plasma ACTH concentration of 100 pg ml^{-1} (151). Fetal plasma ACTH concentrations recorded before the last day of gestation are below 1000 pg ml.$^{-1}$

Since hypophysectomy delays the onset of parturition in the sheep, the goat, and the rhesus monkey, the simplest explanation of the signal to initiate delivery is that it either originates in the fetal pituitary or at least involves this gland as an intermediary. If pituitary ACTH is not the controlling factor it has been suggested that the increased secretion of cortisol by the fetal lamb adrenal may be controlled by another pituitary hormone, such as αMSH or prolactin (PRL). In vivo administration of PRL in doses within the range calculated for the BPR, increases in vitro corticosterone production by adult rat adrenals (115, 131). PRL affects cholesterol metabolism by the adrenal and alters the ratio of different adrenal steroids secreted as a result of its inhibitory action on steroidogenic enzyme systems such as adrenal 5 α-reductase (212). Such an action may make more active steroid available.

The fetal sheep pituitary is capable of secreting PRL. Plasma PRL concentrations increase in late gestation and correlate well with fetal plasma cortisol (1, 2). If PRL is the drive to increased fetal adrenal activity, the rise in fetal plasma PRL concentration should precede the increase in fetal plasma cortisol by at least 24–48 hr, since this is the necessary latent period for the activity of exogenous ACTH. A more detailed correlation of plasma PRL and cortisol in individual fetuses is required. The effect of exogenous PRL on the fetal lamb adrenal in vivo has not been tested.

In the human, cord blood plasma PRL concentrations for neonates born at various stages of gestation show a rise, while plasma ACTH concentration falls, between 16 and 42 weeks of gestation (209, 210). The material from which these data were obtained at the early gestational ages consisted of samples from fetuses removed at total hysterectomy 30 min after clamping of the uterine arteries, whereas those obtained near term were either from cs or vaginal delivery. Thus the extent of anoxic and other forms of stress was variable. However, these results and investigations in the adult mammal justify further investigation of PRL as a pituitary factor with a role in the increased fetal corticosteroidogenesis prior to delivery.

The simplest explanation of observations from fetal hypophysectomy or ACTH infusion to the sheep fetus is that the signal to parturition in this species involves the fetal pituitary. However, other mechanisms will explain the observed experimental facts equally well. Hypophysectomy of the adult rat leads to a rapid decrease in adrenal responsiveness to ACTH over the next 24 hr (122). Four days of ACTH replacement, beginning one week after hypophysectomy, is not sufficient to return steroidogenesis to normal in the adult rat (43). A diminished sensitivity of the adrenal of the hypophysectomized fetal lamb to ACTH has also been demonstrated (195). Therefore, following fetal hypophysectomy, the fetal lamb adrenal is likely to be insensitive to any signals originating from other fetal or maternal sources. The data from fetal hypophysectomy or pituitary stalk section thus do not prove that the signal to parturition originates in the fetal hypothalamo-pituitary system. It may be that fetal hypothalamo-pituitary function is necessary for normal parturition to occur because it supplies a basal tropic input; but by itself it may not be sufficient. The actual signal could originate from some other fetal, placental, or maternal tissue (150). ACTH has been shown to be necessary for the development of ACTH-sensitive adenylate cyclase activity in the fetal rabbit (5). Suppression of fetal ACTH secretion by cortisol administration will inhibit the development of responsiveness to ACTH. Placental influences on the fetal adrenal merit investigation (93). hCG exerts effects similar to those of ACTH on human adrenal ultrastructure in vitro (97). An extra-pituitary site of production of a factor controlling the fetal adrenal may depend on fetal pituitary function. Growth and development of several fetal tissues are impaired following hypophysectomy.

Several recent studies have suggested the existence of a placental ACTH (74, 89, 166). In the pregnant rhesus monkey, cortisol is present in maternal blood following maternal hypophysectomy and fetectomy. When the placenta is removed, maternal plasma cortisol falls to undetectable levels (89). This observation can be explained either by the presence of a placental ACTH or production of cortisol by the placenta. In the pregnant rhesus monkey, dexamethasone completely suppresses maternal plasma cortisol concentration; therefore any placental production of ACTH or cortisol is sensitive to inhibition by high plasma glucocorticoid concentrations. Following hypophysectomy of the fetal lamb at about 110 days gestation, fetal plasma ACTH concentrations measured by radioimmunoassay (98, 108) or cytochemical bioassay on adult guinea pig adrenals (150) fall to low levels. There is thus no evidence that a placental ACTH reaches the fetal circulation in this species. It is however possible that a factor is present in fetal plasma that is stimulatory to the fetal adrenal but not to adult guinea pig adrenals or antigenic in the radioimmunoassay. Heterogeneous forms of ACTH with biological activity have been demonstrated in the adult mammal (48). In the human, detailed analysis of fetal pituitary hormone control has demonstrated a switch from the production of corticotropin-like fragments to authentic corticotropin during the last weeks of gestation (176). The possibility that several different fetal factors are affecting the growth and secretion of the fetal adrenal is supported by the observation that growth of fetal human adrenal cells in vitro is stimulated by fetal calf serum without a concomitant effect on steroidogenesis (168). PG will stimulate corticosteroidogenesis in the adult rat (66). PGE2 but not PGF2α will stimulate cortisol release from the fetal lamb adrenal in vivo at 130 days gestation (85). At this gestational age the fetal lamb adrenal is relatively insensitive to ACTH. It has therefore been suggested that PGE2 plays a role in controlling the increased output of cortisol by the fetal adrenal at term. Fetal plasma PG concentrations do rise in the last day of gestation but this occurs after the increase in fetal plasma cortisol (34).

At 50–90 days gestation, in vitro adrenal sensitivity to ACTH of fetal lamb adrenals is high. Despite continuing high fetal plasma ACTH concentrations, adrenal sensitivity subsequently decreases until just before delivery

(211). In vitro adrenal sensitivity of fetal lamb adrenals in response to a fixed concentration of ACTH (3×10^5 pg ml^{-1}) in a perifusion system increases towards term. This work was performed with adrenal slices containing both medulla and cortex and the results may in part be due to greater growth of the cortex relative to the medulla (16, 147). Taken together, these data suggest the possibility of an inhibitory control of the fetal adrenal that is removed prior to the period of increased fetal adrenal cortisol production.

PROGESTERONE AND ESTROGEN BIOSYNTHESIS

Sheep, Cow, and Goat

The changes in maternal plasma hormone concentrations (the output side of Figure 1) in the ewe before delivery have been well documented. Plasma progesterone concentration falls 2–4 days before delivery (68, 82, 84, 181) and estrogen rises 12–24 hr before delivery (30, 68). There is considerable fluctuation in basal concentrations before parturition and much "hunting" as the concentrations change. Accurate assessments of the time at which the changes in plasma hormone concentrations begin and of their temporal relationship to each other require a larger group of animals and more frequent sampling than has yet been performed.

A clearer indication of the changes brought about by fetal glucocorticoid has been obtained by glucocorticoid administration to the fetus in late gestation (126, 191). In this situation, maternal plasma progesterone begins to fall 30–40 hr after the administration of glucocorticoid, followed by an increase in maternal peripheral plasma estrogen concentration and utero-ovarian PGF2α concentration. It is difficult to determine whether the estrogen concentration increase precedes the rise in PFG2α (68). Increased production of PG can be demonstrated by the administration of estradiol to the ewe (126). It thus appears that the sequence of events in fetal and maternal plasma is a rise in fetal cortisol, a fall in maternal progesterone production, an increase in maternal estrogen production, and a rise in production of PGF2α.

The three major steps in the conversion of progesterone to estrogen by the sheep placenta are (*a*) 17-hydroxylation of progesterone to 17α-hydroxy progesterone, (*b*) cleavage of the 17,20 bond by a 17,20 lyase to produce androstenedione, and (*c*) aromatization to estrone (84, 136, 164, 183). Dexamethasone administration to the fetal sheep around 135 days gestation increases the concentration of androstenedione in the utero-ovarian vein (183). In vivo administration of dexamethasone increases the activity of 17-hydroxylase and 17,20 lyase in placental minces (9, 182). Estrogen production in the placenta is reflected by an increase in fetal plasma estrogen and estrogen-conjugate concentrations just before normal and glucocorticoid induced delivery (52, 65, 213). In both normal and dexamethasone-induced delivery maternal plasma progesterone falls before estrogen increases, supporting the suggestion that progesterone is a precursor for estrogen. Much of the work on the placental conversion of progesterone to estrogen has been carried out using in vitro systems. More in vivo data are required. A major problem results from the fact that in the sheep all the enzyme steps are located within the placenta and the intermediates do not reach the blood in large quantities. Studies on the separate hormone and enzyme links in the chain of different factors that eventually bring about successful labor are increasingly complicated by the need to measure hormone or metabolite concentrations at a site as close to the effector as possible. It should not be automatically assumed that peripheral plasma concentrations accurately reflect local hormone activity.

In the goat and the cow, progesterone production continues in the CL throughout pregnancy (61). Hysterectomy of the pregnant goat between 30–48 days gestation (normal gestation: 150 days) results in CL regression at 147–184 days with the life of the CL exceeding that in pregnant animals in three of the six experimental animals (51). In the later stages of gestation there is a slow fall in caprine placental lactogen (PL) concentration in the maternal circulation. This fall occurs at the same time as the increase in fetal glucocorticoid concentration and it has been suggested that glucocorticoids prevent placental production of caprine PL. However, hysterectomy withdraws caprine PL and yet the CL continues to function. At term the fall in maternal plasma progesterone concentrations is effected by $PGF2\alpha$. $PGF2\alpha$ infused into the utero-ovarian vein will produce lyteolysis and it has been shown that utero-ovarian $PGF2\alpha$ concentration increases before normal and glucocorticoid induced delivery (51). Maternal 17β-estradiol infusion will stimulate $PGF2\alpha$ production within the uterus in the goat (51). Glucocorticoid produced by the fetus stimulates placental estrogen production but whether it does this by enabling the placenta to use more progesterone for the synthesis of estrogen, as in the sheep, remains to be determined. In both the sheep and the goat, glucocorticoid induced parturition is not inhibited by the administration of exogenous progesterone in doses (100 mg per day) that maintain maternal plasma progesterone concentrations. However, administration of very high doses (200 mg per day) will inhibit parturition in the sheep (126). The block to delivery is probably the inhibition of PG release by the elevated maternal progesterone concentration (125, 126).

Primate

Progesterone and estrogens are produced by the placenta in primates (37, 169). Within this group, maternal plasma concentration changes are not as clearly defined as in the sheep. In the human, various patterns of changes in maternal plasma progesterone concentration during late gestation have been demonstrated. In some reports, plasma progesterone has been shown to fall during the last three weeks with a small drop to about 84% of peak values (200) or a more rapid decline in the last week of gestation (50). However, this fall has not always been observed and in the monkey it is clear that maternal plasma progesterone concentration falls after delivery (23, 24, 37, 84, 88, 90, 119, 154). It is difficult to measure progesterone concentration at its site of action and it is possible that there are changes in tissue binding of progesterone. A further problem may be the nature of the steroids estimated by the various methodologies utilized in relation to their progestational activity. As in the human, ovariectomy of the pregnant rhesus monkey following an initial phase of dependence on the CL (24 days) does not result in abortion (152). Progesterone production occurs mainly in the placenta; the possibility of some ovarian contribution and the control of progesterone production by placenta and ovary have already been discussed. The production rate of progesterone in the rhesus monkey is considerably lower than in man and this is reflected in the lower plasma concentration, around 8 ng ml^{-1} at term compared with twice this value in man (37, 154, 200). In summary, as in the sheep, there is no experimental evidence to support the claim that a fall in maternal plasma progesterone concentration in the primate is an indispensible prerequisite to delivery.

Estrogen production during pregnancy in primates differs from sheep in several respects. The fetal primate adrenal lacks both Δ^{5-4}-isomerase and 3β-ol dehydrogenase but is capable of utilizing circulating progesterone. Since it possesses 17α-hydroxylase and C-17,20 lyase activity it can produce C-19 estrogen precursors (37, 53, 156). In vitro studies of primate placental steroid biosynthesis demonstrate aromatase activity but a deficiency of 17 α-hydroxylase and C-17,20 lyase (37, 169). Thus the primate placenta probably depends upon the availability of C-19 estrogen precursors for estrogen biosynthesis at term, whereas the ovine placenta is self-sufficient, utilizing placental progesterone. However, a detailed search for 17α-hydroxylase and 17,20 lyase activity at term has not been made. The maternal ovary, adrenal, and pituitary are not indispensible for estrogen production. It has been calculated following maternal adrenalectomy in man that approximately 50% of the C-19 substrates used by the placenta during pregnancy are of maternal adrenal origin (175). The role of estrogens during pregnancy is uncertain. In arylsulfatase deficiency, failure of hydrolysis of estrogen sulfates results in very low concentrations of unconjugated estrogens in maternal plasma, yet fetal growth and the response of the myometrium to oxytocin is within normal limits (72). It has been suggested that estrogen production removes circulating fetal androgens, thus protecting the fetus against their possible harmful effects (94). Similarly, fetal estriol and estetrol may constitute a method to bypass the more active estrogens as well as androgens. Availability of substrates is the only factor shown to affect the rate of synthesis of placental hormones, including estrogen, in the primate (197). Administration of dehydro-epiandrosterone sulfate (DHEAS) and androstenedione to the catheterized fetal rhesus monkey result in increased concentrations of estrone in fetal and maternal plasma (154). A similarity exists with the sheep, in which it has been shown that the administration of dehydro-epiandrosterone to the fetus at 135–139 days produces an increase in fetal and maternal estrogens in 30 min. The physiological nature of this increase in estrogen production is borne out by the subsequent increase in uterine blood flow after a further 90 min (164).

The various primate species show certain differences in estrogen metabolism (180). It should not be too readily assumed that all primates are good models for the human (180). For example, 16α-hydroxylation by hepatic microsomes of the fetal rhesus monkey is low compared with the human. This observation may explain why estriol excretion by the pregnant rhesus monkey is low (85). Measurement of estrogen concentrations has been performed using various maternal and fetal body fluids. Qualitative differences exist between the estrogens in the maternal and fetal compartments. In the cow, estradiol predominates in the maternal circulation and estrone in the fetus (91). In the primate the reverse situation exists (37, 154). In the rhesus monkey, maternal urinary estrone excretion has been shown to fall on the last day of gestation (132), but this observation conflicts with the maintenance of maternal plasma estrogen concentration at this time (37, 88). Basal plasma estrogen concentrations during pregnancy are lower in the rhesus monkey than in the human (31, 37). In normal human pregnancy, maternal plasma unconjugated 17β-estradiol concentration increases slowly to 30 weeks of gestation, followed by a sharper rise up to 40 weeks (200). A dramatic increase occurs in the last 10 days of pregnancy before premature labor (192). In the pregnant rhesus monkey, a sharp increase in maternal plasma estrogen concentration occurs over the final 7 days of gestation (23, 24, 37). These changes in maternal plasma estrogen concentrations are far less dramatic than those occurring in the sheep. The major role of estrogen at parturition in the primate is likely to be the stimulation of PG synthesis. Amniotic estrone and estrone sulfate concentrations rise in late pregnancy in the rhesus monkey (37, 140), and prolonged infusions of ACTH to the fetus produce a rise in fetal and maternal estrogens (154).

In summary, there is a significant increase in estrogen production in the fetal compartment in the subhuman primate and the sheep fetus. Increased fetal adrenal activity appears to be the cause, but the enzyme mechanisms and their locations may differ in different species. Further work is clearly necessary to determine the stimulus to the increased production of estrogen by the fetoplacental unit in the primate.

THE ROLE OF PROSTAGLANDINS

PGs are twenty-carbon-atom fatty acids related chemically to prostanoic acid. In both the ruminant and the primate the main forms are PGE2 and PGF2α. The major biological precursor of these PGs is arachidonic acid (AA). In the cell AA exists as various esters, predominantly phosphatides from which free AA is produced by the action of phospholipases. The enzyme complex that converts AA to PG is termed PG synthase. In vitro free AA increases PG synthesis immediately (69, 165), and the addition of AA to homogenates of human term myometrium stimulates PG synthesis (190). The intra-amniotic administration of AA in human pregnancy (133) or intra-aortic infusion in the pregnant rabbit (148) initiates parturition. Addition of AA or phospholipase to pregnant rat uterus in vitro increases PG release; this increase can be blocked by indomethacin, a potent inhibitor of PG synthase (159). Thus the availability of substrate for PG synthase is one possible mechanism controlling PG synthesis. Increased activity of PG synthase prior to delivery is suggested by several investigations. The in vitro release of PG from rat uterus increases as parturition approaches (159). Estrogen administration results in stimulation of PG synthesis in the ruminant and monkey, and induces labor (13, 56, 125, 126, 135, 154). Prostaglandin synthase inhibitors will prevent this action of estrogen (135).

A study of PG precursors is needed. We must also investigate the source of the PGs active at term, their metabolic fate, and their mode of action. Phospholipase A_2 specifically splits off fatty acids from position 2 of phospholipids. AAs in this position are then available for PG synthesis. In the sheep, the major sites of phospholipase A_2 activity are the amnion and chorioallantois. ACTH administration to the fetus increases phospholipase A_2 activity in both of these membranes. Enzyme activity is low in the myometrium, maternal placenta, and fetal placenta; ACTH administration produces no increase in activity (125). In the human, phospholipase A_2 activity is also highest in the amnion (76). The free AA produced as a result of phospholipase A_2 activity may be transported to other tissues locally as substrate for PG synthesis since it has been demonstrated in the sheep that the maternal placental layers contain the highest concentration of PG following premature induction of delivery with dexamethasone (126, 127). Since estrogen concentrations are elevated before parturition commences, the major stimulus to PG production in late pregnancy is probably estrogen (68, 125, 126, 202).

A fetal influence on uterine PG production has been shown in the sheep, where fetal cortisol stimulates placental estrogen production (126). In the rat, removal of the fetuses at day 16 or day 17 significantly reduces PGF release and spontaneous uterine activity studied in utero on day 22. Removal of all fetuses from one uterine horn will decrease PGF production by both horns (159). Thus in polytocous species, the fetus exerts an effect on PG synthesis that is not purely local. The intramural generation of PG is proportional to the uterine tone, which suggests that mechanical events in the uterus affect PG synthase activity (113). Inhibition of PG synthase by aspirin or indomethacin delays labor in the human (121), rhesus monkey (155), and rat (41).

PG is metabolized by oxidation of the 15-hydroxyl group by the enzyme prostaglandin dehydrogenase (PGDH) followed by reduction to the 13,14-dihydro derivative by Δ^{13}-reductase. A major site of PG metabolism in the adult is the pulmonary vascular bed. The blood flow through the fetal lung is less than through the adult lung, and pulmonary metabolism of PG is therefore less (157, 163). PG metabolites (PGM) increase in amniotic fluid following intra-amniotic injection of PG (47). Since PGDH activity is lacking in amniotic fluid, PG must have passed into the fetal membranes and PGM entered the amniotic cavity. PGDH has a short cellular half-life [46–75 min (21, 171)] and may be an important step in regulating tissue concentrations of PG and the local release of PG. In the human, PGDH activity in the placenta does not vary with gestational age or with the stage of labor (102). However, evidence of steroid control of uterine PGDH has been obtained in the rat and rabbit (17, 60, 69, 187). In the rat, uterine PGDH concentration rises by 400% from the nonpregnant value by day 18 of pregnancy, begins to fall on day 19, and reaches undetectable levels at day 21–23. These changes follow the fall in progesterone and rise in estrogen concentrations in maternal rat plasma. In addition, administration of 10 μg progesterone daily to the nonpregnant rat causes an increase in uterine PGDH concentration (69). These observations support the suggestion that during pregnancy in the rat, high uterine PGDH concentrations prevent the build-up and release of uterine PG that would lead to abortion. At parturition, the fall in progesterone decreases PGDH concentration; tissue concentrations of PG rise and are able to exert their oxytocic effect. PG is luteolytic in the rat and helps to bring about the fall in production of progesterone from the CL of pregnancy (27). The fall in progesterone production will further decrease tissue PGDH concentration. In species in which progesterone production is placental, PG does not apparently affect progesterone metabolism. PG administration to pregnant rhesus monkeys is not followed by any reproducible pattern of maternal endocrine changes, although labor occurs (37, 111, 112). This observation and the demonstration in the sheep that PG increases the sensitivity of the myometrium to oxytocin (126) indicate that PG acts directly on the myometrium (110) and that PG synthesis, metabolism, and release are the results of the various steroid changes rather than their cause. Hydrocortisone and dexamethasone lower PGDH concentration in rat lung and kidney. Thus increased glucocorticoid concentrations at delivery may directly decrease PG degradation while increasing PG synthesis secondarily due to stimulation of estrogen synthesis (69). Circadian differences in the response of the myometrium to PGF2α have been demonstrated (179).

Tissue concentrations of PG will be determined by the balance of synthesis and specific enzymatic degradation. PGs are powerfully oxytocic (3). Any consideration of their function in labor must attempt an assessment of (a) their various fetal and maternal sites of origin within the uterus, and (b) factors that affect their release, in particular whether PGs produced at different sites can stimulate myometrial contraction. In the sheep, maternally administered progesterone inhibits PG release but not synthesis (126). Decidua and myometrium are able to metabolise PGF2α much more rapidly than the fetal placenta or membranes (105). By contrast, in the human at term, the membranes and placenta have a greater ability to metabolize PGF2α than has the myometrium (101). This difference between the sheep and the human helps to explain the observation that the human myometrium is more irritable than the ovine myometrium at surgery and following PG infusion. The fetal membranes, particularly the chorion, are more active than other tissues in the human uterus, both in the synthesis (104) and degradation of PG (101). However, complete separation of amnion and chorion, or even of fetal from maternal membranes, is not always possible, particularly in the sheep; the membranes used in such studies must be checked by electron microscopy. Fetal death in the rhesus monkey and the human is followed by a fall in estrogen production, but PG concentrations rise (37). Histological studies suggest that fetal death is followed by local tissue destruction. Increase of phospholipase activity following autolysis is the probable mechanism of PG release in this situation (77, 78, 146).

PGF2α is present in human amniotic fluid from 34 weeks of gestation (103, 170). Since vaginal distension and manual dilatation of the cervix causes uterine contraction followed by an increase in utero-ovarian plasma PG concentration in sheep (68), care is required in the interpretation of PG concentrations in samples obtained following vaginal examination. Vibration of the human cervix has been shown to expedite cervical dilatation (26). Tissue damage or cervical stretching during amniotomy probably results in artificially elevated concentrations of PG in amniotic fluid. Although amniotic fluid PGF concentrations are higher at term before labor commences than at 15–20 weeks of gestation (106), no significant increase in PG in late gestation is noted with samples obtained by amniocentesis (198). Once labor has commenced, amniotic PG concentrations rise as cervical dilatation proceeds (103). When labor is induced with oxytocin infusion, amniotic PG concentrations eventually begin to rise; at delivery they reach concentrations similar to those observed during spontaneous delivery (86). Following cs, neonatal umbilical arterial PG concentration is lower than after vaginal delivery (36). In another study, active labor was not shown to increase umbilical plasma PG concentration (49). PG concentrations increased in fetal sheep plasma over the last 24 hr of intrauterine life. No correlation of PG concentration with uterine activity was made in this study (34). The PG increase followed the rise in fetal plasma cortisol concentration.

PG circulating in fetal plasma may play a supportive role in labor since PG injected into the fetal circulation causes uterine contraction. Oxytocin is an additional supportive factor in labor. There is little evidence that fetal or maternal oxytocin concentrations increase before labor commences in either the human or experimental animals. Maternal plasma oxytocin concentrations rise in the second stage of labor (39). Oxytocin and arginine vasopressin concentrations are high in amniotic fluid, fetal urine, and neonatal human cord blood (40, 172). There is a positive umbilical arteriovenous difference for these neurohypophysial hormones. Fetal lamb plasma oxytocin concentrations are low more than 50 hr before delivery and rise steeply in the last 6 hr (70). Oxytocin in fetal circulation can exert an oxytocic effect (149), probably by crossing the fetal membranes directly rather than by gaining access to the maternal circulation across the placenta (71). Oxytocinase activity has been demonstrated in the human placenta but the kinetics of this enzyme do not support the suggestion that it plays a physiological role in the control of the function of oxytocin (177). It has been suggested that oxytocin exerts its action through PG. However, pharmacological doses of oxytocin do cause contraction of the otherwise flaccid, toneless uterus of rhesus monkeys treated with PG synthetase inhibitors (154). Oxytocin may play a role in enhancing PG release in the pregnant sheep (141), thereby setting up an important positive feedback loop since further oxytocin release may be caused by either the uterine contractions that ensue or the PG itself (75).

Oxytocin decreases uterine muscle cAMP concentration. cAMP phosphorylates a tubular binding protein in the myometrial cell, thereby enabling it to bind Ca^{2+}. The fall in intracellular free Ca^{2+} produces muscular relaxation (116). The involvement of cyclic nucleotides in the action of oxytocin and $PGF2\alpha$ has been demonstrated in vivo in the rat and the rabbit. In these two species, theophylline, (a phosphodiesterase inhibitor), cAMP, butyryl-cAMP, and 8-bromo-cGMP all inhibited uterine activity generated by infusions of oxytocin and $PGF2\alpha$ infused directly into the aorta of the pregnant female (28, 95, 96, 117).

CONCLUSION AND SUMMARY

In certain experimental animals, in particular the sheep, cow, and goat, the fetal adrenal apparently plays a central role in the mechanisms that initiate parturition. At the present time the nature of the input signal that stimulates the increased activity of the fetal adrenal is uncertain.

In the sheep, increased fetal glucocorticoid secretion stimulates placental production of estrogen from progesterone, thereby leading to a fall in maternal plasma and tissue progesterone concentrations and a rise in estrogen concentrations. Estrogens are potent stimulators of PG production, and the fall in progesterone enables the release of PG to occur. In addition, maternal and fetal oxytocin secretion may play a supportive role. The interrelationships of estrogen, progesterone, oxytocin, and prostaglandin result in a cascade phenomenon with several interconnected positive feedback loops that ensure rapid and controlled delivery.

In the primate, C-19 estrogen precursors are secreted by the fetal adrenal. Increased fetal adrenal activity will therefore probably result in more of these compounds being made available for placental aromatization to estrogen. Since the placenta does not utilize progesterone, this may explain why it has been a problem to demonstrate a fall in maternal plasma progesterone concentrations before delivery has begun. It should always be borne in mind that myometrial tissue concentrations of various hormones and other important metabolites may not follow maternal plasma concentrations directly. The various steroids synthesized in the ovary and placenta affect the production, release, and metabolism of prostaglandins. Much useful information is now being obtained from studies of the detailed ultrastructure and function of the membranes that separate the maternal and fetal blood and the myometrium. When considering the endocrine events that occur at parturition, we may conveniently divide them into those that are initiatory and those that are supportive. The second group of mechanisms only comes into action once labor has begun. They are, however, of the utmost importance to the successful completion of the delivery of a live fetus in good condition.

Acknowledgments

Investigations by the author were supported by research grants from the Medical Research Council, The Wellcome Trust, and The Lalor Foundation. The author gratefully acknowledges the collaboration of many colleagues, in particular Margaret Abel, Fiona Bass, John Buckle, Carol Horn, Patricia Jack, Sally Ratter, Lesley Rees, and Alan Thomas.

Literature Cited

1. Abel, M. H., Krane, E. J., Thomas, A. L., Bass, F. G., Nathanielsz, P. W. 1977. The use of synthetic TRH to assess fetal pituitary function following section of the pituitary stalk of the fetal sheep. *J. Endocrinol.* 72:32P
2. Abel, M. H., Krane, E. J., Thomas, A. L., Nathanielsz, P. W. 1977. Plasma prolactin concentrations in the fetal sheep: normal concentrations before delivery and the effect of cortisol-induced delivery. *J. Endocrinol.* 72:36–37P
3. Aiken, J. W. 1974. Prostaglandins and prostaglandin synthetase inhibitors: studies on uterine motility and function. In *Prostaglandin Synthetase Inhibitors,* ed. H. J. Robinson, J.R. Vane, pp. 289–301. New York: Raven Press
4. Ainsworth, L., Ryan, K. J. 1966. Steroid hormone transformations by endocrine organs from pregnant mammals. 1. Estrogen biosynthesis by mammalian placental preparations *in vitro. Endocrinology* 79:875–83
5. Albano, J. D. M., Jack, P. M., Joseph, T., Gould, R. P., Nathanielsz, P. W., Brown, B. L. 1976. The development of ACTH-sensitive adenylate cyclase activity in the foetal rabbit adrenal: a correlated biochemical and morphological study. *J. Endocrinol.* 71:333–41
6. Alexander, D. P., Britton, H. G., Forsling, M. L., Nixon, D. A., Ratcliffe, J. G. 1974. Pituitary and plasma concentrations of adrenocorticotrophin, growth hormone, vasopressin, and oxytocin in fetal and maternal sheep during the latter half of gestation and the response to haemorrhage. *Biol. Neonat.* 24:206–19
7. Allen, J. P., Cook, D. M., Kendall, J. W., McGilvra, R. 1973. Maternal-fetal ACTH relationship in man. *J. Clin. Endocrinol. Metab.* 37:230–34
8. Allen, J. P., Greer, M. A., McGilvra, R., Castro, A., Fisher, D. A. 1974. Endocrine function in an anencephalic infant. *J. Clin. Endocrinol. Metab.* 38: 94–98
9. Anderson, A. B. M., Flint, A. P. F., Turnbull, A. C. 1975. Mechanism of action of glucocorticoids in induction of ovine parturition: effect on placental steroid metabolism. *J. Endocrinol.* 66: 61–70
10. Anderson, A. B. M., Laurence, K. M., Davies, K., Campbell, H., Turnbull, A. C. 1971. Fetal adrenal weight and the causes of premature delivery. *J. Obstet. Gynaecol. Br. Commonw.* 78:481–88
11. Anderson, A. B. M., Pierrepoint, C. G., Turnbull, A. C., Griffiths, K. 1973. Steroid investigations in the developing sheep foetus. In *The Endocrinology of Pregnancy and Parturition,* ed. C. G. Pierrepoint, pp. 23–39. Cardiff, U. K: Alpha Omega Alpha
12. Atkinson, L. E., Hotchkiss, J., Fritz, G. R., Surve, A. H., Neill, J. D., Knobil, E. 1975. Circulating levels of steroids and chorionic gonadotropin during pregnancy in the rhesus monkey, with special attention to the rescue of the corpus luteum in early pregnancy. *Biol. Reprod.* 12:335–45
13. Barcikowski, B., Carlson, J. C., Wilson, L., McCracken, J. A. 1974. The effect of endogenous and exogenous estradiol-17β on the release of prostaglandin F2α from the ovine uterus. *Endocrinology* 95:1340–49
14. Barnes, R. J., Comline, R. S., Silver, M., Steven, D. H. 1976. Ultrastructural changes in the placenta of the ewe after foetal hypophysectomy or adrenalectomy. *J. Physiol. London* 263:173P–74P
15. Bass, F., Krane, E. J., Mallon, K., Nathanielsz, P. W., Steven, D. H., Thomas, A. L. 1977. Mobilisation of binucleate cells in the placenta of the ewe following foetal pituitary stalk section. *J. Endocrinol.* 73:36P-37P
16. Bassett, J. M., Thorburn, G. D. 1969. Foetal plasma corticosteroids and the initiation of parturition in sheep. *J. Endocrinol.* 44:285–86
17. Bedwani, J. R., Marley, P. B. 1975. Enhanced inactivation of prostaglandin E2 by the rabbit lung during pregnancy or progesterone treatment. *Br. J. Pharmacol.* 53:547–54
18. Beitins, I. Z., Kowarski, A., Shermeta, D. W., De Lemos, R. A., Migeon, C. J. 1970. Fetal and maternal secretion rate of cortisol in sheep: Diffusion resistance of the placenta. *Pediatr. Res.* 4:129–34
19. Bergland, R., Page, R. 1976. Vascular organization within the mammalian hypophysis. Part II: Interrelationships. *Proc. 5th Int. Cong. Endocrinol. Hamburg.* Abstr. 503
20. Binns, W., James, J. F., Shupe, J. L. 1964. Toxicosis of *Veratrum californicum* in ewes and its relationship to a congenital deformity in lambs. *Ann. NY Acad. Sci.* 111:571–76
21. Blackwell, G. J., Flower, R. J., Vane, J. R. 1975. Rapid reduction of prostaglandin 15-hydroxydehydrogenase activity in rat tissues after treatment with protein synthesis inhibitors. *Br. J. Pharmacol.* 55:233–38

22. Boddy, K., Jones, C. T., Mantell, C., Ratcliffe, J. G., Robinson, J. S. 1974. Changes in plasma ACTH and corticosteroid of the maternal and fetal sheep during hypoxia. *Endocrinology* 94: 588–91

23. Bosu, W. T. K., Johansson, E. D. B., Gemzell, C. 1973. Patterns of circulating oestrone, oestradiol-17β and progesterone during pregnancy in the rhesus monkey. *Acta Endocrinol.* 74: 743–55

24. Bosu, W. T. K., Johansson, E. D. B., Gemzell, C. 1973. Peripheral plasma levels of oestrogens, progesterone and 17α-hydroxyprogesterone during gestation in the rhesus monkey. *Acta Endocrinol.* 74:348–60

25. Bosu, W. T. K., Johansson, E. D. B., Gemzell, C. 1974. Influence of oophorectomy, luteectomy, foetal death and dexamethasone on the peripheral plasma levels of oestrogens and progesterone in the pregnant *Macaca mulatta Acta Endocrinol.* 75:601–16

26. Brant, H. A., Lackelin, G. C. L. 1971. Vibration of the cervix to expedite first stage of labour. *Lancet* 11:686–87

27. Buckle, J. W., Nathanielsz, P. W. 1973. The effect of low doses of prostaglandin F2α infused into the aorta of unrestrained pregnant rats: observations on induction of parturition and effect on plasma progesterone concentration. *Prostaglandins* 4:443–457

28. Buckle, J. W., Nathanielsz, P. W. 1975. Modification of myometrial activity in vivo by administration of cyclic nucleotides and theophylline to the pregnant rat. *J. Endocrinol.* 66:339–47

29. Cawson, M. J., Anderson, A. B. M., Turnbull, A. C., Lampe, L. 1974. Cortisol, cortisone, and 11-deoxycortisol levels in human umbilical and maternal plasma in relation to the onset of labour. *J. Obstet. Gynaecol. Br. Commonw.* 81: 737–45

30. Challis, J. R. G. 1971. Sharp increase in free circulating oestrogens immediately before parturition in sheep. *Nature* 229:208

31. Challis, J. R. G., Davies, I. J., Benirschke, K., Hendrickx, A. G., Ryan, K. J. 1974. The concentrations of progesterone, estrone and estradiol 17-β in the peripheral plasma of the rhesus monkey during the final third of gestation and after the induction of abortion with PGF2α. *Endocrinology* 95:547–53

32. Challis, J. R. G., Davies, I. J., Benirschke, K., Hendrickx, A. G., Ryan, K. J. 1974. The effects of dexamethasone on plasma steroid levels and fetal adrenal histology in the pregnant rhesus monkey. *Endocrinology* 95:1300–1305

33. Challis, J. R. G., Davies, I. J., Benirschke, K., Hendrickx, A. G., Ryan, K. J. 1975. The effects of dexamethasone on the peripheral plasma concentrations of androstenedione, testosterone and cortisol in the pregnant rhesus monkey. *Endocrinology* 96:185–92

34. Challis, J. R. G., Dilley, S. R., Robinson, J. S., Thorburn, G. D. 1976. Prostaglandins in the circulation of the fetal lamb. *Prostaglandins* 11:1041–52

35. Challis, J. R. G., Kendall, J. Z., Robinson, J. S., Thorburn, G. D. 1977. The regulation of corticosteroids during late pregnancy and their role in parturition. *Biol. Reprod.* 16:57–69

36. Challis, J. R. G., Osathanondh, R., Ryan, K. J., Tulchinsky, D. 1974. Maternal and fetal plasma prostaglandin levels at vaginal delivery and caesarean section. *Prostaglandins* 6:281–88

37. Challis, J. R. G., Robinson, J. S., Thorburn, G. D. 1977. Fetal and maternal endocrine changes during pregnancy and parturition in the rhesus monkey. In *The Fetus and Birth,* ed. J. Knight, M. O'Connor, pp. 211–27. Amsterdam: *Ciba Found. Symp. No. 47.* Elsevier/Excerpta Medica/North-Holland

38. Challis, J. R. G., Thorburn, G. D. 1975. Prenatal endocrine function and the initiation of parturition. In *Perinatal Research,* ed. P. W. Nathanielsz. *Br. Med. Bull.* 31(1):57–61

39. Chard, T., Boyd, N. R. H., Forsling, M. L., McNeilly, A. S., Landon, J. 1970. The development of a radioimmunoassay for oxytocin: the extraction of oxytocin from plasma and its measurement during parturition in human and goat blood. *J. Endocrinol.* 48:223–34

40. Chard, T., Hudson, C. N., Edwards, C. R. W., Boyd, N. R. H. 1971. Release of oxytocin and vasopressin by the human foetus during labour. *Nature* 234: 352–54

41. Chester, R., Dukes, M., Slater, S. R., Walpole, A. L. 1972. Delay of parturition in the rat by anti-inflammatory agents which inhibit the biosynthesis of prostaglandins. *Nature* 240:37–39

42. Chez, R. A., Hutchinson, D. L., Salazar, H., Mintz, D. H. 1970. Some effects of fetal and maternal hypophysectomy in pregnancy. *Am. J. Obstet. Gynecol.* 108:643–50

43. Colby, H. D., Malendowicz, L. K., Caffrey, J. L., Kitay, J. I. 1974. Effects of hypophysectomy and ACTH on

adrenocortical function in the rat. *Endocrinology* 94:1346–50
44. Comerford, J. B. 1965. Pregnancy with anencephaly. *Lancet* 1:679–80
45. Comline, R. S., Hall, L. W., Lavelle, R. B., Nathanielsz, P. W., Silver, M. 1974. Parturition in the cow: endocrine changes in animals with chronically implanted catheters in the foetal and maternal circulations. *J. Endocrinol.* 63: 451–72
46. Comline, R. S., Silver, M. 1970. Daily changes in foetal and maternal blood of conscious pregnant ewes with catheters in umbilical and uterine vessels. *J. Physiol. London* 209:567–86
47. Cornette, J. C., Harrison, K. L., Kirton, K. T. 1974. Measurement of prostaglandin F2α metabolites by radioimmunoassay. *Prostaglandins* 5:155–64
48. Coslovsky, R., Yalow, R. S. 1974. Influence of the hormonal forms of ACTH on the pattern of corticosteroid secretion. *Biochem. Biophys. Res. Commun.* 60:1351–56
49. Craft, I. L., Scrivener, R., Dewhurst, C. J. 1973. Prostaglandin F2α levels in the maternal and fetal circulations in late pregnancy. *J. Obstet. Gynaecol. Br. Commonw.* 80(7):616–18
50. Csapo, A. I., Knobil, E., Van der Molen, H. J., Wiest, W. G. 1971. Peripheral plasma progesterone levels during human pregnancy and labour. *Am. J. Obstet. Gynecol.* 110:630–32
51. Currie, W. B., Thorburn, G. D. 1977. The fetal role in timing the initiation of parturition in the goat. In *The Fetus and Birth,* ed. J. Knight, M. O'Connor, pp. 49–66. Amsterdam: *Ciba Found. Symp. No. 47* (new series). Elsevier
52. Currie, W. B., Wong, M. S. F., Cox, R. I., Thorburn, G. D. 1973. Spontaneous or dexamethasone-induced parturition in the sheep and goat: changes in plasma concentrations of maternal prostaglandin F and foetal oestrogen sulphate. *Mem. Soc. Endocrinol.* 20:95–118
53. Davies, I. J., Ryan, K. J. 1972. Comparative endocrinology of gestation. *Vitam. Horm.* 30:223–79
54. Davis, J. N., Carlsson, A. 1973. Effect of hypoxia on tyrosine and tryptophan hydroxylation in unanaesthetised rat brain. *J. Neurochem.* 21:783–90
55. Dawes, G. S., Fox, H. E., Leduc, B. M., Liggins, G. C., Richards, R. T. 1972. Respiratory movements and rapid eye movement sleep in the foetal lamb. *J. Physiol.* 220, 119–43

56. Demers, L. M., Yoshinaga, K., Greep, R. O. 1974. Prostaglandin F in monkey uterine fluid during the menstrual cycle and following steroid treatment. *Prostaglandins* 5:513–19
57. Drost, M. 1968. Bilateral adrenalectomy in the fetal lamb. *Exp. Med. Surg.* 26:61–65
58. Drost, M., Holm, L. W. 1968. Prolonged gestation in ewes after fetal adrenalectomy. *J. Endocrinol.* 40: 293–96
59. Drost, M., Kumagai, L. F., Guzman, M. 1973. Sequential foetal-maternal plasma cortisol levels in sheep. *J. Endocrinol.* 56:483–92
60. Egerton-Vernon, J. M., Bedwani, J. R. 1975. Prostaglandin 15-hydroxydehydrogenase activity during pregnancy in rabbits and rats. *Eur. J. Pharmacol.* 33: 405–8
61. Fairclough, R. J., Hunter, J. T., Welch, R. A. S. 1975. Peripheral plasma progesterone and utero-ovarian prostaglandin F concentrations in the cow around parturition. *Prostaglandins* 9:901–14
62. Fairclough, R. J., Hunter, J. T., Welch, R. A. S., Payne, E. 1975. Plasma corticosteroid concentrations in the bovine foetus near term. *J. Endocrinol.* 65, 139–140
63. Farrell, P. M., Zachman, R. D. 1973. Induction of choline phosphotransferase and lecithin synthesis in the fetal lung by corticosteroids. *Science* 179: 297–98
64. Fencl, M. de M., Tulchinsky, D. 1975. Total cortisol in amniotic fluid and fetal lung maturation. *New Eng. J. Med.* 292:133–37
65. Findlay, J. K., Seamark, R. F. 1973. The occurrence and metabolism of oestrogens in the sheep foetus and placenta. See Ref. 11, pp. 54–64
66. Flack, J. D., Jessup, R., Ramwell, P. W. 1969. Prostaglandin stimulation of rat corticosteroidogenesis. *Science* 163: 691–92
67. Flint, A. P. F., Anderson, A. B. M., Goodson, J. D., Steele, P. A., Turnbull, A. C. 1976. Bilateral adrenalectomy of lambs in utero: effects on maternal hormone levels at induced parturition. *J. Endocrinol.* 69:433–44
68. Flint, A. P. F., Anderson, A. B. M., Patten, P. T., Turnbull, A. C. 1974. Control of utero-ovarian venous prostaglandin F during labour in the sheep: acute effects of vaginal and cervical stimulation. *J. Endocrinol.* 63:67–87
69. Flower, R. J. 1977. The role of prostaglandins in parturition with special ref-

erence to the rat. See Ref. 51, pp. 297–312

70. Forsling, M., Jack, P. M. B., Nathanielsz, P. W. 1975. Plasma oxytocin concentrations in the foetal sheep. *Horm. Metab. Res.* 7:197–98

71. Forsling, M., Jack, P. M. B., Nathanielsz, P. W. 1975. Lack of placental transport of oxytocin from foetal lamb to pregnant ewe between 114 and 134 days gestation. *J. Endocrinol.* 64:41P

72. France, J. T., Seddon, R. J., Liggins, G. C. 1973. A study of a pregnancy with low estrogen production due to placental sulfatase deficiency. *J. Clin. Endocrinol. Metab.* 36:1–9

73. Fylling, P. 1971. Premature parturition following dexamethasone administration to pregnant ewes. *Acta Endocrinol.* 66:289–95

74. Genazzani, A. R., Fraioli, F., Hurlimann, J., Fioretti, P., Felber, J. P. 1975. Immunoreactive ACTH and cortisol plasma levels during pregnancy. Detection and partial purification of corticotrophin-like placental hormone: The human chorionic corticotrophic (HCC). *J. Clin. Endocrinol.* 4:1–14

75. Gillespie, A., Brummer, H. C., Chard, T. 1972. Oxytocin release by infused prostaglandin. *Br. Med. J.* 1:543–44

76. Grieves, S. A., Liggins, G. C. 1976. Phospholipase A activity in human and ovine uterine tissues. *Prostaglandins* 12:229–41

77. Gustavii, B., Brunk, U. 1972. A histological study of the effect on the placenta of intra-amniotically and extra-amniotically injected hypertonic saline in therapeutic abortion. *Acta Obstet. Gynecol. Scand.* 51:121–25

78. Gustavii, B., Green, K. 1972. Release of prostaglandin F2α following injection of hypertonic saline for therapeutic abortion: A preliminary study. *Am. J. Obstet. Gynecol.* 114:1099–1100

79. Hagemenas, F. C., Baughman, W. L., Kittinger, G. W. 1975. The effect of fetal hypophysectomy on placental biosynthesis of progesterone in rhesus. *Endocrinology* 96:1059–62

80. Hamberg, M. 1974. Quantitative studies on prostaglandin synthesis in man. III. Excretion of the major urinary metabolite of prostaglandin F1α and F2α during pregnancy. *Life Sci.* 14:247–52

81. Harbert, G. M. 1977. Biorhythms in the dynamics of a pregnant uterus. *Gynecol. Invest.* 8:57

82. Heap, R. B. 1972. Role of hormones in pregnancy. In *Reproduction in Mammals 3. Hormones in reproduction,* ed. C. R. Austin, R. V. Short, pp. 73–105. London: Cambridge

83. Heap, R. B., Galil, A. K. A., Harrison, F. A., Jenkin, G., Perry, J. S. 1977. Progesterone and oestrogen in pregnancy and parturition: comparative aspects and hierarchical control. See Ref. 51, pp. 127–50

84. Heap, R. B., Perry, J. S., Challis, J. R. G. 1973. Hormonal maintenance of pregnancy. In *American Physiological Society Handbook of Physiology, Section 7. Endocrinology, Vol. II, Part 2.,* ed. R. O. Greep, E. B. Astwood, pp. 217–60. Baltimore: Williams & Wilkins

85. Heinrichs, W. L., Colas, A. 1970. Hepatic microsomal 16-α-hydroxylation of 3-betahydroxyandrost-5-en-17-one (DHA) by fetal, newborn and adult rhesus monkeys. *Gen. Comp. Endocrinol.* 14:159–63

86. Hillier, K., Calder, A. A., Embrey, M. P. 1974. Concentrations of prostaglandin F2α in amniotic fluid and plasma in spontaneous and induced labours. *J. Obstet. Gynaecol. Br. Commonw.* 81:257

87. Hindson, J. C., Schofield, B. M., Turner, C. B. 1967. The effect of a single dose of stilboestrol on cervical dilatation in pregnant sheep. *Res. Vet. Sci.* 8:353–60

88. Hodgen, G. D., Dufau, M. L., Catt, K. J., Tullner, W. W. 1972. Estrogens, progesterone and chorionic gonadotropin in pregnant rhesus monkeys. *Endocrinology* 91:896–900

89. Hodgen, G. D., Gulyas, B. J., Tullner, W. W. 1975. Role of the primate placenta in cortisol secretion by the maternal adrenals. *Steroids* 26:233–40

90. Hodgen, G. D., Tullner, W. W. 1975. Plasma estrogens, progesterone and chorionic gonadotrophin in pregnant rhesus monkeys (*Macaca mulatta*) after ovariectomy. *Steroids* 25:275–82

91. Hoffmann, B., Wagner, W. C., Rattenberger, E., Schmidt, J. 1977. Endocrine relationships during late gestation and parturition in the cow. See Ref. 51, 107–18

92. Holm, L. W., Parker, H. R., Galligan, S. J. 1961. Adrenal insufficiency in postmature calves. *Am. J. Obstet. Gynecol.* 81:1000–1008

93. Honnebier, W. J., Jöbsis, A. C., Swaab, D. F. 1974. The effect of hypophysial hormones and human chorionic gonadotrophin (HCG) on the anencephalic fetal adrenal cortex and on partu-

rition in the human. *J. Obstet. Gynaecol. Br. Commonw.* 81:423–38

94. Hull, M. G. R., Chard, T. 1976. Hormonal aspects of feto-placental function. In *Fetal Physiology and Medicine,* ed. R. W. Beard, P. W. Nathanielsz, pp. 371–94. Philadelphia: Saunders

95. Jack, P. M. B., Nathanielsz, P. W. 1974. Inhibition of the oxytocic action of prostaglandin F2α on the pregnant rabbit uterus by intra-aortic infusion of theophylline in vivo. *J. Endocrinol.* 62:171–72

96. Jack, P. M. B., Nathanielsz, P. W. 1974. The effect of theophylline on oxytocin-induced contractions in the chronically catheterized pregnant rabbit. *Experientia* 30:1218–19

97. Johannisson, E. 1968. Foetal adrenal cortex in human: its ultrastructure at different stages of development and in different functional states. *Acta Endocrinol.* 58(Suppl. 130):7–107

98. Johnson, P., Jones, C. T., Kendall, J. Z., Ritchie, J. W. K., Thorburn, G. D. 1975. ACTH and the induction of parturition in sheep. *J. Physiol. London* 252:64P–66P

99. Jones, C. T., Luther, E., Ritchie, J. W. K., Worthington, D. 1975. The clearance of ACTH from the plasma of adult and fetal sheep. *Endocrinology* 96: 231–34

100. Kaplan, S. L., Grumbach, M. M., Aubert, M. L. 1976. The ontogenesis of pituitary hormones and hypothalamic factors in the human fetus: maturation of central nervous system regulation of anterior pituitary function. *Rec. Prog. Horm. Res.* 32:

101. Keirse, M. J. N. C., Turnbull, A. C. 1975. Metabolism of prostaglandins within the pregnant uterus. *Br. J. Obstet. Gynaecol.* 82:887–93

102. Keirse, M. J. N. C., Hicks, B. R., Turnbull, A. C. 1976. Prostaglandin dehydrogenase in the placenta before and after the onset of labour. *Br. J. Obstet. Gynaecol.* 83:152–55

103. Keirse, M. J. N. C., Turnbull, A. C. 1973. E prostaglandins in amniotic fluid during late pregnancy and labour. *J. Obstet. Gynaecol. Br. Commonw.* 80: 970–73

104. Keirse, M. J. N. C., Turnbull, A. C. 1976. The fetal membranes as a possible source of amniotic fluid prostaglandins. *Brit. J. Obstet. Gynaecol.* 83:146–51

105. Keirse, M. J. N. C., Hicks, B. R., Turnbull, A. C. 1975. Comparison of intrauterine metabolism of prostaglandin

F2α in ovine and human pregnancy. *J. Endocrinol.* 67:24–25P

106. Keirse, M. J. N. C., Flint, A. P. F., Turnbull, A. C. 1974. F Prostaglandins in amniotic fluid during pregnancy and labour. *J. Obstet. Gynaecol. Br. Commonw.* 81:131–35

107. Kendall, J. W., Roth, J. G. 1969. Adrenocortical function in monkeys after forebrain removal or pituitary stalk section. *Endocrinology* 84:686–91

108. Kendall, J. Z., Challis, J. R. G., Jones, C. T., Ritchie, J. W. K., Thorburn, G. D. 1975. Steroid changes associated with the induction of premature parturition in intact and hypophysectomised fetal lambs. *Acta Endocrinol.* Suppl. 199, Abstr. 33

109. Kennedy, P. C., Kendrick, J. W., Stormont, C. 1957. Adenohypophyseal aplasia, an inherited defect associated with abnormal gestation in Guernsey cattle. *Cornell Vet.* 47:160–78

110. Kimball, F. A., Kirton, K. T., Wyngarden, L. J. 1975. Prostaglandin E1 specific binding in rhesus myometrium. *Prostaglandins* 10:853–64

111. Kirton, K., Duncan, G., Oesterling, T., Forbes, A. 1971. Prostaglandins and reproduction in the rhesus monkey. *Ann. N.Y. Acad. Sci.* 180:445–55

112. Kirton, K. T., Pharriss, B. B., Forbes, A. D. 1970. Some effects of prostaglandin E2 and F2α on the pregnant rhesus monkey. *Biol. Reprod.* 3:163–68

113. Kloeck, F. K., Jung, H. 1973. In vitro release of prostaglandins from the human myometrium under the influence of stretching. *Am. J. Obstet. Gynecol.* 115:1066–69

114. Kloosterman, G. J. 1968. The obstetrician and dysmaturity. In *Aspects of Prematurity and Dysmaturity,* ed. J. H. P. Jonxis, H. K. A. Visser, J. A. Troelstra, pp. 263–80. Leiden: Stenfert Kroese

115. Koch, Y., Chow, Y. F., Meites, J. 1971. Metabolic clearance and secretion rates of prolactin in the rat. *Endocrinology* 89:1303–8

116. Krall, J. F., Korenman, S. G. 1977. Control of uterine contractility via cyclic AMP dependent protein kinase. See Ref. 51, pp. 319–38

117. Kuehl, F. A. 1974. Prostaglandins, cyclic nucleotides and cell function. *Prostaglandins* 5:325–38

118. Lanman, J. T. 1968. Delays during reproduction and their effects on the embryo and fetus. *New Eng. J. Med.* 278:993–999, 1047–54, 1092–99

119. Lanman, J. T. 1977. Parturition in non-human primates. *Biology of Reproduction* 16:28–38

120. Lanman, J. T., Thau, R., Sundaram, K., Brinson, A., Bonk, R. 1975. Ovarian and placental origins of plasma progesterone following fetectomy in monkeys (*Macaca mulatta*). *Endocrinology* 96:591–97

121. Lewis, R. B., Schulman, J. D. 1973. Influence of acetylsalicylic acid, an inhibitor of prostaglandin synthesis, on the duration of human gestation and labour. *Lancet* (2):1159–61

122. Liddle, G. W., Island, D., Meador, C. K. 1962. Normal and abnormal regulation of corticotropin secretion in man. *Rec. Prog. Horm. Res.* 8:125–53

123. Liggins, G. C. 1968. Premature parturition after infusion of corticotrophin or cortisol into foetal lambs. *J. Endocrinol.* 42:323–29

124. Liggins, G. C. 1969. The foetal role in the initiation of parturition in the ewe. In *Foetal Autonomy*, ed. G. E. W. Wolstenholme, M. O'Connor, pp. 218–44. *Ciba Found. Symp.*

125. Liggins, G. C., Fairclough, R. J., Grieves, S. A., Forster, C. S., Knox, B. S. 1977. See Ref. 51, pp. 5–25. Parturition in the sheep.

126. Liggins, G. C., Fairclough, R. J., Grieves, S. A., Kendall, J. Z., Knox, B. S. 1973. The mechanism of initiation of parturition in the ewe. *Rec. Prog. Horm. Res.* 29:111–59

127. Liggins, G. C., Forster, C. S., Grieves, S. A., Schwartz, A. L. 1977. Control of parturition in man. *Biol. Reprod.* 16:39–56

128. Liggins, G. C., Holm, L. W., Kennedy, P. C. 1966. Prolonged pregnancy following surgical lesions of the foetal lamb pituitary. *J. Reprod. Fertil.* 12:419

129. Liggins, G. C., Kennedy, P. C. 1968. Effects of electrocoagulation of the foetal lamb hypophysis on growth and development. *J. Endocrinol.* 40:371–81

130. Liggins, G. C., Kennedy, P. C., Holm, L. W. 1967. Failure of initiation of parturition after electrocoagulation of the pituitary of the foetal lamb. *Am. J. Obstet. Gynecol.* 98:1080–86

131. Lis, M., Gilardeau, C., Chretien, M. 1973. Effect of prolactin on corticosterone production by rat adrenals. *Clin. Res.* 21:1027

132. Liskowski, L., Wolf, R. C., Chandler, S., Meyer, R. K. 1970. Urinary estrogen excretion in pregnant rhesus monkeys. *Biol. Reprod.* 3:55–60

133. MacDonald, P. C., Schultz, F. M., Duenhoelter, J. H., Gant, N. F., Jimencz, J. M., Pritchard, J. A., Porter, J. C., Johnston, J. M. 1974. Initiation of Human Parturition. 1. Mechanism of Action of Arachidonic Acid. *Obstet. Gynecol.* 44:629–36

134. Madill, D., Bassett, J. M. 1973. Corticosteroid release by adrenal tissue from foetal and newborn lambs in response to corticotrophin stimulation in a perifusion system in vitro. *J. Endocrinol.* 58:75–87

135. Manaugh, L. C., Novy, M. J. 1976. Effects of indomethacin on corpus luteum function and pregnancy in rhesus monkeys. *Fertil. Steril.* 27:588–98

136. Mann, M. R., Curet, L. B., Colas, A. E. 1975. Aromatizing activity of placenta microsomal fractions from ewes in late gestation. *J. Endocrinol.* 65:117–25

137. Mati, J. K. G., Horrobin, D. F., Bramley, P. S. 1973. Induction of labour in sheep and in humans by single doses of corticosteroids. *Br. Med. J.* 2:149–51

138. Mellor, D. J., Slater, J. S. 1971. Daily changes in amniotic and allantoic fluid during the last three months of pregnancy in conscious, unstressed ewes, with catheters in their foetal fluid sacs. *J. Physiol.* 217:573–604

139. Mellor, D. J., Slater, J. S. 1972. Daily changes in foetal urine and relationships with amniotic and allantoic fluid and maternal plasma during the last two months of pregnancy in conscious, unstressed ewes with chronically implanted catheters. *J. Physiol. London* 227:503–25

140. Mitchell, M. D., Patrick, J. E., Robinson, J. S., Thorburn, G. D., Challis, J. R. G. 1976. Prostaglandins in the plasma and amniotic fluid of rhesus monkeys during pregnancy and after intra-uterine foetal death. *J. Endocrinol.* 71:67–76

141. Mitchell, M. D., Flint, A. P. F., Turnbull, A. C. 1975. Effects of oxytocin on plasma prostaglandin F levels in the pregnant and postpartum ewe. *J. Endocrinol.* 64:16–17P

142. Mueller-Heubach, E., Myers, R. E., Adamsons, K. 1972. Effects of adrenalectomy on pregnancy length in the rhesus monkey. *Am. J. Obstet. Gynecol.* 112:221–26

143. Murphy, B. E. P. 1973. Does the human fetal adrenal play a role in parturition? *Am. J. Obstet. Gynecol.* 115:521–25

144. Murphy, B. E. P., Clark, S. J., Donald, I. R., Pinsky, M., Vedady, D. 1974. Conversion of maternal cortisol to cor-

tisone during placental transfer to the human fetus. *Am. J. Obstet. Gynecol.* 118:538–41

145. Murphy, B. E. P., Patrick, J., Denton, R. L. 1975. Cortisol in amniotic fluid during human gestation. *J. Clin. Endocrinol. Metab.* 40:164–67

146. Myers, R. E., Symchych, P., Strauss, L., Comas, A., Figueroa-Longo, J., Kerenyi, T., Adamsons, K. 1974. Morphologic changes of uterine wall following intra-amniotic injection of hypertonic saline in the rhesus monkey. *Am. J. Obstet. Gynecol.* 119:877–88

147. Nathanielsz, P. W. 1976. *Fetal Endocrinology—An Experimental Approach,* Amsterdam: North-Holland; New York: Oxford. 261 pp.

148. Nathanielsz, P. W., Abel, M., Smith, G. W. 1973. Hormonal factors in parturition in the rabbit. In *Foetal and Neonatal Physiology, Proc. Sir Joseph Barcroft Centenary Symp.*, ed. R. S. Comline, K. W. Cross, G. S. Dawes, P. W. Nathanielsz, pp. 594–602. London: Cambridge

149. Nathanielsz, P. W., Comline, R. S., Silver, M. 1973. Uterine activity following intravenous administration of oxytocin to the foetal sheep. *Nature* 243:471–72

150. Nathanielsz, P. W., Comline, R. S., Silver, M., Paisey, R. B. 1972. Cortisol metabolism in the fetal and neonatal sheep. *J. Reprod. Fertil.* Suppl. 16: 39–59

151. Nathanielsz, P. W., Jack, P. M. B., Krane, E. J., Thomas, A. L., Ratter, S., Rees, L. H. 1977. The role and regulation of corticotropin in the fetal sheep. See Ref. 51, pp. 73–91

152. Neill, J. D., Johansson, E. D. B., Knobil, E. 1969. Patterns of circulating progesterone concentrations during the fertile menstrual cycle and the remainder of gestation in the rhesus monkey. *Endocrinology* 84:45–48

153. Newton, W. H. 1935. "Pseudo-parturition" in the mouse and the relation of the placenta to post-partum oestrus. *J. Physiol. London* 84:196–207

154. Novy, M. J. 1977. Endocrine and pharmacological factors which influence the onset of labour in rhesus monkeys. See Ref. 51, pp. 259–88

155. Novy, M. J., Cook, M. J., Manaugh, L. 1973. Indomethacin block of normal onset of parturition in primates. *Am. J. Obstet. Gynecol.* 118:412–16

156. Oakey, R. E. 1970. The progressive increase in estrogen production in human pregnancy. An appraisal of the factors responsible. *Vitam. Horm.* 28:1–36

157. Olley, P. M., Coceani, F., Kent, G. 1974. Inactivation of prostaglandin E_1 by the lungs of the foetal lamb. *Experientia* 30:58–59

158. Page, R., Bergland, R. 1976. Vascular organization within the mammalian hypophysis. Part 1: Median eminence. *Proc. 5th Int. Congr. Endocrinol., Hamburg, July 18–24, 1976,* ed. V. H. T. James. In press

159. Parnham, M. J., Sneddon, J. M., Williams, K. I. 1975. Evidence for a possible foetal control of prostaglandin release from the pregnant rat uterus in vitro. *J. Endocrinol.* 65:429–37

160. Patrick, J. E., Challis, J. R. G., Johnson, P., Robinson, J. S., Thorburn, G. D. 1976. Cortisol in amniotic fluid of rhesus monkeys. *J. Endocrinol.* 68: 161–62

161. Pepe, G. J., Townsley, J. D. 1975. Cortisol metabolism in the baboon during pregnancy and the post-partum period. *Endocrinology* 96:587–91

162. Pierrepoint, C. G., Anderson, A. B. M., Griffiths, K., Turnbull, A. C. 1971. The short term maintenance of the isolated sheep foetus in the last fifth of pregnancy. *Acta Endocrinol.* 66:35–49

163. Piper, P. J., Vane, J. R., Wyllie, J. H. 1970. Inactivation of prostaglandins by the lungs. *Nature* 225:600–4

164. Pupkin, M. J., Schomberg, D. W., Nagey, D. A., Crenshaw, C. 1975. Effect of exogenous dehydroepiandrosterone upon the fetoplacental biosynthesis of estrogens and its effect upon uterine blood flow in the term pregnant ewe. *Am. J. Obstet. Gynecol.* 121: 227–32

165. Ramwell, P. W., Leovey, E. M. K., Sintetos, A. L. 1977. Regulation of the arachidonic acid cascade. *Biol. Reprod.* 16:70–87

166. Rees, L. H., Burke, C. W., Chard, T., Evans, S. W., Letchworth, A. T. 1975. Placental origin of ACTH in normal human pregnancy. *Nature* 254:620–22

167. Rees, L. H., Jack, P. M. B., Thomas, A. L., Nathanielsz, P. W. 1975. Role of foetal adrenocorticotrophin during parturition in sheep. *Nature* 253:274–75

168. Roos, B. A. 1974. Effect of ACTH and cAMP on human adrenocortical growth and function in vitro. *Endocrinology* 94:685–90

169. Ryan, K. J., Hopper, B. R. 1974. Placental biosynthesis and metabolism of steroid hormones in primates. *Contrib. Primatol.* 3:258–83

170. Salmon, J. A., Amy, J. J. 1973. Levels of prostaglandin F2α in amniotic fluid

during pregnancy and labour. *Prostaglandins* 4:523–33

171. Schlegel, W., Demers, L. M., Hildebrandt-Stark, H. E., Behrman, H. R., Greep, R. O. 1974. Partial purification of human placental 15-hydroxy-prostaglandin dehydrogenase kinetic properties. *Prostaglandins* 5:417–33

172. Seppala, M., Aho, I., Tissari, A., Ruoslahti, E. 1972. Radioimmunoassay of oxytocin in amniotic fluid, fetal urine and meconium during late pregnancy and delivery. *Am. J. Obstet. Gynecol.* 114:788–95

173. Shearman, R. P., Jools, N. D., Smith, I. D. 1972. Maternal and fetal venous plasma steroids in relation to parturition. *J. Obstet. Gynaecol. Br. Commonw.* 79:212–15

174. Sherwood, O. D., Chang, C. C., Bevier, G. W., Diehl, J. R., Dziuk, P. J. 1976. Relaxin concentrations in pig plasma following administration of prostaglandin F2α during late pregnancy. *Endocrinology* 98:875–79

175. Siiteri, P. K., MacDonald, P. C. 1966. Placental estrogen biosynthesis during human pregnancy. *J. Clin. Endocrinol. Metab.* 26:751–61

176. Silman, R. E., Chard, T., Lowry, P. J., Smith, I., Young, I. M. 1976. Human fetal pituitary peptides and parturition. *Nature* 260:716–18

177. Small, C. W., Watkins, W. B. 1975. Oxytocinase—Immuno-histochemical demonstration in the immature and term human placenta. *Cell Tiss. Res.* 162:531–39

178. Smith, I. D., Shearman, R. P. 1974. Fetal plasma steroids in relation to parturition. *J. Obstet. Gynaecol. Br. Commonw.* 81:11–15

179. Smith, I. D., Shearman, R. P. 1974. Circadian aspects of prostaglandin F2α-induced termination of pregnancy. *J. Obstet. Gynaecol. Br. Commonw.* 81: 841–48

180. Solomon, S., Leung, K. 1972. Steroid hormones in non-human primates during pregnancy. In *The Use of Non-human Primates for Research on Problems of Human Reproduction*, ed. E. Diczfalusy, C. C. Diczfalusy, pp. 178–190. New York: W.H.O.

181. Stabenfeldt, G. H., Drost, M., Franti, C. E. 1972. Peripheral plasma progesterone levels in the ewe during pregnancy and parturition. *Endocrinology* 90:144–50

182. Steele, P. A., Flint, A. P. F., Turnbull, A. C. 1976. Activity of steroid C-17,20 lyase in the ovine placenta: effect of exposure to foetal glucocorticoid. *J. Endocrinol.* 69:239–46

183. Steele, P. A., Flint, A. P. F., Turnbull, A. C. 1976. Increased utero-ovarian androstenedione production before parturition in sheep. *J. Reprod. Fert.* 46: 443–45

184. Steven, D. H. 1975. Separation of the placenta in the ewe: an ultrastructural study. *Q. J. Exp. Physiol.* 60:37–44

185. Strott, C. A., Sundel, H., Stahlman, M. T. 1974. Maternal and fetal plasma progesterone, cortisol, testosterone and 17 β-estradiol in preparturient sheep: response to fetal ACTH infusion. *Endocrinology* 95:1327–39

186. Stryker, J. L., Dziuk, P. J. 1975. Effects of fetal decapitation on fetal development, parturition and lactation in pigs. *J. Anim. Sci.* 40:282–87

187. Sun, F. F., Armour, S. B. 1974. Prostaglandin 15-hydroxydehydrogenase and Δ^{13}-reductase levels in the lungs of maternal, fetal and neonatal rabbits. *Prostaglandins* 7:327–38

188. Swaab, D. F., Boer, K., Honnebier, W. J. 1977. The fetal hypothalamus and pituitary in the onset and the course of parturition. See Ref. 51, pp. 379–93

189. Swaab, D. F., Honnebier, W. J. 1974. The role of the fetal hypothalamus in development of the feto-placental unit and in parturition. In *Progress in Brain Research, Vol. 41: Integrative Hypothalamic Activity*, ed. D. F. Swaab, J. P. Schadé, pp. 255–80. Amsterdam: Elsevier

190. Sykes, J. A. C., Williams, K. I., Rogers, A. F. 1975. Prostaglandin production and metabolism by homogenates of pregnant human deciduum and myometrium. *J. Endocrinol.* 64:18–19P

191. Talbert, L. M., Easterling, W. E., Potter, H. D. 1973. Maternal and fetal plasma levels of adrenal corticoids in spontaneous vaginal delivery and cesarian section. *Am. J. Obstet. Gynecol.* 117:554–59

192. Tamby Raja, R. L., Anderson, A. B. M., Turnbull, A. C. 1974. Endocrine changes in premature labour. *Br. Med. J.* 4:67–71

193. Thorburn, G. D., Challis, J. R. G., Currie, W. B. 1977. Control of parturition in domestic animals. *Biol. Reprod.* 16:18–27

194. Thorburn, G. D., Cox, R. I., Currie, W. B., Restall, B. J., Schneider, W. 1973. Prostaglandin F and progesterone concentrations in the utero-ovarian venous plasma of the ewe during the oestrous

cycle and early pregnancy. *J. Reprod. Fert.* Suppl. 18:151–58

195. Thorburn, G. D., Nicol, D. H., Bassett, J. M., Shutt, D. A., Cox, R. I. 1972. Parturition in the goat and sheep: changes in corticosteroids, progesterone, oestrogens and prostaglandin F. *J. Reprod. Fert.* Suppl. 16:61–84

196. Thorburn, G. D., Schneider, W. 1972. The progesterone concentration in the plasma of the goat during the oestrous cycle and pregnancy. *J. Endocrinol.* 52:23–36

197. Townsley, J. D., Rubin, E. J., Crystle, C. D. 1973. Evaluation of placental steroid 3-sulfatase and aromatase activities as regulators of estrogen production in human pregnancy. *Am. J. Obstet. Gynecol.* 117:345–50

198. Turnbull, A. C., Anderson, A. B. M., Flint, A. P. F., Jeremy, J. Y., Keirse, M. J. N. C., Mitchell, M. D. 1977. Human parturition. See Ref. 51, pp. 427–52

199. Turnbull, A. C., Anderson, A. B. M. 1969. The influence of the foetus on myometrial contractility. In *Progesterone: its regulatory effect on the myometrium*, ed. G. E. W. Wolstenholme, J. Knight, pp. 106–13. London: Churchill

200. Turnbull, A. C., Patten, P. T., Flint, A. P. F., Keirse, M. J. N. C., Jeremy, J. Y., Anderson, A. B. M. 1974. Significant fall in progesterone and rise in oestradiol levels in human peripheral plasma before onset of labour. *Lancet* 1: 101–4

201. Tyson, J. E., Hwang, P., Guyda, H., Friesen, H. G. 1972. Studies of prolactin secretion in human pregnancy. *Am. J. Obstet. Gynecol.* 113:14–20

202. Umo, I., Fitzpatrick, R. J., Ward, W. R. 1976. Parturition in the goat: plasma concentrations of prostaglandin F and steroid hormones and uterine activity during late pregnancy and parturition. *J. Endocrinol.* 68:383–89

203. Van Wagenen, G., Newton, W. H. 1943. Pregnancy in the monkey after removal of the fetus. *Surg. Gynecol. Obstet.* 77:539–43

204. Walker, A. M., Oakes, G. K., Ehrenkranz, R. A., McLaughlin, M., Chez, R. A. 1976. 24-hour rhythms in uterine and umbilical blood flows of pregnant sheep. *Gynecol. Invest.* 7:23

205. Walsh, S. W., Wolf, R. C., Meyer, R. K. 1974. Progesterone, progestins and 17-hydroxypregn-4-ene-3,20-dione in the utero-ovarian, uterine and peripheral blood of the pregnant rhesus monkey. *Endocrinology* 95:1704–10

206. Webel, S. K., Rimers, R. J., Martin, P., Dziuk, P. J. 1972. Plasma progesterone and embryo survival in gilts. *J. Anim. Sci.* 35:256–61

207. Welsch, C. W., Squiers, M. D., Cassell, E., Chen, C. L., Meites, J. 1971. Median eminence lesions and serum prolactin: influence of ovariectomy and ergocornine. *Am. J. Physiol.* 221:1714–17

208. Wiener, M. 1976. Control of placental 3β-hydroxy-Δ5-steroid dehydrogenase: comparison of enzyme characteristics in man, cow, goat, rat and rhesus monkey. *Biol. Reprod.* 14:306–13

209. Winters, A. J., Colston, C., MacDonald, P. C., Porter, J. C. 1975. Fetal plasma prolactin levels. *J. Clin. Endocrinol. Metab.* 41:626–29

210. Winters, A. J., Oliver, C., Colston, C., MacDonald, P. C., Porter, J. C. 1974. Plasma ACTH levels in the human fetus and neonate as related to age and parturition. *J. Clin. Endocrinol. Metab.* 39:269–73

211. Wintour, E. M., Brown, E. H., Denton, D. A., Hardy, K. J., McDougall, J. G., Oddie, C. J., Whipp, G. T. 1975. The ontogeny and regulation of corticosteroid secretion by the ovine foetal adrenal. *Acta Endocrinol.* 79:301–16

212. Witorsch, R. J., Kitay, J. I. 1972. Pituitary hormones affecting adrenal 5α-reductase activity: ACTH, growth hormone and prolactin. *Endocrinology* 91: 764–69

213. Wong, M. S. F., Cox, R. I., Currie, W. B., Thorburn, G. D. 1972. Changes of oestrogen sulphoconjugates in the foetal plasma of sheep and goats during late gestation. *Proc. 15th Annu. Meet. Endocrine Society of Australia, Sydney,* Vol. 15, Abstr. 8

Ann. Rev. Physiol. 1978. 400:447–69
Copyright © 1978 by Annual Reviews Inc. All rights reserved

ACTIVITY METABOLISM OF THE LOWER VERTEBRATES

❖1198

Albert F. Bennett

School of Biological Sciences, University of California, Irvine, California 92717

INTRODUCTION

The physiology of animals during activity has become a topic of widespread investigation. Studies concerning activity have generally been done on mammals, and several aspects of these have been reviewed elsewhere (87, 102, 139, 149). Fewer data are available for avian systems (64). The present review summarizes a growing body of literature concerning activity metabolism in the lower vertebrates: reptiles, amphibians, and fish. It includes a discussion of oxygen consumption during activity, emphasizing maximal oxygen consumption; aerobic scope; the cost of locomotion; and the influence of body temperature on these processes. Anaerobic metabolism, principally the production of lactic acid, is reviewed and its magnitude, thermal dependence, and effect on recovery and oxygen debt are discussed. Finally, the magnitudes of these two factors are compared at different levels of exertion, and phylogenetic differences in activity patterns are emphasized. Aspects of these topics have been reviewed previously for reptiles (21, 63, 65, 151) and, more extensively, for fish (28, 40, 74, 79, 80, 82, 117, 160).

Major differences in ecology, physiology, and morphology exist between and within each of the classes of lower vertebrates; within this diversity, I have tried to emphasize common themes and point out where the groups differ from each other and from the mammals and birds. Such a comparative examination of these different classes is not frequently attempted (49), and the literature concerning these animals has largely developed independently with little intercommunication. I hope this review will stimulate increased interest among people working with these animals and with activity metabolism in mammals and birds, so that a broader comparative outlook on the capacities of and limitations on activity in vertebrates may be achieved.

447

0066-4278/78/0301-0447$01.00

AEROBIC METABOLISM

The analysis of aerobic metabolism of vertebrates historically has concentrated on determination of standard or basal metabolism: the minimal maintenance requirement in the absence of external stimulation. Allometric equations predicting resting metabolic rate as a function of body mass and temperature have been generated for several vertebrate classes: mammals (53, 114), birds (1, 116), reptiles (21), amphibians (162), and fish (167). The mass-dependence of resting oxygen consumption is similar in all these groups and is proportional to body mass raised to the 0.75–0.80 power. These relationships have also demonstrated a basic equality among the resting metabolic requirements of the lower vertebrates (reptiles, amphibians, and fish) and a similarity to resting metabolic rates of most invertebrate groups (97). Basal metabolic rates of mammals and birds, however, are six to ten times greater than are those of the poikilothermic groups, even at equal body temperatures (16, 21, 66, 97). The greater aerobic heat production in these former groups is, of course, the basis of their homeothermic condition.

Maximal Oxygen Consumption

More recently, attention has been directed to the determination of the greatest capacity of these organisms for oxygen uptake. Maximal levels of oxygen consumption have been elicited by electrically stimulating animals with low votage shocks or having them swim against a current of water (46, 49, 80). Spontaneous struggling does not appear to produce the highest levels of oxygen uptake (46, 80, 164). Maximal oxygen consumption has now been measured in a number of different species of lower vertebrates: fish (12, 47, 48, 50–52, 68, 76, 78, 86, 89, 94, 107, 115, 133, 136, 145, 146), amphibians (25, 27, 98, 143, 156), and reptiles (2, 7, 8, 17, 20, 22, 23, 69, 83, 90, 125, 134, 138, 164, 166). Maximal levels of oxygen consumption in these animals exceed standard levels by factors of five- to fifteen-fold; consequently, active oxygen consumption by members of these groups approximates basal oxygen consumption of birds and mammals. These homeotherms are capable of similar factorial increments in oxygen consumption (64, 149, 154, 171), achieving much greater absolute levels of uptake. For example, standard and maximal levels of oxygen consumption of a 1 kg reptile at 30°C are 0.07 and 0.40 cm^3O_2 $(g \cdot hr)^{-1}$, respectively; comparable values for a bird are 0.79 and 9.49 cm^3O_2 $(g \cdot hr)^{-1}$ (1, 21, 95). Thus, resting and active oxygen consumption appear to be linked. This factorial increment in aerobic metabolism of approximately ten-fold appears to be a rather standard feature of vertebrate physiology and may represent a basic limitation of the oxygen delivery or utilization systems.

Maximal levels of oxygen consumption of lower vertebrates appear more closely correlated with the behavioral capacities of these organisms than are standard levels. More active animals tend to be able to sustain much higher levels of oxygen consumption (152), at least among the reptiles and fish. Among the snakes studied this correlation is clear. Racers (*Masticophis, Coluber*), very fast snakes that actively pursue their prey, have high levels of active oxygen consumption: $1.05 \ cm^3O_2 \ (g \cdot hr)^{-1}$; rattlesnakes (*Crotalus*), sit-and-wait predators capable of rapid striking, have lower levels: $0.52 \ cm^3O_2 \ (g \cdot hr)^{-1}$; boas (*Lichanura*), animals incapable of rapid locomotion which rely on constriction to kill prey, have the lowest levels: $0.25 \ cm^3O_2 \ (g \cdot hr)^{-1}$ (138). Similar correlations are apparent among lizards: monitor lizards (*Varanus*), carnivorous predators, achieve substantially higher levels of oxygen transport than do herbivorous iguanid and agamid lizards of equal size (7, 17, 164). Active oxygen uptake is rather low in the sluggish rhynchocephalian *Sphenodon* (166). A similar situation exists in fish: maximum oxygen consumption in active sockeye salmon (*Oncorhynchus*), $0.63 \ cm^3O_2 \ (g \cdot hr)^{-1}$ (47), exceeds that of the more sluggish goldfish (*Carassius*), $0.30 \ cm^3O_2 \ (g \cdot hr)^{-1}$ (82), or largemouth bass (*Micropterus*), $0.37 \ cm^3O_2 \ (g \cdot hr)^{-1}$ (12). Maximal oxygen consumption is even lower in reclusive cave-adapted fishes: $0.06-0.16 \ cm^3O_2 \ (g \cdot hr)^{-1}$ (33). Unfortunately only fragmentary data are available for oxygen consumption in the tunas (55), highly active, predatory, and homeothermic animals that might be expected to achieve the highest aerobic levels among the fishes.

These correlations between activity and oxygen consumption do not apply to amphibians. In this group, animals capable of the greatest amount of short-term activity have the lowest levels of maximal oxygen consumption (25). For example, leopard frogs (*Rana*), with considerable powers for rapid locomotion, have a lower maximal oxygen consumption, $0.49 \ cm^3O_2 \ (g \cdot hr)^{-1}$, than those of the more sluggish toad (*Bufo*), $1.53 \ cm^3O_2 \ (g \cdot hr)^{-1}$ (143).

The correlation between maximal oxygen consumption and behavior complicates an examination of the mass dependence of this factor. Maximal oxygen consumption in 14 species of reptiles was found to be proportional to body mass to the 0.80–0.82 power (21, 165), an exponent similar to that describing standard oxygen consumption. Consequently, smaller reptiles can achieve higher rates of mass-specific oxygen consumption than can larger animals. A similar mass-dependence of maximal oxygen consumption has been reported for both birds (95) and mammals (130). Not enough data have been collected under comparable conditions to permit interspecific comparisions among fish or amphibians. However, within four different species of fish, maximal oxygen consumption has been found to be directly proportional to body mass rather than to a fractional power of it

(12, 48, 51, 88, 136, 137). The ratio of active to standard oxygen consumption increases with increasing body size in these groups. However, in speckled trout (*Salvelinus*), the mass dependence of active oxygen consumption is temperature-dependent. Values of the mass-dependent exponent b (in the equation $Y = a X^b$, where Y is organismal oxygen consumption and X is body mass and a and b are constants) decrease from 0.91 at 5°C to 0.73 at 20°C (105). More extensive examinations will be required before the mass-dependence of active metabolism in fish or amphibians can be stated with confidence.

Maximal oxygen consumption is strongly affected by body temperature in the lower vertebrates, as are most other physiological processes. In many species, active oxygen consumption increases exponentially with increasing temperature, generally with Q_{10}'s of 1.5–2.0, up to lethal or debilitating thermal levels (2, 7, 8, 17, 69, 78, 79, 83, 90, 143, 164). However, in a large number of species investigated, maximal oxygen consumption is attained at some intermediate, nonlethal temperature and remains constant at higher temperatures ($Q_{10} = 1.0$) (12, 17, 20, 22, 23, 47, 68, 81, 86, 89, 125, 164, 166). This latter type of response is particularly apparent and is highly consistent among iguanid and agamid lizards. The lowest temperature at which maximal oxygen consumption is attained is often the same as preferred body temperature or body temperature of the animal in its natural environment (21, 164). A limitation of oxygen transport at higher temperatures is clearly suggested, either because of internal physiological factors (18) or limitation of environmentally available oxygen (47).

Aerobic Metabolic Scope

Normal behavioral activities require levels of oxygen consumption intermediate between standard and maximal levels. The capacity to which activity can be aerobically supported is indicated by the difference between these maximal and minimal levels of oxygen consumption in any particular physiological state. This difference, the *scope for activity*, was utilized by Fry (78), in his seminal paper on activity metabolism in fish, as an index of work capacity. Determination of this metabolic scope has been an important theme in the study of energetics of lower vertebrates. Since anaerobic metabolism may play a major role in activity energetics of these animals (125), this measurement of oxygen consumption is currently referred to as *aerobic metabolic scope* (17).

The use of aerobic scope as a predictor of activity capacity is recognized to have certain limitations. It assumes that the efficiency of aerobic energy transduction is constant under different physiological conditions, e.g. at different temperatures (6). It also assumes that maintenance processes are sustained at pre-activity levels (125); and if these are temporarily abandoned, activity capacity is underestimated. On the other hand, in order to supply oxygen to the contracting skeletal musculature, the ventilatory and circulatory systems must also increase work output and consume a fraction of the increased oxygen uptake. An estimated 20% of the aerobic scope is required for these systems in active fish (112). Increased gill ventilation also increases osmoregulatory costs for fish (136, 137). It is estimated that as much as 40% of the aerobic scope associated with swimming at maximal sustained speed in fish is devoted to these systems (160).

Another potential difficulty with the association between aerobic scope and work capacity is the assumption that maximal levels of oxygen consumption are achieved simultaneously with maximal work output. This may not be the case for some lizards at lower than preferred thermal levels (22, 23), or for amphibians (25). Measurement of aerobic scope may thus overestimate work capacity. If these provisions are kept in mind, aerobic scope presents a convenient method of assaying the potential aerobic work component of an organism's metabolism.

More active animals among fish and reptiles tend to have higher aerobic scopes, a reflection of their greater levels of maximal oxygen consumption. The aerobic scopes of very active sockeye salmon (*Oncorhynchus*) and more sluggish goldfish (*Carassius*) are 0.58 and 0.28 cm^3O_2 $(g \cdot hr)^{-1}$, respectively (47, 78). The more active aquatic turtle *Pseudemys* has an aerobic scope 75% greater than that of the more terrestrial *Terrapene* (83). Homeotherms have aerobic scopes far exceeding those of the lower vertebrates: 8.70 and 0.33 cm^3O_2 $(g \cdot hr)^{-1}$ for a 1 kg bird and reptile, respectively (1, 21, 95). Aerobic scope is temperature-dependent and is often maximal at normal field temperatures or preferred body temperature in organisms in which maximal oxygen consumption has a thermal plateau (78, 164). This maximization is a consequence of increased maintenance levels at higher temperatures. In species lacking this thermal plateau, aerobic scope increases with temperature up to lethal levels.

Cost of Transport

As physical performance (e.g. speed of locomotion) increases, oxygen consumption increases until maximal values are attained. The exact form of that increase varies considerably and depends upon the type of locomotion employed, the species in question, and its body mass and temperature. To determine this dependence, oxygen consumption is measured while an animal walks on a treadmill, flies in a wind tunnel, or swims against a current.

As swimming speed increases in fish, oxygen consumption increases exponentially according to the relationship $Y = ae^{bX}$, where Y is oxygen consumption, X is swimming speed, and a and b are constants (47). Although a linear relationship between activity and oxygen consumption was reported earlier (13, 147), more recent studies have all found a logarithmic dependence of aerobic metabolism on swimming speed (12, 47, 51, 52, 76, 78, 86, 115, 127, 136, 137, 145, 146, 157, 159). The difference between the observed oxygen consumption and standard metabolism generally increases as the square of the cruising speed (79). This exponential increase has also been found for oxygen consumption during swimming by a sea turtle (*Chelonia*) (134); however, a linear approximation may describe these data equally well.

In contrast to fish swimming, oxygen consumption increases as a linear function of speed in terrestrial mammals (139, 150) and in walking birds (77). Studies on terrestrial reptiles (3, 57, 70, 126, 149) have also found a linear increment in oxygen consumption with increasing speed. Oxygen consumption of birds during flight has a low dependence on speed or has a minimal value at intermediate air speeds (28, 153, 155). The physical bases of the differences in the power requirements of different locomotory patterns in water and air and on land are not fully understood.

Aerobic locomotory energetics are most commonly compared by calculation of the *cost of transport,* the amount of energy required to move a unit of mass over a unit distance (139, 154, 161). The cost of transport is obtained by dividing the mass-specific oxygen consumption by the speed; the *net cost of transport* first subtracts the resting oxygen consumption from the total (139). The net cost of transport is velocity-dependent in animals that have nonlinear aerobic energetics as a function of speed, such as fish and flying birds. It is independent of speed in terrestrial reptiles and mammals. The cost of transport is very dependent on body mass. A large animal expends less energy to move a unit of its mass than does a smaller animal. The net cost of locomotion decreases as the −0.40 and −0.33 power of body mass in terrestrial mammals and reptiles, respectively (139, 149). The minimal cost of locomotion in fish decreases as the −0.24 power of mass (47, 139). Consequently, the velocity-dependence of aerobic metabolism is considerably less in larger animals. Higher speeds can be attained before aerobic scope is reached. For instance, larger fish are capable of sustaining much higher speeds than are smaller individuals (12, 48, 51).

Expression of metabolic data as the cost of transport permits comparision of the various locomotory modes. Animals adapted for swimming have a much lower net cost of transport than do those specialized for flying or running; fliers have lower net locomotory costs than do runners (139, 154). The minimal cost of locomotion is least for fish, being only one eighth that of a terrestrial runner if both animals weigh 1.0 kg (139). The cost of transport is similar in equal-sized fish of several different families of very different anatomy, stamina, and swimming mode: salmonids, cyprinids, anguillids, and sparids (47, 136, 139, 145, 170). These differences appear to have little influence on locomotory costs at low speeds. The net cost of transport in swimming sea turtles (*Chelonia*) is twice that predicted for a fish of equal size (134). In spite of the fact that the turtle is well-adapted for aquatic existence, it must surface to breathe; this behavior undoubtedly decreases its swimming efficiency.

The net cost of transport of lizards running at low speeds is equal to or slightly less than that of mammals of equal size (3, 70, 126, 149). Consequently, the sprawling gait and "push-up" position of the limbs of these animals do not result in a less efficient means of locomotion (3, 149). The net cost of locomotion in a snake (*Thamnophis*), however, is only half that predicted for a quadruped runner of equal weight (57). Relatively few experiments have been carried out on reptiles moving on treadmills; reptiles are generally difficult to train and tend to engage in rapid bursts of speed. No measurements have been reported on aerobic cost of transport in amphibians.

Comparisions based on the net cost of transport obscure the real differences in energetic expense of locomotion in homeotherms and poikilotherms. The much lower maintenance costs of the latter animals are reflected by the fact that the metabolic rate of a poikilotherm moving at a certain speed is considerably below that of a homeotherm moving at the same speed. Thus, a 630 g lizard has a metabolic rate of 0.58 cm^3O_2 $(g \cdot hr)^{-1}$ when walking at 0.5 km hr^{-1}. This is below the resting metabolic rate of a mammal of equal size [0.70 cm^3O_2 $(g \cdot hr)^{-1}$], which would consume 1.5 cm^3O_2 $(g \cdot hr)^{-1}$ walking at this speed (149). Given, however, the equality of transport costs in the two groups, the poikilotherm reaches the limit of its aerobic scope at a much lower speed than does the homeotherm. The highest walking speed that can be sustained by the lizard *Iguana* for one hour without exhaustion is 0.4 km hr^{-1} (126). A large oxygen debt is accumulated by the agamid lizard *Uromastix* while walking at 0.5 km hr^{-1}, indicating anaerobic metabolism at this speed (70). These speeds are considerably below those sustained by mammals: a ground squirrel of a size comparable to these lizards can sustain running at nearly 3 km hr^{-1} (150). A similar relationship holds for aquatic homeotherms and poikilotherms. However, the lower cost of transport during swimming is reflected in the greater speeds that can be sustained by aquatic poikilotherms: sockeye salmon (*Oncorhynchus*) weighing 1–2 kg can swim at 4.6 km hr^{-1} without becoming exhausted (51). Higher levels of speed in all these animals entail the use of anaerobic metabolism.

Temperature sometimes influences the cost of transport. In fish, oxygen consumed while swimming at any particular speed is positively temperature-dependent; swimming is more expensive at higher temperatures (12, 47, 136). If, however, the standard oxygen consumption is subtracted from the observed, the temperature-dependence is reduced. In sockeye salmon (*Oncorhynchus*) as speed increases, the temperature-dependence decreases until at burst speed the aerobic increment is temperature-independent (147). This is not the case for rainbow trout (*Salmo*) or largemouth bass (*Micropterus*), in which the temperature-dependence of the aerobic increment increases with increasing temperature (12, 136). In lizards, the cost of walking at any speed is independent of body temperature (70, 126). Consequently, the added aerobic increment above resting levels decreases with increasing temperature. For all these organisms, maximal sustainable speeds will be attained at the temperature at which aerobic scope is maximal. For example, maximal cruising speed is attained at 20°C in goldfish (*Carassius*), which coincides with maximal aerobic scope (81, 82).

A detailed analysis of the efficiencies involved in aerobically supported locomotion will not be undertaken here. Such an examination has generally only been attempted for fish [but see (134)], and Webb (160) has recently prepared an excellent summary of that literature.

ANAEROBIC METABOLISM

Both intense activity and exposure to hypoxic environments result in anaerobic metabolism in skeletal muscle. Under both these circumstances, demand for high-energy phosphate groups exceeds the supply that can be sustained through aerobic metabolism. The fact that both of these circumstances in vertebrates result in the formation of large quantities of the same compound, lactic acid, has tended to emphasize their similarities. However, the selective demands of each situation are quite different. During hypoxia or anoxia, it is important to sustain anaerobic metabolism for as long as possible since the time of return to aerobic conditions is not always predictable. During activity, the purpose of anaerobic metabolism is to generate in the shortest period of time as many high-energy phosphate compounds as can be utilized. These distinct demands cannot always be satisfied by the same metabolic pathways, and the invertebrate groups with the highest tolerance of anoxia generally do not accumulate lactic acid under anoxic conditions (100). One cannot easily extrapolate from anoxic tolerance to anaerobic activity capacity. For instance, among the reptiles, turtles have an immense anoxic tolerance in comparison with other groups and can form much greater quantities of lactic acid under anoxic conditions (14, 21, 106). However, their capacity for anaerobic activity metabolism does not appear to be any greater than that of other reptiles (83, 84). Likewise, although cyprinid fish appear to have impressive tolerance of anoxia (43, 146), their capacities for anaerobic activity metabolism are smaller than those of the salmonids (71), which also have a greater aerobic capacity. Consequently, the applicability of data on hypoxic tolerance to activity metabolism appear somewhat limited and the literature on the former is not reviewed here.

Because of the limited aerobic metabolic scope of the lower vertebrates and their low aerobically sustainable speeds, anaerobic metabolism is particularly important in activity energetics, particularly for terrestrial poikilotherms. Methods of measuring anaerobic metabolism have generally consisted of assaying changes during activity of metabolites within the blood or skeletal muscle. Because of diffusion of compounds into the blood and inhomogeneities of metabolite formation in different areas of skeletal muscle (36, 37), it is difficult to quantify the contribution of anaerobic to total activity metabolism by these techniques. Analysis of whole body homogenates has been used for these comparisons (20, 24).

Lactic Acid Metabolism

The principal form of anaerobic metabolism during activity in the vertebrates is the catabolism of carbohydrates to lactic acid. In the lower vertebrates, blood lactate concentration increases greatly after a bout of intense activity, generally five- to ten-fold (5, 18, 22, 24, 31–34, 36–39, 59, 62, 67, 73, 84, 93, 96, 104, 122, 125, 142, 143, 148, 158, 164). In a summary of blood lactate data for reptiles (21), the following values were associated with different activity levels: resting, 0.5–2.0 mM; moderate and sustainable activity, 3.0–9.0 mM; vigorous and exhausting activity, 9.0–20 mM. Similar values have been reported for fish (40, 117) and amphibians (104, 143) with comparable activity levels; however, lower values for sustained activity may be obtained if blood is removed through a cannula rather than by heart puncture (73). These ranges may be contrasted with those of the blood of anoxic reptiles, which may reach 33 mM in diving lizards (126) and 108 mM in turtles (106). Concentrations of lactate in skeletal muscle are substantially higher than blood levels and reach values as high as 42 mmoles kg^{-1} muscle in lizards (24), 27 mmoles kg^{-1} in frogs (104), and 59 mmoles kg^{-1} in fish (36) after exhausting activity. These high concentrations of lactate can cause major disruptions in blood and muscle pH and disrupt enzymatic function and oxygen transport. The very limited data available on lactic acid formation during voluntary activity suggest that animals avoid the formation of very high concentrations of lactic acid when possible (24, 58, 143).

Muscle glycogen appears to be the principal source of the lactic acid formed, although quantitative comparisons between the two components are few. In rainbow trout (*Salmo*), all of the lactate formed in the muscle can be accounted for by glycogen breakdown and vice versa (148). Essentially all the lactic acid formed during activity in the lizard *Iguana* is the result of glycogen catabolism (124). Glycogen is very rapidly depleted during intense activity (37, 67, 122), being 50% catabolized in 2 min, and 80% depleted if activity is continued (11, 40, 148). Liver glycogen generally does not change during short-term activity (39, 40, 67, 99, 108, 124, 169) but it does decrease in some species (67, 109, 110). It may be utilized to replenish other carbohydrate stores if the animal is not fed (40, 99). Levels of blood glucose either remain constant (32, 93, 113, 125, 144) or increase (33, 67, 104, 141) during activity. Skeletal muscle in fish and amphibians possesses very low levels of hexokinase and consequently may be unable to utilize glucose as a rapidly expendable fuel for activity (60, 118). It has consequently been concluded that blood glucose contributes little to activity metabolism (39); however, until turnover studies using labeled glucose are completed, this conclusion is premature.

The maximal rate of lactic acid formation during activity has been investigated in reptiles and amphibians and is termed the *anaerobic scope* (24). This is assayed as the increment in lactic acid content of the whole body over short (e.g. 30 sec) periods of maximal activity. In small lizards, there is little interspecific variability in anaerobic scope; values range between 11 and 19 mmoles (kg body weight·min)$^{-1}$ at 30°–37°C (24). In amphibians, however, pronounced interspecific differences exist, and anaerobic scope varies over a ten-fold range [1.6–14 mmoles (kg·min)$^{-1}$] at 20°C (25, 26). Slower moving and aquatic amphibians have low anaerobic scopes; more active, saltatory forms produce lactic acid rapidly. The temperature-dependence of anaerobic scope in lizards is quite low, with Q_{10}'s ranging from 1.1 to 1.3 above 20°C; anaerobic scope in amphibians is more sensitive to temperature (Q_{10}'s = 1.5–3.9).

The *anaerobic capacity* is the amount of lactic acid formed during activity to exhaustion (24). As with aerobic scope, values for small lizards show little interspecific variation (10–17 mmoles kg^{-1} body mass) in contrast to amphibians (–1.2–16 mmoles kg^{-1}) (4, 24, 26, 27, 61, 104). Active racer snakes (*Masticophis, Coluber*) have higher anaerobic capacities than do rattlesnakes (*Crotalus*) or boas (*Lichanura*) (138). More sluggish box turtles (*Terrapene*) have a greater lactate formation during activity than aquatic *Pseudemys* (83). Neotenic salamanders (*Ambystoma*) form less lactate while swimming vigorously than do metamorphosed individuals of the same species (61). The thermal dependence of anaerobic capacity is low, with Q_{10}'s generally below 1.5 for both lizards and amphibians (24, 26). There is some indication that anaerobic capacity is maximized at preferred body temperature in iguanid lizards (20, 23). Few comparable data exist for fish, but the temperature-dependence of maximal blood lactate concentration after activity is very low (32, 67). In fact, such concentrations can in certain instances be greater at lower temperatures than higher.

Although the maximal capacities for lactate formation found among fish, amphibians, and reptiles are similar, fish appear more sensitive to its effects than do members of the other groups. Exercised reptiles and amphibians rarely die after intense activity, unlike some species of fish, which do so frequently enough to be a considerable problem in the fisheries industry (35, 158). Mortality is common in fish of several species with average blood lactate concentrations of 17–26 mM after exercise (10, 34, 128, 129). Mortality is positively correlated with concentration of lactic acid in the blood (10, 128). Physical damage to the scales and mucus is not a contributory cause (41); nor is the lactate ion per se involved. Acidosis associated with lactic acid diffusion into the blood is probably the important factor (35, 111). The decreased pH is associated with a depression of blood oxygen-capacity, decrease of blood bicarbonate, and disruption of circulation (35). Similar acidosis after activity in reptiles is also observed, but is never lethal (18, 84, 163).

Other anaerobically generated products appear to play a distinctly minor role in the overall energetics of activity in the lower vertebrates. The concentration of pyruvic acid in fish blood and skeletal muscle doubles during strenuous activity; however, its concentrations are only 1% of those of lactic acid and its accumulation does not account for much high-energy phosphate production (37, 40, 62, 169). Changes in concentrations of other glycolytic or Krebs-cycle intermediates do not occur or are small in comparison with increments in lactic acid concentration during activity in carp (*Cyprinus*) muscle (72). Whole-body concentrations of pyruvate, succinate, and alanine remain constant or increase very little during burst activity in small lizards (*Sceloporus, Xantusia*) and amphibians (*Xenopus, Batrachoseps*) (A. F. Bennett, unpublished observations). Anaerobically formed compounds, succinate and alanine, accumulate in the blood of sea turtles (*Chelonia*) during diving, but their concentration is again only 1% of that of the lactic acid accumulated (101). A study on hypoxic metabolism in fish suggested the anaerobic production of short-chain volatile acids (43). However, further studies on hypoxic fish have not found an accumulation of these compounds (56, 71). No change in the concentration of any of 17 amino acids was found during hypoxia (71). Respiratory quotients (RQ) in excess of 1.0 have been reported in goldfish (*Carassius*) (RQ = 1.32) and trout (*Salmo*) (RQ = 1.16) during enforced swimming (115), indicating some form of anaerobic metabolism. These values declined to 1.03 and 0.91, respectively, during steady-state swimming. In spontaneously active fish, RQs in excess of 1.0 developed only in goldfish and only under hypoxic conditions. The source of the excess carbon dioxide is unknown but may come from blood bicarbonate as a result of lactic acid entry into the blood.

Currently, no evidence exists for the operation of other anaerobic pathways during activity in normoxic situations.

Recovery and Oxygen Debt

The effects of physical activity persist a long time in the lower vertebrates. Fish in particular require a long recovery period until the pre-active state is reestablished. Blood lactate levels continue to increase for 2–3 hr after activity to exhaustion (36–40, 62, 142); resting levels are not restored for 8–24 hr (10, 11, 32–34, 36–39, 93, 96, 132). Tunas may eliminate a lactate burden more rapidly (5). A very long post-active period is also required for elimination of white-muscle lactate (37, 62, 93, 110) and resynthesis of white-muscle glycogen (11, 37, 99, 122); recovery of pre-active levels is more rapid in red muscle (110). Exercise-trained or fed fish recover more rapidly than untrained or starved individuals (39, 93, 99, 122).

Several ideas have been advanced to explain this slow recovery. The temperatures at which these experiments have been done have been generally low (10°–15°C), and diffusion of lactic acid from the muscle might have been impaired; however, lactate appears very rapidly in the blood during activity even at low temperatures (37). Some evidence suggests impairment of blood circulation after activity, but this has not been quantified (37, 40). The oxygen-carrying capacity of the blood may become depressed by low blood pH and thus retard aerobic catabolism of the lactate (37, 140, 158). Probably a combination of all these factors is involved in slowing recovery in fish. Blood lactate also requires several hours to return to pre-active levels in amphibians and reptiles (25, 104, 125). Rate of elimination of blood lactate in the lizard *Iguana* is maximal at 35°C (the preferred body temperature and the temperature of maximal aerobic scope) (125).

The time required for elimination of the oxygen debt per se—the oxygen consumption in excess of pre-active levels—is quite variable. In fish, oxygen consumption has been reported to return to pre-active levels in 3 (47), 4–6 (99), and more than 10 hr (96). In amphibians, similar variability is reported, with values ranging from 1–1.5 hr (25, 143) to 4–6 hr (61, 156). Oxygen debts in large lizards are mostly eliminated in 30 min (17). It is unclear whether these differences reflect methodology or physiological differences between the species investigated. The size of the debt is generally temperature-dependent and is greatest at the highest temperature examined (17, 143, 156). In sockeye salmon (*Oncorhynchus*), however, maximal debt occurs at 15°C (the temperature of maximal oxygen consumption and aerobic scope) and decreases at higher temperatures (47). The oxygen debt is most rapidly repaid at the temperature of maximal aerobic scope (17, 47, 143, 156).

The time course of the oxygen debt repayment is generally shorter than that of lactate elimination. Oxygen debt in one species of amphibian is completely eliminated before any net amount of lactate is catabolized (25). In other members of this group, oxygen consumption returns to resting levels long before lactate is eliminated (25, 104, 156). Oxygen consumption and blood lactate concentration return to pre-active values in 3 hr and 8 hr, respectively, in sockeye salmon (*Oncorhynchus*) (34, 47). In view of these results, these processes do not seem tightly coupled in the lower vertebrates and the oxygen debt is thus primarily alactacid. It is consequently inadvisable to attempt to estimate lactic acid production or total energetic output during activity from measurements of oxygen consumption alone or to estimate the excess oxygen consumption required to eliminate a lactate burden.

The general topic of lactate catabolism and elimination, mainly in mammalian systems, has been reviewed and details of the general process may be found in (123). The fate of the large amounts of lactate formed during strenuous activity in the lower vertebrates is largely unknown and may well be different from that of mammalian systems. The original experiments on the fate of lactate were performed on isolated amphibian skeletal muscle, and about 80% of the lactate utilized was estimated to be reconverted to carbohydrate stores, the remainder being oxidized (120, 121). A similar ratio was estimated for in vivo lactate metabolism in trout (*Salmo*) (99). A smaller amount of glycogen is resynthesized in mammalian than in amphibian white muscle under identical in vitro conditions (15). In mammalian systems in vivo during recovery from activity, most of the lactate is rapidly oxidized to carbon dioxide (54, 75). Since similar in vivo experiments have not been performed in lower vertebrates, it is not known whether most of the lactate is resynthesized to glycogen or glucose, is oxidized to carbon dioxide, or is synthesized into other compounds, e.g. fatty acids. Excretion of lactate has not been observed, even in an aquatic medium (61, 119, 160). Muscle glycogen levels are eventually reestablished, but the site of lactate catabolism or carbohydrate mobilization is in doubt. Trout (*Salmo*) liver has been shown to have a high capacity for lactate catabolism (30). However, in another study, 27 of 36 species of fish examined had very low levels of lactic dehydrogenase in their livers, and it was concluded that this organ has a negligible role in metabolizing blood lactate in fish (62). Skeletal muscle, both white and red, has some capacity for lactate oxidation (15, 30). Considerable interspecific variation may exist in the fate of the lactate; only further experimentation, particularly in vivo experimentation, will resolve the rather uncertain situation that now exists.

COMPARISON OF AEROBIC AND ANAEROBIC METABOLISM

The relative contributions made by aerobic and anaerobic pathways to activity metabolism is dependent upon work output. At low-level sustainable locomotion, aerobic catabolism of carbohydrates and fats probably accounts for all of the work output. It is expected that a certain amount of anaerobic metabolism, causing a rise in blood lactate, may occur at the initiation of exercise until oxygen supply systems catch up with oxygen requirements. If activity is prolonged, this initial anaerobiosis will make little contribution to overall energetics. This viewpoint is largely supported by the relatively low levels of blood lactate maintained during moderate activity in lizards and fish (11, 39, 73, 122, 126). In experiments using cannulated fish, blood lactate remained at resting levels up to 93% of critical swimming speed (73). However, muscle lactate levels may increase even during sustained swimming in fish (109), so that it is not possible without whole body studies to rule out a net anaerobic contribution to low speed locomotion. It is necessary to distinguish here between lactic acid formation and a net accumulation of lactic acid. As long as no lactate accumulates or is excreted, oxygen consumption totally accounts for the energetic output of an animal. Lactate may be formed in white muscle or other tissue, enter the blood, and be catabolized aerobically elsewhere, especially in red muscle or gill tissue (30, 168, 169). In the former case, white muscle could provide a readily metabolizable compound to support contractile activity in the red muscle.

There is a large literature on different muscle fiber types and differential reliance upon them during locomotion in fish. This topic has been well reviewed (29) and is only summarized here. Skeletal muscle tissue is generally divided into red and white fiber types, although there are several intermediate categories in fish (131). The red fibers show higher concentrations of aerobic enzymes, greater oxygen consumption, and higher concentrations of glycogen and lipid than do white fibers. The former are thought to be primarily aerobic, whereas the latter are primarily anaerobic. It is important to keep in mind, however, that these are only distinctions in a continuum of function. Red fibers have some anaerobic ability and white fibers also function aerobically. More active fish have a greater proportion of red fibers in their total body musculature, generally localized in discrete superficial bands, than do more sedentary, sluggish animals (44, 92). These red muscle bands are primarily responsible for low-speed locomotion, and white muscle only becomes active at intermediate or maximal swimming speeds (45, 91, 103, 108–110, 135, 146, 159). The exact contributions made by each system are in some dispute and are probably highly species-specific. In general, however, aerobically supported metabolism functions at low speeds, supplemented by anaerobic metabolism during burst speeds. For sustainable (1 hr) swimming by trout (*Salmo*) at critical speed, the anaerobic contribution to total energetic output is less than 5% (159).

However, when pursued, lower vertebrates cannot sustain such activity and often are exhausted within 1–2 min (9, 23, 24, 26, 31, 40, 67, 85, 96). Fatigued and unresponsive, the animals lose their orientation and equilibrium. Schooling species of fish break their schools and move to concealment (40). Efforts have been made to quantify the energetics of this burst behavior, both to determine the total amount of energy an organism can mobilize and to partition that metabolism into its aerobic and anaerobic components. This is done by simultaneously measuring oxygen consumption and lactic acid production during the active period (20), a method that does not take into account the anaerobic contribution made by dephosphorylation of adenosine triphosphate (ATP) and creatine phosphate. The contribution from these sources may be relatively minor (72) or large (110). Full analysis and determination of the time course await further experimentation.

In many reptiles and amphibians, burst behavior is fueled mainly, in some cases almost exclusively, by anaerobic metabolism. During 2–5 min of activity, lactic acid formation accounts for 58–96% of the total ATP production (20–25, 83, 125, 138). During the first half-minute of activity, the anaerobic contribution is even greater (24, 25). Between 95 and 99.7% of the glycogen utilized during 2 min of activity is converted to lactic acid (22, 23). Because of the large and rapidly mobilized anaerobic potential and the relatively low levels of oxygen consumption, burst activity is essentially oxygen-independent in these animals. The relative temperature-independence of lactate formation in comparison to aerobic scope (24, 26) provides the functional basis for the temperature-independence of burst behavior (22, 32, 42) and the anaerobic metabolic mode exerts an even greater influence on total metabolism at low body temperature. Although recovery from activity requires much longer at these lower temperatures, anaerobic metabolism provides the organism with a capacity for rapid activity and escape.

The relative extents of aerobic and anaerobic metabolism vary among different groups of lower vertebrates. Among small lizards interspecific variation is small; anaerobic scope varies little between species (24) and aerobic scope is mass-dependent (21, 165). Small lizards rely on anaerobiosis for burst activity. Total scope, both in its aerobic and anaerobic components, may be maximal at preferred body temperature, at least in iguanid lizards. The total energy output varies between 28 and 52 μmoles ATP

g^{-1} body weight for three species of iguanids at preferred body temperature during 2 min of activity (20, 22, 23).

Among the snakes examined, anaerobic metabolism during activity accounts for over half of the total ATP formation (138). However, aerobic and anaerobic scopes are positively correlated: Both are highest in racers (*Coluber, Masticophis*), intermediate in rattlesnakes (*Crotalus*), and lowest in boas (*Lichanura*). Minimal and maximal values for metabolism by these species during 5 min of activity differ by a factor of five: racers, 52 μmoles g^{-1}; rattlesnakes, 28 μmoles g^{-1}; boas, 10 μmoles g^{-1}. The minimal value is similar to those of turtles during activity (9–15 μmoles g^{-1}). The overall activity capacities and performance abilities of these species are well-reflected in these measurements of total metabolism.

Aerobic and anaerobic capacities of amphibians are inversely correlated in a series of species (25). The animals with the greatest aerobic scopes (e.g. *Bufo, Scaphiopus*) do not produce large amounts of lactic acid during activity; animals with high anaerobic scopes (e.g. *Rana, Batrachoseps, Hyla*) have low aerobic scopes (25, 26, 143). These differences appear to have an enzymatic basis (14, 19). This inverse relationship tends to equalize total metabolism, which ranges from 12–20 μM ATP g^{-1} for 2 min of activity. Animals that rely on burst activity for rapid escape do so by utilizing anaerobic metabolism. The more aerobically competent animals are incapable of this rapid activity and rely on static defense mechanisms: noxious skin secretions, protective postures, and counterattack (26).

Simultaneous determination of aerobic and anaerobic capacities during short-term activity has not been undertaken for fish. Measurements of oxygen consumption during activity are generally longer-term than the 1–2 min required for exhaustion. While is it premature to speculate, the data available suggest that considerable interspecific and/or interfamilial variability exists in both aerobic and anaerobic capacities. Both capacities appear greater in salmonids than in goldfish (*Carassius*) (71). In view of the considerable range of aerobic scopes reported for fish, activity metabolism in these animals may be similar to that of snakes, in which very active species have both high aerobic and anaerobic capacities.

SUMMARY

Aerobic capacities of the lower vertebrates (fish, amphibians, and reptiles) are considerably lower then those of homeothermic birds and mammals. The low rate of oxygen consumption of the former animals has decided consequences for their capacity for sustaining activity. Maximal oxygen consumption is approximately ten times the resting level, approximating that of a resting homeotherm. Since locomotor costs appear similar for both groups, the birds and mammals have much more extensive capacities for sustained, aerobically supported activity. In contrast, the lower vertebrates rely on anaerobic metabolism (i.e. lactic acid production) to a great extent during intense activity. Anaerobic metabolism is independent of oxygen delivery systems, which operate at comparatively lower rates. Efficient in supplying energy quickly, anaerobic metabolism provides a capacity for rapid activity. It may be temperature-insensitive. It entails a long recovery period (hours), during which the animal is fatigued and unresponsive. Major differences in the aerobic and anaerobic partitioning of activity metabolism exist among different groups of lower vertebrates, but the most active animals of each group rely heavily on anaerobic metabolism to support vigorous activity.

Acknowledgment

Partial support for this review was provided by Grant PCM75-10100 from the National Science Foundation.

Literature Cited

1. Aschoff, J., Pohl, H. 1970. Rhythmic variations in energy metabolism. *Fed. Proc. Fed. Am. Soc. Exp. Med.* 29: 1541–52
2. Asplund, K. K. 1970. Metabolic scope and body temperatures of whiptail lizards (*Cnemidophorus*). *Herpetologica* 26:403–11
3. Bakker, R. T. 1972. Locomotor energetics of lizards and mammals compared. *Physiologist* 15:76
4. Baldwin, J., Friedman, G., Lillywhite, H. 1977. Adaptation to temporary muscle anoxia in anurans: Activities of glycolytic enzymes in muscles from species differing in their ability to produce lactate during exercise. *Aust. J. Zool.* 25:15–18
5. Barrett, I., Connor, A. R. 1962. Blood lactate in yellow fin tuna, *Neothunnus macropterus,* and skipjack, *Katsuwonus pelamus,* following capture and tagging. *Bull. Inter.-Am. Trop. Tuna Comm.* 6:231–80
6. Bartholomew, G. A., Tucker, V. A. 1963. Control of changes in body temperature, metabolism, and circulation by the agamid lizard, *Amphibolurus barbatus. Physiol. Zool.* 36:199–218
7. Bartholomew, G. A., Tucker, V. A. 1964. Size, body temperature, thermal conductance, oxygen consumption, and heart rate in Australian varanid lizards. *Physiol. Zool.* 37:341–54
8. Bartholomew, G. A., Tucker, V. A., Lee, A. K. 1965. Oxygen consumption, thermal conductance, and heart rate in the Australian skink *Tiliqua scincoides. Copeia* 1965:169–73
9. Beamish, F. W. H. 1966. Swimming endurance of some northwest Atlantic fishes. *J. Fish. Res. Bd. Can.* 23:341–47
10. Beamish, F. W. H. 1966. Muscular fatigue and mortality in haddock, *Melanogrammus aeglefinus,* caught by otter trawl. *J. Fish. Res. Bd. Can.* 23:1507–21
11. Beamish, F. W. H. 1968. Glycogen and lactic acid concentrations in the Atlantic cod (*Gadus morhua*) in relation to exercise. *J. Fish. Res. Bd. Can.* 25:837–51
12. Beamish, F. W. H. 1970. Oxygen consumption of largemouth bass, *Micropterus salmoides,* in relation to swimming speed and temperature. *Can. J. Zool.* 48:1221–28
13. Beamish, F. W. H., Mookherjii, P. S. 1964. Respiration of fishes with special emphasis on standard oxygen consumption. I. Influence of weight and temperature on respiration of goldfish, *Carassius auratus* L. *Can. J. Zool.* 42:161–75
14. Belkin, D. A. 1963. Anoxia: Tolerance in reptiles. *Science* 139:492–93
15. Bendall, J. R., Taylor, A. A. 1970. The Meyerhof quotient and the synthesis of glycogen from lactate in frog and rabbit

muscle: A reinvestigation. *Biochem. J.* 118:887–93
16. Benedict, F. G. 1932. *The Physiology of Large Reptiles.* Washington, DC: Carnegie Inst. Wash. 539 pp.
17. Bennett, A. F. 1972. The effect of activity on oxygen consumption, oxygen debt, and heart rate in the lizards *Varanus gouldii* and *Sauromalus hispidus. J. Comp. Physiol.* 79:259–80
18. Bennett, A. F. 1973. Blood physiology and oxygen transport during activity in two lizards, *Varanus gouldii* and *Sauromalus hispidus. Comp. Biochem. Physiol.* 46A:673–90
19. Bennett, A. F. 1974. Enzymatic correlates of activity metabolism in anuran amphibians. *Am. J. Physiol.* 226:1149–51
20. Bennett, A. F., Dawson, W. R. 1972. Aerobic and anaerobic metabolism during activity in the lizard *Dipsosaurus dorsalis. J. Comp. Physiol.* 81:289–99
21. Bennett, A. F., Dawson, W. R. 1976. Metabolism. In *Biology of the Reptilia,* ed. C. Gans, W. R. Dawson, 5:127–223. London / New York / San Francisco: Academic. 556 pp.
22. Bennett, A. F., Dawson, W. R., Bartholomew, G. A. 1975. Effects of activity and temperature on aerobic and anaerobic metabolism in the Galapagos marine iguana. *J. Comp. Physiol.* 100:317–29
23. Bennett, A. F., Gleeson, T. T. 1976. Activity metabolism in the lizard *Sceloporus occidentalis. Physiol. Zool.* 49:65–76
24. Bennett, A. F., Licht, P. 1972. Anaerobic metabolism during activity in lizards. *J. Comp. Physiol.* 81:277–88
25. Bennett, A. F., Licht, P. 1973. Relative contributions of anaerobic and aerobic energy production during activity in amphibia. *J. Comp. Physiol.* 87:351–60
26. Bennett, A. F., Licht, P. 1974. Anaerobic metabolism during activity in amphibians. *Comp. Biochem. Physiol.* 48A:319–27
27. Bennett, A. F., Wake, M. 1974. Metabolic correlates of activity in the caecilian *Geotrypetes seraphinii. Copeia* 1974:764–69
28. Bernstein, M. H., Thomas, S. P., Schmidt-Nielsen, K. 1973. Power input during flight of the fish crow, *Corvus ossifragus. J. Exp. Biol.* 58:401–10
29. Bilinski, E. 1974. Biochemical aspects of fish swimming. In *Biochemical and Biophysical Perspectives in Marine Biology,* ed. D. C. Malins, J. R. Sargent, 1:239–88. London / New York / San Francisco: Academic. 343 pp.
30. Bilinski, E., Jonas, R. E. E. 1972. Oxidation of lactate to carbon dioxide by rainbow trout (*Salmo gairdneri*) tissues. *J. Fish. Res. Bd. Can.* 29:1467–71
31. Black, E. C. 1955. Blood levels of haemoglobin and lactic acid in some freshwater fishes following exercise. *J. Fish. Res. Bd. Can.* 12:917–29
32. Black, E. C. 1957. Alterations in the blood level of lactic acid in certain salmonid fishes following muscular activity. I. Kamloops trout, *Salmo gairdneri. J. Fish. Res. Bd. Can.* 14:117–34
33. Black, E. C. 1957. Alterations in the blood level of lactic acid in certain salmonid fishes following muscular activity. II. Lake trout, *Salvelinus namaycush. J. Fish. Res. Bd. Can.* 14:645–49
34. Black, E. C. 1957. Alterations in the blood level of lactic acid in certain salmonid fishes following muscular activity. III. Sockeye salmon, *Oncorhynchus nerka. J. Fish. Res. Bd. Can.* 14:807–14
35. Black, E. C. 1958. Hyperactivity as a lethal factor in fish. *J. Fish. Res. Bd. Can.* 15:573–86
36. Black, E. C., Chiu, W.-G., Forbes, F. D., Hanslip, A. R. 1959. Changes in pH, carbonate and lactate of the blood of yearling Kamloops trout, *Salmo gairdneri,* during and following severe muscular activity. *J. Fish. Res. Bd. Can.* 16:391–402
37. Black, E. C., Connor, A. R., Lam, K.-C., Chiu, W.-G. 1962. Changes in glycogen, pyruvate and lactate in rainbow trout (*Salmo gairdneri*) during and following muscular activity. *J. Fish. Res. Bd. Can.* 19:409–36
38. Black, E. C., Manning, G. T., Hayashi, K. 1966. Changes in levels of haemoglobin, oxygen, carbon dioxide, pyruvate and lactate in venous blood of rainbow trout (*Salmo gairdneri*) during and following severe muscular activity. *J. Fish. Res. Bd. Can.* 23:783–95
39. Black, E. C., Robertson, A. C., Hanslip, A. R., Chiu, W.-G. 1960. Alterations in glycogen, glucose and lactate in rainbow and kamloops trout, *Salmo gairdneri,* following muscular activity. *J. Fish. Res. Bd. Can.* 17:487–500
40. Black, E. C., Robertson, A. C., Parker, R. R. 1961. Some aspects of carbohydrate metabolism in fish. In *Comparative Physiology of Carbohydrate Metabolism in Heterothermic Animals,* ed. A. W. Martin, pp. 89–124. Seattle: Univ. Washington. 144 pp.
41. Black, E. C., Tredwell, S. J. 1967. Effect of a partial loss of scales and mucus on carbohydrate metabolism in rainbow

trout (*Salmo gairdneri*). *J. Fish. Res. Bd. Can.* 24:939–53
42. Blaxter, J. H. S., Dickson, W. 1959. Observations on the swimming speeds of fish. *J. Cons., Cons. Perma. Int. Explor. Mer* 24:472–79
43. Blažka, P. 1958. The anaerobic metabolism of fish. *Physiol. Zool.* 31:117–28
44. Boddeke, R., Slijper, E. J., Van der Stelt, A. 1959. Histological characteristics of the body musculature of fishes in connection with their mode of life. *Proc. Kon. Ned. Akad. Wetensch. Ser. C* 62:576–88
45. Bone, Q. 1966. On the function of the two types of myotomal muscle fibre in Elasmobranch fish. *J. Mar. Biol. Ass. UK* 46:321–50
46. Brett, J. R. 1962. Some considerations in the study of respiratory metabolism in fish, particularly salmonids. *J. Fish. Res. Bd. Can.* 19:1025–38
47. Brett, J. R. 1964. The respiratory metabolism and swimming performance of young sockeye salmon. *J. Fish. Res. Bd. Can.* 21:1183–1226
48. Brett, J. R. 1965. The relation of size to rate of oxygen consumption and sustained swimming speed of sockeye salmon (*Oncorhynchus nerka*). *J. Fish. Res. Bd. Can.* 22:1491–1501
49. Brett, J. R. 1972. The metabolic demand for oxygen in fish, particularly salmonids, and a comparison with other vertebrates. *Resp. Physiol.* 14:183–92
50. Brett, J. R. 1973. Energy expenditure of sockeye salmon, *Oncorhynchus nerka*, during sustained performance. *J. Fish. Res. Bd. Can.* 30:1799–1809
51. Brett, J. R., Glass, N. R. 1973. Metabolic rates and critical swimming speeds of sockeye salmon (*Oncorhynchus nerka*) in relation to size and temperature. *J. Fish. Res. Bd. Can.* 30:379–87
52. Brett, J. R., Sutherland, D. B. 1965. Respiratory metabolism of pumpkinseed (*Lepomis gibbosus*) in relation to swimming speed. *J. Fish. Res. Bd. Can.* 22:405–9
53. Brody, S. 1945. *Bioenergetics and Growth.* New York/London: Hafner. 1023 pp.
54. Brooks, G. A., Brauner, K. E., Cassins, R. G. 1973. Glycogen synthesis and metabolism of lactic acid after exercise. *Am. J. Physiol.* 224:1162–66
55. Brown, C. E., Muir, B. S. 1970. Analysis of ram ventilation of fish gills with application of skipjack tuna (*Katsuwonus pelamis*). *J. Fish. Res. Bd. Can.* 27:1637–52
56. Burton, D. T., Spehar, A. M. 1971. A re-evaluation of the anaerobic end products of fresh-water fish exposed to environmental hypoxia. *Comp. Biochem. Physiol.* 40A:945–54
57. Chodrow, R. E., Taylor, C. R. 1973. Energetic cost of limbless locomotion in snakes. *Fed. Proc. Fed. Am. Soc. Exp. Med.* 32:422 (Abstr.)
58. Connor, A. R., Elling, C. H., Black, E. C., Collins, G. B., Gauley, J. R., Trevor-Smith, E. 1964. Changes in glycogen and lactate levels in migrating salmonid fishes ascending experimental "endless" fishways. *J. Fish. Res. Bd. Can.* 21:255–90
59. Coulson, R. A., Hernandez, T. 1964. *Biochemistry of the Alligator.* Baton Rouge: Louisiana State Univ. 138 pp.
60. Crabtree, B., Newsholme, E. A. 1972. Activities of phosphorylase, hexokinase, phosphofructokinase, lactate dehydrogenase and the glycerol 3-phosphate dehydrogenases in muscles from vertebrates and invertebrates. *Biochem. J.* 126:49–58
61. Cushman, J. R., Packard, G. C., Boardman, T. J. 1976. Concentrations of lactic acid in neotenic and transformed tiger salamanders (*Ambystoma tigrinum*) before and after activity. *J. Comp. Physiol.* 112:273–81
62. Dando, P. R. 1969. Lactate metabolism in fish. *J. Mar. Biol. Ass. UK* 49:209–23
63. Dawson, W. R. 1967. Interspecific variation in physiological responses of lizards to temperature. In *Lizard Ecology: A Symposium,* ed. W. W. Milstead, pp. 230–57. Columbia: Univ. Missouri. 300 pp.
64. Dawson, W. R. 1975. Avian physiology. *Ann. Rev. Physiol.* 37:441–65
65. Dawson, W. R. 1975. On the physiological significance of the preferred body temperatures of reptiles. In *Perspectives in Biophysical Ecology,* ed. D. M. Gates, R. B. Schmerl, pp. 443–73. New York/ Heidelberg/ Berlin: Springer. 609 pp.
66. Dawson, W. R., Bartholomew, G. A. 1956. Relation of oxygen consumption to body weight, temperature, and temperature acclimation in lizards *Uta stansburiana* and *Sceloporus occidentalis. Physiol. Zool.* 29:40–51
67. Dean, J. M., Goodnight, C. J. 1964. A comparative study of carbohydrate metabolism in fish as affected by temperature and exercise. *Physiol. Zool.* 37: 280–99
68. Dickson, I. W., Kramer, R. H. 1971. Factors influencing scope for activity and active and standard metabolism of

rainbow trout (*Salmo gairdneri*). *J. Fish. Res. Bd. Can.* 28:587–96

69. Dmi'el, R. 1972. Effect of activity and temperature on metabolism and water loss in snakes. *Am. J. Physiol.* 223:510–16

70. Dmi'el, R., Rappeport, D. 1976. Effect of temperature on metabolism during running in the lizard *Uromastix aegyptius. Physiol. Zool.* 49:77–84

71. Driedzic, W. R., Hochachka, P. W. 1975. The unanswered question of high anaerobic capabilities of carp white muscle. *Can. J. Zool.* 53:706–12

72. Driedzic, W. R., Hochachka, P. W. 1976. Control of energy metabolism in fish white muscle. *Am. J. Physiol.* 230:579–82

73. Driedzic, W. R., Kiceniuk, J. W. 1976. Blood lactate levels in free-swimming rainbow trout (*Salmo gairdneri*) before and after strenuous exercise resulting in fatigue. *J. Fish. Res. Bd. Can.* 33:173–76

74. Drummond, G. I., Black, E. C. 1960. Comparative physiology: Fuel of muscle metabolism. *Ann. Rev. Physiol.* 22:169–90

75. Drury, D. R., Wick, A. N. 1956. Metabolism of lactic acid in the intact rabbit. *Am. J. Physiol.* 184:304–8

76. Farmer, G. J., Beamish, F. W. H. 1969. Oxygen consumption in *Tilapia nilotica* in relation to swimming speed and salinity. *J. Fish. Res. Bd. Can.* 26:2807–21

77. Fedak, M. A., Pinshow, B., Schmidt-Nielsen, K. 1974. Energy cost of bipedal running. *Am. J. Physiol.* 227:1038–44

78. Fry, F. E. J. 1947. Effects of the environment on animal activity. *Publ. Ont. Fish. Res. Lab.* 68. 62 pp.

79. Fry, F. E. J. 1957. The aquatic respiration of fish. In *Physiology of Fishes*, ed. M. E. Brown, 1:1–63. New York: Academic. 447 pp.

80. Fry, F. E. J. 1971. The effect of environmental factors on the physiology of fish. In *Fish Physiology*, ed. W. S. Hoar, D. J. Randall, 6:1–98. New York/London: Academic. 559 pp.

81. Fry, F. E. J., Hart, J. S. 1948. Cruising speed of goldfish in relation to water temperature. *J. Fish. Res. Bd. Can.* 7:169–75

82. Fry, F. E. J., Hochachka, P. W. 1970. Fish. In *Comparative Physiology of Thermoregulation*, ed. G. C. Whittow, 1:79–134. New York/London: Academic. 333 pp.

83. Gatten, R. E. Jr. 1974. Effects of temperature and activity on aerobic and an-

aerobic metabolism and heart rate in the turtles *Pseudemys scripta* and *Terrapene ornata. Comp. Biochem. Physiol.* 48A:619–48

84. Gatten, R. E. Jr. 1975. Effects of activity on blood oxygen saturation, lactate, and pH in the turtles *Pseudemys scripta* and *Terrapene ornata. Physiol. Zool.* 48:24–35

85. Giaja, J., Markovic-Giaja, L. 1957. La fatigue des poissons. *C. R. Soc. Biol.* 151:1204–5

86. Gibson, E. S., Fry, F. E. J. 1954. The performance of the lake trout, *Salvelinus namaycush,* at various levels of temperature and oxygen pressure. *Can. J. Zool.* 32:252–60

87. Gollnick, P. D., Hermansen, L. 1973. Biochemical adapatations to exercise: Anaerobic metabolism. In *Exercise and Sport Sciences Reviews,* ed. J. H. Wilmore, 1:1–43. New York/London: Academic. 457 pp.

88. Gordon, M. S., Chow, P. H. 1974. Unusual patterns of aerobic metabolism in fishes: Effects of swimming speed and environmental temperature on the tropical "staring *weke*" goatfish (*Mulloidichthys samoensis*) and the temperate zone jack mackerel (*Trachurus symmetricus*). *Am. Zool.* 14:1258 (Abstr.)

89. Graham, J. M. 1949. Some effects of temperature and oxygen pressure on the metabolism and activity of the speckled trout, *Salvelinus fontinalis. Can. J. Res., Sect. D* 27:270–88

90. Greenwald, O. E. 1971. The effect of body temperature on oxygen consumption and heart rate in the Sonora gopher snake, *Pituophis catenifer affinis* Hallowell. *Copeia* 1971:98–106

91. Greer Walker, M., Pull, G. A. 1973. Skeletal muscle function and sustained swimming speeds in the coalfish *Gadus virens* L. *Comp. Biochem. Physiol.* 44A:495–501

92. Greer Walker, M., Pull, G. A. 1975. A survey of red and white muscle in marine fish. *J. Fish Biol.* 7:295–300

93. Hammond, B. R., Hickman, C. P. Jr. 1966. The effect of physical conditioning on the metabolism of lactate, phosphate, and glucose in rainbow trout, *Salmo gairdneri. J. Fish. Res. Bd. Can.* 23:65–83

94. Hart, J. S. 1968. Respiration of the Winnipeg goldeneye (*Hiodon alosoides*). *J. Fish. Res. Bd. Can.* 25:2603–8

95. Hart, J. S., Berger, M. 1972. Energetics, water economy and temperature regulation during flight. *Proc. 15th Int. Ornithol. Congr.,* 189–99

96. Heath, A. G., Pritchard, A. W. 1962. Changes in the metabolic rate and blood lactic acid of bluegill sunfish, *Lepomis macrochirus*, Raf. following severe muscular activity. *Physiol. Zool.* 35: 323–29

97. Hemmingsen, A. M. 1960. Energy metabolism as related to body size and respiratory surfaces, and its evolution. *Rep. Steno. Mem. Hosp. Nord. Insulinlab.* 9. 110 pp.

98. Hillman, S. S. 1976. Cardiovascular correlates of maximal oxygen consumption rates in anuran amphibians. *J. Comp. Physiol.* 109:199–207

99. Hochachka, P. W. 1961. The effect of physical training on oxygen debt and glycogen reserves in trout. *Can. J. Zool.* 39:767–76

100. Hochachka, P. W., Mustafa, T. 1972. Invertebrate facultative anaerobiosis. *Science* 178:1056–60

101. Hochachka, P. W., Owen, T. G., Allen, J. F., Whittow, G. C. 1975. Multiple end products of anaerobiosis in diving vertebrates. *Comp. Biochem. Physiol.* 50B:17–22

102. Holloszy, J. O., Booth, F. W. 1976. Biochemical adaptations to endurance exercise in muscle. *Ann. Rev. Physiol.* 38:273–91

103. Hudson, R. C. L. 1973. On the function of the white muscles in teleosts at intermediate swimming speeds. *J. Exp. Biol.* 58:509–22

104. Hutchison, V. H., Turney, L. D. 1975. Glucose and lactate concentrations during activity in the leopard frog, *Rana pipiens*. *J. Comp. Physiol.* 99:287–95

105. Job, S. V. 1955. The oxygen consumption of *Salvelinus fontinalis*. *Publ. Ont. Fish. Res. Lab.* 73. 39 pp.

106. Johlin, J. M., Moreland, F. B. 1933. Studies of the blood picture of the turtle after complete anoxia. *J. Biol. Chem.* 103:107–14

107. Johnson, M. C., Charlton, W. H. 1960. Some effects of temperature on metabolism and activity of the largemouth bass, *Micropterus salmoides* Lacepede. *Progr. Fish. Cult.* 22:155–63

108. Johnston, I. A., Goldspink, G. 1973. Quantitative studies of muscle glycogen utilization during sustained swimming in crucian carp (*Carassius carassius* L.) *J. Exp. Biol.* 59:607–15

109. Johnston, I. A., Goldspink, G. 1973. A study of glycogen and lactate in the myotomal muscles and liver of the coalfish (*Gadus virens* L.) during sustained swimming. *J. Mar. Biol. Ass. UK* 53:17–26

110. Johnston, I. A., Goldspink, C. 1973. A study of the swimming performance of the Crucian carp *Carassius carassius* (L.) in relation to the effects of exercise and recovery on biochemical changes in the myotomal muscles and liver. *J. Fish. Biol.* 5:249–60

111. Jonas, R. E. E., Sehdev, H. S., Tomlinson, N. 1962. Blood pH and mortality in rainbow trout (*Salmo gairdneri*) and sockeye salmon (*Oncorhynchus nerka*). *J. Fish. Res. Bd. Can.* 19:619–24

112. Jones, D. J. 1971. Theoretical analysis of factors which may limit the maximum oxygen uptake of fish: The oxygen cost of the cardiac and branchial pumps. *J. Theor. Biol.* 32:341–49

113. Kiermeir, A. 1939. Über den Blutzucker der Süsswasserfische. *Z. Vergleich. Physiol.* 27:460–91

114. Kleiber, M. 1975. *The Fire of Life.* Huntington, NY: Krieger. 453 pp. 2nd ed.

115. Kutty, M. N. 1968. Respiratory quotients in goldfish and rainbow trout. *J. Fish. Res. Bd. Can.* 25:1689–1728

116. Lasiewski, R. C., Dawson, W. R. 1967. A re-examination of the relation between standard metabolic rate and body weight in birds. *Condor* 69:13–23

117. Love, R. M. 1970. *The Chemical Biology of Fishes.* London/New York: Academic. 547 pp.

118. MacLeod, R. A., Jonas, R. E. E., Roberts, E. 1963. Glycolytic enzymes in the tissues of a Salmonid fish (*Salmo gairdnerii gairdnerii*). *Can. J. Biochem. Physiol.* 41:1971–81

119. Mearns, A. J. 1971. *Lactic acid regulation in salmonid fishes.* PhD thesis. Univ. Washington, Seattle. 151 pp.

120. Meyerhof, O. 1920. Über die Energieumwandlungen in Muskel. II. Das Schicksal der Milchsäure in der Erholungsperiod des Muskels. *Pfluegers Arch.* 182:284–317

121. Meyerhof, O. 1922. Die Energieumwandlungen in Muskel. VI. Mitteilung über den Ursprung der Kontraktionswärme. *Pfluegers Arch.* 195:22–74

122. Miller, R. B., Sinclair, A. C., Hochachka, P. W. 1959. Diet, glycogen reserves and resistance to fatigue in hatchling rainbow trout. *J. Fish. Res. Bd. Can.* 16:321–28

123. Minaire, Y. 1973. Origine et destinée du lactate plasmatique. *J. Physiol. Paris* 66:229–57

124. Moberly, W. R. 1966. *The physiological correlates of activity in the common iguana, Iguana iguana.* PhD thesis. Univ. Michigan, Ann Arbor. 123 pp.

125. Moberly, W. R. 1968. The metabolic responses of the common iguana, *Iguana iguana*, to activity under restraint. *Comp. Biochem. Physiol.* 27: 1–20

126. Moberly, W. R. 1968. The metabolic responses of the common iguana, *Iguana iguana*, to walking and diving. *Comp. Biochem. Physiol.* 27:21–32

127. Muir, B. S., Nelson, G. S., Bridges, K. W. 1965. A method for measuring swimming speed in oxygen consumption studies on the aholehole, *Kuhlia sanddvicensis. Trans. Am. Fish. Soc.* 94:378–82

128. Parker, R. R., Black, E. C. 1959. Muscular fatigue and mortality in troll-caught chinook salmon (*Oncorhynchus tshawytscha*). *J. Fish. Res. Bd. Can.* 16:95–106

129. Parker, R. R., Black, E. C., Larkin, P. A. 1959. Fatigue and mortality in troll-caught Pacific salmon (*Oncorhynchus*). *J. Fish. Res. Bd. Can.* 16:429–48

130. Pasquis, P., Lacaisse, A., Dejours, P. 1970. Maximal oxygen uptake in four species of small mammals. *Resp. Physiol.* 9:298–309

131. Patterson, S., Johnston, I. A., Goldspink, G. 1975. A histochemical study of the lateral muscles of five teleost species. *J. Fish. Biol.* 7:159–66

132. Piiper, J., Meyer, M., Drees, F. 1972. Hydrogen ion balance in the elasmobranch *Scyliorhinus stellaris* after exhausting activity. *Resp. Physiol.* 16:290–303

133. Poulson, T. C. 1963. Cave adaptation in amblyopsid fishes. *Am. Midl. Nat.* 70:257–90

134. Prange, H. D. 1976. Energetics of swimming of a sea turtle. *J. Exp. Biol.* 64:1–12

135. Pritchard, A. W., Hunter, J. R., Lasker, R. 1971. The relation between exercise and biochemical changes in red and white muscle and liver in the jack mackerel, *Trachurus symmetricus. Fish. Bull.* 69:379–86

136. Rao, G. M. M. 1968. Oxygen consumption of rainbow trout (*Salmo gairdneri*) in relation to activity and salinity. *Can. J. Zool.* 46:781–86

137. Rao, G. M. M. 1971. Influence of activity and salinity on the weight-dependent oxygen consumption of the rainbow trout *Salmo gairdneri. Mar. Biol.* 8: 205–12

138. Ruben, J. A. 1976. Aerobic and anaerobic metabolism during activity in snakes. *J. Comp. Physiol.* 109:147–57

139. Schmidt-Nielsen, K. 1972. Locomotion: Energy cost of swimming, flying, and running. *Science* 177:222–28

140. Secondat, M. 1950. Influence de l'exercice sur la capacité pour l'oxygène du sang de la Carpe (*Cyprinus carpio* L.) *C. R. Acad. Sci. Paris* 230:1787–88

141. Secondat, M. 1950. Influence de l'exercise musculaire sur le valeur de la glycémie de la carpe *Cyprinus carpio* L. *C. R. Acad. Sci. Paris* 231:796–97

142. Secondat, M., Diaz, D. 1942. Recherches sur la lactacidémie chez le poisson d'eau douce. *C. R. Acad. Sci. Paris.* 215:71–73

143. Seymour, R. S. 1973. Physiological correlates of forced activity and burrowing in the spadefoot toad, *Scaphiopus hammondii. Copeia* 1973:103–15

144. Simpson, W. W. 1926. The effects of asphyxia and isletectomy on the blood sugar of *Myoxocephalus* and *Ameiurus. Am. J. Physiol.* 77:409–18

145. Smit, H. 1965. Some experiments on the oxygen consumption of goldfish (*Carassius auratus* L.) in relation to swimming speed. *Can. J. Zool.* 43:623–33

146. Smit, H., Amelink-Koutstaal, J. M., Vijverberg, J., von Vaupel-Klein, J. C. 1971. Oxygen consumption and efficiency of swimming goldfish. *Comp. Biochem. Physiol.* 39:1–28

147. Spoor, W. A. 1946. A quantitative study of the relationship between activity and oxygen consumption of the goldfish, and its application to the measurement of respiratory metabolism in fishes. *Biol. Bull.* 91:312–15

148. Stevens, E. D., Black, E. C. 1966. The effect of intermittent exercise on carbohydrate metabolism in rainbow trout, *Salmo gairdneri. J. Fish. Res. Bd. Can.* 23:471–85

149. Taylor, C. R. 1973. Energy cost of animal locomotion. In *Comparative Physiology: Locomotion, Respiration, Transport and Blood,* ed. L. Bolis, K. Schmidt-Nielsen, S. H. P. Maddrell, pp. 23–42. Amsterdam/New York: North-Holland. 634 pp.

150. Taylor, C. R., Schmidt-Nielsen, K., Raab, J. L. 1970. Scaling of energetic cost of running to body size in mammals. *Am. J. Physiol.* 219:1104–7

151. Templeton, J. R. 1970. Reptiles. See Ref. 82, pp. 167–221

152. Tucker, V. A. 1967. The role of the cardiovascular system in oxygen transport and thermoregulation in lizards. See Ref. 63, pp. 258–69

153. Tucker, V. A. 1968. Respiratory exchange and evaporative water loss in the

flying budgerigar. *J. Exp. Biol.* 48: 67–87

154. Tucker, V. A. 1970. Energetic cost of locomotion in animals. *Comp. Biochem. Physiol.* 34:841–46

155. Tucker, V. A. 1972. Metabolism during flight in the laughing gull, *Larus atricilla. Am. J. Physiol.* 222:237–45

156. Turney, L. D., Hutchison, V. H. 1974. Metabolic scope, oxygen debt, and diurnal oxygen consumption cycle of the leopard frog, *Rana pipiens. Comp. Biochem. Physiol.* 49A:583–601

157. Tytler, P. 1969. Relationship between oxygen consumption and swimming speed in the haddock, *Melanogrammus aeglefinus. Nature* 221:274–75

158. von Buddenbrock, W. 1938. What physiological problems are of interest to the marine biologist in his studies of the most important species of fish? Part II. Beobachtungen über das Sterben gefangener Seefische und über den Milchsäuregehalt des Fischblutes. *Int. Counc. Explor. Sea, Rapp. Proc.-Verb.* 101:3–7

159. Webb, P. W. 1971. The swimming energetics of trout. II. Oxygen consumption and swimming efficiency. *J. Exp. Biol.* 55:521–40

160. Webb, P. W. 1975. Hydrodynamics and energetics of fish propulsion. *Bull. Fish. Res. Bd. Can.* 190. 159 pp.

161. Weis-Fogh, T. 1952. Weight economy of flying insects. *Trans. 9th Int. Congr. Entomol.* 1:341–47

162. Whitford, W. G. 1973. The effects of temperature on respiration in the amphibia. *Am. Zool.* 13:505–12

163. Wilson, K. J. 1971. *The relationships of activity, energy, metabolism, and body temperature in four species of lizards.* PhD thesis. Monash Univ., Clayton, Victoria, Australia

164. Wilson, K. J. 1974. The relationship of oxygen supply for activity to body temperature in four species of lizards. *Copeia* 1974:920–34

165. Wilson, K. J. 1974. The relationships of maximum and resting oxygen consumption and heart rates to weight in reptiles of the order Squamata. *Copeia* 1974: 781–85

166. Wilson, K. J., Lee, A. K. 1970. Changes in oxygen consumption and heart rate with activity and body temperature in the tuatara, *Sphenodon punctatum. Comp. Biochem. Physiol.* 33:311–22

167. Winberg, G. G. 1961. New information on metabolic rate in fishes. *Vopr. Ikhtiol.* 1:157–65 (*Fish. Res. Bd. Can. Transl. Ser.* 362)

168. Wittenberger, C. 1968. Biologie du chinchard de la Mer Noire (*Trachurus mediterraneus*). XV. Recherches sur le métabolisme d'effort chez *Trachurus* et *Gobius. Mar. Biol.* 2:1–4

169. Wittenberger, C., Diaciuc, I. V. 1965. Effort metabolism of lateral muscles in carp. *J. Fish. Res. Bd. Can.* 22:1397–1406

170. Wohlschlag, D. E., Cameron, J. N., Cech, J. J. Jr. 1968. Seasonal changes in the respiratory metabolism of the pinfish (*Lagodon rhomboides*). *Contrib. Mar. Sci.* 13:89–104

171. Wunder, B. A. 1970. Energetics of running activity in Merriam's chipmunk, *Eutamias merriami. Comp. Biochem. Physiol.* 33:821–36

Ann. Rev. Physiol. 1978. 40:471–99
Copyright © 1978 by Annual Reviews Inc. All rights reserved

COMPARATIVE ASPECTS OF ❖1199
VERTEBRATE CARDIORESPIRATORY
PHYSIOLOGY[1]

Fred N. White

Physiological Research Laboratory, Scripps Institution of Oceanography, and
Department of Medicine, University of California, San Diego, La Jolla,
California 92093

INTRODUCTION

This review is largely restricted to nonmammalian vertebrates; it touches
only tangentially on invertebrate cardiorespiratory physiology. By cardiorespiratory physiology I mean those aspects of functional morphology and
physiology that bear on the phenomena of gas exchange. Mammals are
treated only in a comparative sense; from the voluminous literature on the
cardiorespiratory physiology of commonly used laboratory mammals and
of man, material of interest to comparative physiologists has been selected.
Recent developments regarding hemoglobin are not discussed, for recent
reviews on this subject are available (see below).

[1]Glossary of symbols:

C = concentration
D = coefficient for diffusion
E = coefficient of extraction
F = fractional concentration in dry
    gas phase
G = conductance
P = gas pressure (or, partial pressure)
P_{50} = partial pressure O_2 at which
    Hb is 50% oxygenated
$\dot{Q}$ = blood flow
R = respiratory exchange ratio
$\dot{V}$ = volume per unit time
V_T = tidal volume

X = conductance ratio
A = alveolar
E = expired
a = arterial
b = blood
g = gill
m = medium (i.e. air, water)
$\bar{v}$ = mean venous
w = water
diff = diffusion
perf = perfusion
vent = ventilation
β = capacitance coefficient

471

0066-4278/78/0301-0471$01.00

While comparative physiology often emphasizes differences among species or among adaptations within species, many of the papers and reviews referred to here illustrate functional similarities among species or groups that should provide the basis for meaningful generalizations.

Several important reviews and symposia have appeared in recent years: hemoglobin (8, 127); acid-base regulation (115, 123); respiration in amphibious vertebrates (54); respiratory, metabolic, and circulatory physiology of reptiles (9, 158, 168); neural control of respiration (128, 170); receptors and control of respiration in birds (133); comparative physiology of the cardiorespiratory system (107); carbon dioxide and metabolic regulation (100). A most useful overview of the varied aspects of comparative cardiorespiratory physiology has appeared (33).

While I hope that established investigators will find this review helpful, it is my special wish that it will stimulate in students and others new to the discipline a level of creative discomfort that will lead them to the field or laboratory for relief from the pleasant pain of a disquieting idea.

CONVECTION REQUIREMENTS

The convection requirements for air, water, and blood represent the ratio of the volume of medium moved to the gas consumption expressed in l mmol^{-1} ($\dot{V}m/\dot{V}_{O_2}$; $\dot{Q}b/\dot{V}_{O_2}$). A water convection requirement of 17 for *Octopus* indicates that 17 l H_2O are ventilated for each mmol O_2 consumed. Dejours et al (33, 34) have tabulated these requirements for O_2 for a variety of species. Plots of $\dot{V}m/\dot{V}_{O_2}$ and $\dot{Q}b/\dot{V}_{O_2}$ reveal that both convection requirements are high in water breathers in comparison to air breathers. The convection requirements are inversely related to the C_{O_2} of the medium. For blood, the requirement is highly dependent upon hemoglobin level. Aquatic forms, owing to the relatively low C_{O_2} of H_2O, exhibit ventilation requirements of 10–30 times those of air breathers. However, Em_{O_2} for aquatic species is roughly twice that of aerial animals. The countercurrent vascular arrangement of the gill vessels of fishes contributes importantly to extraction efficiency. For a given Cm_{O_2} the convection requirement for blood is generally lower than that for the medium breathed, whereas Eb_{O_2} appears always to be higher than Em_{O_2}. Blood convection requirement ranges from 0.33–0.56 l mmol^{-1} O_2 in birds and mammals and is variably higher in ectotherms, reaching the extreme value of 8.36 in icefishes, which lack hemoglobin (46). An inverse relationship between blood hemoglobin content (above 3 gm%) and the blood convection requirement exists in vertebrates from all classes (85); this suggests a strong influence of O_2 capacity of blood on perfusion requirements. Below [Hb] of 3 gm% the requirement rises sharply.

Endotherms maintain relatively constant $\dot{V}_E/\dot{Q}$ when going from rest to activity. Thus, a close match exists between ventilatory and circulatory convections at elevated $\dot{V}_{O_2}$. The data for lower vertebrates are extremely sparse, especially in regard to $\dot{Q}/\dot{V}_{O_2}$, most measures being taken only at a single body temperature or in the resting state. At constant body temperature, the dogfish, *Scyliorhinus stellaris*, maintains relatively constant $\dot{V}_w/\dot{V}_{O_2}$ when going from rest to activity, the value increasing by only 3% (108). However, an associated 15% increase occurred in $\dot{Q}/\dot{V}_{O_2}$. $\dot{V}_w/\dot{Q}$ thus fell by around 11%. While the conductance ratio G_{vent}/G_{perf} increased, G_{diff}/G_{perf} decreased. The decrease in utilization of inspired O_2 during swimming was attributable to diffusion limitation in branchial transfer. Certain contrasts and similarities exist between these observations and those on trout going from rest to activity (117): Trout and dogfish increase $\dot{V}_g$ primarily by increasing stroke volume; the same is true for $\dot{Q}$; branchial and systemic vascular resistance decreased in both species; $\dot{O}_2$ utilization remained unchanged in trout but decreased in dogfish; following exercise, the ratio of O_2 debt to net uptake of O_2 during swimming was much lower for trout than dogfish. This latter contrast may be related to the swimming habits of the two species; trout must attain a balance between energy and O_2 budgets if they are to swim for long periods.

Resting turtles (*Pseudemys scripta, P. floridana*) exhibit an inverse relationship between $\dot{V}_E/\dot{V}_{O_2}$ and body temperature as E_{O_2} increases (58, 73); $\dot{Q}/\dot{V}_{O_2}$ based on mean estimates of $\dot{Q}$ at various body temperatures remains constant (73). Thus, $\overline{\dot{V}_E/\dot{Q}}$ falls as resting O_2 demand increases with body temperature. The increase in E_{O_2} is highly dependent on blood flow at constant arteriovenous O_2 difference. Since Pa_{CO_2} increases as a result of the decline in $\dot{V}_E/\dot{V}_{O_2}$, both temperature and the Bohr effect increasingly influence tissue O_2 extraction at higher temperatures. Construction of O_2 dissociation curves at physiological temperatures and pHa for *Iguana iguana* (168) reveals that P_{50} values shift from P_{O_2} of 12 torr at 15°C and pH 7.78 to around 53 torr at 37°C and pH 7.4. This shift in the Hb-dissociation curve is accompanied by an increase in $(Ca_{O_2} - C\bar{v}_{O_2})$.

While both mean systemic and pulmonary blood flows remain approximately equal at various body temperatures and in direct proportion to $\dot{V}_{O_2}$ in the turtle *Pseudemys floridana*, redistribution of blood flow between these circuits takes place during the respiratory cycle. Ventilatory periods are brief and are interrupted by relatively protracted apneic pauses. Immediately preceding and during the ventilatory phase, a left-to-right intracardiac shunt develops in association with an increase in heart rate (157, 160).

During apnea the shunt is reversed to right-to-left. No critical evaluation of these shunts in relationship to O_2 and CO_2 exchange across the alveoli has been made. One result of right-to-left shunting during apnea is the recirculation of a fraction of the mixed venous blood to the systemic circuit. The decline in hemoglobin saturation of arterial blood is presumably offset at the tissue level through intensification of the Bohr effect. The events during passage of blood through the lungs are complicated by the fact that alveolar partial pressures are constantly changing as apnea progresses. A decrease in convective effect on gas transport may also occur during the long breathhold, with consequent stratification. An increase in frequency of cholinergically mediated lung smooth muscle contractions with increased body temperature may play a role in reducing stratification of lung gases (159). When such contractions occur, the pressure difference between the lungs augments convective gas flow.

The air convection requirement for lung breathers appears to be reduced as metabolic intensity increases with temperature (58). This adjustment has been related to the necessity for adjusting the Pa_{CO_2} in a manner that maintains arterial $[OH^-]/[H^+]$ at a constant level. Since a relative decrease in air convective intensity occurs as $\dot{V}O_2$ rises, an increase in EO_2 is required to support metabolism. In the limited cases studied, circulatory convection appears to be directly proportional to metabolic intensity; tissue extraction is augmented by local vascular adjustments favoring gas exchange and by the behavior of hemoglobin.

GAS EXCHANGE MODELS

Four major gas exchange systems can be distinguished among vertebrates from the relationships between the direction of flow of the medium breathed and that of the flow of capillary blood: (a) countercurrent (fish gills—water and blood flow in opposite directions); (b) crosscurrent (avian lung—capillary flow at right angle to air flow); (c) ventilated pool (mammalian lung —capillary blood equilibrates with an external pool, the alveolar space, where partial pressures are uniform); (d) infinite pool (amphibian skin— network of capillaries in skin exposed to external medium). An anatomical study has concluded that while the avian parabronchial gas flow is crosscurrent to pulmonary arterial blood, a countercurrent relation exists at the gas exchange site, i.e. the air capillaries (1). Gas flow in the avian lung is unidirectional throughout the respiratory cycle (15, 19, 20, 135, 136).

Earlier attempts to analyze the absolute and relative efficacies of these systems have been usefully extended (109, 110). Derived from the Fick principle, the analysis replaces concentration differences by introducing the term "capacitance coefficient," β, which is the ratio of the difference in incurrent and excurrent gas concentration to the difference in partial pressures. This is applied to the medium breathed, βm, or to the blood, βb.

Under "ideal" conditions where distributional inhomogeneity and diffusion limitations are absent, the partial pressures in excurrent medium and blood, relative to entering partial pressures, depend upon the medium-to-blood conductance ratio [$X = (\dot{V}\beta)m/(\dot{V}\beta)b$). The extent of gas transfer at similar X values increases from ventilated pool to crosscurrent to countercurrent (109). On the basis of both experimental data and theory, these studies have been extended to analyses of the models in terms of conductances, relative partial pressure differences, and limitations that can be attributed to ventilation, medium/blood transfer, and perfusion (110). Although distinct differences exist among the models in maximum efficiencies, the actual efficiency values based on experimental data are fairly uniform. Lower than maximal theoretical conductance may be attributed to either diffusion limitation or functional inhomogeneities. In the mammalian lung, stratified inhomogeneities in the absence of convective gas mixing in the alveolar space would seriously limit alveolar gas exchange (142). This limitation could become important for animals that exhibit protracted apneic periods (reptiles, amphibia) in the normal ventilatory cycle. The analyses contained in (109, 110) form a foundation for comparisons between animals of different groups and in different conditions (rest, exercise, thermal influences, altitude, etc). However, along with cyclic changes in ventilation and perfusion and functional inhomogeneities, uncertainty regarding the appropriate values of β for CO_2 and O_2 in blood, and for CO_2 in sea water, present difficulties in application.

Useful analyses of contrasts in gas exchange at sea level and high altitude, and between rest and exercise, are presented in the monograph of Dejours (33).

Hills (49) has evaluated arterial partial pressure differences of transmitted gases across gills and lungs at steady state. The overall gradient was expressed as the simple sum of terms representing airway convection, airway diffusion, membrane diffusion, blood convection, ventilation/perfusion inequalities, and shunt. These, excepting shunts, were weighted by ventilation rate. The approach avoids equations defining physiological dead space and mixed alveolar air.

The roles of convective and diffusive gas transport and mixing in the alveolar lung have been analyzed and different mathematical approaches compared (29, 142). In the latter study, a single-breath technique was used for analysis of the equilibration of various test gases for varying breath-holding times. The results were incorporated into a serial three-compartment lung model. Both diffusion and convection were effective in achieving equilibration of test gases during breath-holding. In the absence of convective mixing, stratified inhomogeneities were shown to limit gas exchange seriously.

Hill et al (48) have presented a mathematical model of alveolar gas exchange that assumes constant or sinusoidally varying alveolar gas where this compartment represents an infinite source for O_2 and a sink for CO_2. The model concentrates on blood-gas reactions during passage through the alveolar capillaries. The model predicts that CO_2 exchange enhances O_2 delivery by only 2% through the Bohr effect; the Haldane effect (dependence of CO_2 exchange on O_2) accounted for 46% of the CO_2 exchange. P_{CO_2}, $[HCO_3^-]$, and pH of blood all continue to exhibit slight change following transit, and thus complete CO_2 equilibrium is not reached on passage through the respiratory unit. Blood flow and mixed venous gas tensions, rather than diffusion or reaction rates, were most determinative for O_2 and CO_2 exchange rates.

Gas exchange across the placenta has been extensively reviewed in an international symposium (90), and mathematical models for O_2 (47, 91) and CO_2 transfer (48) have been presented.

Embryos of birds must achieve gas exchange with the ambient air across the barriers of the shell, the outer shell membrane, the air cell, and the chorioallantoic membrane. Since this transport must be accomplished by diffusion, the relationship between metabolic rate and shell permeability is important in establishing the P_{O_2} and P_{CO_2} in the air cell. The barrier between chorioallantoic blood and the air cell appears more important for transport of CO_2 than for O_2 (150). Bird eggs vary widely in size, shell thickness, and relative surface area. Shell pore diameter and length are additional variables.

Water conductance, Gw, is reported to follow the relationship Gw = $0.432 \times W^{0.78}$ for eggs ranging in mass (W) from 1–1000 g (2). Water loss appears to be independent of metabolic rate; since metabolic rate varies with mass raised to a power similar to that for water loss, it has been suggested that the pore geometry that influences gas conductance evolved in response to the metabolic needs of the embryo. The fact that Gw varies with $W^{0.78}$ apparently reflects its dependence on the metabolic requirements for gas exchange. The plot of water loss from eggs in nests against egg mass exhibits a slope similar to that for the body mass dependence of Gw(37).

Using sections of chicken egg shells for determining permeabilities for CO_2, H_2O, and O_2, Wangensteen et al (152) concluded that as a barrier to gas diffusion the inner and outer shell membranes are negligible compared with the shell; shell porosity, which is set at laying time, is thus the prime factor determining gas exchange. However, Kutchai & Steen (82) found that the O_2 and CO_2 permeabilities of shell plus membranes of newly laid eggs are not sufficient to support later developmental gas exchange, and that permeabilities increase with incubation time. Drying the shell membranes was shown to increase permeability; the water content of the membranes was said to decrease from 70% at fertilization to 40% by day 17. No such change was observed in unfertilized eggs.

Using previously determined Gw (2) to calculate O_2 conductance, and utilizing the product of O_2 conductance and ΔP_{O_2} across the shell as an estimate of O_2 consumption, Rahn et al found O_2 consumption to be proportional to $W^{0.78}$. Incubation time had been found to vary with $W^{0.22}$. Combining these mass functions, the investigators concluded that in different species the incubation period is inversely related to metabolic rate or eggshell gas conductance (113). The reported role of the state of hydration of the membranes on gas conductances (82) across the shell would presumably influence these calculations by lowering the conductance values used in estimating O_2 consumption. Lomholt (88) has found that eggs of species from wet habitats lose mass at a higher rate than those from drier habitats under identical incubation conditions. This suggested that the conductance of the egg shell to water vapor may be adapted to the conditions of humidity in the environment. These observations raise the possibility of many families of in vivo Gw vs W curves reflecting different environmental relations among avian eggs. Parental behavior and nest structure of four species maintain the relative humidity at a level (30–50% RH) higher than if ambient air were heated to incubation temperature (88).

An analysis of the shell porosity (151) of eggs laid by chickens acclimatized to an altitude of 3800 m showed a reduction in total pore area that should just offset the increase in diffusion coefficient of water vapor at this altitude. P_{O_2} and P_{CO_2} across the shell were less than at sea level; $\dot{V}_{O_2}$ was reduced by a factor of 0.58. G_{O_2} was similar at both altitudes. So far as O_2 exchange is concerned the major adaptation to altitude appears to be reduced metabolism, which decreases P_{O_2} across the shell; the gas conductance remains unchanged.

Eggs of varying size (9–39 g) among seven species of terns all lost 14% of their initial weight during their natural incubation times (21–36 days). A species-specific Gw (i.e. pore geometry) is said to determine water-vapor conductance, provided that a water-vapor pressure difference of around 27 torr is maintained between egg and nest microenvironment. Maintenance of this gradient requires of the incubating bird an appropriate nest ventilation (114).

D_{O_2} for the chorioallantoic membrane of chicks is reported to increase about six-fold between days 10 and 18 of incubation. Mass-specific D_{O_2} and capillary blood volume are similar to those for the human lung during late incubation (146).

Around 100 eggs, buried near a meter in depth, comprise a clutch of green turtle (*Chelonia mydas*) eggs. Damp sand minimizes the problems of water loss; however, diffusional gas exchange must support metabolism, and convection is low. During early development, O_2 and CO_2 levels in the nest are 18.4% and 2.24%, respectively. The metabolism of the young turtles rises sharply as their activity increases near and during hatching, and O_2 levels may fall to as low as 12%. The activity of the nest mates is known to be synchronous and periodic; periodicity may be related to O_2 demand, for the turtles cease activity when the system becomes diffusion limited. By flushing the soil with fresh air, rainfall may trigger emergence. This may augment O_2 availability during the vigorous burst of activity involved in emergence (111).

CONTROL OF RESPIRATION

Significant progress has been made toward revealing the nature of neural control of respiration in invertebrates and lower vertebrates. Several articles of importance are to be found in a recent symposium (128). Kammer (71) presented evidence that rhythmic ventilatory activity in insects is dependent on an endogenous central oscillator that can generate output without sensory feedback, although normally subject to such feedback. The oscillator is probably linked by interneurons to a number of motor units and is coupled to motor neurons in a labile manner, which permits the oscillator to be used several ways. Central neural oscillators that play a role in coordination of ventilation and gill perfusion have been described in decapod crustacea (162). Sensory feedback is important in maintenance of the normal rates of scaphognathite beating. Both cardiac and ventilatory oscillators show direct responses to hypoxia. The king crab, *Limulus,* has been shown to generate central respiratory motor output patterns that require no sensory feedback (171). The fact that antidromic stimulation of motoneurons has little effect on other motoneurons suggests that the central pattern is generated at interneuronal levels. Proprioceptive reflexes have little modulating effect on the centrally generated pattern but may entrain rhythm at gill plate cycling frequencies near the respiratory rate. The observed proportionality between ambient P_{O_2} and respiratory rate involves three types of O_2 receptors in the gills: units excited by O_2; those inhibited by O_2; and mechanoreceptors, the activity of which is O_2 dependent. Command fibers of these units may modulate respiration.

The neural control and proprioceptive aspects of respiratory movements of fishes have been reviewed by Ballintijn & Roberts (4). Similarity in location and function of units within the medulla of fishes with the small respiratory neurons in the rostral medulla of mammals is noted. Unlike mammalian motoneurons, the motoneurons of fish exit in cranial nerves to head muscles, no spinal centers being evident. These observations suggest that the neural modifications of terrestrial vertebrates may have occurred without a fundamental alteration of the central pattern generator. The study of lower vertebrates in order better to comprehend the nature of central control of respiration in higher forms thus gains validity from this view. Recordings from several sites in the medulla of trout revealed units that are phase coupled. Evidence for a diffuse distribution of interneurons contradicts the proposal (140) that fish respiratory interneurons are clustered in small groups, within which timing is closer than between groups.

Experiments in which muscles were paralyzed to eliminate proprioceptive feedback allow the identification of three categories of central neurons: A-cells, which are oscillator-dependent; B-cells, which are proprioception-dependent; and C-cells, of mixed function. The latter stop firing during paralysis; however, abduction of the lower jaw induces rhythmic activity. The presence of direct, proprioceptive loops is implied from fast compensating changes in electrical activity of respiratory muscle when respiratory movements are mechanically modified. Motor and proprioceptive neurons are close together within the medulla (93), and fast disynaptic reflex arcs appear to exist in the trigeminal system. Reflex modulation of motoneuron activity may be important in load matching (4). The transition from rhythmic gill ventilation to the ram mode transfers work load from branchial to swimming muscles. Recordings from medullary sites in fishes undergoing the transition from rhythmic to ram ventilation revealed rhythmic firing patterns only at speeds below the ram transition, i.e. during rhythmic breathing. These cells may have been either Ballintijn's B or C type neurons. Receptors (as yet unlocated) sensitive to some aspect of flow rate may be involved in the transition between ventilatory modes.

Proprioceptive influence on respiratory rhythm is implied from the 1:1 synchrony of ventilatory and locomotory movements in *Cymatogaster aggregata,* a fish that propels itself with the pectoral fins (155). The coupling became 2:1 under hypoxic conditions. No coordination in ventilatory and locomotor rhythms was found for the shark, *Scyliorhinus stellaris;* however, increase in speed of swimming was associated with elevated $\dot{V}g$ due to mechanical-passive and/or nervous coupling between respiratory and locomotor centers (108).

Sensitivity to changes in environmental oxygen concentration is well established in fishes; however, control pathways remain obscure (33). Chemoreceptors apparently similar in function to those of mammals have been suggested (5) but have not been located. Recordings from the pseudobranchial nerve of the trout revealed an increase in discharge frequency of more than 1% per torr below a P_{O_2} of 100 torr. This finding led to the suggestion that O_2 receptors that influence respiration may reside in the pseudobranch (83). However, the fact that bilateral deafferentiation of the pseudobranch had no significant effect on the ventilatory response to hypoxia or hyperoxia has cast doubt on the presence of such putative receptors (119). Elevation of Pa_{CO_2} of rainbow trout results in a rise in $\dot{V}g$ while changes in pH have little effect. The CO_2-sensitive receptors involved in this reflex (62) have not been located.

The variety of structural specializations exhibited by animals with a bimodal gas exchange is testimony to the richness of nature's means for making the transition from aquatic to aerial respiration (54). Rahn & Howell (112) have presented an overall view of the elimination of CO_2 by the gill-skin and the lung systems for 21 species of fishes and amphibians. They reveal that the percentage contribution of each system to CO_2 elimination is rather constant (76% in gill-skin system; 24% for lung system). When the lung system is more dominant in O_2 exchange (as in *Lepidosiren*), the exchange ratio, R, for the gill-skin system reaches very high values. Thus, CO_2 elimination by this system remains unaltered. The relative inadequacy of lungs in CO_2 elimination necessitates an increase in blood P_{CO_2}. Furthermore, air-breathing fishes may inhabit hypercarbic waters (32); as Wood & Lenfant point out (167), CO_2 receptors become important in controlling respiratory mode and $\dot{V}_E$ in lungfishes (63, 65). In *Amphipnous cuchia,* an amphibious fish in which gas exchange is accomplished principally by air breathing, the ventilation of the pharyngeal air sacs was enhanced more in response to hypoxia than to hypercapnia; ventilation was augmented only at inspired CO_2 levels above 4% (89).

Hypercapnia is an effective respiratory stimulant in many reptiles, but it depresses the respiratory rate of *Acrochordus jovanicus,* a highly aquatic snake (44). Metabolically produced CO_2 escapes readily to the water across the skin in this species. The system governing its breathing pattern appears sensitive to hypoxia, although it allows effective depletion of oxygen stores during periods of submergence which may extend over 90% of the time.

As pointed out by Wood & Lenfant (168), comparison of CO_2 sensitivity in different species is complicated by variable and often large alveolar-arterial differences in P_{CO_2} and P_{O_2} which result from intracardiac shunting and imbalances in ventilation-perfusion ratio. Differences in metabolic rate and body temperature further complicate comparisons. Jackson et al (60) found for turtles that at 10°C, 2% CO_2 in inspired gas caused a decrease in $\dot{V}_E$, whereas 6% CO_2 caused only a small increase compared to the effects of the same CO_2 concentrations at 20° and 30°C. However, when the effect was measured by $\dot{V}_E/\dot{V}_{O_2}$ the ventilatory responses were approximately the same. Among the reptiles a trend toward reduced CO_2 sensitivity seems to exist in those forms normally experiencing elevated Pa_{CO_2} (168).

The characterization and general location of CO_2-sensitive receptors in the airways of birds (21, 22, 133) has stimulated a search for such receptors in lower vertebrates. Experiments on the lizard *Tupinambis nigropunctatus,* (in which the unidirectional ventilation allowed observation of ventilatory responses to changes in gas composition) show that elevation in inspired CO_2 induces rapid ventilatory augmentation (43). Occlusion of the pulmonary circulation did not alter the response. Cervical vagotomy abolished it. CO_2-sensitive stretch or irritant receptors could not be excluded. More direct evidence from unit recording in the vagus nerve of *T. nigropunctatus* indicates that both stretch- and CO_2-sensitive receptors are present, with those receptors responsive to elevation in CO_2 showing an inverse relationship between firing rate and P_{CO_2}, as in birds (40, 133, 134). Indirect evidence, similar to that obtained for *T. nigropunctatus,* has been reported for turtles (99). Clearly, more data based on unit recording from these putative CO_2 receptors during carefully controlled ventilation are needed. The possible role of such receptors in the establishment of the demonstrated inverse relationship between $\dot{V}_E/\dot{V}_{O_2}$ and body temperature (58, 73, 159) in turtles is in need of investigation.

Sensitivity of the avian respiratory center to hypercapnia is well documented (16, 27). While hypercapnia normally causes increased $\dot{V}_E$, paralyzed ducks exhibited respiratory center inhibition (67); hypoxia had no observable effect in paralyzed ducks or chickens. The effect was evaluated by recording respiratory motor discharge from the intercostal nerve. Vagotomy abolished all response to CO_2; apparently the airway CO_2-sensitive receptors (133), cardiac receptors (39), or carotid bodies (17, 69) were involved. The abolition of normal CO_2 and O_2 responses in paralyzed birds led to the suggestion that rhythmic pulmonary afferent feedback may be essential to the maintenance of normal sensitivity of the respiratory center to CO_2.

Avian intrapulmonary chemoreceptors can detect sinusoidal variations in F_{CO_2} at frequencies above 160 cpm (104). The bidirectional rate sensitivity of the receptors over physiological ranges of airway P_{CO_2} suggests that information concerning direction and rate changes in P_{CO_2} is transmitted to the central nervous system. Airway CO_2 receptors and systemic chemoreceptors can act independently in controlling respiratory amplitude and frequency (105): Intrapulmonary CO_2-sensitive receptors can dominate the control of respiratory amplitude during hypocapnia, while systemic receptors dominate during hypercapnia.

In dogs on cardiopulmonary bypass, ventilatory responses to alterations in inspired CO_2 are independent of arterial CO_2 and are abolished by vagotomy (7). These observations raise the question of whether avian-type CO_2 receptors are present in the airways of mammals. Wasserman et al (154) have offered evidence from dogs that the hyperpnea associated with induced elevation in cardiac output and CO_2 flow to the lungs is accompanied by precise regulation of Pa_{CO_2}; they suggest that a rapidly responding respiratory chemoreceptor is involved. In a later study (153), $P\bar{v}_{CO_2}$ was elevated without change in $\dot{Q}$. $\dot{V}E$ increased in direct proportion to the additional CO_2 and Pa_{CO_2} remained at the control level. It was concluded that the CO_2-linked hyperpnea was not mediated by arterial chemoreceptors. However, recordings of single unit vagal activity (120 units) firing in phase with ventilation failed to demonstrate avian-type CO_2-sensitive units in the lungs of the cat (81). The study was designed to differentiate between stretch of lung tissue and intrapulmonary CO_2 concentration.

Anesthetic dissection (101) and brainstem section (102) were used to study the central control of respiration in crocodilian reptiles. Neither study provided evidence for an apneustic center. Stem-sectioning experiments demonstrated the presence of inspiratory, expiratory, and glottal closure centers. All of these areas were immediately under the nucleus laminaries in the medulla. The presence of a pneumotaxic center was not confirmed.

The central neural areas involved in controlling polypnea in fowl were located by stimulation of specific multiple loci in the brainstem (125). The midbrain was found to contain a panting center. Its location at the level of the nucleus mesencephalicus lateralis, pars dorsalis (i.e. mammalian inferior colliculus), and its spatial relationships to other structures, suggested homology with the mammalian pneumotaxic center. A study (80) of central inhibitory loci in fowl revealed that apnea or partial respiratory inhibition was associated with (a) an anteriolateral thalamic field near nucleus rotundus, (b) the total course of the quintofrontal tract and, (c) a medial and lateral mesencephalic area. The accompanying cardiovascular responses associated with the mesencephalic quintofrontal tract showed features of the diving reflex.

Recent reviews deal with central control of mammalian respiratory rhythmicity and pattern generation (30, 169, 170).

CONTROL OF PERFUSION

Circulation through gas exchange organs and ventilation are regulated in a linked manner. Although various stimuli are known to influence cardiac output and vascular resistance in gas exchange organs, our knowledge of the integrative mechanisms controlling flow and its distribution within gas exchangers, especially in lower vertebrates, is rather limited. A useful review of comparative aspects of circulation in gills, skin, and lungs has been presented by Johansen (64).

Direct neural control of cardiac output in elasmobranchs appears to be exclusively cholinergic, there being no cardiac sympathetic innervation (25). Butler et al attribute the increase in stroke volume accompanying the vagally induced bradycardia of hypoxia to the operation of Starling's law. Teleosts appear to possess sympathetic cardiac innervation causing cardio-acceleration (131). While the role of neural innervation of the gill vessels is obscure, considerable evidence shows that the branchial vessels possess both α and β adrenergic receptors (11, 64, 164, 165). Acetylcholine increases branchial vascular resistance, an effect that is abolished by atropine (64, 164). Blood flow appears to be equally distributed through anterior and posterior gills of *Raja rhina* at rest; a redistribution favoring the posterior gills, where water flow is greatest, occurs during exercise (132). The humoral or neurogenic basis for regional redistribution of $\dot{V}w/\dot{Q}$ is not understood. Investigators using influx of ^{14}C-urea to evaluate the functional surface areas of isolated-perfused gills of trout demonstrated that both norepinephrine and epinephrine increase functional surface area and decrease overall branchial vascular resistance; acetylcholine induced the reverse effect (11). Although the mechanisms are unclear, it appears that both the vascular and mucosal sides of fish gills can be adjusted by recruitment of perfused or ventilated channels. It is possibile that both the capacity rate ratio in different parts of the system and the overall capacity flow rate can be adjusted (55).

The question of arteriovenous anastomoses (AVAs) in the gills of fishes has received recent morphological and physiological scrutiny. The possibility that a circulatory shunt may bypass the gill lamellae (124, 144) appeared doubtful on morphological grounds [see the literature cited in (106)]. Arteriovenous anastomoses between the efferent filament artery and the central venous sinus of gill filaments have been demonstrated for *Tilapia* (149) and *Salmo* (148). These studies did not reveal AVAs originating from afferent gill vessels, but recent observations have verified the presence of such vessels in *Salmo* (W. Vogel, personal communication). The vessels were said to originate from the two small arteries that parallel the main afferent artery (41). Thus the bypass of lamellae by afferent arterial blood is again of concern; the functional significance of efferent arterial to venous sinus connections is still obscure. The latter AVAs have been reported to close under an α-vasoconstrictor effect of epinephrine (106). A ten-fold increase in circulating catecholamine level is associated with exercise in trout (103).

The pulmonary circulation and lung parenchymal smooth muscle of both frogs and turtles have long been known to possess an excitatory cholinergic innervation (92). Sympathetic inhibitory innervation to lung muscle and blood vessels has been demonstrated in the lizard *Trachydosaurus rugosus* (10, 24). The cholinergic pulmonary constrictor effect appears to reside in arteries distal to the transition between the main pulmonary arteries and their highly muscular continuance near the hilus of the lung. This transition in arterial structure was described by Koch in 1934 (75) and has recently been redescribed (158). Cholinergic control of pulmonary vascular state appears to be a major determinant of the distribution of the cardiac output between systemic and pulmonary circuits in noncrocodilian reptiles; in crocodilians, cholinergic control of pulmonary outflow tract contractile state governs distribution between the major circuits (158). The role of autonomic control of pulmonary vascular state in determining the distributional patterns of blood flow during ventilation has yet to be evaluated critically. Ventilation in turtles is associated with left-to-right intracardiac shunts, whereas in apnea and during diving a right-to-left shunt develops (97, 141, 145, 158, 160, 161). The functional significance of these changes in $\dot{V}_E/\dot{Q}$ remains obscure.

A number of fishes exhibit varying degrees of synchrony between ventilation and cardiac frequencies (131). Where it occurs, synchrony may adjust the instantaneous $\dot{V}_w/\dot{Q}$ to a more favorable value for gas exchange. The degree of cardiorespiratory coupling is variable in trout and the percentage of coupling shows an inverse relationship to inspired P_{O_2} (55), an observation confirming earlier results in the tench (116). Evidence for the reflex nature of cardiorespiratory synchrony in fishes is discussed by Satchell (131).

Ventilation tachycardia is common in reptiles in which ventilation is interrupted by apnea of variable duration. Variation in vagal parasympathetic activity to the heart represents the efferent limb of the reflex. While the nature of the sensory and central neural components of the reflex is obscure, the variations in pulmonary vascular resistance throughout the respiratory cycle and during diving (see below) may be linked with cardiac output control by the respiratory center (23). Such an integrative system would adjust $\dot{V}_E/\dot{Q}$ to more favorable levels as the partial pressure differences favoring gas exchange improved during ventilation and early apnea.

OXIDATIVE COST OF BREATHING

Estimations of the oxidative cost of maintaining the convective flow of the external medium across the respiratory surfaces are rare. With a cooperative human subject such estimates can be gained with relative ease by evaluating differences in $\dot{V}_{O_2}$ under different voluntary ventilatory regimes. This is not possible with other vertebrates. Estimates of ventilatory cost in fishes (when paralysis of the respiratory muscles was used to eliminate the O_2 cost of powering the pump) ranged from 30% $\dot{V}_{O_2}$ at rest to 50% when ventilation was trebled (138). These estimates are high by comparison to those obtained for trout by Jones & Schwarzfeld (70), who compared $\dot{V}_{O_2}$ of normally breathing fish with that when ventilation ceases as water is forced through the gills. This technique yielded an estimate of 10.7%. This is still a rather high figure when compared with estimates of 1–2% for healthy resting man. The high cost must be largely attributable to the physical characteristics of water. Ballintijn (3) has presented evidence that positional changes of the gill filaments during breathing reduces ventilatory work and that strong coupling between buccal and opercular pumps maintains uniform water movement and constant hydrodynamic efficiency. As ventilatory demand increases active muscle is recruited; energy is conserved because muscle contraction efficiency is optimal at a specific load.

Submergence of frogs is followed by a period in which $\dot{V}_{O_2}$ is elevated. This period is associated with elevated blood lactate; however, the major increase in post-submergence $\dot{V}_{O_2}$ should be attributed to the oxidative cost of hyperventilation (68). Inflation of the anuran lung is accomplished by a buccal force pump. From analysis of pressure-volume loops from buccal cavity and lungs, it was shown that work is done on the lungs by the buccal pump (156). Mean efficiency of the buccal pump was 8%, and $\dot{V}_{O_2}$ per 100 g of respiratory muscle was 0.89 ml O_2 min^{-1}. The O_2 cost of breathing at rest was estimated to be around 5% total resting $\dot{V}_{O_2}$. Since frogs elevate Pa_{CO_2} in support of acid-base homeostasis as body temperature increases (52), it seems likely that $\dot{V}_E/\dot{V}_{O_2}$ may be decreased as body temperature rises. If this is so, a range must exist of relative ventilatory costs that are inversely related to body temperature.

The shift of limb girdles into the rib cage and fusion of the skeletal elements into protective armor prevents turtles from using abdominal or thoracic excursions to inflate or deflate the lungs. Respiration involves rotation of the limb girdles, and both expiration and inspiration are active processes (42). Turtles (*Pseudemys floridana*) stop breathing with the glottis closed if the lungs are ventilated through implanted cannulae at air flow rates slightly in excess of normal. The inhibition of respiratory drive is thought to be due to the decrease in Pa_{CO_2}. Comparisons of $\dot{V}_{O_2}$ during artificial ventilation and normal ventilation provide the basis for computing the oxidative cost of moving a volume of gas (74). At 22°C this cost was estimated at 4.7×10^{-3} ml O_2 per ml gas ventilated, a value about ten times that reported for man (33). Jackson (58) found an inverse relationship between body temperature and $\dot{V}_E/\dot{V}_{O_2}$ in *P. scripta,* an observation which has been confirmed (73). In the latter study, the air convection requirement for man and turtle were found to be similar at 37°C; thus the oxidative cost of ventilation (percentage of resting $\dot{V}_{O_2}$) for the turtle at 37°C was 5–10 times that of man. When cost estimates were applied to the known values for $\dot{V}_E$ and $\dot{V}_{O_2}$ at various body temperatures, it was found that although absolute cost rises with body temperature, relative cost (i.e. percentage of resting $\dot{V}_{O_2}$) shows an inverse relationship with body temperature (at 10°C,

30%; at 37°C, 10%). In addition to its influence on acid-base homeostasis (see the section below on acid-base regulation), the inverse relationship between $\dot{V}_E/\dot{V}_{O_2}$ and body temperature means that the relative ventilatory cost decreases as metabolism increases with temperature.

ACID-BASE REGULATION

The acid-base status of the arterial blood is importantly influenced by the prevailing Pa_{CO_2} and $[HCO_3^-]$ through the Henderson-Hasselbalch relationship. In endotherms, departures from normal levels in blood pH are compensated by renal regulation of $[HCO_3^-]$ or respiratory adjustments in P_{CO_2}. Arterial pH is closely regulated in mammals at around pH 7.4, but this is not the case for a number of vertebrates and invertebrates at body temperatures other than 37°C. Arterial pH varies inversely with BT in numerous ectotherms (52), including invertebrates (53, 147); the slope of that variation is the same as for the pH of neutrality of H_2O and the pOH (52). A constant relative alkalinity ($[H^+]/[OH^-]$) results over the temperature range. $\Delta pH/°C$ is about $-.014$, a slope similar to that seen in blood held at a constant CO_2 level in vitro (129). The intercept of the in vivo pH vs temperature curve is such that both ectotherms and endotherms exhibit a similar pH at 37°C. Changes that elevate or reduce the intercept of the pH slope must be regarded as producing alkalosis or acidosis. When the pHs of arterial blood at various body temperatures are evaluated by the Henderson-Hasselbalch relationship it becomes clear that the observed changes must be accompanied by organismal regulation of $[HCO_3^-]$ or PA_{CO_2}. If the required adjustment were solely ventilatory, a fall in $\dot{V}_E/\dot{V}_{O_2}$ would be expected on transition from low to higher body temperature. Jackson (58) has demonstrated such a fall in the turtle, *Pseudemys scripta*, while $[HCO_3^-]$ remained fixed. The response is rapid and does not depend on prolonged exposure to a transitional temperature (59). The reduction in $\dot{V}_E/\dot{V}_{O_2}$ with increasing $\dot{V}_{O_2}$ may at first appear to contrast with the relatively constant $\dot{V}_E/\dot{V}_{O_2}$ of mammals undergoing alterations in $\dot{V}_{O_2}$ with exercise. However, different levels of $\dot{V}_{O_2}$ at stable body temperature in the turtle exhibit constant $\dot{V}_E/\dot{V}_{O_2}$. Thus, each body temperature is characterized by a $\dot{V}_E/\dot{V}_{O_2}$ appropriate to achieving the characteristic arterial pH.

Gill-breathing fishes, such as the trout, must expose their respiratory surfaces to a continuous stream of water representing an almost infinite sink for CO_2. This results in a characteristically low Pa_{CO_2} (2-3 torr). Arterial pH at varying temperatures is regulated by control of $[HCO_3^-]$ via active transport across the gills (118). Amphibians and certain turtles appear to exhibit intermediate dependence on adjustments of $[HCO_3^-]$ and P_{CO_2} (52). Reeves (123) has suggested that the regulation of the arterial pH in this fashion is important in maintaining the net charge of proteins, in preventing abnormal Donnan distribution, and in assuring optimal enzyme activity (121, 122). Parallel shifts in intracellular pH have been demonstrated (95).

Blood contains a buffer that maintains the slope of the pH–temperature relationship. The necessary characteristic is met by the imidazole group of protein histidine residues (120). Adjustment of pH in accordance with that exhibited by animals acclimated at different temperatures markedly influenced enzyme kinetics in goldfish, in contrast to the result obtained when pH was maintained constant (163). For example, the temperature coefficient of the reaction velocity for catalysis by the M_4 isozyme of lactate dehydrogenase was greater than when pH was adjusted. These results were interpreted in terms of the charge state of histidine imidazole at the LDH active site.

At endothermic body temperature, arterial pH is similar in ectotherms and endotherms. What, then, is the appropriate pH for endotherms at other than their regulated temperatures? The answer to this question should bear importantly on the rationale for acid-base control during hypothermia, and on construction of perfusion fluids for human organ storage. The pH of arterial blood circulating through cool peripheral tissues of mammals is higher than that of blood circulating in warmer core tissues; however, $[OH^-]/[H^+]$ remains constant (115). A comparison of lactate and pyruvate in rat blood and cardiac muscle during normo- and hypothermia showed little change in these parameters when $[OH^-]/[H^+]$ was held constant by adjusting Pa_{CO_2}. Increasing the ratio by three times caused a marked rise in both blood and muscle lactate levels. It was postulated that the maintenance of constant $[OH^-]/[H^+]$ rather than the absolute hydrogen ion concentration was responsible for stability of lactate/pyruvate (130). Cardiac function curves, myocardial blood flow, and the O_2 and lactate consumption of the dog heart at 25°C were markedly improved when pH was raised from 7.4 to 7.7 (96).

In contrast to ectotherms, hibernating mammals (marmots, hamsters) exhibited a shift from pH 7.4 (37°C) to 7.57 (8–9°C). The equivalent shift for ectotherms would have been 0.5 units (94). Further work on hibernating mammals and torpid endotherms is needed.

A recent review by Reeves (123) should be consulted for a more comprehensive overview of comparative aspects of acid-base relationships.

DIVING

The invasion of an aqueous environment by air-breathing vertebrates was linked with the evolution of a number of physiological responses known collectively as the "diving reflex." Familiar components of this complex response in mammals and birds are bradycardia and intense peripheral vasoconstriction in vascular beds other than heart, brain, and lungs. Peripheral tissues undergoing ischemia revert to anaerobic metabolic pathways, and upon termination of diving, lactate is released into the blood. Myoglobin levels and circulating O_2 stores are generally high in mammalian and avian divers owing to a larger blood volume and O_2 capacity. Peripheral vasoconstriction accompanies diving and allows a preferential redistribution of the circulating O_2 stores to brain and heart. Protracted diving in marine mammals is associated with very low Pa_{O_2} and a mixed acidosis; a high buffer capacity blunts this trend, while the combination of increasing Bohr and Haldane effects favors tissue exchange. The Bohr factor tends to be large in certain whales and seals.

A review of the comparative physiology and duration and depth of diving among marine birds and mammals has been presented by Kooyman (76). Marine mammals are attractive subjects of study, in part because they are amenable to training. Seals, porpoises, and small whales can be trained to vary diving time and depth, and to breathe into gas collection devices both underwater and on the surface. Some of these techniques are graphically described, along with associated findings, in (126). A new type of depth-time recorder has been used to monitor free-ranging seals at sea (77). This device should yield accurate information on depth and duration of diving, feeding behavior, and energy budgets.

Several marine mammals are deep divers: the sperm whale descends to 1100 m, the elephant seal to 200 m, and the Weddell seal to 600 m. Decompression sickness (bends) must be avoided when surfacing. Scholander (137) suggested that nitrogen tensions remain low because the volume of gas in the lung at the beginning of the dive is small and owing to collapse of the thorax, the gas is forced into nonexchange areas of the respiratory tree as the animal dives to depth. Assessments of the N_2 distribution in harbor and elephant seals before and during compression dives in a chamber revealed that the seals dove with about 40% of inspiratory volume. Blood N_2 tensions remained below theoretical estimates. Widespread alveolar collapse occurred on compression (79). In contrast to those of terrestrial mammals, the lungs of sea lions empty more completely on compression (36). This finding supports Scholander's hypothesis (137) that the sea lion's airway is reinforced by cartilage. Anatomical observations on seals and sea otters have verified reinforcement of the airways by muscle and/or cartilage (18, 35). The reinforcement in otariid seals is apparently extreme, and it has been suggested that such airway strength may prevent collapse of the airways during the rapid ventilation at the surface between dives (35).

The lung volume of the Weddell seal changed greatly between breathing at rest, submergence, and recovery during the post-dive period (78). At rest, $\dot{V}E$ was 0.05 1 kg^{-1} min^{-1}; it rose to 0.53 following a dive. V_T increased about three-fold on emergence. Lung volume after inspiration was four times that of the diving volume. The diving volume would still have been sufficient to cause inert gas tensions to increase to several atmospheres in blood and tissue during deep dives if the gases remained in exchange areas of the lungs. Unrestrained Weddell seals, after a resting apneusis of 4.5 min, exhibited a $P_{A_{O_2}}$ of 59 torr, and a $P_{A_{CO_2}}$ of 50 torr. After deep dives of 11 min the $P_{A_{O_2}}$ was 70 torr, the $P_{A_{CO_2}}$ 28 torr. Corresponding values after dives ranging from 25–47 min were: $P_{A_{O_2}}$ 40 torr, $P_{A_{CO_2}}$ 36 torr. These differences were attributable to hyperventilation prior to diving and subsequent lung collapse during submergence. $\dot{V}_{O_2}$ during diving was found to be significantly less than during surface breathing.

The marked reduction in $P_{A_{O_2}}$ during submergence in seals suggests that their tolerance of cerebral hypoxia is greater than that of terrestrial mammals. Harbor seals exhibited reversible hypoxic patterns in the EEG only when $P_{A_{O_2}}$ fell to 10 torr with cerebral venous P_{O_2} of 2.5 torr (72). These values are lower than for laboratory mammals. In the latter period of an 18-min dive, when cerebral (a-v) CO_2 fell the cerebral (v-a) lactate content rose. According to Hochachka et al (50), the glucose supply to the brain of diving Weddell seals is supplemented by glucose production in lung tissue. Having analyzed lactate and glucose levels in pulmonary artery and vein, these workers concluded that circulating lactate is utilized by lung tissue in preference to glucose as a carbon and energy source; a gluconeogenic capacity of this tissue supplies supplemental glucose to the brain.

Bradycardia is associated with a substantial fall in cardiac output during diving. The reduction in cardiac work was accompanied by a 90% reduction in coronary blood flow in grey seals (14). Calculated coronary vascular resistance increased by a factor of 8. Given the very low values of $P_{A_{O_2}}$ during protracted diving, the roles of myoglobin and anaerobic metabolic pathways in the support of cardiac metabolism are in need of assessment.

No significant adaptive features in O_2-Hb affinity were found in hippopotamus (84), or in otariid seal, walrus or sea otter (87), but both killer and beluga whale bloods showed comparatively large Bohr factors— Δlog $P_{50}/\Delta pH = -0.6$ and -0.78, respectively. Concentration of 2, 3-diphosphoglycerate was high in killer whale blood. Beluga blood contained one major hemoglobin component on starch gel electrophoresis; killer whale blood contained two.

Pa_{O_2} and Pa_{CO_2} reach 10 and 100 torr, respectively, when *Phoca vitulina* dives for up to 25 min. In the nondiving state these chemical alterations provide a strong ventilatory drive, which must be inhibited during dives. Stimulation of carotid bodies by hypoxic hypercapnic blood or cyanide in anesthetized *Phoca* produces hyperventilation and bradycardia. When the seal's face was covered with water trigeminal sensory stimulation caused apnea and bradycardia. In the latter situation, perfusion of the carotid bodies with blood of normal Po_2 and Pco_2 was accompanied by acceleration in heart rate. Resubstitution of hypoxic hypercapnic blood reinstated a slower heart rate; but due to the inhibitory effect of the trigeminal stimulation, it did not initiate respiration (31). It was shown that the trigeminal chemoreceptor activity arriving in the expiratory phase of respiration prolongs the expiratory phase and that this system facilitates the carotid-body cardio-inhibitory response during progressive asphyxia (38).

Upon submersion, ducks display a prompt but modest bradycardia that later intensifies. This progressive response is dependent upon the development of arterial asphyxia (12, 13). Carotid body stimulation produced bradycardia in ducks only when the head was submerged, whether the lungs were ventilated or not. Apparently receptors associated with the head allow, by central interaction, the operation of a reflex path mediating bradycardia once hypoxia has stimulated chemoreceptors (51). This contrasts with the conclusion that bradycardia results from apnea and not from stimulation of water sensitive receptors (6, 26). The heart rate responses of unrestrained pochards (*Arythya ferina*) are different from those observed in forced laboratory dives (28). While these ducks swam on a pond, respiratory and heart rates more than doubled during the 2.5 sec preceding natural submersion. Submersion heart rates were only slightly lower than those associated with gentle surface swimming. Instead of an intensification of bradycardia with submergence time, heart rate progressively increased; at surfacing, the rate was similar to that prior to the dive. Ducks, like seals, apparently exhibit anticipatory changes in heart rate, and there may be striking differences between forced and natural dives.

Denervation of arterial baroreceptors of ducks produces, during diving, a more profound fall in arterial pressure and less intense peripheral vasoconstriction than in intact animals at similar heart rates (66). Maintenance of arterial pressure and redistribution of blood flow are thus dependent upon the baroreceptors.

The lack of rhythmic pulmonary afferent nerve discharge during apnea is apparently sufficient to modify the CO_2 sensitivity of the avian respiratory center. Progressive CO_2 inhibition of the respiratory center during apnea would aid in explaining the protracted apnea of diving, when stimuli that normally drive respiration during rhythmic breathing are intensified (67).

Diving reptiles exhibited bradycardia and peripheral vasoconstriction while submerged; upon surfacing after prolonged apnea, such reptiles showed markedly elevated circulating lactate levels (158, 168). These responses are qualitatively similar to those of avian and mammalian divers. A peculiarity of both crocodilian and noncrocodilian forms is the redistribution of the cardiac output via a right-to-left intracardiac shunt, which appears to intensify with diving time (158). The consequence for gas exchange of bypassing the lungs and mixing a portion of the venous with the systemic blood has not been analyzed. It is likely that the Bohr effect intensifies as the lung O_2 stores are metered out to the tissues.

The Pa_{O_2} of the Nile monitor lizard may fall from around 110 to 10 torr as Pa_{CO_2} rises from 20 to 28 torr during a 15-minute voluntary dive (166). In spite of the fall in Ca_{O_2} the Bohr shift ensures almost complete utilization of the O_2 stores. The Bohr effect is not universally great in all diving reptiles, but it is large in crocodilians ($\Delta \log P_{50}/\Delta pH = -0.76$ to -0.8) and reaches the extreme level of -1.64 in the highly aquatic snake *Acrochordus javanicus* (168).

Although marked elevations in circulating and alveolar P_{CO_2} may occur in many reptiles during submergence, the Pa_{CO_2} may not reflect total CO_2 production. The turtle *Chelys fimbriatus* exhibits a marked decrease in the respiratory exchange ratio while submerged, suggesting cutaneous CO_2 elimination (86). Cutaneous CO_2 loss through the skin presumably also occurs in *Pseudemys scripta;* however, severe respiratory and lactic acidosis occurs after 2–4 hr of apnea. Hyperventilation corrected blood pH to normal values within 2 hr following such dives (61). The snake *Achrocordus* exchanges 92% of the CO_2 through the skin (143). Interestingly, this snake does not exhibit ventilatory augmentation in response to CO_2 breathing (44). Sea snakes (*Pelamis platurus*) exchange 94% of their CO_2 across the skin and transcutaneous equilibration of inert gases may prevent caisson disease (45). The blood respiratory properties of the banded sea snake (*Laticauda colubrina*) do not appear to be different from terrestrial species (139).

In Lake Titicaca (altitude 3812 m) a frog (*Telmatobius culeus*) exhibits a combination of behavioral, morphological, and physiological adaptations to the cool (10°C) O_2-saturated (100 torr) waters (56). The lungs are small and capillaries reach the outer layers of the pronounced folds of the skin. P_{50} is low, while erythrocyte count is the highest reported for an amphibian. O_2 capacity, Hb, and hematocrit are all elevated, while the Bohr factor is small. The frogs have low metabolic rates but in hypoxic water they increase convective transport by "bobbing behavior."

Submersion will be accompanied by excessive energy expenditures if the specific gravity does not approach a state of neutral buoyance. This is apparently one of the chief advantages to marine mammals of diving with a small lung volume. The fresh water turtle, *Pseudemys scripta,* follows the ballasting principle of submarines by adjusting the fluid stores in cloacal bursae against the lung volume (57). Although not possessing cloacal bursae, the sea turtle *Caretta caretta* is able to vary lung volume in response to specific gravity changes caused by attaching weights or floats to the animal. The lung volume adjustments maintained total specific gravity at a relatively constant level (98).

SUMMARY

The field of comparative physiology of gas exchange is rapidly emerging from an era of descriptive studies of diverse organisms toward more synthetic, comprehensive, and perspective analysis. One revelation of such analysis is that mechanisms for control of external respiration can be quite similar in representatives of different phylogenetic lines, such as arthropods and vertebrates. Perhaps this reflects constraints in general design and function of "early" nervous and respiratory systems that have persisted in these lines (128). However, evolutionary convergence cannot be excluded. Rhythmic and coordinated muscular movements that propel an oxygen-containing medium across a thin interface with circulating body fluids accomplish renewal of the medium. Among aquatic vertebrates these movements are often closely associated with feeding as well as respiration. This mechanism depends on establishment of repetitive motor activity through neural pattern generators. Compensation for variable concentrations of O_2 and CO_2 in the external medium or body fluids requires modulation of these neural patterns. Both external and internal sensory elements have appeared in diverse forms, and they constitute the afferent limbs of reflexes influencing central pattern generators. Both chemical and mechano-sensitive sensors aid in modulating the intensity and sequencing of motor events. While anatomical details subserving respiratory function differ for vertebrates, the properties of the control system conform to the general pattern of central pattern generators modulated by peripheral chemical and mechanical receptors serving to fine-tune ventilatory intensity.

The exposition of convective requirements for medium breathed and for blood flow through gas exchangers emphasizes the importance of the physical characteristics of both external and internal media in determining these flows. Thus, water breathers have characteristically large external convective requirements compared to air breathers, owing primarily to the low O_2 capacitance of water. These high requirements for ventilation are ameliorated by the presence of special vascular arrangements that promote greater extraction of O_2 from the medium. Although circulatory requirements for O_2 vary widely from endotherms to icefishes, which have hemoglobin-free blood, a strong indication exists that the variation is closely correlated with the O_2 content of blood leaving the gas exchanger, which in turn is highly dependent on hemoglobin concentration. While these broad trends are evident, the air convection requirements of ectothermic vertebrates are by no means fixed, as evidenced by declining $\dot{V}E/\dot{V}O_2$ accompanying rising body temperature in turtles. Although it appears paradoxical that the convective requirement should decline with rising O_2 demand and CO_2 production, the behavior of hemoglobin and apparent steadiness of $\dot{Q}/\dot{V}O_2$ allows increased EO_2 even though the relative flow of air declines. The air convection requirement for man and turtle are quite similar at the same body temperature and this similarity can be related to the apparent necessity of regulating the Pa_{CO_2} in such a manner that an appropriate $[OH^-]/[H^+]$ is achieved. The increase in $\dot{V}E/\dot{V}O_2$ of turtles at lower body temperature apparently has the same role. The regulatory mechanisms surrounding these adjustments are in need of investigation. As a start, we need to know how intrapulmonary CO_2 receptors interact with the respiratory center as temperature changes.

The observations on acid-base regulation much emphasized by Rahn (115) and Reeves (123) are fruits of comparative physiology and biochemistry that challenge the concepts of 'normality' surrounding mammalian and cellular physiology and biochemistry. It seems highly appropriate that the "rules of the game" that apply to ectotherms be evaluated by clinicians whose work entails induction of hypothermia in human tissues. Likewise, such considerations of acid-base regulation deserve attention in determining the composition of physiological media for the study of cellular and biochemical processes.

The study of the overall convective requirements of animals is a prerequisite to the more complete analysis of gas transport in the various gas exchangers found in animals. These models now stand in a conceptual framework, as exemplified by the studies of Piiper & Scheid (109, 110), within which useful experimental approaches can be taken to the study of gas exchange and transport in various environments and physiological states. They also provide a basis for comparisons among species from which generalizations may be derived.

ACKNOWLEDGMENT

Preparation of this manuscript was aided by National Science Foundation Grant No. PCM77-12754. My special thanks are extended to Mrs. Jo Manning for her help in the library search and literature organization.

Literature Cited

1. Abdalla, M. A., King, A. S. 1975. The functional anatomy of the pulmonary circulation of the domestic fowl. *Respir. Physiol.* 23:267–290
2. Ar, A., Paganelli, C. V., Reeves, R. B., Greene, D. G., Rahn, H. 1974. The avian egg: water vapor conductance, shell thickness and functional pore area. *Condor* 76:153–58
3. Ballintijn, C. M. 1972. Efficiency, mechanics and motor control of fish respiration. *Respir. Physiol.* 14:125–41
4. Ballintijn, C. M., Roberts, J. L. 1976. Neural control and proprioceptive load matching in reflex respiratory movements of fishes. *Fed. Proc.* 35:1983–91
5. Bamford, O. S. 1974. Oxygen reception in the rainbow trout (*Salmo gairdneri*). *Comp. Biochem. Physiol.* 48A:69–76
6. Bamford, O. S., Jones, D. R. 1974. On the initiation of apnoea and some cardiovascular responses to submergence in ducks. *Respir. Physiol.* 22:199–216
7. Bartoli, A., Cross, B. A., Guz, A., Jain, S. K., Noble, M. I. M., Trenchard, D. W. 1974. The effect of carbon dioxide in the airways and alveoli on ventilation; a vagal reflex studied in the dog. *J. Physiol. Lond.* 240:91–109
8. Bauer, C. 1974. On the respiratory function of haemoglobin. *Rev. Physiol. Biochem. Pharmacol.* 70:1–31
9. Bennett, A. F., Dawson, W. R. 1976. Metabolism. In *Biology of the Reptilia*, ed. C. Gans, W. R. Dawson, 5A:127–223. London: Academic. 556 pp.
10. Berger, P. J. 1973. Autonomic innervation of the visceral and vascular smooth muscle of the lizard lung. *Comp. Gen. Pharmacol.* 4:1–10
11. Bergman, H. L., Olson, K. R., Fromm, P. O. 1974. The effects of vasoactive agents on the functional surface area of isolated-perfused gills of rainbow trout. *J. Comp. Physiol.* 94:267–86
12. Blix, A. S. 1975. The importance of asphyxia for the development of diving bradycardia in ducks. *Acta Physiol. Scand.* 95:41–45
13. Blix, A. S., Lundgren, O., Folkow, B. 1975. The initial cardiovascular responses in the diving duck. *Acta Physiol. Scand.* 94:539–41
14. Blix, A. S., Kjekshus, J. K., Enge, I., Bergan, A. 1976. Myocardial blood flow in the diving seal. *Acta Physiol. Scand.* 96:277–80
15. Bouverot, P., Dejours, P. 1971. Pathway of respired gas in the air sacs–lung apparatus of fowl and ducks. *Respir. Physiol.* 13:330–42
16. Bouverot, P., Hill, N., Jammes, Y. 1974. Ventilatory responses to CO_2 in intact and chronically chemodenervated Pekin ducks. *Respir. Physiol.* 22:137–56
17. Bouverot, P., Leitner, L.-M. 1972. Arterial chemoreceptors in the domestic fowl. *Respir. Physiol.* 15:310–20
18. Boyd, R. B. 1975. A gross and microscopic study of the respiratory anatomy of the antarctic Weddell seal, *Leptonychotes weddelli. J. Morphol.* 147:309–36
19. Bretz, W. L., Schmidt-Nielsen, K. 1971. Bird respiration: flow patterns in the duck lung. *J. Exp. Biol.* 54:103–18
20. Bretz, W. L., Schmidt-Nielsen, K. 1972. The movement of gas in the respiratory system of the duck. *J. Exp. Biol.* 56:57–65
21. Burger, R. E., Coleridge, J. C., Coleridge, H. M., Nye, P. C. G., Powell, F. L., Ehlers, C., Banzett, R. B. 1976. Chemoreceptors in the paleopulmonic lung of the emu: discharge patterns during cyclic ventilation. *Respir. Physiol.* 28:249–59
22. Burger, R. E., Nye, P. C. G., Powell, F. L., Ehlers, C., Barker, M., Fedde, M. R. 1976. Response to CO_2 of intrapulmonary chemoreceptors in the emu. *Respir. Physiol.* 28:315–24
23. Burggren, W. W. 1975. A quantitative analysis of ventilation tachycardia and its control in two chelonians, *Pseudemys scripta* and *Testudo graeca. J. Exp. Biol.* 63:367–80
24. Burnstock, G., Wood, M. J. 1967. Innervation of the lungs of the sleepy lizard (*Trachydosaurus rugosus*). II. Physiology and Pharmacology. *Comp. Biochem. Physiol.* 22:815–31
25. Butler, P. J., Short, S., Taylor, E. W. 1976. Factors affecting blood flow through the ventral aorta of the dogfish (*Scyliorhinus canicula*). *J. Physiol. London* 256:74P
26. Butler, P. J., Taylor, E. W. 1973. The effect of hypercapnic hypoxia, accompanied by different levels of lung ventilation on heart rate in the duck. *Respir. Physiol.* 19:176–87
27. Butler, P. J., Taylor, E. W. 1974. Responses of the respiratory and cardiovascular systems of chickens and pigeons to changes in Pa_{O_2} and Pa_{CO_2}. *Respir. Physiol.* 21:351–63
28. Butler, P. J., Woakes, A. J. 1976. Changes in heart rate and respiratory frequency associated with natural

submersion of ducks. *J. Physiol. London* 256:73P

29. Chang, H.-K., Cheng, R. T., Farhi, L. E. 1973. A model study of gas diffusion in alveolar sacs. *Respir. Physiol.* 18: 386–97

30. Cohen, M. I., Piercey, M. F., Gootman, P. M., Wolotsky, P. 1976. Respiratory rhythmicity in the cat. *Fed. Proc.* 35: 1974–76

31. Daly, M. deB., Elsner, R., Angell-James, J. E. 1976. The role of the carotid body chemoreceptors in the control of respiration and heart rate during dives in the harbour seal. *IRCS Med. Sci.: Respir. Syst.* 4:182

32. Dehadrai, P. V., Tripathi, S. D. 1976. Environment and ecology of freshwater and air-breathing teleosts. See Ref. 54, pp. 39–72

33. Dejours, P. 1975. *Principles of Comparative Respiratory Physiology.* New York: American Elsevier. 253 pp.

34. Dejours, P., Garey, W. F., Rahn, H. 1970. Comparison of ventilatory and circulatory flow rates between animals in various physiological conditions. *Respir. Physiol.* 9:108–17

35. Denison, D. M., Kooyman, G. L. 1973. The structure and function of the small airways in pinniped and sea otter lungs. *Respir. Physiol.* 17:1–10

36. Denison, D. M., Warrell, D. A., West, J. B. 1971. Airway structure and alveolar emptying in the lungs of sea lions and dogs. *Respir. Physiol.* 13:253–60

37. Drent, R. H. 1970. Functional aspects of incubation in the herring gull. *Behaviour* 17:1–132 (Suppl.)

38. Elsner, R., Angell-James, J. E., Daly, M. deB. 1976. Interactions of the trigeminal and carotid body respiratory and cardiac reflexes in the harbor seal. *IRCS Med. Sci.: Respir. Syst.* 4:182

39. Estavillo, J., Burger, R. E. 1973. Avian cardiac receptors: activity changes by blood pressure, carbon dioxide and pH. *Am. J. Physiol.* 225:1067–71

40. Fedde, M. R., Kuhlmann, W. D., Scheid, P. 1977. Intrapulmonary receptors in the Tegu lizard: I. Sensitivity to CO_2. *Respir. Physiol.* 29:35–48

41. Fromm, P. O. 1974. Circulation in trout gills. Presence of "Blebs" in afferent filamental vessels. *J. Fish. Res. Bd. Can.* 31:1793–96

42. Gans, C. 1976. Ventilatory mechanisms and problems in some amphibious aspiration breathers (*Chelydra, Caiman-Reptilia*). See Ref. 54, pp. 357–74

43. Gatz, R. N., Fedde, M. R., Crawford, E. C. 1975. Lizard lungs: CO_2-sensitive

receptors in *Tupinambis nigropunctatus. Experientia* 31:455–56

44. Glass, M., Johansen, K. 1976. Control of breathing in *Acrochordus javanicus,* an aquatic snake. *Physiol. Zool.* 49: 328–40

45. Graham, J. B. 1974. Aquatic respiration in the sea snake *Pelamis platurus. Respir. Physiol.* 21:1–7

46. Hemmingsen, E. A., Douglas, E. L., Johansen, K., Millard, R. W. 1972. Aortic blood flow and cardiac output in the hemoglobin-free fish (*Chaenocephalus aceratus*). *Comp. Biochem. Physiol.* 43A:1045–51

47. Hill, E. P., Power, G. G., Longo, L. D. 1972. A mathematical model of placental O_2 transfer with consideration of hemoglobin reaction rates. *Am. J. Physiol.* 222:721–29

48. Hill, E. P., Power, G. G., Longo, L. D. 1973. Mathematical simulation of pulmonary O_2 and CO_2 exchange. *Am. J. Physiol.* 224:904–17

49. Hills, B. A. 1972. Diffusion and convection in lungs and gills. *Respir. Physiol.* 14:105–14

50. Hochachka, P. W., Liggins, G. C., Qvist, J., Schneider, R., Snider, M. T., Wonders, T. R., Zapol, W. M. 1977. Pulmonary metabolism during diving: Conditioning blood for the brain. *Science.* In press

51. Holm, B., Sorensen, S. C. 1972. The role of the carotid body in the diving reflex in the duck. *Respir. Physiol.* 15: 302–9

52. Howell, B. J., Baumgardner, W. F., Bondi, K., Rahn, H. 1970. Acid-base balance in cold-blooded vertebrates as a function of body temperature. *Am. J. Physiol.* 218:600–606

53. Howell, B. J., Rahn, H., Goodfellow, D., Herreid, C. 1973. Acid-base regulation and temperature in selected invertebrates as a function of temperature. *Am. J. Zool.* 13:557–63

54. Hughes, G. M., ed. 1976. *Respiration of Amphibious Vertebrates.* London: Academic. 402 pp.

55. Hughes, G. M., 1976. Fish respiratory physiology. In *Perspectives in Experimental Biology, Vol. 1, Zool.,* ed. P. Spencer Davies, pp. 235–45. Oxford: Pergamon

56. Hutchison, V. H., Haines, H. B., Engbertson, G. 1976. Aquatic life at high altitude: Respiratory adaptations in the Lake Titicaca frog, *Telmatobius culeus. Respir. Physiol.* 27:115–29

57. Jackson, D. C. 1971. Mechanical basis for lung volume variability in the turtle

Pseudemys scripta elegans. Am. J. Physiol. 220:754–58

58. Jackson, D. C. 1971. The effect of temperature on ventilation in the turtle, *Pseudemys scripta elegans. Respir. Physiol.* 12:131–40

59. Jackson, D. C., Kagen, R. D. 1976. Effects of temperature transients on gas exchange and acid-base status of turtles. *Am. J. Physiol.* 230:1389–93

60. Jackson, D. C., Palmer, S. E., Meadow, W. L. 1974. The effects of temperature and carbon dioxide breathing on ventilation and acid-base status of turtles. *Respir. Physiol.* 20:131–46

61. Jackson, D. C., Silverblatt, H. 1974. Respiration and acid-base status of turtles following experimental dives. *Am. J. Physiol.* 226:903–9

62. Janssen, R. G., Randall, D. J. 1975. The effects of changes in pH and P_{CO_2} in blood and water on breathing in rainbow trout, *Salmo gairdneri. Respir. Physiol.* 25:235–45

63. Johansen, K. 1966. Chemoreception in respiratory control of lungfish, *Neoceratodus. Fed. Proc.* 25:389

64. Johansen, K. 1972. Heart and circulation in gill, skin and lung breathing. *Respir. Physiol.* 14:193–210

65. Johansen, K., Lenfant, C. J. M. 1968. Respiration in the African lungfish, *Protopterus aethiopicus,* II. Control of breathing. *J. Exp. Biol.* 49:453–68

66. Jones, D. R. 1973. Systemic arterial baroreceptors in ducks and the consequences of their denervation on some cardiovascular responses to diving. *J. Physiol. London* 234:499–518

67. Jones, D. R., Bamford, O. S. 1976. Open-loop respiratory chemosensitivity in chickens and ducks. *Am. J. Physiol.* 230:861–67

68. Jones, D. R., Mustafa, T. 1973. The lactacid oxygen debt in frogs after one hour's apnoea in air. *J. Comp. Physiol.* 85:15–24

69. Jones, D. R., Purves, M. J. 1970. The effect of carotid body denervation upon the respiratory response to hypoxia and hypercapnia in the duck. *J. Physiol. London* 211:295–309

70. Jones, D. R., Schwarzfeld, T. 1974. The oxygen cost to the metabolism and efficiency of breathing in trout (*Salmo gairdneri*). *Respir. Physiol.* 21:241–54

71. Kammer, A. E. 1976. Respiration and the generation of rhythmic outputs in insects. *Fed. Proc.* 35:1992–99

72. Kerem, D., Elsner, R. 1973. Cerebral tolerance to asphyxial hypoxia in the harbor seal. *Respir. Physiol.* 19:188–200

73. Kinney, J. L., Matsuura, D. T., White, F. N. 1977. Ventilation-perfusion relationships in a turtle, *Pseudemys floridana. Respir. Physiol.* In press

74. Kinney, J. L., White, F. N. 1977. Oxidative cost of ventilation in a turtle, *Pseudemys floridana. Respir. Physiol.* In press

75. Koch, W. 1934. Lungengefässe und Kreislauf der Schildkröten. *Biol. Gen.* 10:359–82

76. Kooyman, G. L. 1974. Behavior and physiology of diving. In *The Biology of Penguins,* ed. B. Stonehouse, pp. 115–37. London: Macmillan. 555 pp.

77. Kooyman, G. L., Gentry, R. L., Urquhart, D. L. 1976. Northern fur seal diving behavior: A new approach to its study. *Science* 193:411–12

78. Kooyman, G. L., Kerem, D. H., Campbell, W. B., Wright, J. J. 1971. Pulmonary function in freely diving Weddell seals, *Leptonychotes weddelli. Respir. Physiol.* 12:271–82

79. Kooyman, G. L., Schroeder, J. P., Denison, D. M., Hammond, D. D., Wright, J. J., Bergman, W. P. 1972. Blood nitrogen tensions of seals during simulated deep dives. *Am. J. Physiol.* 223:1016–20

80. Kotilainen, P. V., Putkonen, P. T. 1974. Respiratory and cardiovascular responses to electrical stimulation of the avian brain with emphasis on inhibitory mechanisms. *Acta Physiol. Scand.* 90:358–69

81. Kunz, A. L., Kawashiro, T., Scheid, P. 1976. Study of CO_2 sensitive vagal afferents in the cat lung. *Respir. Physiol.* 27:347–55

82. Kutchai, H., Steen, J. B. 1971. Permeability of the shell and shell membranes of hen's eggs during development. *Respir. Physiol.* 11:265–78

83. Laurent, P., Rouzeau, J. -D. 1972. Afferent neural activity from pseudobranch of teleosts. Effects of P_{O_2}, pH, osmotic pressure and Na^+ ions. *Respir. Physiol.* 14:307–31

84. Leivestad, H., Richardson, D., Wright, P. G. 1973. The respiratory properties of the blood of the hippopotamus. *Respir. Physiol.* 19:19–25

85. Lenfant, C., Johansen, K., Hanson, D. 1970. Bimodal gas exchange and ventilation perfusion relationships in lower vertebrates. *Fed. Proc.* 29:1124–29

86. Lenfant, C., Johansen, K., Petersen, J. A., Schmidt-Nielsen, K. 1970. Respiration in the fresh water turtle, *Chelys fimbriata. Respir. Physiol.* 8:261–75

87. Lenfant, C., Johansen, K., Torrance, J. D. 1970. Gas transport and oxygen storage capacity in some pinnipeds and the sea otter. *Respir. Physiol.* 9:277–86

88. Lomholt, J. P. 1976. Relationship of weight loss to ambient humidity of birds eggs during incubation. *J. Comp. Physiol.* 105:189–96

89. Lomholt, J. P., Johansen, K. 1974. Control of breathing in an amphibious fish, *Amphipnous cuchia. Acta Physiol. Scand.* 91:47A

90. Longo, L. D., Bartels, H., eds. 1972. Respiratory gas exchange and blood flow in the placenta. *DHEW Publication No. (NIH) 73–361.* 570 pp.

91. Longo, L. D., Hill, E. P., Power, G. G. 1972. Theoretical analysis of factors affecting placental O_2 transfer. *Am. J. Physiol.* 222:730–39

92. Luckhardt, A. B., Carlson, A. J. 1921. Studies on the visceral sensory nervous system. VIII. On the presence of vasomotor fibers in the vagus nerve to the pulmonary vessels of the amphibian and the reptilian lung. *Am. J. Physiol.* 56:72–112

93. Luiten, P. G. M. 1975. The central projections of the trigeminal, facial and anterior lateral nerves in the carp (*Cyprinus carpio L.*). *J. Comp. Neurol.* 160:399–417

94. Malan, A., Arens, H., Waechter, A. 1973. Pulmonary respiration and acid-base state in hibernating marmots and hamsters. *Respir. Physiol.* 17:45–61

95. Malan, A., Wilson, T. L., Reeves, R. B. 1976. Intracellular pH in cold-blooded vertebrates as a function of body temperature. *Respir. Physiol.* 28:29–47

96. McConnell, D. H., White, F. N., Nelson, R. L., Goldstein, S. M., Maloney, J. V., DeLand, E. C., Buckberg, G. D. 1975. Importance of alkalosis in maintenance of "ideal" blood pH during hypothermia. *Surg. Forum* 26:263–65

97. Millen, J. E., Murdaugh, H. V. Jr., Bauer, C. B., Robin, E. D. 1964. Circulatory adaptation to diving in the freshwater turtle. *Science* 145:591–93

98. Milsom, W. K., Johansen, K. 1975. The effect of buoyancy induced lung volume changes on respiratory frequency in a Chelonian (*Caretta caretta*). *J. Comp. Physiol.* 98:157–60

99. Milsom, W. K., Jones, D. R. 1975. Inhibition by CO_2 of respiratory related, vagal discharge in turtles. *Physiologist* 18:322

100. Nahas, G., Schaefer, K. E., eds. 1974. *Carbon Dioxide and Metabolic Regulations.* New York: Springer 372 pp.

101. Naifeh, K. H., Huggins, S. E., Hoff, H. E. 1971. Study of the control of crocodilian respiration by anesthetic dissection. *Respir. Physiol.* 12:251–60

102. Naifeh, K. H., Huggins, S. E., Hoff, H. E. 1971. Effects of brain stem section on respiratory patterns of crocodilian reptiles. *Respir. Physiol.* 13:186–97

103. Nakano, R., Tomlinson, N. 1967. Catecholamine and carbohydrate concentrations in rainbow trout (*Salmo gairdneri*) in relation to physical disturbances. *J. Fish. Res. Bd. Can.* 24:1701–15

104. Osborne, J. L., Burger, R. E., Stoll, P. J. 1977. Dynamic responses of CO_2-sensitive avian intrapulmonary chemoreceptors. *Am. J. Physiol.* In press

105. Osborne, J. L., Mitchell, G. S., Powell, F. 1977. Ventilatory responses to CO_2 in the chicken: Intrapulmonary and systemic chemoreceptors. *Respir. Physiol.* In press

106. Payan, P., Girard, J.-P. 1977. Adrenergic receptors regulating patterns of blood flow through the gills of trout. *Am. J. Physiol.* 232:H18–23

107. Piiper, J. 1972. Comparative physiology of respiration in vertebrates. *Respir. Physiol.* 14:1–236 (Symp.)

108. Piiper, J., Meyer, M., Worth, H., Willmer, H. 1977. Respiration and circulation during swimming activity in the dogfish *Scyliorhinus stellaris. Respir. Physiol.* 30:221–39

109. Piiper, J., Scheid, P. 1972. Maximum gas transfer efficacy of models for fish gills, avian lungs and mammalian lungs. *Respir. Physiol.* 14:115–24

110. Piiper, J., Scheid, P. 1975. Gas transport efficacy of gills, lungs and skin: theory and experimental data. *Respir. Physiol.* 23:209–21

111. Prange, H. D., Ackerman, R. A. 1974. Oxygen consumption and mechanisms of gas exchange of green turtle (*Chelonia mydas*) eggs and hatchlings. *Copeia* 3:758–63

112. Rahn, H., Howell, B. J. 1976. Bimodal gas exchange. See Ref. 54, pp. 217–85

113. Rahn, H., Paganelli, C. V., Ar, A. 1974. The avian egg: Air-cell gas tension, metabolism and incubation time. *Respir. Physiol.* 22:297–309

114. Rahn, H., Paganelli, C. V., Nisbet, I. C. T., Whittow, G. C. 1976. Regulation of incubation water loss in eggs of seven species of terns. *Physiol. Zool.* 49:245–59

115. Rahn, H., Reeves, R. B., Howell, B. J. 1975. Hydrogen ion regulation, temperature and evolution. The 1975 J. Burns

Amberson Lecture. *Am. Rev. Respir. Dis.* 112:165–72

116. Randall, D. J. 1966. The nervous control of cardiac activity in the tench (*Tinca tinca*) and the goldfish (*Carassius auratus*). *Physiol. Zool.* 39:185–92

117. Randall, D. J. 1970. Gas exchange in fishes. In *Fish Physiology*, ed. W. S. Hoar, D. J. Randall, 4:253–92. New York: Academic. 532 pp.

118. Randall, D. J., Cameron, J. N. 1973. Respiratory control of arterial pH as temperature changes in rainbow trout *Salmo gairdneri. Am. J. Physiol.* 225: 997–1002

119. Randall, D. J., Jones, D. R. 1973. The effect of deafferentation of the pseudobranch on the respiratory response to hypoxia and hyperoxia in the trout (*Salmo gairdneri*). *Respir. Physiol.* 17:291–301

120. Reeves, R. B. 1972. An imidazole alphastat hypothesis for vertebrate acid-base regulation: Tissue carbon dioxide content and body temperature in bullfrogs. *Respir. Physiol.* 14:219–36

121. Reeves, R. B. 1976. Temperature-induced changes in blood acid-base status: pH and P_{CO_2} in a binary buffer. *J. Appl. Physiol.* 40:752–61

122. Reeves, R. B. 1976. Temperature-induced changes in blood acid-base status: Donnan R_{cl} and red cell volume. *J. Appl. Physiol.* 40:762–67

123. Reeves, R. B. 1977. The interaction of body temperature and acid-base balance in ectothermic vertebrates. *Ann. Rev. Physiol.* 39:559–86

124. Richards, B. D., Fromm, P. O. 1969. Patterns of blood flow through filaments and lamellae of isolated-perfused rainbow trout (*Salmo gairdneri*). *Comp. Biochem. Physiol.* 29:1063–70

125. Richards, S. A. 1970. A pneumotaxic centre in avian brain. *J. Physiol. London* 207:57P

126. Ridgway, S. H., ed. 1972. *Mammals of the Sea.* Springfield, Ill: Thomas. 812 pp.

127. Riggs, A. 1976. Factors in the evolution of hemoglobin function. *Fed. Proc.* 35:2115–18

128. Roberts, J. L., ed. 1976. Neural control of respiration. *Fed. Proc.* 35:1965–66

129. Rosenthal, T. B. 1948. The effect of temperature on the pH of blood and plasma *in vitro. J. Biol. Chem.* 173: 25–30

130. Saborowski, F., Lang, D., Albers, C. 1973. The effect of temperature and of relative acidity on the concentration of lactate in cardiac muscle. *Experientia* 29:47–48

131. Satchell, G. H. 1971. *Circulation in Fishes.* London: Cambridge. 131 pp.

132. Satchell, G. H., Hanson, D., Johansen, K. 1970. Differential blood flow through the afferent branchial arteries of the skate, *Raja rhina. J. Exp. Biol.* 52:721–26

133. Scheid, P., ed. 1974. Receptors and control of respiration in birds. *Respir. Physiol.* 22:1–216

134. Scheid, P., Kuhlmann, W. D., Fedde, M. R. 1977. Intrapulmonary receptors in the Tegu lizard: II. Functional characteristics and localization. *Respir. Physiol.* 29:49–62

135. Scheid, P., Piiper, J. 1971. Direct measurement of the pathway of respired gas in duck lungs. *Respir. Physiol.* 11: 308–14

136. Scheid, P., Slama, H., Piiper, J. 1972. Mechanisms of unidirectional flow in parabronchi of avian lungs: Measurements in duck lung preparations. *Respir. Physiol.* 14:83–95

137. Scholander, P. F. 1940. Experimental investigations on the respiratory function in diving mammals and birds. *Hvalradets Skr.* 22:1–131

138. Schumann, D., Piiper, J. 1966. Der Sauerstoffbedarf: Atmung bei Fischen nach Messungen an der narkotisierten Schleie (*Tinca tinca*). *Pfluegers Arch.* 288:15–26

139. Seymour, R. S. 1976. Blood respiratory properties in a sea snake and a land snake. *Aust. J. Zool.* 24:313–20

140. Shelton, G. 1970. The regulation of breathing. See Ref. 117, 4:293–359

141. Shelton, G., Burggren, W. 1976. Cardiovascular dynamics of the Chelonia during apnoea and lung ventilation. *J. Exp. Biol.* 64:323–43

142. Sikand, R. S., Magnussen, H., Scheid, P., Piiper, J. 1976. Convection and diffusive gas mixing in human lungs: Experiments and model analysis. *J. Appl. Physiol.* 40:362–71

143. Standaert, T., Johansen, K. 1974. Cutaneous gas exchange in snakes. *J. Comp. Physiol.* 89:313–20

144. Steen, J. B., Kruysse, A. 1964. The respiratory function of teleostean gills. *Comp. Biochem. Physiol.* 12:127–42

145. Steggerda, F. R., Essex, H. E. 1957. Circulation and blood pressure in the great vessels and heart of the turtle (*Chelydra serpentina*). *Am. J. Physiol.* 190:310–26

146. Tazawa, H., Mochizuki, M. 1976. Estimation of contact time and diffusing capacity for oxygen in the chorioallantoic

vascular plexus. *Respir. Physiol.* 28: 119–28

147. Truchot, J. P. 1973. Temperature and acid-base regulation in the shore crab *Carcinus maenas* (L.). *Respir. Physiol.* 17:11–20

148. Vogel, W., Vogel, V., Pfautsch, M. 1976. Arterio-venous anastomoses in rainbow trout gill filaments. *Cell Tissue Res.* 167:373–85

149. Vogel, W., Vogel, V., Scholte, W. 1974. Ultrastructural study of arterio-venous anastomoses in gill filaments of *Tilapia mossambica. Cell Tissue Res.* 155:491–512

150. Wangensteen, O. D. 1972. Gas exchange by a bird's embryo. *Respir. Physiol.* 14:64–74

151. Wangensteen, O. D., Rahn, H., Burton, R. R., Smith, A. H. 1974. Respiratory gas exchange of high altitude adapted chick embryos. *Respir. Physiol.* 21: 61–70

152. Wangensteen, O. D., Wilson, D., Rahn, H. 1970–71. Diffusion of gases across the shell of the hen's egg. *Respir. Physiol.* 11:16–30

153. Wasserman, K., Whipp, B. J., Casaburi, R., Huntsman, D. J., Castagna, J., Lugliani, R. 1975. Regulation of arterial P_{CO_2} during intravenous CO_2 loading. *J. Appl. Physiol.* 38:651–56

154. Wasserman, K., Whipp, B. J., Castagna, J. 1974. Cardiodynamic hyperpnea: Hyperpnea secondary to cardiac output increase. *J. Appl. Physiol.* 36: 457–64

155. Webb, P. W. 1975. Synchrony of locomotion and ventilation in *Cymatogaster aggregata. Can. J. Zool.* 53:904–7

156. West, N. H., Jones, D. R. 1975. Breathing movements in the frog *Rana pipiens.* I. The mechanical events associated with lung and buccal ventilation. *Can. J. Zool.* 53:332–44

157. White, F. N. 1970. Central vascular shunts and their control in reptiles. *Fed. Proc.* 29:1149–53

158. White, F. N. 1976. Circulation. See Ref. 9, pp. 275–334

159. White, F. N., Kinney, J. L. 1976. Ventilation-perfusion relationships in the turtle. *Physiologist* 19:409

160. White, F. N., Ross, G. 1965. Blood flow in turtles. *Nature* 208:759–60

161. White, F. N., Ross, G. 1966. Circulatory changes during experimental diving in the turtle. *Am. J. Physiol.* 211:15–18

162. Wilkens, J. L. 1976. Neural control of respiration in decapod crustacea. *Fed. Proc.* 35:2000–2006

163. Wilson, T. L. 1975. *pH-temperature interrelations: Theory and application to the M_4 isozyme of goldfish lactate dehydrogenase.* Ph.D. thesis. Univ. Illinois, Urbana-Champaign. 161 pp.

164. Wood, C. M. 1975. A pharmacological analysis of the adrenergic and cholinergic mechanisms regulating branchial vascular resistance in the rainbow trout (*Salmo gairdneri*). *Can. J. Zool.* 53: 1569–77

165. Wood, C. M., Shelton, G. 1975. Physical and adrenergic factors affecting systemic vascular resistance in the rainbow trout: A comparison with branchial vascular resistance. *J. Exp. Biol.* 63:505–23

166. Wood, S. C., Johansen, K. 1974. Respiratory adaptations to diving in the Nile monitor lizard, *Varanus niloticus. J. Comp. Physiol.* 89:145–58

167. Wood, S. C., Lenfant, C. J. M. 1976. Physiology of fish lungs. See Ref. 54, pp. 257–70

168. Wood, S. C., Lenfant, C. J. M. 1976. Respiration: Mechanics, control and gas exchange. See Ref. 9, pp. 225–74

169. Wyman, R. J. 1976. Neurophysiology of the motor output pattern generator for breathing. *Fed. Proc.* 35:2013–23

170. Wyman, R. J. 1977. Neural generation of the breathing rhythm. *Ann. Rev. Physiol.* 39:417–48

171. Wyse, G. A., Page, C. H. 1976. Sensory and central nervous control of gill ventilation in *Limulus. Fed. Proc.* 35: 2007–12

Ann. Rev. Physiol. 1978. 40:501–26
Copyright © 1978 by Annual Reviews Inc. All rights reserved

THE PHYSIOLOGY ❖1200
OF CIRCADIAN PACEMAKERS

Michael Menaker

Department of Zoology, University of Texas, Austin, Texas 78712

Joseph S. Takahashi

Department of Zoology, University of Texas, Austin, Texas 78712

Arnold Eskin

Department of Biology, Rice University, Houston, Texas 77001

INTRODUCTION

In order to appreciate what is currently known about the physiology of circadian pacemakers, it is necessary to place that knowledge in the context of the much broader field of circadian biology and to look, if only briefly, at the way that field has developed over the past 25 years. Whatever pacemakers may underlie the many circadian rhythms expressed by almost all living things, their physiology is of necessity reflected in the behavior of commonly measured overt rhythms. Some important and firmly founded generalizations concerning the behavior of these overt rhythms can be made.

Most organisms living under natural conditions express daily rhythms in their behavior, their physiology, and their biochemistry. Much of what organisms do is temporally organized with respect to the environmental day-night cycle. This observation, in spite of its simplicity, is central to circadian biology. It is, after all, what work in circadian biology seeks to explain: the evolutionary history of daily rhythms; their adaptive significance; their ontogeny, physiology, and biochemistry. The importance of circadian biology—not as an example of some broader class of phenomena,

501

0066-4278/78/0301-0501$01.00

but as the study of a kind of biological organization that demands explanation in its own right—follows directly from the fact that daily rhythms are ubiquitous among living things.

Most daily rhythms persist in the absence of periodic environmental input. In laboratory environments from which periodic fluctuations have been eliminated, activities that are expressed as daily rhythms in the field continue as free-running circadian rhythms with periods close to, but rarely exactly, 24 hours. This fact, which could not have been deduced from field observation alone—which indeed contradicts naive expectation—has implications that underpin the entire modern study of circadian biology. It implies that organisms contain "systems" capable of continued, self-generated oscillation and that the daily rhythms observed in the field result from the action of the periodic environment on the organism's internal oscillators. The major action of the environment is to synchronize (entrain) the internal system to a period of precisely 24 hours, so that it and those expressed rhythms that it controls will be in adaptive temporal relationship with the day-night cycle. By now daily rhythms in a very large number of organisms and in many functions within a single individual have been shown to persist in nonperiodic environments. We are justified in assuming that most of the widespread daily rhythmicity seen in nature is underlain by internal "circadian systems."

Circadian rhythms can be entrained by only a few environmental variables. Light and temperature cycles are the dominant synchronizing agents, and most of the experimental work has employed light cycles. A great deal is known concerning the entrainment process, about which a bit more will be said below.

Circadian systems are used by organisms as clocks to measure astronomical time and to organize many aspects of internal temporal structure. The timing functions of circadian systems have been extensively documented in several elegantly analyzed particular cases (28, 50, 112). Furthermore a large number of well-defined properties of circadian systems can be reasonably understood only as features of an adaptively significant biological clock (89).

Compared with most other major areas in physiology, the study of circadian rhythms is very young. Although there was some fine early work, the major questions were not widely recognized or appreciated until the 1950s. Modern interest was sparked by the creative act of combining the long-observed fact of daily rhythmicity with the concept of real biological timekeeping demanded by new observations. First Bünning suggested a relationship between the daily rhythms of leaf movements in plants and the measurement of day length as expressed in the photoperiodic control of flowering (22). Then Pittendrigh hypothesized (88) that daily rhythms were an expression of the same timing system that enabled birds and bees to engage in time-compensated celestial orientation. Following this line of reasoning Pittendrigh deliberately sought, and found, clock-like properties in the system controlling the daily rhythm of emergence of *Drosophila* from its puparium (88). Of these properties it was the temperature compensation of the period of the rhythm that most engaged the imagination of other workers (129). There followed a period of rapid development in which clock-like properties were discovered in a wide variety of organisms and a number of specific rhythmic processes. These discoveries and the solid beginnings of analysis of the regularities of entrainment and other environmental effects on circadian rhythms, were summarized at the Cold Spring Harbor Symposium of 1959. With the publication of those proceedings (46) it became clear that there existed a new field, circadian biology, with a set of reasonably well-defined questions of broad biological and medical importance.

Questions about the *physiology* of circadian rhythms fell into two broad categories: those concerned with systematizing and analyzing the effects of environmental variables on circadian rhythms; and those concerned with the anatomical location, biochemical mechanism, and physiological relationships to other systems, of the internal clock mechanism. Answers to questions in the first category came relatively rapidly. Analogies between the circadian system and nonlinear physical oscillators were drawn and proved extremely fruitful. By the mid-1960s there existed relatively sophisticated mathematical models of the entrainment process that were consistent with a great deal of solid experimental data (86, 90). In this work the internal clock was treated as a black box and its behavior was inferred from the response of overt rhythms in whole organisms to environmental cycles, steps, and pulses. This approach ("dry" physiology) was pursued and is still being pursued vigorously and productively (93). On the other hand, progress in finding and taking apart the internal clock itself was very slow. Great difficulty was encountered in affecting the circadian system chemically (46), and this may have been responsible for the growing feeling that it was exceedingly difficult to discover experimental handles with which to approach the "wet" physiology of the circadian system. Partly as a result, many biologists not working in the area themselves concluded that it was heavily steeped in mysticism.

During the past ten years, there have been a small but increasing number of successful approaches to the wet physiology of circadian systems in particular organisms. These developments have grown directly out of and could not have occurred without the dry physiology that preceded them. They are the results of more or less serendipitous discovery of biological systems that have clear circadian properties and can also be manipulated by the traditional experimental approaches of wet physiology, especially those of endocrinology and neurophysiology.

Circadian biology is at an exciting point in its development. General, conspicuous, and clearly important regularities have been described that demand, and are beginning to get, explanations in terms of mechanism. Such explanations are of particular significance when they have been brought to the level of anatomy, physiological interaction, and biochemistry, not alone because these are intrinsically interesting aspects of the problem, but especially because appreciation of circadian biology by those scientists not working directly in it requires at least some progress in this direction. Many biologists will not fully "believe in" circadian rhythms or "take them seriously" (i.e. recognize applications to their own areas of interest) until mechanisms have been elucidated.

In this paper we review current attempts to find, open, and understand the contents of the black box that has so often stood for the internal clock. We limit our discussion to several specific systems that appear to hold special promise of further insights. In none of them do we yet have even the outlines of a complete explanation, but we have at least been able with certainty to tie circadian properties to specific groups of cells in multicellular organisms. In some cases these groups of cells can be ablated, transplanted, even cultured. With the material at hand we are now in a position to study the wet physiology of circadian organization and to develop in vitro model systems with which to study the cellular physiology of biological clocks.

CIRCADIAN PACEMAKERS

Broadly defined, the pacemaker is that part of the circadian system that confers upon the system the ability to persist in its rhythmicity without rhythmic environmental input. Without rhythmic input, the period of the rhythm expressed by the system will reflect the period of the pacemaker and thus its physico-chemical properties. Other things being equal, the properties of the pacemaker will determine the phase relationship of the expressed rhythm to an entraining cycle (86).

An entire circadian system must, of necessity, consist of much more than the pacemaker. There are at least two classes of input to the pacemaker: those that carry to it information about features of the environment to which it has evolved adaptive responses, and those that feed back to it information about the internal state of the organism. Because pacemakers determine temporal organization of a great many physiological processes concurrently in a single individual, they must have extensive outputs. Furthermore, the fact that expressed rhythms of different physiological parameters (e.g. locomotor activity, body temperature, drug sensitivity) can have very different phase relationships to a single entraining cycle, suggests that the output circuitry may be not only extensive but also complex—perhaps containing sub-oscillators not themselves capable of pacemaking but functioning to adjust the phase of particular physiological rhythms (71).

The enterprise of localizing pacemakers and attempting to understand their concrete functioning is fraught with difficulties. Perhaps the most serious of these arise from the ambiguities in interpretation that plague experiments in which a particular treatment produces an effect on an overt rhythm (e.g. locomotor activity) that is clearly linked to its pacemakers by an unknown but potentially very long chain of intermediate events. Many experimentally produced effects on overt rhythms can be ascribed to perturbations of events on either the input or the output side of pacemakers with as much reason as they can be ascribed to effects on pacemakers themselves. One of the most ambiguous effects—the abolition of free-running rhythmicity—is also one of the most commonly observed. In dealing with these ambiguities physiologists have as guidelines only those formal regularities (and the models that have come from them) that have resulted from the extensive black box analysis to which circadian systems have been subjected. The logical relationship between the dry and the wet approaches to analysis of circadian systems is directly analogous to that between the formalism of Mendelian genetics and discovery of the structure of DNA. Without the formalisms, both the molecular biologist and his circadian counterpart would be doomed forever to make observations, the relevance of which to the central questions could not be assessed.

In order to illustrate how the analysis of circadian pacemakers can be brought to the concrete level we have chosen to review experimental work on five circadian systems in three diverse phyla of multicellular animals. These particular cases were chosen because each involves both a reasonably large number of observations and good general agreement on the facts (if not always on their interpretation). The reader wishing broader acquaintance with the phenomenology of circadian rhythms and pacemakers should consult (14, 47, 49, 72, 91, 110).

SPECIFIC SYSTEMS

The Silkmoth Brain

Silkmoths of several species have long been used as experimental subjects by insect endocrinologists. They are also exceptionally well suited for certain kinds of work on circadian pacemakers. They are large, easily operable, and exhibit stereotyped behavior. In particular, the pupal stage has a relatively simple internal organization which allows drastic experimental manipulation such as brain removal and reimplantation. Implanted brains do not form new neural connections but remain competent to secrete hormones. Williams & Adkisson (137) used implantation to demonstrate direct photosensitivity of the brain of *Antheraea pernyi*. Pupal diapause in that species is controlled by environmental photoperiod. In normal pupae, the anterior but not the posterior end of the body responds to appropriate photoperiods by releasing the insect from diapause. If the brain is surgically transplanted from the anterior end to the posterior end, photosensitivity moves with it.

This general approach has been used by Truman and his associates in an elegant series of studies of the circadian system of silkmoths (131–133). They first established that adult moths eclosed (emerged from their pupal cases) only during a particular part of the day-night cycle. The duration of this eclosion "gate" as well as its phase was different in each of three species studied, (*Antheraea pernyi, A. polyphemus, Hyalophora cecropia*), but in all three species the rhythm of eclosion in a population of moths persisted in constant darkness. Eclosion in silkmoths was thus shown to be clock-controlled as it is in the much more extensively studied *Drosophila* (88). Moths whose brains were removed during the pupal stage eclosed at random times even in the presence of light cycles, indicating that the brain contained either the photoreceptor, the circadian pacemaker, outputs from the pacemaker, links among these components, or some combination of these elements. Two further experiments demonstrated that the brain probably contains all of these elements. Brainless pupae were arranged so that their anterior and posterior ends were exposed to different light cycles. Brains were implanted in either the anterior or posterior end; when the moths eclosed, it was with the normal phase relationship to the light cycle seen by whichever end contained the brain. This established that the photoreceptor that synchronizes the eclosion rhythm with the environmental light cycle is in the brain. In the second experiment, brains were exchanged between moths of two species that have very different eclosion-gate widths and phases. The temporal pattern with which these chimeras eclosed was characteristic of the species that had contributed the brain, suggesting strongly that this structure contains the circadian pacemaker as well as the links between the photoreceptor and the pacemaker and between the pacemaker and its clearly hormonal output. Although it seems unlikely, it is logically possible that the pacemaking in these experiments was done by the light cycle that was present throughout. The circadian temporal pattern appears to be coded in brain; but the temporal patterning of the act of eclosion is elsewhere, for the chimeras eclosed with a pattern of muscular contractions characteristic of the host species.

The entire brain is not required to maintain the free-running eclosion rhythm or to allow its synchronization by light cycles. The optic lobes can be removed without abolishing rhythmicity, although this operation does reduce the sharpness of synchronization somewhat. This experiment localizes the mechanism of interest to the cerebral lobes, but further localization has not yet been accomplished.

The above experiments were possible only because coupling between the pacemaker and the eclosion mechanism is humoral. This point is underlined by a later study of the circadian flight rhythm in adult silkmoths (*Hyalophora cecropia*) (132). That rhythm is abolished by either brain removal or section of the nerves connecting the brain with the thoracic motor centers. Transplantation approaches are precluded in the analysis of this system by the need for intact neural circuitry, and the conclusion—that the pacemaker is probably in the brain—seems reasonable primarily because of the earlier work on the eclosion pacemaker.

The Cockroach Brain

The physiological basis of circadian rhythmicity was first examined experimentally in the cockroach. In a series of papers from 1954 to 1960 Harker reported that the rhythm of locomotor behavior in *Periplaneta americana* was controlled hormonally by a secretion from the subesophageal ganglion. She proposed that the hormonal rhythm in the subesophageal ganglion was maintained by neurosecretion from the corpora cardiaca and that phase shifting was controlled by a second clock responding to photic information mediated by the ocelli (43–45). These results were reexamined by Roberts (101) and later Brady (16, 17). Neither Roberts nor Brady was able to transfer rhythmicity by transplanting subesophageal ganglia as Harker had reported. Furthermore, they found that the corpora cardiaca were not necessary for the expression of the rhythm and that the compound eyes, not the ocelli, mediated photic information for entrainment.

By the late 1960s, it had been clearly established that photic entrainment was neurally mediated by the compound eyes and that lesions in the vicinity of the pars intercerebralis could produce arrhythmicity. In 1968, Nishiitsutsuji-Uwo & Pittendrigh (81, 82) reported an important finding: that bilateral transection of the optic lobes produced arrhythmicity under all lighting conditions. They proposed that the driving oscillators controlling the locomotor rhythm were located in the optic lobes and were neurally connected to the pars intercerebralis. A hormonal substance secreted by the pars intercerebralis was believed to couple the driving oscillators in the protocerebrum to the locomotor centers in the thoracic ganglia. To the contrary, Brady (17) had previously reported that severing the neural connections (i.e. the circumesophageal connectives) between the brain and thoracic ganglia resulted in apparent arrhythmicity. A reexamination of this question by Roberts, Skopik & Driskill (103) clearly showed that a neural pathway mediated rhythmic information from the brain to the thoracic ganglia. It is now firmly established that the only operations that abolish the locomotor rhythm are those that interrupt the neural pathways between the optic lobes and the brain, and between the brain and the thorax. A clear hormonal role for the pars intercerebralis has not been established, although recent parabiosis experiments once again have raised the possibility of hormonal involvement (26).

Focusing attention upon the optic lobes, Roberts (102) and Sokolove (117) set out to localize the region within the optic lobes necessary for the expression of circadian rhythmicity. Roberts reported that the two innermost synaptic areas of the optic lobes (the lobula and the medulla) were the crucial elements because cuts proximal to the lobula always resulted in arrhythmicity and cuts distal to the lobula did not. Using microlesions Sokolove concluded that the crucial area consisted primarily of cell bodies bordering the second optic chiasm and the lobula. Although Robert's interpretation is different, his results are consistent with Sokolove's lesion study for the cuts through the synaptic areas undoubtedly damaged neuronal cell bodies as well.

Page, Caldarola & Pittendrigh (84) examined in detail the long-known observation that only a single optic lobe was necessary for rhythmicity. They found no evidence for a difference in the left and right optic lobe "pacemakers" as judged by the postoperative free-running period lengths. However, they did find a consistent increase in the period length following unilateral optic lobe section. In addition they showed that either compound eye alone was sufficient to entrain both left and right optic lobe "pacemakers." These results strongly suggest that two separate pacemakers exist in the cockroach brain, one in each optic lobe, and that they interact probably through mutual excitation, for the compound pacemaker's period is shorter than each of the constituent pacemakers.

In cockroaches [and other orthopterans (118)], it appears that photic entrainment is mediated by the compound eyes alone, that the optic lobes contain circadian pacemakers whose output is neurally coupled to the brain, and, in the case of locomotion, that the brain is neurally coupled to the thorax.

The Eye of the Aplysia

Interest in *Aplysia* as an organism for research in circadian rhythms is traceable to the relative simplicity of its nervous system and the large, identifiable neurons in its ganglia. Strumwasser first made use of *Aplysia californica* to probe for circadian rhythms in individual nerve cells (124). Most of the subsequent research has been based on experimental approaches established by Strumwasser: the application of electrophysiological and pharmacological techniques to isolated portions of the nervous system.

Strumwasser, and later others, made intracellular recordings from a spontaneously active cell, R15, in the isolated abdominal ganglion. The frequency of action potentials peaks during the first 24 hours after isolation, and occasionally a second peak is observed about 24 hours later. R15 apparently contains a heavily damped oscillator: Attempts to measure circadian rhythms for longer periods have failed. Both the oscillation in R15 and the weakly persistent rhythm of locomotor activity of the entire animal have been extensively studied (4a, 61, 66, 116, 125), but it is the very tiny eyes of the animal that contain one of the clearest examples of pacemaking function yet discovered among multicellular organisms. The eye shows a clear circadian rhythm even when isolated from the animal, and may also play an organizing role in the intact animal by influencing other circadian rhythms (54, 67, 125).

The eye is about 0.5–1.0 mm in diameter. It contains a spherical lens surrounded by receptor and pigmented support cells; below these are other neurons and neurosecretory cells (55). It is attached by about a centimeter of optic nerve to the cerebral ganglion. Spontaneous and light-evoked optic nerve impulses from the eye occur in the form of compound action potentials (CAPs), indicating that at least some neurons in the eye are coupled and are active in synchrony. The optic nerve also carries spontaneous activity to the eye from the cerebral ganglion (29).

When an eye is removed from the animal and placed in constant darkness, the frequency of CAPs varies with a clear circadian rhythm of large amplitude with the peak of activity occurring within a few hours of the first projected dawn (54). The rhythm persists for about 5 days when the eyes are run in buffered sea water (32). Longer recordings are possible if an organ culture medium is used (29, 59). Two eyes isolated from a single animal have very similar rhythms. The difference in peak times for six pairs of eyes that were compared over four cycles averaged 2 min ± 50 min (SD) (104). Clearly a circadian pacemaker exists in each eye and thus each animal has at least two pacemakers. Because of the similarity in their rhythms, one eye can serve as a control while the other receives an experimental treatment.

Jacklet & Geronimo (57, 63) have reported that tissue reduction of the eye shortens the free-running period; below a critical size (about 20% remaining), noncircadian, high-frequency (ultradian) rhythms are expressed. They have proposed that the circadian rhythm of CAPs results from a mutually coupled population of oscillators possessing ultradian periodicities. Attempting to repeat this experiment, Sener (115) removed over 90% of the cells and found no difference in period for one cycle. Although Jacklet & Geronimo's hypothesis has many attractive features, the data do not exclude other interpretations. It is equally plausible that a single pacemaker exists whose period is changed when the eye is cut, perhaps due to ionic changes, and that when the pacemaker is removed the rhythm becomes aperiodic.

The CAP rhythm can be phase-shifted almost 13 hours by exposure of the intact animal to only one shifted cycle of white light. The phase of the rhythm is assayed by recording the rhythm of isolated eyes in constant darkness after they have been exposed to the shifted light cycle while still attached to the animal. Isolated eyes are also entrainable by light-dark cycles to which they are exposed during culture. For reasons that are not clear, entrainment requires a longer time when the eyes are exposed in vitro than when they are exposed in vivo (29). This difference in rate of entrainment does not seem to depend on the neural connection between the eye and the cerebral ganglion (13, 29).

The CAP rhythm can also be entrained in vivo with red light but only if the eye remains attached to the cerebral ganglion by the optic nerve (12). This indicates either that (a) there is an extraocular photoreceptor that can entrain the eye pacemaker via the optic nerve, (b) if the eye is acting as its own photoreceptor for red light its sensitivity must be modified by its connection to the cerebral ganglion; or (c) the entrainment pathway must run through the cerebral ganglion and back to the eye.

Light applied to one eye apparently cannot phase-shift the rhythm of the other eye (56, 66). However, these experiments would only have shown positive effects if there were strong coupling between the eyes. Recent evidence indicates that the eye pacemakers are in fact coupled to one another (51). Animals were placed in constant conditions and their eyes were removed at progressively later times. After the animals had been held in constant conditions for eight days, the peaks of the CAP rhythms of the two eyes were still within a few hours of each other. By day nine and thereafter, pairs of eyes with rhythms about 180° out of phase with one another were found. The difference in phase between the individual eyes of a pair was thus either a few hours or 10–12 hours. This result is expected of two oscillators that are weakly coupled and mutually entrain one another. The nature and pathway of the coupling mechanism remain to be elucidated.

The physiological processes involved in entrainment of the eye rhythm have been studied by determining whether pharmacological agents or ion substitutions can block phase shifts produced by single light pulses (32). A solution containing high magnesium, low calcium (HiMgLoCa) and tetrodotoxin did not block phase shifting by light, demonstrating that neither a secretory step nor action potentials are required for information about environmental light to reach the pacemaker. Low sodium (LoNa) solutions, which significantly affect receptor potentials, blocked the phase shift, indicating that phase shifting information is translated into photoreceptor potentials. These results are consistent with either of two possible pathways for the flow of phase-shifting information to the pacemaker. The pacemaker might be contained within receptor cells; if so the entrainment pathway would include a step involving the photoreceptor potential. Alternatively, the pacemaker might be in secondary cells and receive entrainment information from receptor cells via photoreceptor potentials and passive spread of current through gap junctions. It seems unlikely that cells of higher than second order are involved in the entrainment pathway (32).

A body of morphological and electrophysiological information exists that is consistent with either of the two entrainment pathways proposed above: (a) Photoreceptors in the *Aplysia* eye do not appear to generate action potentials (55, 57, 60); (b) gap junctions exist between receptor cells and between receptor and second order cells (126); (c) there are additional neuronal cells in the eye that exhibit spontaneous activity synchronized with optic nerve impulses (60); and (d) there is additional evidence that a secretory step does not seem to be required for the expression of the CAP rhythm (58). The data strongly suggest that the pathway for entrainment as well as the pacemaker responsible for the CAP rhythm are localized within the first two orders of cells in the *Aplysia* eye.

If, as suggested by the ion substitution experiments, membrane potential changes couple photic information to the pacemaker, then exposing eyes to treatments that change membrane potentials should phase-shift their rhythms. Two depolarizing stimuli, elevated extracellular potassium and a sodium-potassium pump inhibitor, strophanthidin, have been shown to produce advance or delay phase shifts depending on the phase of the eye rhythm at which they are administered [i.e. there is a "phase response curve" to the effects (30, 33)]. Thus, the results of two different kinds of experiments converge to stress the importance of membrane potential changes in coupling the phase-shifting effects of environmental light to the circadian pacemaker in the eye.

The circadian rhythm of the isolated eye has proven quite susceptible to chemical manipulation. Table 1 summarizes the effects of treatments that either change the free-running period of the eye or phase-shift its rhythm. It also includes several treatments that have been ineffective. Treatments in groups I and II are very general in their effects on cells. Those in group III have primary effects on protein synthesis and produce response curves with both advance and delay phase shifts. Group IV treatments have primary effects on energy metabolism and on intracellular concentrations of divalent cations (Ca^{2+}, Mg^{2+}); they produce response curves with only delay phase shifts. Group V treatments have primary effects on processes associated with membranes and produce response curves with both advance and delay phase shifts. Of the treatments in group VI, procaine and mephenesin have primary effects on membranes and cause phase shifts, but response curves are not yet available for these substances. Finally, large variations in the extracellular concentrations of some ions do not produce phase shifts (Na^+, Ca^{2+}, Mg^{2+}) whereas variations in the extracellular concentrations of other ions do cause phase shifts (K^+, Li^+, Mn^{2+}). (See references in Table 1.)

The results of these studies may provide some clues to the molecular mechanism of the pacemaker, and may also place some constraints on molecular models. They emphasize the potential usefulness of obtaining phase response curves for treatments that affect pacemakers in contrast to looking only at effects on free-running period, which may not reveal differences among treatments. Treatments that produce different response curves (e.g. puromycin and HiK vs DNP and LiCl) may be exerting their effects on different processes or elements of the underlying oscillating system; alternatively, they may be affecting the entrainment pathway to the oscillator and not directly affecting the oscillator itself.

The Avian Pineal Gland

In birds, as in other vertebrates, extra-retinal photoreceptors located in the brain are partially responsible for entrainment of the circadian system by

Table 1 Effects of various chemical agents on the *Aplysia* eye rhythm

Treatments		Effect[a]
I.	D_2O	Period increases (6)
II.	Temperature pulses	Delay phase shifts (7)
III.	Puromycin, cycloheximide, Anisomycin	Advance and delay response curves (62, 104, 105)
IV.	Manganese, A23187 (Ionophore) 2,4-Dinitrophenol, Na-cyanide, LiCl	All delay response curves (33, 34)
V.	HiK, Strophanthidin, Serotonin	Advance and delay response curves (30, 31, 33, 35)
VI.	Procaine, mephenesin, hypertonic sea water, hypotonic sea water, propionate substituted for Cl	Phase shifts (32)
VII.	LoNa, HiCa, LoCa, HiMgLoCa, LoNaHiMgLoCa	No phase shifts (32, 34)

[a]Numbers refer to the bibliography.

environmental light cycles (72, 136). Attempting to localize the brain photoreceptors, Gaston & Menaker removed pineal glands from house sparrows (*Passer domesticus*). They found that pinealectomized sparrows still entrained to light cycles; unexpectedly, however, these animals did not express free-running circadian locomotor rhythms in constant conditions as do unoperated birds (39). If the sparrow pineal is photoreceptive, as it may well be, it cannot be the sole brain photoreceptor with input to the circadian system, for sparrows that are both blind and pinealectomized still entrain. However, the abolition of the free-running rhythm following pineal gland removal indicates clearly that, photoreceptive or not, this gland is a part of the sparrow's circadian system. As the early results also made clear, the pineal cannot contain all or even most of that system (as does the brain of silkmoths): Pinealectomized birds entrained to some light cycles begin their activity several hours before the onset of light (38) and when they are transferred to constant darkness they become arrhythmic gradually over as many as seven or eight cycles (39). These results have been interpreted to mean that following pinealectomy sparrows retain at least a damped oscillator coupled on its input side to photoreceptors and on its output side to locomotor behavior. On the other hand, the data leave open, among others, the intriguing possibility that the pineal is a pacemaker in the sparrow's circadian system normally coupled to and driving that damped oscillator (73).

Pinealectomized sparrows are more or less continuously active in constant darkness; when their perching behavior is recorded with an event recorder, it appears arrhythmic. This impression was confirmed by statistical analysis of numerical perching data (11). Circadian periodicities were undetectable; within broad limits, pinealectomy did not appear to increase the absolute amount of perching activity, but rather caused it to spread out across the entire 24 hours. Not only locomotor activity but also body temperature and uric acid excretion are made arrhythmic by pinealectomy of house sparrows (10; A. L. Mackey & M. Menaker, unpublished). In white-crowned sparrows (*Zonotrichia leucophrys*) pinealectomy abolishes the free-running rhythm of nocturnal activity that occurs seasonally when the birds are prepared to migrate (69). The effect of pinealectomy in house sparrows was shown to depend on complete removal of the gland. Remnants of pineal tissue, especially if they maintained the normal follicular organization, supported free-running locomotor rhythmicity with varying degrees of precision and for variable times (38).

Zimmerman & Menaker determined that the neural inputs to and outputs from the pineal gland of *P. domesticus* could be destroyed without abolishing free-running rhythmicity (140). Disconnecting the pineal stalk from its ventral attachments severs the tract of small unmyelinated fibers that leave the pineal through its stalk and are the only known neural output from the gland. Systematic injection of large doses of 6-hydroxydopamine depletes sympathetic nerve terminals at the pineal of their norepinephrine and presumably severs the functional connection between the pineal and the superior cervical ganglia. That connection is the only known neural input to the pineal. Neither of these treatments nor both of them together abolishes free-running circadian rhythmicity. This demonstrates that the pineal's output links to the rest of the circadian system are humoral and strongly suggests that it does not require neural input to perform its function within the system.

If the pineal does not require neural coupling and in addition produces a humoral signal, then it should be possible to restore free-running rhythmicity to arrhythmic pinealectomized birds by transplanting the pineal of a donor bird (73). Success in this endeavor was first reported by Gaston, who was able on two occasions out of many attempts to produce rhythmicity by transplanting into the pineal site of *P. domesticus* (38). By transplanting into the anterior chamber of the eye and by making several cuts in the body of the donor gland before inserting it, Zimmerman & Menaker were able to achieve regular success in restoring free-running rhythmicity to arrhythmic pinealectomized birds. In many cases this rhythmicity appeared within 48 hours of implantation of the donor gland, persisted for many months, and disappeared when the eye bearing the transplanted pineal was removed (140). While confirming the hypothesis of humoral coupling between the pineal and the rest of the circadian system, these data left open two alternatives concerning the pineal's role within that system. Either the pineal tonically secretes a humoral factor necessary for the expression of free-running rhythmicity—in that case the pacemaking machinery would all reside elsewhere—or it rhythmically secretes a product the level of which oscillates and drives or entrains the rest of the system. In the latter case the pineal would be a true pacemaker conferring its endogeneous rhythmicity on the sparrow's circadian system in the absence of rhythmic environmental input.

These alternatives were tested by determining whether the phase of the rhythm produced by a transplanted pineal did or did not reflect the phase of the locomotor rhythm of the bird from which it came. Two groups of donors were entrained to light cycles 10 hours out of phase. At the same real time, pineals from both groups were transplanted into pinealectomized arrhythmic hosts. The phases of the induced rhythms were not distributed at random, did not correlate with the time of surgery, but did correlate with the previous phase of the donor (139). The transplanted pineal appears not simply to permit the expression of rhythmicity but to carry with it a specific and identifiable feature of the rhythm of its previous owner. These results and the others reported above make it difficult to escape the conclusion that the pineal gland functions as a pacemaker in the circadian system of the house sparrow.

A good deal is known about the physiology and biochemistry of the avian pineal gland itself (as distinct from its participation in the control of locomotor and other rhythms) that supports and extends the above conclusion. The activity of the pineal enzyme N-acetyltransferase (NAT) is dramatically rhythmic in chicks exposed to light-dark cycles, with peak values in the dark phase of the cycle about 30 times those of the troughs that occur during the light. This rhythm is circadian: It persists for at least two cycles in chicks held in constant darkness (9). Regulation of pineal NAT—which in mammals is under the control of norepinephrine from the sympathetic fibers that innervate the pineal—appears to be free of sympathetic control in birds (8). Although it is not at all clear how the oscillation in NAT activity in the avian pineal is generated, it is consistent with the data to conclude that the controlling mechanism is within rather than outside the pineal. This possibility is especially intriguing in view of the fact that the pineal's role in the circadian system of the sparrow does not seem to require neural input.

Because under most circumstances NAT activity is the rate-limiting step in the synthesis of the pineal hormone melatonin, rhythmicity in pineal NAT activity is reflected in circadian rhythmicity of plasma melatonin levels (97). Pinealectomy, which in chickens reduces plasma melatonin to below detectable levels (87), abolishes free-running locomotor rhythmicity in sparrows. Constant light of relatively high intensity abolishes rhythms of NAT activity (96), pineal melatonin (96), and locomotor activity (70). Melatonin secreted by the avian pineal may be involved in coupling the pineal gland with the rest of the circadian system.

That hypothesis receives some support from experiments in which melatonin was administered to sparrows via implanted silastic capsules. Sparrows free-running in constant darkness responded to low constant levels of exogenous melatonin either by becoming continuously active or with shortening of the free-running period of the locomotor rhythm (134). This effect is especially significant because of the great difficulty usually encountered in affecting free-running period with specific chemical agents. On the other hand these results, while adding weight to the supposition that melatonin is involved in mediating avian locomotor rhythms, do not confirm the specific hypothesis that pineal melatonin affects the rest of the bird's circadian system. They can be explained equally well by assuming that the effect of the exogenous melatonin is on the pineal gland itself. This and many other questions about the organization of the avian circadian system remain to be answered. However, it does appear that in birds the pineal gland is a pacemaker—perhaps the dominant one—and that its relationships to the rest of the system are experimentally tractable.

The Mammalian Suprachiasmatic Nuclei

Over a decade ago, Richter (99, 100), who was studying circadian rhythms in rats, concluded that the rat "clock" must be located in the brain because removal of virtually all the endocrine glands did not abolish circadian rhythmicity. At the same time, after making literally hundreds of lesions throughout the brains of rats, he reported that only those in a small area in the ventral median nucleus of the hypothalamus disrupted the free-running rhythm. This initial result and an earlier report (25) that lesions in the suprachiasmatic region affect estrous cyclicity in rats apparently went unnoticed for many years in the field of circadian biology. It was not until recently that Richter's result was "rediscovered' by two laboratories employing a somewhat different strategy in localizing the elusive mammalian "clock." Their reasoning was as follows: It had been long known that the photoreceptors for entrainment of rodent rhythms were in the retina—blinded rodents free-run under all lighting conditions (18, 99). Since lighting information must have access to the circadian pacemaker for entrainment to light cycles, it is likely that a pathway exists from the retina to the pacemaker. Identifying the visual pathways mediating entrainment might then help in localizing the pacemaker itself since a functional connection must exist.

Adopting this strategy, Moore & Eichler (75) and Stephan & Zucker (121) found that interrupting both the primary optic tracts and the accessory optic system did *not* affect entrainment. This surprising result led to the proposal that a direct retinohypothalamic pathway, whose existence at the time was unsubstantiated (80), mediated photic information for entrainment. A reinvestigation of this pathway using autoradiographic tracing methods indeed revealed a direct retinohypothalamic tract (RHT) terminating in the suprachiasmatic nuclei (SCN) (48, 78). In an attempt to interrupt the RHT, both laboratories lesioned the terminal nuclei of this projection (i.e. the SCN) and found that not only was entrainment lost, but in addition, circadian rhythmicity was abolished in three different parameters (adrenal corticosterone content, drinking behavior, wheel-running activity) (75, 122).

In the last five years, it has become clear that the SCN play an important role in the maintenance of a diverse number of circadian rhythms in rodents. The initial results of SCN lesions have been generally confirmed by many laboratories assaying different circadian rhythms and using other species. Table 2 lists the various circadian rhythms that are disrupted by SCN lesions.

Unfortunately most of the early SCN experiments were performed on populations of animals or involved only short periods of observation of the rhythms. It is therefore difficult to assess the degree of arrhythmicity caused by SCN lesions and to know whether entrainment to light has been abolished. These distinctions are necessary in evaluating the role of the SCN in the mammalian circadian system. An exception is Rusak's study of the effects of SCN lesions on the wheel-running activity of hamsters (*Mesocricetus auratus*) (107). By recording from individual animals for long periods of time, Rusak found a wide spectrum of effects of SCN lesions. Two results are especially interesting. Entrainment is not abolished but rather is disrupted after lesions that appear to destroy both the RHT and the SCN. Two classes of synchronization to the light cycle are apparent. Some hamsters convincingly show entrainment, although the pattern is abnormal and generally unstable. Other hamsters appear to be passively driven by the light cycle. In both cases, it is clear that photic information can have access to locomotor behavior, perhaps at different levels, to exert either entraining or masking effects. In constant conditions, the precise and coherent circadian activity rhythms of intact hamsters are unambiguously abolished by SCN lesions. Total arrhythmicity, however, is rarely achieved. There are residual components in the activity records that appear to dissociate, to free-run, and to interact with one another. Fourier analysis of the data indicates the presence of 8-hr and sometimes 12-hr components in the locomotor activity of many of the lesioned hamsters (107).

As a result of the behavioral work, interest in the anatomy of the SCN has increased. In the rat, the two eggshaped SCN lie directly upon the optic chiasm. They are 300–350 μm in transverse diameter and 600 μm in length. Each nucleus contains about 10,000 extremely small, densely packed neu-

Table 2 Circadian rhythms disrupted by suprachiasmatic nuclei lesions in mammals

Rhythm	Animal[a]
Wheel running activity, drinking behavior	Rat (120, 122)
Adrenal corticosterone content	Rat (75)
Pineal N-acetyltransferase activity	Rat (77)
Sleep-wake rhythms	Rat (24, 52, 53, 120)
Temperature	Rat (120)
Ovulation	Rat (19, 95)
Wheel running activity	Hamster (107, 123)
Drinking behavior	Hamster (107)
Estrous cyclicity	Hamster (123)
Photoperiodic time measurement	Hamster (109, 123)

[a] Numbers refer to the bibliography.

rons. Ultrastructural studies reveal that SCN neurons make reciprocal dendro-dendritic synapses that are unique in the hypothalamus (40, 41). The retinohypothalamic tract projects bilaterally to the ventral and lateral portions of the SCN with the contralateral nucleus receiving twice as many fibers as the ipsilateral one (48). RHT innervation is apparent by day four of neonatal life, and coincides with the time that the first rhythms in pineal NAT activity can be detected (36, 37, 65, 119).

In addition to the retinal input to the SCN, two other afferents are known in the rat. There is a second, presumably photic, input from the ventral nucleus of the lateral geniculate body (98, 128). An additional input arises from the midbrain raphe nuclei (1). This projection is serotonergic and accounts for the relatively high content of serotonin in the SCN (111). No other afferents to the SCN are well documented; however, it is likely that others exist.

Neither the lateral geniculate nuclei (LGN) or the raphe nuclei are necessary for the generation of free-running rhythms. In rats LGN lesions do not affect steady-state entrainment (27); however, in hamsters LGN lesions reduce the rate of phase shifting to a 12-hour phase delay (141). Although the SCN may have a rhythmic uptake of serotonin (74), raphe lesions and treatments with para-chlorophenylalanine (treatments that deplete serotonin levels in the SCN) have no clear effect on the persistence of free-running rhythmicity in constant conditions; however, both treatments increase the level of activity (15, 64, 141). Lateral hypothalamic lesions do not affect circadian wheel-running activity and drinking behavior according to Rowland (106); however, in another study, similar lesions apparently abolished both activity and temperature rhythms in the rat (76). The discrepancy may be due to the extent of damage to the medial forebrain bundle, which is probably a major descending pathway for central sympathetic regulation and a potential output pathway from the SCN (77).

The output pathways leaving the SCN are not well documented. Presently, the only known fibers project caudally in a diffuse manner and appear to terminate entirely within the medial hypothalamus (127, 130). Electrophysiological studies have confirmed the functional connectivity of some of these pathways (68, 83). Humoral substances may be potential output pathways also since there is immunofluorescent and ultrastructural evidence for secretory activity in the perikarya of SCN cells (23, 79). No direct evidence exists for humoral coupling: Knife cuts caudal to the SCN are just as effective in abolishing rhythmicity as SCN lesions. In contrast, cuts placed anterior to the SCN have no effect (77). These experiments agree well with the known efferent anatomy and suggest that the SCN are neurally coupled on their output sides.

To summarize, it appears that the RHT alone are sufficient for entrainment to light. However, for several reasons it seems likely that photic information has access to the circadian system through other pathways: (a) Residual entrainment and masking occur in the absence of the RHT (107); (b) primary optic tract lesions affect phase and period of hamster rhythms (108); (c) LGN lesions affect phase-shifting rates (141); and (d) superior colliculus lesions alter the day/night ratio of activity (2). Thus, the RHT appear to play a dominant role in coupling the mammalian circadian system to the external light-dark cycle to achieve stable entrainment. The other photic inputs apparently play a lesser, modulating role of as yet undefined function and complexity.

In free-running conditions, the SCN maintain the integrity of hamster circadian rhythms. The way in which the SCN exert their integrative influence remains to be determined. The mammalian circadian system appears to be a multi-oscillatory one. Dissociation of different rhythms within individual humans (4), and splitting of activity rhythms into two components (92, 94), suggest that more than one oscillator is involved. Additionally, there is weak evidence that isolated mammalian tissues and organs express circadian rhythms in vitro (3, 42). The residual ultradian components and their complex patterns of interaction in SCN-lesioned hamster activity records, are suggestive of the interactions of a population of oscillators (138). Whether the SCN act as a pacemaker exerting period and phase on a population of other oscillators, or whether they couple circadian oscillators located elsewhere remain open questions.

Regardless of the role of the SCN—as pacemaker or coupler—two facts are especially intriguing: The metabolic rate as measured by 2-deoxy-D-glucose uptake of the SCN themselves oscillates with an apparently circadian rhythm (113); and, melatonin, the pineal "hormone," is found in high concentrations although there is no evidence for its synthesis there (20).

CONCLUSIONS

We have described some of what is known about the location and physiology of circadian pacemakers (or strong candidates for that role) in a variety of multicellular animals. For the nonspecialist perhaps the most important conclusion to be drawn comes from the dramatic way in which some of the findings reported here underline the reality of the circadian system. It is a demonstrable fact that organisms have circadian systems just as—and more generally than—they have circulatory or nervous systems. It has been somewhat difficult to perceive this fact because the adaptive significance of circadian function lies in temporal organization and must therefore be inferred from observed regularities. Classically, understanding of many physiological systems has progressed by attempting to make increasingly precise descriptions of what an organ that is obviously there, is doing. Questions of the type "What does the heart do?" have been much more common than those like "What moves the blood around the body?" Although there has for quite some time been the strongest inferential evidence for the reality and biological importance of circadian systems, the identification of isolateable, transplantable circadian pacemakers resident in specific organs and groups of cells convinces as no amount of inference can.

We do not yet have nearly enough information about the physiological detail to attempt to identify common features among the known or strongly suspected pacemakers. That is likely to be a difficult undertaking because as yet we do not have formal criteria to guide the search for physiological generalities. At the moment there is no reason to reject models of circadian pacemakers in which (*a*) one element oscillates with a circadian period and drives others, (*b*) several, or many, elements with periods very different from the circadian interact to produce a circadian output (85), (*c*) no element oscillates but circadian periodicity is an emergent property of an entire network (114), or (*d*) some combination of the above or any of several other possibilities. Furthermore, as use of the word "element" is meant to imply, the conceptual difficulty extends from the level of organ systems to molecular events within any cell that in the future may be identified as a pacemaker. Similarities among circadian pacemakers may turn out to be great or they may exist only at a very abstract level.

In spite of these difficulties, the comparative physiology of circadian systems is likely to produce meaningful insights in the coming years. In fact the outlines of such a comparative physiology are already appearing in the vertebrates: The pineal gland of lizards has a role in the circadian system similar to, but not identical with, that of birds (135); the mammalian pineal is involved in photoperiodic control of the reproductive system, quite possibly as a time measuring device (F. W. Turek, personal communication); SCN lesions appear to affect locomotor rhythms in sparrows (J. S. Takahashi & M. Menaker, unpublished observations); melatonin has been reported in the SCN of rats (20), and is widespread in the pineals and the retinae of vertebrates (21); and complex, often extraretinal, photic inputs to the circadian system are the rule (72).

The five specific systems discussed in this review share one feature that is worth emphasizing because it may be more significant than it superficially appears. They were all discovered in much the same way. Although the research strategy was more explicit in some cases than in others, in all, the pacemakers (or putative pacemakers) turned up in the course of studies of the photoreceptive input to the circadian system. The silkmoth brain contains both photoreceptors and pacemaker. The pacemaker in cockroaches is very near the compound eyes. The eye of *Aplysia* is itself a pacemaker. The avian pineal may well have photoreceptive as well as pacemaking properties and is phylogenetically derived from unambiguous photoreceptors in the lower vertebrates. The mammalian SCN receive unusually direct photic input via the retinohypothalamic tract. These correlations convey both a general and perhaps a more specific message. In general it would appear to be good research strategy in attempting to localize components of the circadian system and understand their interactions, to follow known sensory inputs into the system or to work "upstream" from known outputs. The success of this approach will depend primarily on the length and complexity of the path—initially unknown—that one chooses. Specifically it appears that the path from photoreceptor to pacemaker may be particularly short and straight. It may well be that the connection between light and the circadian system is a much more intimate one than is implied by the statement that light is the dominant natural entraining agent. Perhaps it is not even too vain a hope that systems will be found in which photopigments are directly involved in the underlying biochemical oscillations. In that case it might be possible to follow light into the heart of the mechanism.

ACKNOWLEDGMENTS

We thank Sharon Wiener and Sharon Nugent for technical assistance. This review was prepared while M. M. was supported by NIH grant HD-03803, J. S. T. by a NSF graduate fellowship, and A. E. by NSF grant BNS75-23452.

Literature Cited

1. Aghajanian, G. K., Bloom, F. E., Sheard, M. H. 1969. Electron microscopy of degeneration within the serotonin pathway of rat brain. *Brain Res.* 13:266–73
2. Altman, J. 1962. Diurnal activity rhythm of rats with lesions of superior colliculus and visual cortex. *Am. J. Physiol.* 202:1205–7
3. Andrews, R. V. 1968. Temporal secretory responses of cultural hamster adrenals. *Comp. Biochem. Physiol.* 26: 179–93
4. Aschoff, J., Wever, R. 1976. Human circadian rhythms: a multioscillatory system. *Fed. Proc.* 35:2326–32
4a. Audesirk, G., Strumwasser, F. 1975. The circadian rhythm of the neuron R15 of *Aplysia californica: in vivo*

photoentrainment. *Proc. Natl. Acad. Sci. USA* 72:2408–12
5. Beiswanger, C. M., Jacklet, J. W. 1975. *In vitro* tests for a circadian rhythm in the electrical activity of a single neuron in *Aplysia californica. J. Comp. Physiol.* 103:19–37
6. Benson, J. A., Jacklet, J. W. 1977. Circadian rhythm of output from neurons in the eye of *Aplysia.* I. Effect of deuterium oxide and temperature. *J. Exp. Biol.* In press
7. Benson, J. A., Jacklet, J. W. 1977. Circadian rhythm of output from neurons in the eye of *Aplysia.* II. Effects of cold pulses on a population of coupled oscillators. *J. Exp. Biol.* In press
8. Binkley, S. 1976. Pineal gland biorhythms: N-acetyltransferase in chickens and rats. *Fed. Proc.* 35:2347–52

9. Binkley, S., Geller, E. B. 1975. Pineal N-acetyltranferase in chickens: rhythm persists in constant darkness. *J. Comp. Physiol.* 99:67–70

10. Binkley, S., Kluth, E., Menaker, M. 1971. Pineal function in sparrows: circadian rhythms and body temperature. *Science* 174:311–14

11. Binkley, S., Kluth, E., Menaker, M. 1972. Pineal and locomotor activity. Levels and arrhythmia in sparrows. *J. Comp. Physiol.* 77:163–69

12. Block, G. D., Hudson, D. J., Lickey, M. E. 1974. Extraocular photoreceptors can entrain the circadian oscillator in the eye of *Aplysia. J. Comp. Physiol.* 89:237–49

13. Block, G. D., Page, T. L. 1977. Lack of centrifugal effects on speed of phase shifting in the *Aplysia* eye. *Neurosci, Abstr.* 3:172

14. Block, G. D., Page, T. L. 1978. Circadian pacemakers in the nervous system. *Ann. Rev. Neurosci.* In press

15. Block, M., Zucker, I. 1976. Circadian rhythms of rat locomotor activity after lesions of the midbrain raphe nuclei. *J. Comp. Physiol.* 109:235–47

16. Brady, J. 1967. Control of the circadian rhythm of activity in the cockroach. I. The role of the corpora cardiaca, brain, and stress. *J. Exp. Biol.* 47:153–63

17. Brady, J. 1967. Control of the circadian rhythm of activity in the cockroach. II. The role of the subesophageal ganglion and ventral nerve cord. *J. Exp. Biol.* 47:165–78

18. Browman, L. G. 1937. Light in its relation to activity and estrous rhythms in the albino rat. *J. Exp. Zool.* 75:375–88

19. Brown-Grant, K., Raisman, G. 1977. Abnormalities in reproductive function associated with the destruction of the suprachiasmatic nuclei in female rats. *Proc. R. Soc. Lond. Ser. B.* 198:279–96

20. Bubenik, G. A., Brown, G. M., Grota, L. J. 1976. Differential localization of N-acetylated indolealkylamines in CNS and the Harderian gland using immunohistology. *Brain Res.* 118:417–28

21. Bubenik, G. A., Brown, G. M., Uhlir, I., Grota, L. J. 1974. Immunohistological localization of N-acetylindolealkaylamines in pineal gland, retina and cerebellum. *Brain Res.* 81:233–42

22. Bünning, E. 1936. Die endonome Tagesperiodik als Grundlage der photoperiodischen Reaktion. *Ber. Dtsch. Bot. Ges.* 54:590–607

23. Clattenburg, R. E., Singh, R. P., Montemurro, D. G. 1972. Postcoital ultrastructural changes in neurons of the su-

prachiasmatic nucleus of the rabbit. *Z. Zellforsch.* 125:448–59

24. Coindet, J., Chouvet, G., Mouret, J. 1975. Effects of lesions of the suprachiasmatic nuclei on paradoxical sleep and slow wave sleep circadian rhythms in the rat. *Neurosci. Lett.* 1:243–47

25. Critchlow, V. 1963. The role of light in the neuroendocrine system. In *Advances in Neuroendocrinology,* ed. A. V. Nalbandov, pp. 377–402. Urbana, Ill.: Univ. Illinois Press

26. Cymborowski, B., Brady, J. 1972. Reexamination of the evidence for transmission by parabiosis in insects. *Nature New Biol.* 236:221–22

27. Dark, J. G., Asdourian, D. 1975. Entrainment of the rat's activity rhythm by cyclic light following lateral geniculate nucleus lesions. *Physiol. Behav.* 15:295–301

28. Elliott, J. A. 1976. Circadian rhythms and photoperiodic time measurement in mammals. *Fed. Proc.* 25:2339–46

29. Eskin, A. 1971. Properties of the *Aplysia* visual system: in vitro entrainment of the circadian rhythm and centrifugal regulation of the eye. *Z. Vgl. Physiol.* 74:353–71

30. Eskin, A. 1972. Phase shifting a circadian rhythm in the eye of *Aplysia* by depolarizing high potassium pulses. *J. Comp. Physiol.* 80:353–76

31. Eskin, A. 1974. Circadian rhythmicity in the isolated eye of *Aplysia:* mechanism of entrainment. In *The Neurosciences: Third Study Program,* ed. F. O. Schmitt, F. G. Worden, pp. 531–35. Cambridge: MIT

32. Eskin, A. 1977. Neurophysiological mechanisms involved in photoentrainment of the circadian rhythm from the *Aplysia* eye. *J. Neurobiol.* 8:273–99

33. Eskin, A. 1977. Entraining a circadian rhythm from the isolated eye of *Aplysia:* The involvement of changes in membrane potential. *Neurosci. Abstr.* 3:176

34. Eskin, A., Corrent, G. 1977. Effects of divalent cations and metabolic poisons on the circadian rhythm from the *Aplysia* eye. *J. Comp. Physiol.* 117:1-21

35. Eskin, A., Corrent, G. 1977. Pathways for entrainment of eye circadian rhythms. *Physiologist* 10:26 (Abstr.)

36. Felong, M. 1976. Development of the retinohypothalamic projection in the rat. *Anat. Rec.* 184:400–401

37. Felong, M., Moore, R. Y. 1976. Development of a circadian rhythm in pineal N-acetyltransferase in the rat. *Neurosci. Abstr.* 2:670

38. Gaston, S. 1971. The influence of the pineal organ on the circadian activity rhythm in birds. In *Biochronometry*, ed. M. Menaker, pp. 541–48. Washington: Natl. Acad. Sci.

39. Gaston, S., Menaker, M. 1968. Pineal function: the biological clock in the sparrow? *Science* 160:1125–27

40. Güldner, F.-H. 1976. Synaptology of the rat suprachiasmatic nucleus. *Cell Tiss. Res.* 165:509–44

41. Güldner, F.-H., Wolff, H. R. 1974. Dendro-dendritic synapses in the suprachiasmatic nucleus of the rat hypothalamus. *J. Neurocytol.* 3:245–50

42. Hardeland, R., Hohmann, D., Rensing, L. 1973. The rhythmic organization of rodent liver: a review. *J. Interdiscip. Cycle Res.* 4:89–118

43. Harker, J. E. 1954. Diurnal rhythms in *Periplaneta americana* L. *Nature* 173:680–90

44. Harker, J. E. 1956. Factors controlling the diurnal rhythm of activity in *Periplaneta americana*. *J. Exp. Biol.* 33:224–34

45. Harker, J. E. 1960. Internal factors controlling the subesophageal ganglion neurosecretory cycle in *Periplaneta americana*. *J. Exp. Biol.* 37:164–70

46. Hastings, J. W. 1960. Biochemical aspects of rhythms: phase shifting by chemicals. *Cold Spring Harbor Symp. Quant. Biol.* 25:131–43

47. Hastings, J. W., Schweiger, H.-G., eds. 1976. *The Molecular Basis of Circadian Rhythms*. Berlin: Dahlem Konferenzen. 464 pp.

48. Hendrickson, A. E., Wagoner, N., Cowan, W. M. 1972. Autoradiographic and electron microscopic study of retino-hypothalamic connections. *Z. Zellforsch.* 125:1–26

49. Hillman, W. S. 1976. Biological rhythms and physiological timing. *Ann. Rev. Plant Physiol.* 27:159–79

50. Hoffmann, K. 1960. Experimental manipulation of the orientational clock in birds. See Ref 46, pp. 379–87

51. Hudson, D. J., Lickey, M. E. 1977. Weak negative coupling between circadian pacemakers of the eyes of *Aplysia*. *Neurosci. Abstr.* 3:179

52. Ibuka, N., Inouye, S. I. T., Kawamura, H. 1977. Analysis of sleep-wakefulness rhythms in male rats after suprachiasmatic nucleus lesions and ocular enucleation. *Brain Res.* 122:33–48

53. Ibuka, N., Kawamura, H. 1975. Loss of circadian rhythm in sleep-wakefulness cycle in the rat by suprachias-matic nucleus lesions. *Brain Res.* 96:76–81

54. Jacklet, J. W. 1969. Circadian rhythm of optic nerve impulses recorded in darkness from isolated eye of *Aplysia*. *Science* 164:562–63

55. Jacklet, J. W. 1969. Electrophysiological organization of the eye of *Aplysia*. *J. Gen. Physiol.* 53:21–42

56. Jacklet, J. W. 1971. A circadian rhythm in optic nerve impulses from an isolated eye in darkness. See Ref. 38, pp. 351–62

57. Jacklet, J. W. 1973. Neuronal population interactions in a circadian rhythm in *Aplysia*. In *Neurobiology of Invertebrates*, ed. J. Salanki, pp. 363–80. Budapest: Akademiai Kiado

58. Jacklet, J. W. 1973. The circadian rhythm in the eye of *Aplysia*: effects of low calcium and high magnesium. *J. Comp. Physiol.* 87:329–38

59. Jacklet, J. W. 1974. The effects of constant light and light pulses on the circadian rhythm in the eye of *Aplysia*. *J. Comp. Physiol.* 90:33–45

60. Jacklet, J. W. 1976. Dye marking neurons in the eye of *Aplysia*. *Comp. Biochem. Physiol.* 55A:373–77

61. Jacklet, J. W. 1976. Circadian rhythms in the nervous system of a marine gastropod, *Aplysia*. In *Biological Rhythms in the Marine Environment*, ed. P. J. DeCoursey, pp. 17–31. Columbia, SC: Univ. S. Carolina Press

62. Jacklet, J. W. 1977. Neuronal circadian rhythms: phase shifting by a protein synthesis inhibitor. *Science* 198:69–71

63. Jacklet, J. W., Geronimo, J. 1971. Circadian rhythm: Population of interacting neurons. *Science* 174:299–302

64. Kam, L. M., Moberg, G. P. 1977. Effect of raphe lesions on the circadian pattern of wheel running in the rat. *Physiol. Behav.* 18:213–17

65. Lenn, N. J., Beebe, B., Moore, R. Y. 1977. Postnatal development of the suprachiasmatic hypothalamic nucleus of the rat. *Cell Tiss. Res.* 178:463–75

66. Lickey, M. E., Block, G. D., Hudson, D. J., Smith, J. T. 1976. Circadian oscillators and photoreceptors in the gastropod, *Aplysia*. *Photochem. Photobiol.* 23:253–73

67. Lickey, M. E., Wozniak, J. A., Block, G. D., Hudson, D. J., Augter, G. K. 1977. The consequences of eye removal for the circadian rhythm of behavioral activity in *Aplysia*. *J. Comp. Physiol.* 118:121–43

68. Makara, G. B., Hodács, L. 1975. Rostral projections from the hypothalamic arcuate nucleus. *Brain Res.* 84:23–29

524   MENAKER, TAKAHASI & ESKIN

69. McMillan, J. P. 1972. Pinealectomy abolishes the circadian rhythm of migratory restlessness. *J. Comp. Physiol.* 79:105–12
70. McMillan, J. P., Elliott, J. A., Menaker, M. 1975. On the role of the eyes and brain photoreceptors in the sparrow: arrhythmicity in constant light. *J. Comp. Physiol.* 102:263–68
71. Menaker, M. 1974. Aspects of the physiology of circadian rhythmicity in the vertebrate central nervous system. See Ref. 31, pp. 479–89
72. Menaker, M., ed. 1976. Symposium on extraretinal photoreception in circadian rhythms and related phenomena. *Photochem. Photobiol.* 23:213–306
73. Menaker, M., Zimmerman, N. 1976. Role of the pineal in the circadian system of birds. *Am. Zool.* 16:45–55
74. Meyer, D. C., Quay, W. B. 1976. Hypothalamic and suprachiasmatic uptake of serotonin in vitro: twenty-four-hour changes in male and proestrous female rats. *Endocrinol.* 98:1160–65
75. Moore, R. Y., Eichler, V. B. 1972. Loss of a circadian adrenal corticosterone rhythm following suprachiasmatic lesions in the rat. *Brain Res.* 42:201–6
76. Moore, R. Y., Eichler, V. B. 1976. Central neural mechanisms in diurnal rhythm regulation and neuroendocrine responses to light. *Psychoneuroendocrinol.* 1:265–79
77. Moore, R. Y., Klein, D. C. 1974. Visual pathways and the central neural control of a circadian rhythm in pineal serotonin N-acetyltransferase activity. *Brain Res.* 71:17–33
78. Moore, R. Y., Lenn, N. J. 1972. A retinohypothalamic projection in the rat. *J. Comp. Neur.* 146:1–14
79. Naik, D. V. 1975. Immunoreactive LH-RH neurons in the hypothalamus identified by light and fluorescent microscopy. *Cell Tiss. Res.* 157:423–36
80. Nauta, W. J. H., Haymaker, W. 1969. Hypothalamic nuclei and fiber connections. In *The Hypothalamus*, ed. W. Haymaker, E. Anderson, W. J. H. Nauta, pp. 136–209. Springfield, Ill.: Thomas
81. Nishiitsutsuji-Uwo, J., Pittendrigh, C. S. 1968. Central nervous system control of circadian rhythmicity in the cockroach. II. The pathway of light signals that entrain the rhythm. *Z. Vgl. Physiol.* 58:1–13
82. Nishiitsutsuji-Uwo, J., Pittendrigh, C. S. 1968. Central nervous control of circadian rhythmicity in the cockroach.

83. III. The optic lobes, locus of the driving oscillation? *Z. Vgl. Physiol.* 58:14–46
83. Nishino, H., Koizumi, K., Brooks, C. M. 1976. The role of suprachiasmatic nuclei of the hypothalamus in the production of circadian rhythm. *Brain Res.* 112:45–59
84. Page, T. L., Caldarola, P. C., Pittendrigh, C. S. 1977. Mutual entrainment of bilaterally distributed circadian pacemakers. *Proc. Natl. Acad. Sci. USA* 74:1277–81
85. Pavlidis, T. 1969. Populations of interacting oscillators and circadian rhythms. *J. Theor. Biol.* 22:418–36
86. Pavlidis, T. 1973. *Biological Oscillators: Their Mathematical Analysis.* New York: Academic. 207 pp.
87. Pelham, R. W. 1975. A serum melatonin rhythm in chickens and its abolition by pinealectomy. *Endocrinol.* 96:543–46
88. Pittendrigh, C. S. 1954. On temperature independence in the clock system controlling emergence time in *Drosophila. Proc. Natl. Acad. Sci. USA* 40:1018–29
89. Pittendrigh, C. S. 1960. Circadian rhythms and the circadian organization of living systems. See Ref. 46, pp. 159–84
90. Pittendrigh, C. S. 1965. On the mechanism of entrainment of a circadian rhythm by light cycles. In *Circadian Clocks*, ed. J. Aschoff, pp. 277–97. Amsterdam: North-Holland
91. Pittendrigh, C. S., ed. 1974. Circadian oscillations and organization in nervous systems. See Ref. 31, pp. 432–542
92. Pittendrigh, C. S. 1974. Circadian oscillations in cells and the circadian organization of multicellular systems. See Ref. 31, pp. 437–58
93. Pittendrigh, C. S., Daan, S. 1976. A functional analysis of circadian pacemakers in nocturnal rodents. IV. Entrainment: pacemaker as clock. *J. Comp. Physiol.* 106:291–331
94. Pittendrigh, C. S., Daan, S. 1976. A functional analysis of circadian pacemakers in nocturnal rodents. V. Pacemaker structure: A clock for all seasons. *J. Comp. Physiol.* 106:333–55
95. Raisman, G., Brown-Grant, K. 1977. The "suprachiasmatic syndrome": Endocrine and behavioral abnormalities following lesions of the suprachiasmatic nuclei in the female rat. *Proc. R. Soc. London Ser. B.* 198:297–314
96. Ralph, C. L., Binkley, S., MacBride, S. E., Klein, D. C. 1975. Regulation of pineal rhythms in chickens: effects of blinding, constant light, constant dark,

and superior cervical ganglionectomy. *Endocrinol.* 97:1373–78

97. Ralph, C. L., Pelham, R. W., Mac-Bride, S. E., Reilly, D. P. 1974. Persistent rhythms of pineal and serum melatonin in cockerels in continuous darkness. *J. Endocrinol.* 63:319–24

98. Ribak, C. E., Peters, A. 1975. An autoradiographic study of the projections from the lateral geniculate body of the rat. *Brain Res.* 92:341–68

99. Richter, C. P. 1965. *Biological Clocks in Medicine and Psychiatry.* Springfield, Ill.: Thomas. 109 pp.

100. Richter, C. P. 1967. Sleep and activity: their relation to the 24-hour clock. *Proc. Assoc. Res. Nerv. Ment. Dis.* 45:8–27

101. Roberts, S. K. 1966. Circadian activity rhythms in cockroaches. III. The role of endocrine and neural factors. *J. Cell. Physiol.* 67:473–86

102. Roberts, S. K. 1974. Circadian rhythms in cockroaches. Effects of the optic lobe lesions. *J. Comp. Physiol.* 88:21–30

103. Roberts, S. K., Skopik, S. D., Driskill, R. J. 1971. Circadian rhythms in cockroaches: does brain hormone mediate the locomotor cycle? See Ref. 46, pp. 505–15

104. Rothman, B. S., Strumwasser, F. 1976. Phase shifting the circadian rhythm of neuronal activity in the isolated *Aplysia* eye with puromycin and cycloheximide: electrophysiological and biochemical studies. *J. Gen. Physiol.* 68:359–84

105. Rothman, B. S., Strumwasser, F. 1977. Manipulation of a neuronal circadian oscillator with inhibitors of macromolecular synthesis. *Fed. Proc.* 36: 2050–55

106. Rowland, N. 1976. Endogenous circadian rhythms in rats recovered from lateral hypothalamic lesions. *Physiol. Behav.* 16:257–66

107. Rusak, B. 1977. The role of the suprachiasmatic nuclei in the generation of circadian rhythms in the golden hamster, *Mesocricetus auratus. J. Comp. Physiol.* 118:145–64

108. Rusak, B. 1977. Involvement of the primary optic tracts in mediation of light effects on hamster circadian rhythms. *J. Comp. Physiol.* 118:165–72

109. Rusak, B., Morin, L. P. 1976. Testicular responses to photoperiod are blocked by lesions of the suprachiasmatic nuclei in golden hamsters. *Biol. Reprod.* 15: 366–74

110. Rusak, B., Zucker, I. 1975. Biological rhythms and animal behavior. *Ann. Rev. Psychol.* 26:137–71

111. Saavedra, J. M., Palkovits, M., Brownstein, M. J., Axelrod, J. 1974. Serotonin distribution in the nuclei of the rat hypothalamus and preoptic region. *Brain Res.* 77:157–65

112. Saunders, D. S. 1976. *Insect Clocks.* Oxford: Pergamon. 280 pp.

113. Schwartz, W. J., Gainer, H. 1977. Suprachiasmatic nucleus: use of ^{14}C 2-deoxy-D-glucose uptake as a functional marker. *Science.* 197:1089–91

114. Selverston, A. I., Mulloney, B. 1974. Synaptic and structural analysis of a small neural system. See Ref. 31, pp. 389–95

115. Sener, R. 1972. Site of circadian rhythm production in *Aplysia* eye. *Physiologist* 15:261

116. Smith, J. T. 1976. *Long term in vitro recording from the optic nerve and neuron R15 of Aplysia: R15 does not reveal a circadian rhythm but is highly temperature sensitive.* PhD thesis. Univ. of Oregon, Eugene. 181 pp.

117. Sokolove, P. G. 1975. Localization of the cockroach optic lobe circadian pacemaker with microlesions. *Brain Res.* 87:13–21

118. Sokolove, P. G., Loher, W. 1975. Role of eyes, optic lobes, and pars intercerebralis in locomotory and stridulatory circadian rhythms of *Teleogryllus commodus. J. Insect Physiol.* 21:785–99

119. Stanfield, B., Cowan, W. M. 1976. Evidence for a change in the retinohypothalamic projection in the rat following early removal of one eye. *Brain Res.* 104:129–36

120. Stephan, F. K., Nunez, A. A. 1977. Elimination of circadian rhythms in drinking, activity, sleep, and temperature by isolation of the suprachiasmatic nuclei. *Behav. Biol.* 20:1–16

121. Stephan, F. K., Zucker, I. 1972. Rat drinking rhythms: Central visual pathways and endocrine factors mediating responsiveness to environmental illumination. *Physiol. Behav.* 8:315–26

122. Stephan, F. K., Zucker, I. 1972. Circadian rhythms in drinking behavior and locomotor activity of rats are eliminated by hypothalamic lesions. *Proc. Natl. Acad. Sci. USA,* 69:1583–86

123. Stetson, M. H., Watson-Whitmyer, M. 1976. Nucleus suprachiasmaticus: the biological clock in the hamster? *Science* 191:197–99

124. Strumwasser, F. 1965. The demonstration and manipulation of a circadian rhythm in a single neuron. See Ref. 90, pp. 442–62

125. Strumwasser, F. 1974. Neuronal principles organizing periodic behaviors. See
Ref. 31, pp. 459–78
126. Strumwasser, F., Alvarez, R. 1974. Gap
junctions between photoreceptor cells
in the eye of *Aplysia californica*. *Caltech
Biol. Ann. Rep.* pp. 225–26
127. Swanson, L. W., Cowan, W. M. 1975.
The efferent connections of the suprachiasmatic nucleus of the hypothalamus. *J. Comp. Neur.* 160:1–12
128. Swanson, L. W., Cowan, W. M., Jones,
E. G. 1974. An autoradiographic study
of the efferent connections of the ventral
lateral geniculate nucleus in the albino
rat and the cat. *J. Comp. Neur.* 156:
143–64
129. Sweeney, B. M., Hastings, J. W. 1960.
Effects of temperature upon diurnal
rhythms. See Ref. 46, pp. 87–104
130. Szentágothai, J., Flerko, B., Mess, B.,
Halász, B. 1968. *Hypothalamic Control
of the Anterior Pituitary.* Budapest:
Akadémiai Kiado. 3rd ed.
131. Truman, J. W. 1972. Physiology of insect rhythms. II. The silkmoth brain as
the location of the biological clock controlling eclosion. *J. Comp. Physiol.*
81:99–114
132. Truman, J. W. 1974. Physiology of insect rhythms. IV. Role of the brain in
the regulation of the flight rhythm of
the giant silkmoths. *J. Comp. Physiol.*
95:281–96
133. Truman, J. W., Riddiford, L. M. 1970.
Neuroendocrine control of ecdysis in
silkmoths. *Science* 167:1624–26
134. Turek, F. W., McMillan, J. P.,
Menaker, M. 1976. Melatonin: Effects
on the circadian locomotor rhythm of
sparrows. *Science* 194:1441–43
135. Underwood, H. 1977. Circadian organization in lizards: the role of the pineal
organ. *Science* 195:587–89
136. Underwood, H., Menaker, M. 1976.
Extraretinal photoreception in lizards.
Photochem. Photobiol. 23:227–43
137. Williams, C. M., Adkisson, P. L. 1964.
Physiology of insect diapause. XIV. An
endocrine mechanism for the photoperiodic control of pupal diapause in the
oak silkmoth, *Antheraea pernyi. Biol.
Bull.* 127:511–25
138. Winfree, A. T. 1967. Biological
rhythms and the behavior of populations of coupled oscillators. *J. Theoret.
Biol.* 16:15–42
139. Zimmerman, N. H. 1976. *Organization
within the circadian system of the house
sparrow: hormonal coupling and the location of a circadian oscillator.* PhD
thesis. Univ. of Texas, Austin. 157 pp.
140. Zimmerman, N. H., Menaker, M. 1975.
Neural connections of sparrow pineal:
role in circadian control of activity.
Science 190:477–79
141. Zucker, I., Rusak, B., King, R. G. 1976.
Neural basis for circadian rhythms in
rodent behavior. In *Advances in Psy-
chobiology,* ed. A. H. Riesen, R. F.
Thompson, 3:35–74. New York: Wiley

Ann. Rev. Physiol. 1978. 40:527–52
Copyright © 1978 by Annual Reviews Inc. All rights reserved

BRAINSTEM MECHANISMS FOR ❖1201
RAPID AND SLOW EYE MOVEMENTS

Theodore Raphan and Bernard Cohen

Department of Neurology, Mount Sinai School of Medicine of the City
University of New York, New York, NY 10029

INTRODUCTION

The primary function of the oculomotor system is to subserve vision. It
accomplishes this by holding the eyes steady while they fixate objects or by
moving the eyes to stabilize images on the retina. Dodge (60) first distinguished the various types of eye movements; Westheimer (215, 216) and
Rashbass (167) recognized that the oculomotor system is organized into
separate subsystems to produce fast and slow eye movements. Fast or rapid
movements include saccades and quick phases of nystagmus. They bring the
eyes rapidly from one fixation point to another or reset the eyes during
compensatory movements induced by vestibular or optokinetic stimulation.
Slow eye movements include pursuit movements and slow phases of vestibular and optokinetic nystagmus.[1] They fix moving images on the retina so
they can be seen and usually have lower velocities than saccades. Most
visual input is processed during slow movements and periods of fixation.

Activity responsible for producing eye movements originates in the visual
and vestibular systems as well as in other parts of the brain and is transmitted to parts of the oculomotor system that lie in the brainstem. Models for
this organization have been formulated that help us to understand how
visual and vestibular information is processed centrally to move the eyes.
These models give insight into the structure of the oculomotor system and
supply a theoretical basis for understanding neurophysiological data. In this
review we consolidate information about where and how rapid and slow eye
movements are generated in the brainstem and relate neurophysiological
data to models of the oculomotor system.

---

[1]Vergence movements are also slow movements but will not be considered here
[see (217, 231) for review].

0066-4278/78/0301-0527$01.00

SIGNAL PROCESSING FOR PRODUCING RAPID EYE MOVEMENTS

The first model to incorporate separate saccadic and smooth pursuit systems was developed by Young & Stark (224). The model was based on the work of Westheimer (215, 216), who had shown that in response to steps in target displacement there was an obligatory refractory period of 150–250 msec between successive saccades. This indicated intermittancy, and was modeled using sampled-data control theory (224). Young & Stark divided the oculomotor system into two distinct subsystems: a smooth pursuit and a saccadic system. The pursuit system acted as a sampled-data velocity servomechanism that rotated the eyes at the angular velocity of the target. The saccadic system was a sampled-data positional servomechanism that directed the eyes toward the target. As suggested by Westheimer (215), Young & Stark assumed a second-order underdamped system for the dynamics of the ocular "plant."[2] This implies that a saccade-like trajectory results when a step in tension is applied to the eye muscles.

The Young–Stark model was the first to predict eye movements when both smooth movements and saccades were required. In addition, it formalized the theoretical and experimental data in a model that could be tested by experimentation. Subsequent studies showed that for certain stimuli the model did not predict the behavior of the human oculomotor system. These stimuli were pulse-steps of target displacement (218) or target movements combining smooth displacements with steps in the opposite direction (167). In response to two steps of target displacement within 50–100 msec, first to one side and then to the other, the eye frequently made a single saccade to the final position (218). The model predicted two saccades under all circumstances. If a target moved in a step to one side and then returned at a constant velocity, crossing the original position within 150–200 msec, there was frequently no saccadic response (167); that is, the eyes followed only the smooth component. The model predicted that eyes would follow both the target step and the smooth movement. These deficiencies led Young, Forster & Van Houtte (225) to modify the original Young–Stark model to include a finite sampling interval and a nonsychronous sampler.

Quick phases of nystagmus have characteristics similar to those of saccades and both are presumably generated by the same neural mechanism (39, 41, 43, 44, 167, 179). Therefore, quick phases were modeled using sampled-data theory (200, 222). A limitation of these models was that they did not predict variations in frequency of nystagmus based on input velocity. To compensate for this deficiency, Barnes & Benson (14) incorpo-

---

[2]The "plant" comprises the orbital contents, including the eye muscles and globe.

rated a threshold element in the quick phase generator rather than a fixed sampler. Robinson (174) also used concepts of threshold to formulate models of the saccadic generator. These models attempted to give structure to the sampling process and expand the movement repertoire that could be predicted. As yet neither the mechanism of sampling nor its site is known.

Inherent in these models is an assumption that saccades or quick phases of nystagmus are ballistic—that is, these rapid eye movements are pre-programmed and once initiated must run their course (215). This follows as a logical consequence of the use of a sampler. Until the next sample is taken, the ongoing movement cannot be affected. Both the ballistic nature of saccades and the sampling concept have been questioned (176, 229). These objections are based on findings that activity for two saccades can be processed simultaneously if the information arrives up to at least 80 msec prior to a saccade (15, 17). In addition, "slow" saccades that occur in patients with cerebellar disease can be interrupted in mid-flight (229). In normal subjects, however, saccades can generally be interrrupted only by vestibular input (23), which commonly occurs during combined head and eye movement in lateral gaze shifts (23, 59). As the head begins to move, the saccade is truncated and reverses direction in a compensatory movement. With this exception the ballistic nature of saccadic movements still seems valid (91, 92). Similarly, the concept of sampling still seems correct, although the sampler may not operate at a constant rate under all circumstances.

Another important property of saccadic generation is prediction (57, 68, 197, 215, 216). When responding to a periodic target, the eyes can follow with zero phase (no delay) or can even lead the target. The mechanism of anticipation is unknown, but must be considered in evaluating oculomotor system properties studied with periodic stimuli (68, 197).

Precisely how the central nervous system generates saccades is still speculative. However, the immediate supranuclear mechanism for generating saccades has been identified, and models of this mechanism have been formulated that can be supported by neurophysiological data.

Robinson (169) presented evidence that the oculomotor plant was over-damped, and inferred that a combined pulse and step of contraction, a "pulse-step", was required to produce saccades. Cook & Stark (55) and Fuchs (71) concurred in this finding. As a result the Young-Stark model (224) required restructuring to produce a pulse-step rather than a step in activity to drive the plant dynamics (72, 174).

With the development of techniques for recording the activity of single neurons in alert animals (22, 65, 172) it became possible to study internal signals in the oculomotor system and determine its internal structure.

Recordings in alert monkeys indicated that many motoneurons display a pulse-step in activity during saccades (73, 94, 95, 118, 119, 172, 177, 183). They fire at constant rates during positions of fixation and have bursts of activity just prior to and during saccades; the burst is followed by a return of the firing rate to a new steady level during the following period of fixation. The change in the tonic frequency from one period of fixation to the next represents a step in activity, while the burst in motoneurons is probably composed of both the pulse and the rising phase of the step.

In addition to "burst-tonic" motoneurons there are motoneurons that are predominantly phasic (94). These cells have little or no tonic activity and probably contribute mainly to the production of the pulse. There are also predominantly tonic motoneurons that have little or no phasic activity when the eyes change position. They would contribute mainly to the step in activity. Under normal conditions the pulse-step is well synchronized. However, overshoots and undershoots in saccadic eye movement of normal subjects (6) and of patients (214) have been described. These appear to be due to desynchronization of the pulse-step.

The different characteristics of the motoneurons are reflected in functional differences among the eye muscle fibers (4; reviewed in 5, 157). There are a variety of eye muscle fibers, and they respond differently during saccadic eye movements. Some are predominantly phasic, while others are phasic-tonic or tonic in character (53). Together they produce a pulse-step in tension (54).

During saccades, the number of impulses in the motoneuron burst determines the amount of shortening on contraction and consequently the component of movement in the pulling direction of the activated muscles (95, 97). This suggests that the impulses in the burst sum on the muscle to determine the size of the saccade. Presumably, the instantaneous frequency during the burst determines the velocity characteristics of the saccade. The number of impulses in the burst is also related to the difference in steady frequency before and after the saccade (95). This suggests that the activity for the step was co-determined with the pulse. As will be described, the step could be produced by an integration of the activity in the burst.

In summary, models of the oculomotor system indicate that incoming visual information is sampled in the central oculomotor system, that saccades are essentially ballistic, and that a pulse-step of activity to the eye muscle is necessary to produce rapid eye movements. Studies of motoneurons during saccades are in general agreement with the concept that saccades are produced by a pulse-step change in tension. They show that the number of impulses in the burst is summed on the muscle during the rapid eye movement to produce the component of movement in its pulling plane. Where and how this pulse-step is formed in the central nervous system are considered next.

SUPRANUCLEAR NEURAL MECHANISMS
FOR GENERATION OF RAPID EYE MOVEMENTS

Saccades and quick phases of nystagmus in the horizontal plane appear to be generated in the paramedian zone of the pontine reticular formation (PPRF) (21, 39–45, 97, 98, 116, 131, 132). Stimulation of the PPRF causes ipsilateral eye movements similar to spontaneously occuring slow and rapid eye movements (45, 116). Lesions of this region cause paralysis of ipsilateral conjugate gaze (21, 42, 70, 78); rapid eye movements are affected most (42). Gross potential changes in this region are associated with every rapid eye movement (41); unit activity before, during, and after rapid eye movements is also found in the PPRF (43, 44, 61, 63, 97, 98, 116, 132, 192, 193).

Firing patterns of units found in rostral portions of the PPRF are different from those of units found in portions of the PPRF around, or caudal to, the abducens nucleus. This suggests that there are two functionally separate areas of the PPRF. In the rostral PPRF, unit activity is predominantly phasic, and is associated mainly with rapid eye movements (43, 44, 97, 98, 132). These neurons have little tonic activity associated with eye position. It would appear that the pulse of activity that produces saccades is generated in this region. In support of this hypothesis, Henn & Cohen (97, 98) have shown that activity necessary to produce rapid eye movements is coded in the firing rates of units located in the rostral PPRF. This activity is organized according to a polar coordinate system; i.e. individual bursts code direction, duration or amplitude, and the component of movement in the plane of the individual eye muscles. The component of movement is directly related to the number of spikes in the burst. This is the information the motoneurons need to fire during saccades and quick phases (95, 97, 98). Raphan (164, 165) has shown that if the several types of cells most frequently encountered in the PPRF of the monkey were properly coupled, they could generate the bursts of activity that drive the motoneurons.

In contrast, units in the periabducens region have both bursts of activity in association with rapid eye movements and steady levels of tonic activity associated with eye position (116, 132). In addition, activity of some periabducens units is related solely to eye position. This shows that a step is present in some periabducens neurons that could contribute to the step in activity transmitted to motoneurons. The finding that conjugate paralysis of horizontal gaze follows abducens (35) or periabducens lesions (42, 56, 78) is consistent with the idea that the periabducens region lies on or close to the final common path for horizontal gaze. It seems probable that the step in the periabducens neurons is formed by an integration of the pulse from the rostral PPRF.

The presence of an integrator in oculomotor pathways has been inferred from stimulation studies (45, 116) and from studies on the vestibulo-ocular reflex arc (171, 173, 175, 190, 201). This integrator has a time constant longer than 20 sec in man (16). However, after cerebellar lesions its time constant can fall to 1 sec (37, 175). Although integration seems to be a basic building block in oculomotor organization, how it is realized at the neuronal level is still unknown. The motoneuron by itself is probably not capable of such integration, since it needs continuous excitation to fire at steady rates (180). Nor is this integration likely to take place on the eye muscles, because activity related to position of the eyes is already present in motoneurons. Therefore it must occur centrally (131, 173, 190).

Once the step in activity has been formed by an integration of the pulse, i.e. by integrating the spike activity in the burst from the PPRF, the pulse-step necessary for exciting the motoneurons could be realized by simultaneous addition of the activity from the integrator to the pulse itself.

How various cells in the PPRF and periabducens region are coupled to motoneurons is still not clear, nor is it known how the visual system couples to the PPRF units. Raybourn & Keller (168) have demonstrated that long-lead burst units in the PPRF of the monkey are monosynaptically activated by superior colliculus stimulation, while short-lead burst units are activated from the superior colliculus via a disynaptic link. There is also a disynaptic path from the superior colliculus to abducens motoneurons in the cat (86, 162), with an intermediate synapse in the PRF (86). The role of the individual cell types in pulse generation is also unknown, although Raphan (164, 165) has suggested that these cells might be the state variables of a pulse generating network. Some of the high-frequency burst neurons in the PRF of the cat transmit inhibition onto motoneurons (79, 103, 106), and pause units may be responsible for inactivating saccadic generation (116). Further work is necessary before the organization of the PPRF is completely understood.

There is evidence to indicate that the vestibular system may also contribute to the production of the pulse-step in activity. Spiegel & Price (194) originally proposed that quick phases of nystagmus are generated in the vestibular nuclei; this could occur via commissural pathways (186, 188). On the other hand, Lorente de Nó (131) maintained that quick phases arise in the pontine reticular formation. Unit recordings show that there are burst, burst-tonic, pause, and tonic units in the vestibular nuclei that are associated with rapid eye movements (74, 120, 121, 147). Lending support to this idea of Spiegel & Price (194) is the finding that vestibular commissural interneurons project excitation and inhibition directly onto abducens motoneurons before and during quick phases (137, 138). However, there are relatively few of these neurons (84, 85), and even after massive bilateral destruction of the vestibular nuclei it is possible to induce nystagmus by appropriate stimulation (141, 158). Therefore it would appear that the vestibular nuclei are not essential for production of rapid eye movements. Rather, they probably provide supplementary activation for quick phases and saccades.

PATHWAYS FROM THE PPRF TO MOTONEURONS

Excitory Pathways and the Median Longitudinal Fasciculus (MLF)

Until recently, there was little evidence for direct pathways from the PPRF to eye muscle motoneurons, but electrophysiological and anatomical studies have now provided a firm basis for understanding the transmission of the "pulse" of activity from the PPRF. In order for the eyes to move horizontally, there must be a pulse-step to the agonists, the ipsilateral lateral rectus and the contralateral medial rectus, and a negative pulse-step to the antagonists, the ipsilateral medial rectus and contralateral lateral rectus. The negative pulse-step would be realized by a sudden reduction in firing during saccades, followed by a lower level of tonic activity after the saccade (55). Since each of the 12 eye muscles has a vector of force in the horizontal plane, the vertical recti and obliques also receive similar excitation and inhibition during horizontal movements (95).

In the monkey, direct pathways extend from the PPRF to ipsilateral abducens motoneurons and to neurons in the periabducens region (32). In the cat, cells in a similar region of the pontine reticular formation, at the junction of nucleus reticularis pontis oralis (NRPO) and nucleus reticularis pontis caudalis (NRPC), also project directly to ipsilateral abducens motoneurons (86, 87, 101). This provides the basis for monosynaptic excitation of the ipsilateral abducens motoneurons and contraction of the lateral rectus msucle.

There are two potential pathways from the PPRF to medial rectus motoneurons carrying excitation. Cells in the NRPO-PC region send axons directly to oculomotor neurons (100, 131, 182, 203), carrying excitation and inhibition (100). However, the bulk of excitation from the PPRF to the contralateral medial rectus motoneurons probably takes a more circuitous route. Graybiel & Hartwieg (88) demonstrated that neurons lying in and around the abducens nucleus have axons that project to the region of the oculomotor nucleus. Baker & Highstein (11) extended this finding by showing that these neurons, which they termed "internuclear neurons," project excitation monosynaptically to contralateral medial rectus motoneurons. The internuclear neurons, in turn, receive activation directly from the PPRF and from the vestibular nuclei (101). Their axons cross the brainstem at the level of the abducens nucleus to ascend in the medial longitudinal fasciculus (102). This group of neurons appears to provide the major excitatory drive for contraction of the medial rectus muscle and ocular adduction during all types of spontaneous and induced eye movements. Destruction of these neurons due to damage of the MLF is probably responsible for the paresis or paralysis of adduction of the ipsilateral eye that follows these lesions (11, 18, 19, 196). Other parts of the MLF syndrome ("internuclear ophthalmoplegia") include nystagmus in the contralateral eye when it abducts, vertical nystagmus, and a loss of vertical vestibular responses (39, 40, 66, 185). Convergence is preserved after MLF lesions.

Unit activity in the MLF associated with horizontal saccades or quick phases is burst-tonic in type, suggesting that the MLF fibers carry a pulse-step to the ipsilateral medial rectus motoneurons (122, 163). Other unit activity in the MLF is related to vertical compensatory movements (122). Inhibitory pathways to medial rectus motoneurons do not appear to be located in the MLF (12).

The MLF is usually considered to be the major ascending pathway carrying activity from the medial vestibular nucleus and horizontal canals for adduction during compensatory eye movements (131, 142, 202). However, Baker & Highstein (12) have recently found that medial rectus motoneurons were activated from the vestibular system via the lateral ascending tract of Deiters (76) rather than through the MLF. This would be generally in accord with the results of unit studies (122, 163), which show that few if any MLF units are directly associated with horizontal head velocity. Thus, activity in the MLF that is responsible for horizontal eye movements is probably almost entirely under control of internuclear neurons.

Inhibitory Pathways

Since every eye movement is produced by a combination of excitation and inhibition of yoked agonist and antagonist pairs (99), there must also be pathways from the PPRF to the antagonists. Less is known about PPRF-inhibitory than about PPRF-excitatory pathways. Stimulation of the NRPO-PC region causes disynaptic inhibition of contralateral abducens motoneurons (86, 101). The pathway utilizes an inhibitory interneuron whose cell body appears to lie in the medial vestibular nucleus (101). In addition there are cells mediating contralateral inhibition on abducens motoneurons from the periabducens region (79), including the area caudal to the abducens nucleus (103). The inhibitory pathway from each PPRF to the ipsilateral medial rectus muscle is still unclear, but could utilize direct NRPC-PO-oculomotor pathways (100). Whether there are inhibitory pathways from the vestibular system to medial rectus motoneurons has also been questioned by Baker & Highstein (12). They could find no sign of disynaptic inhibition in identified medial rectus motoneurons of the cat on stimulating the ipsilateral vestibular nerve or nucleus. These findings are contrary to generally accepted notions of disynaptic vestibulo-oculomotor organization (131, 202).

In addition to the major antagonists, the vertical recti and oblique muscles also participate in every horizontal movement (95, 99). The presence of PPRF units that code information suitable for driving the vertical eye movers could provide the basis for exciting or inhibiting superior and inferior rectus and oblique motoneurons during horizontal saccades (98). Monosynaptic pathways from the NRPO-PC region to the oculomotor nucleus (100) could carry this activity from the PPRF. More work is necessary to clarify this connection.

MECHANISM FOR VERTICAL SACCADES AND QUICK PHASES OF NYSTAGMUS

Because the oculomotor "plant" is the same for vertical as for horizontal eye movements, a pulse-step in activity would also be necessary to move the eyes in the vertical direction during saccades and quick phases of nystagmus. Patients with pontine lesions can have an isolated paralysis of horizontal gaze, while those with pretectal or mesencephalic reticular formation (MRF) lesions can have an isolated paralysis of vertical gaze (70, 107, 115, 159, 231). This indicates that the immediate supranuclear mechanisms for vertical and horizontal gaze are separate and are located in different regions of the brainstem (39, 40, 231). There is probably also a separation of the mechanisms responsible for upward and downward eye movements. Lesions of the pretectum are associated with paralysis of upward gaze (155, 156, 231) while more rostral lesions cause paralysis of downward gaze (113, 123, 231).

The immediate supranuclear mechanism for vertical gaze has recently been investigated by Buettner, Buettner-Ennever & Henn (33). At the mesodiencephalic junction they found a portion of the MRF where unit activity is associated with vertical saccades. This region receives ascending projections from the PPRF (33). The ascending fibers lie lateral to the MLF and degenerate after PPRF lesions (78). Burst units in the MRF are related to amplitude and direction of eye movement as well as to components of movements in the planes of the vertical recti and oblique muscles. Thus they have the requisite activity for producing the pulse for vertical rapid eye movements. How this activity reaches the oculomotor and trochlear nuclei from the MRF, how the pulse-step for vertical movements is formed, as well as the location of the vertical integrators responsible for the step associated with fixation are unknown.

Although parts of the neural mechanism for vertical and horizontal gaze are separate, there is fragmentary evidence to suggest that all rapid eye movements may originate in a single region of the PPRF. There may be asynchrony in horizontal and vertical components of saccades (210), but generally coordination of rapid eye movements is precise, whether the movements are horizontal, vertical or oblique. In addition, omnidirectional gaze paralysis can be produced by large bilateral PPRF lesions, but not by MRF lesions (21, 70, 107). Finally, stimulation of pause units in the PPRF causes inhibition of vertical as well as horizontal saccades (116). Differences between PPRF lesions that cause paralysis of conjugate horizontal gaze (21, 42, 78) and those that cause paralysis of gaze in all directions (21) may provide clues to the location of the neurons responsible for the various functions.

A comparison of unit activity in the PPRF and MRF is consistent with the notion that the MRF may be driven at least in part by the PPRF. PPRF units associated with eye movements have "on-directions" in planes of all the eye muscles, whereas the on-directions of units in the MRF lie only in planes of the vertical movers. The latency between the onset of activity in MRF units and the onset of movement is generally shorter than in corresponding PPRF units. Thus the MRF may receive its activation from the PPRF. In addition, long-lead burst units and pause units, believed to be utilized in the timing and switching of pulse generation (164, 165), are present in the PPRF, but not in the MRF.

In the MRF as in the PPRF, the neurons code the component of movement in the plane of the vertical recti and obliques by the number of spikes in the burst (33). This is the information the vertical rectus and oblique muscles need to move the eyes during saccades. Direction of movement is coded in terms of a polar coordinate system, and is represented by firing frequencies related to the cosine of the angle formed by the plane of movement and a reference plane (33).

For the hypothesis to be accepted, that parts of the PPRF contain the timing mechanism for all rapid eye movements, there must be better differentiation of pontine lesions associated with a loss of horizontal movements from those associated with a loss of all eye movements. Unit activity in these separate regions must also be studied.

Bender (20) originally noted that stimulation of both sides of the brain induces pure vertical movements, and that bilateral lesions cause pure vertical nystagmus. This suggests that vertical movements are produced by activity of cells that lie on both sides of the brain. On-directions of MRF and PPRF units are in accord with this idea. In both the MRF and PPRF there are no units with pure vertical on-directions (33, 98). Rather, the on-directions are "off vertical", i.e. 5°–15° from the vertical plane. These planes are close to the pulling planes of the vertical recti and obliques (99).

In summary, available evidence suggests that the rostral PPRF may contain the neural substrate for originating and coordinating quick eye movements in all directions. The immediate supranuclear mechanism for vertical saccadic eye movements appears to lie in the MRF and pretectal regions, with some separation of the mechanisms for upward and downward gaze. Pathways from the MRF to the oculomotor and trochlear nuclei, and sites of integrators where pulses of activity associated with vertical saccades would be converted into pulse-steps are still unknown. It is also not clear how the PPRF and MRF are coordinated and coupled.

SIGNAL PROCESSING FOR PRODUCING SLOW EYE MOVEMENTS

Slow eye movements can be induced by either vestibular or visual stimuli. In either case stimulus velocity has been shown to be the primary signal driving the oculomotor system (47, 48, 50, 52, 144, 146, 167, 170, 173, 190). Eye movements induced by the vestibular system can compensate for head movements over a frequency band up to 5 Hz (74, 117). Compensatory eye velocities can approach speeds of $400°$ sec^{-1} (3), the velocity range of rapid movements (134, 136). Thus, the term "slow eye movement" is imprecise. Nevertheless, it has come to designate movements that are not ballistic and are probably not processed through the pulse generation mechanism of the PPRF.

Slow eye movements generated by the vestibular system are essentially a response to head velocity (144–146, 190). The labyrinths respond to angular or linear acceleration (64, 199); but over a frequency range that includes the frequency of most head movements (.05 Hz–5 Hz), the canals perform an integration of acceleration due to their fluid mechanics (69, 80, 81, 146, 199). Thus the signal they generate is proportional to head velocity rather than to head acceleration (80, 144). Models of the vestibular system that account for these characteristics have been reviewed elsewhere (143, 145, 227, 228). Because the canals only perform one integration, a second integration is necessary to convert head velocity information to an eye position signal that drives the muscles to produce compensatory eye movements (190). This integration is performed centrally since the frequency of firing in motoneurons is related to eye position (73, 95, 118, 119, 172, 183). A similar integration is necessary for converting visual system signals related to target velocity to eye position. This is considered in more detail below.

Rashbass (167) was the first to show that the control system mediating visually guided smooth pursuit[3] is primarily responsive to target velocity.

[3]Smooth pursuit refers to eye movements made tracking a small target without regard to background motion.

He used a target that stepped to one side and then moved slowly in the opposite direction. The eyes initially followed the slowly moving part of the stimulus, though they were deviating from the target. Smooth pursuit is also responsive to positional errors, and the eyes can move onto target during tracking (170). The limit of pursuit tracking is generally taken to be about 45° sec[-1] (167, 170, 216, 224). However, in response to whole-field rotation, i.e. during optokinetic nystagmus (OKN), slow-phase eye velocity can be close to target velocity up to 60°–90° sec[-1] in man (90, 135) and to 180° sec[-1] in the monkey (47). The slow eye-movement control system can be selective in responding to one of many targets moving in the visual field (60, 151).

Signals from the visual system mediating smooth pursuit and slow phases of OKN probably originate in direction-sensitive retinal ganglion cells (153, 154), but how this velocity information reaches the oculomotor system is not clear. Modeling of the oculomotor system has given some insight into the nature of the signal processing. Fender & Nye (68) were among the first to model the input-output response of the oculomotor system to a visual stimulus. They moved a point source sinusoidally, and measured the steady-state response. At lower frequencies this stimulus primarily elicited smooth pursuit. The upper cutoff frequency of visual tracking was about 1.0 Hz, which is considerably lower than the frequency response of the vestibular system (117). This indicates that the vestibular system is better able to promote tracking for rapidly changing velocities (high frequencies), while the visual system responds better to slowly changing velocities (low frequencies). This study showed that a velocity or "regenerative" feedback had to be added to retinal slip[4] to model oculomotor frequency and phase behavior properly. The feedback could originate either from eye muscle proprioceptors or as an efference signal from "outflow" information (93, 195, 211). The Fender-Nye model attributed the less than minimum phase behavior in the frequency response to prediction. It is not clear how prediction is realized in the nervous system (67).

Fender & Nye provided useful information about overall oculomotor behavior, but did not distinguish the separate saccadic and smooth subsystems. This was accomplished by Young & Stark (224), who modeled smooth pursuit as a sampled-data velocity servomechanism driving an underdamped plant (see the section on Signal Processing for Producing Rapid Eye Movements, above). The pursuit portion of the model nulled the error rate estimate from successive samples. Sampling of smooth pursuit was originally suggested by Westheimer (216). Attempts to verify the Young-Stark model experimentally resulted in certain modifications.

---

[4]Retinal slip is the difference between target velocity and eye velocity.

It was shown that eye velocity can change during pursuit with latencies as short as 75 msec (170). This indicates that target motion is probably monitored continuously rather than intermittently (13, 170, 198). In addition, there is a high foward gain in the input-output relationship during pursuit. This is shown by the exact matching of eye velocity to target velocity at low speeds (226). It is also demonstrated by the "runaway" response to target velocity under open-loop conditions when one eye is paralyzed (48, 124, 152) or when there is positive feedback (68, 170). The continuous nature of smooth pursuit coupled with high gain and with the delay inherent during following would lead to instability.

Implicit in the Young-Stark (224) model was the assumption that the appropriate stimulus for inducing pursuit was a target moving across the retina. Childress & Jones (38) pulled the eye to one side and suddenly released it. As the eye returned to its original position there was retinal slip, but smooth pursuit was not induced. Retinal slip alone was not sufficient to induce smooth following.

These results led Young, Forster & Van Houtte (225) to modify the pursuit portion of the original model. Using Helmholtz's concept of efference copy (93), they assumed that a signal representing eye velocity was fed back from the oculomotor to the visual system. When combined with the retinal error signal, it gave a "perceived" target velocity, which then drove the oculomotor system. This supposition avoided the instability of the original model and accounted for its high open-loop gain. Yasui (222) and Yasui & Young (223) provided evidence for the "perceptual feedback" hypothesis. They recorded nystagmus induced by angular rotation in darkness with a foveal after-image. Although there was no retinal error in either case, compensatory eye movements were improved by the after-image. They suggested that the difference was due to a perceptual feedback loop that had been activated by the after-image. Similar assumptions about efference copy have beeen made to explain open and closed loop behavior of OKN (47, 124). As yet, these signals have not been identified in unit recordings.

More information is available about the motor and premotor signals used to drive the eyes during slow eye movements. The finding that the ocular plant was overdamped rather than underdamped (169) suggested that the information the eye muscles need to produce a constant velocity smooth movement is a step plus a ramp of contraction, a "step-ramp" (170). For saccadic generation it was inferred that a pulse was integrated to produce a step, and the pulse and step were then combined to form a pulse-step (see the section on Supranuclear Neural Mechanisms, above). Similarly, to induce slow eye movements the step representing eye velocity could be integrated to produce a ramp. The two could then be combined to form a step-ramp, the adequate signal to drive the motoneurons (173, 175). A step-ramp in motoneuron firing during nystagmus is present in motoneuron recordings from the alert rabbit by Schaefer (181) and has been inferred from motoneuron recordings in the monkey during slow eye movements regardless of stimulus origin (119, 190). A step-ramp is also present in axons from the vestibular nuclei that drive the motoneurons (104). The integrator that produces the ramp from the step during slow movement generation is presumably the same integrator that produces the step from the pulse during rapid eye movements. Pause units in the PPRF could serve as a switch enabling this integrator to accept information related to either saccadic or to slow movements (116).

During pursuit of small targets (foveal or perifoveal), the step in stimulus velocity appears to be transmitted directly to the integrator, which converts it to a position signal for use by the motoneurons. However, during full-field stimulation that excites the peripheral retina (24), another integrator or storage mechanism appears to be activated. It acts to store the internal velocity signal and participates in production of optokinetic nystagmus (OKN) and optokinetic after-nystagmus (OKAN). Collewijn (48–50) recorded OKN of rabbits in response to steps of velocity and to sinusoidal velocities under open and closed loop conditions. The animals did not respond to steps in position from 0.5° to 4°. In response to steps in velocity there was a small jump in slow-phase eye velocity, followed by a longer, more gradual rise to a steady-state level. The gradual rise in eye velocity was taken by Collewijn (50) to indicate that there was a second integrator in the neural mechanism for OKN. Cohen, Matsuo & Raphan (47) identified a similar integrator in the monkey and analyzed its dynamic characteristics. It has a time constant of 12–20 sec, and is responsible for driving the eyes during OKAN. Activity from the OKN-OKAN integrator appears to sum with activity in the direct pathways from the visual system that extend around this integrator (47). This sum forms the velocity signal that drives the "step-ramp" integrator that transforms the velocity signal to a position signal.

It has generally been assumed that the functional significance of OKN and OKAN is to stabilize a moving environment on the retina (114, 150, 207). The OKN-OKAN integrator could contribute to the ocular response by stabilizing slow-phase velocity, thereby reducing its variation. It would also make following possible at higher velocities. Activity in direct pathways could add to activity from the OKN-OKAN integrator to produce a faster combined response. This integrator is closely related to the vestibular system (47), and appears to be important for the perception of self motion during visual stimulation (24, 25, 133). It also appears to be involved in the proper functioning of the vestibulo-ocular reflex. Time constants of cupular return after deflections caused by a step in velocity (80, 187) are much shorter than time constants of nystagmus induced by the same step (166, 178). This implies that the cupulary deflection excites a central storage mechanism to produce the long-lasting nystagmus (166, 178). Preliminary evidence indicates that the OKN-OKAN integrator is the same integrator that participates in the production of per and post-rotatory nystagmus (166). This would represent an efficient use of the vestibular system by the visual system in producing slow phases of nystagmus. Thus although OKN and OKAN would on first sight appear to be predominantly visual-oculomotor reflexes, data now suggests that the vestibular system is intimately involved in the generation of these responses.

In summary the following are inferred about the slow eye movement control system: Slow eye movements change continuously rather than discretely (as in the case of saccades). Head velocity is the major driving signal for smooth movements from the vestibular system. Over a wide frequency range (.05–5 Hz) in which normal head movements occur, an internal velocity signal results from an integration of head acceleration by the semicircular canals. Target velocity is postulated as the major driving signal for smooth pursuit and OKN. It is presumably formed by a combination of retinal error velocity and an efferent signal that is fed back to the visual system from the oculomotor system. The slow eye movement control system is capable of predictive and selective following of targets. Eye position is realized by an integration of a head or target velocity signal to form a step-ramp. A step-ramp in frequency is the signal adequate to drive the motoneurons during constant velocity slow phases of nystagmus or pursuit movement. The ramp is presumably achieved by using the same integrator used for "pulse" integration by the rapid eye movement subsystem. A separate integrator is used in generating the slow phases of OKN and OKAN. This integrator also appears to participate in the production of per and post-rotatory nystagmus.

NEURAL MECHANISMS FOR SLOW MOVEMENT GENERATION

How visual-oculomotor information is transmitted to the brainstem is not entirely clear. Pathways in the MRF have been postulated to carry activity responsible for generating both slow and rapid eye movements (125). Descending pathways from the accessory optic system through the inferior olive ending in the flocculus (140); descending pathways from the visual system to the prepositus nucleus, which are as yet of unknown origin (89); and corticopontine-cerebellar pathways (7, 30, 31) are probably important in initiating and/or maintaining slow eye movements. There are pathways from the superior colliculus to the PPRF and periabducens region (34, 86, 87, 162). However, since unit activity in the colliculus is related to rapid and not to slow eye movements (184, 191, 221), collicular-reticular pathways are probably more closely related to generation of saccades than to production of slow movements.

A great deal more is known about how vestibular information is transmitted to the oculomotor system. [See (26, 27, 29, 39, 40, 126, 127, 160, 161, 219) for reviews of this subject.] Suffice it to say that there are monosynaptic and multisynaptic pathways from the vestibular nuclei to each of the eye-muscle motoneurons. Pathways also exist for activation of the reticular formation of the pons and medulla and adjacent regions of the brainstem and cerebellum.

As previously noted, rostral PPRF neurons do not appear to carry information related either to pursuit movements or to slow phases of nystagmus. Sparks & Sides (193) found rostral PPRF units whose activity was related to pursuit, but the sensitivity of these neurons to position or velocity was low. Few such units have been encountered in other studies of the rostral PPRF (43, 98, 132). Thus although rapid eye movements are probably generated in the rostral PPRF, it is unlikely that slow eye movements are produced there.

However, neurons with activity related to eye position and eye velocity during slow movement are widely distributed in the periabducens region of the caudal PPRF and rostral medulla (116, 132), in the vestibular nuclei (74, 120, 121, 147) and prepositus nucleus (9), and in the flocculus (75, 128–130, 149). Each of these regions has direct or indirect connections to the abducens and oculomotor nuclei and could be associated with the integrators described above. Integration of velocity to position information for producing rapid and slow movements must take place in or close to the final common pathway for horizontal gaze. Therefore, lesions involving this integrator should affect all types of horizontal movements. Lesions in the periabducens region do cause striking changes in conjugate horizontal gaze (35, 42, 56, 78), while vestibular nuclei (208), prepositus (208, 209), or flocculus (206) lesions have less dramatic effects on horizontal eye movements. This suggests that the output of the "pulse-step" and "step-ramp" integration is probably in the periabducens region. Presumably, direct pathways then carry the excitation from the periabducens region to the abducens motoneurons. These same pathways are probably also responsible for exciting internuclear neurons, which in turn cause activation of contralateral medial rectus motoneurons (see the section on Excitatory Pathways, above).

In contrast, the OKN-OKAN integrator appears to be more closely related to the vestibular system and to the prepositus nucleus (47, 204, 208, 209). OKN is irregular and of low velocity after bilateral labyrinthectomy, and OKAN is permanently lost (46, 51, 208, 209, 230). This signifies that the OKN-OKAN integrator is inactivated by the loss of the labyrinths (47). OKN and OKAN are also strongly affected by lesions of the ventral part of the lateral vestibular nucleus, rostral portions of the descending vestibular nucleus, and closely associated regions of the medullary reticular formation including the prepositus nucleus (208, 209). The lesion studies suggest that each of these structures may help to maintain the integrity of the integration process. In accord with this view, unit activity in the vestibular nuclei closely follows slow-phase velocities of OKN and OKAN (212, 213).

Recent unit studies indicate that oculomotor function is more widely represented in the vestibular nuclei. If animals are anesthesized or drowsy, most vestibular nucleus neurons respond primarily to vestibular stimuli (146, 187, 188). However, if animals are alert, a large proportion of cells, especially in the rostral parts of the vestibular nuclei, modulate their firing rates during both slow and rapid eye movement (74, 105, 120, 121, 147). Tonic activity of vestibular nuclei cells is also affected by visual stimulation in accord with the direction of excitation or inhibition associated with angular head movement (96). Linear movements of the visual surround produce similar changes in firing rates of cells that respond to otolith organ excitation (58). Activity of vestibular nuclei cells is related to slow-phase velocity during OKN and OKAN, and also follows slow-phase velocity during per and post-rotary nystagmus (212, 213). These data suggest that the vestibular nuclei are an important area for generating slow eye movements whether from optokinetic or vestibular stimulation.

The prepositus nucleus must also play a role in processing vestibular system signals and in generating slow eye movements. Eye movements are induced by stimulation in the region of the prepositus (108). Baker & Berthoz (10) first showed that prepositus neurons received disynaptic projections from the vestibular nerve. The prepositus also receives fibers from the flocculus (2) and from the NRPO-PC region (87) as well as activity from neck afferents (9) and from the visual system (89). Axons of prepositus neurons project directly to the oculomotor nucleus (10, 87), to the flocculus (1), and to the vestibular nuclei (87). Thus the prepositus has the requisite connections for combining visual, vestibular, and cervical information (10). Burst tonic neurons, associated with both horizontal and vertical slow and fast eye movements, are found in the prepositus (9). Confirming the close association between the prepositus and slow eye movements, slow-phase velocities of OKN and caloric nystagmus are affected by prepositus lesions (208), and OKAN is lost bilaterally after unilateral prepositus destruction (208, 209). The latter finding also suggests a close link between the prepositus nucleus and the OKN-OKAN integrator.

The flocculus is also an important site for visual-vestibular interaction. It receives direct projections from the vestibular nerve (28, 36) and nuclei (26, 27, 29), and from the neck (220), as well as visual input over climbing fiber projections from the inferior olive and accessory optic system (139, 140, 189). In turn floccular Purkinje cells project to the vestibular nuclei (8, 26, 111) and to the prepositus nucleus (2, 26). The oculomotor system can be affected through each of these connections. In the monkey, floccular Purkinje cells are mainly driven by mossy fibers (75, 128–130, 149). Whence these mossy fibers reach to the cerebellum is unknown. Floccular Purkinje cells respond to movements of large areas of the visual fields and saturate at low velocities in the rabbit (189).

Ito (109, 110) originally pointed out that the flocculus might adapt or control the vestibulo-ocular reflex arc by virtue of its neural connections. This has been borne out by subsequent experiments (77, 112). Single unit recordings from Purkinje cells and from axons in the stalk of the flocculus have shown that Purkinje cells receive inputs related to head velocity (128, 129), target velocity (149), eye position (128), and eye velocity (75, 128–130, 149). Based on latency, Miles & Fuller (149) suggest that the flocculus may support pursuit but probably does not initiate it.

During head movement the floccular Purkinje cells are silent. However, if ocular compensation for head movement is suppressed, or if the eyes pursue a moving target without head movement, then Purkinje cells fire (77, 129, 130, 149). Presumably they feed inhibition back onto both the vestibulo-ocular reflex and the oculomotor system to inhibit or sustain slow-phase following. In accord with this idea the velocity of slow phases of OKN is reduced after flocculectomy (206), and visual suppression of caloric or spontaneous nystagmus (205) is reduced or lost (206). OKAN can still be elicited after bilateral flocculectomy (206), which indicates that integrity of the flocculus is not essential for activation of the OKN-OKAN integrator. Changes in gain of the vestibulo-ocular reflex (111, 112) or "plasticity" associated with reversing (82, 83) or magnifying prisms (148) are also probably mediated through the flocculus or associated cerebellar structures.

In summary, the output of the integrator that provides the step-ramp for driving motoneurons during slow movements appears to be located in the periabducens region. Inputs to this region that carry activity responsible for producing slow phases of OKN and vestibular nystagmus come from the vestibular nuclei, as well as from the prepositus nucleus and the flocculus. Descending pathways from the visual system responsible for the organization of smooth pursuit and OKN are still unclear. These should project to the periabducens region as well as to the oculomotor and vestibular systems. Another integrator associated with slow eye movement control has been identified. It is separate from the integrator postulated to lie in the periabducens region and participates in production of OKN and OKAN. It appears to engage neural circuitry in the vestibular nuclei and the adjacent prepositus nucleus, and also appears to participate in production of vestibular nystagmus.

ACKNOWLEDGMENTS

This work was supported by NIH Research Grant NS00294. T. Raphan was supported by NINCDS Fellowship NS 52970.

Literature Cited

1. Alley, K., Baker, R., Simpson, J. I. 1975. Afferents to the vestibulo-cerebellum and the origin of the visual climbing fibers in the rabbit. *Brain Res.* 98:582–89
2. Angaut, P., Brodal, A. 1967. The projection of the vestibulo cerebellum onto the vestibular nuclei in the cat. *Arch. Ital. Biol.* 105:441–79
3. Atkin, A., Bender, M. B. 1968. Ocular stabilization during oscillatory head movements. *Arch. Neurol. Chic.* 19:559–66
4. Bach-y-Rita, P., Ito, F. 1966. In vivo studies on fast and slow muscle fibers in cat extraocular muscles. *J. Gen. Physiol.* 49:1177–98
5. Bach-y-Rita, P. 1971. Neurophysiology of eye movements. In *The Control of Eye Movements*, ed. P. Bach-y-Rita, C. C. Collins, J. E. Hyde, pp. 7–45. New York: Academic
6. Bahill, A. T., Clark, M. R., Stark, L. 1975. Dynamic overshoot in saccadic eye movements is caused by neurological control signal reversals. *Exp. Neurol.* 48:107–22
7. Baker, J., Gibson, A., Glickstein, M., Stein, J. 1976. Visual cells in the pontine nuclei of the cat. *J. Physiol. London.* 225:415–33
8. Baker, R., Precht, W., Llinas, R. 1972. Cerebellar modulatory action of the vestibulo-trochlear pathway in the cat. *Exp. Brain Res.* 15:364–85
9. Baker, R., Gresty, M., Berthoz, A. 1975. Neural activity in the prepositus hypoglossi nucleus correlated with vertical and horizontal eye movement in the cat. *Brain Res.* 101:366–71
10. Baker, R., Berthoz, A. 1975. Is the prepositus hypoglossi the source of another vestibulo-ocular pathway? *Brain Res.* 86:121–27
11. Baker, R., Highstein, S. M. 1975. Physiological identification of interneurons and motoneurons in the abducens nucleus. *Brain Res.* 91:292–98
12. Baker, R., Highstein, S. M. 1976. Vestibular projections to medial rectus motoneurons in the cat. *Neurosci. Soc. Abstr.* 6:226
13. Barmack, N. H. 1970. Modification of eye movements by instantaneous changes in the velocity of visual targets. *Vision Res.* 10:1431–41
14. Barnes, G. R., Benson, A. J. 1973. A model for the prediction of the nystagmic response to angular and linear acceleration stimuli. *AGARD Conf. Proc. Use of Nystagmography in Aviation Medicine*, pp. a-23-1 to a23-13
15. Becker, W., Fuchs, A. F. 1969. Further properties of the human saccadic system: Eye movements and correction saccades with and without visual fixation points. *Vision Res.* 9:1247–58
16. Becker, W., Klein, H. 1973. Accuracy of saccadic eye movements and maintenance of eccentric eye positions in the dark. *Vision Res.* 13:1021–34
17. Becker, W., Jürgens, R. 1975. Saccadic reactions to double-step stimuli: evidence for model feedback and continuous information uptake. In *Basic Mechanisms of Ocular Motility and Their Clinical Implications*, ed. G. Lennerstrand, P. Bach-Y-Rita, pp. 519–24. Oxford: Pergamon
18. Bender, M. B., Weinstein, E. A. 1944. Effects of stimulation and lesion of the medial longitudinal fasciculus in the monkey. *Arch. Neurol. Psychiatry* 52:106–13
19. Bender, M. B., Weinstein, E. A. 1950. The syndrome of the medial longitudinal fasciculus. *Proc. Assoc. Res. Nerv. Ment. Dis.* 28:414–20
20. Bender, M. B. 1960. Comments on the physiology and pathology of eye movements in the vertical plane. *J. Nerv. Ment. Dis.* 130:456–66
21. Bender, M. B., Shanzer, S. 1964. Oculomotor pathways defined by electric stimulation and lesions in the brainstem of the monkey. In *The Oculomotor System*, ed. M. B. Bender, pp. 81–140. New York: Harper & Row
22. Bizzi, E. 1968. Discharge of frontal eye field neurons during saccadic and following eye movements in unanesthetized monkeys. *Exp. Brain Res.* 10:69–80
23. Bizzi, E., Kalil, R. E., Tagliasco, V. 1971. Eye-head coordination in monkeys: evidence for centrally patterned organization. *Science.* 173:452–54

23a. Blanks, R. H. I., Volkind, R., Precht, W., Baker, R. 1977. Responses of cat prepositus hypoglossi neurons to horizontal angular acceleration. *Neuroscience.* 2:391–403

24. Brandt, T., Dichgans, J., Koenig, E. 1973. Differential effects of central versus peripheral vision on egocentric and exocentric motion perception. *Exp. Brain Res.* 16:476–91

25. Brandt, T., Dichgans, J., Büchele, W. 1974. Inverted self motion perception and optokinetic after-nystagmus. *Exp. Brain Res.* 21:337–52

26. Brodal, A. 1974. Anatomy of the vestibular nuclei and their connections. See Ref. 126, pp. 239–352

27. Brodal, A., Pompeiano, D., Walberg, S. 1962. *The Vestibular Nuclei and Their Connections, Anatomy and Functional Correlations.* Springfield, Ill: Thomas. 193 pp.

28. Brodal, A., Hodivik, G. 1964. Site and mode of termination of primary vestibulo cerebellar fibers in the cat. *Arch. Ital. Biol.* 102:1–21

29. Brodal, A., Pompeiano, D. 1972. Basic aspects of central vestibular mechanisms. *Prog. Brain Res.* 37:1–656

30. Brodal, P., 1972. The corticopontine projection from the visual cortex of the cat. I. The total projection and the projection from area 17. *Brain Res.* 39:297–317

31. Brodal, P. 1972. The corticopontine projection from the visual cortex of the cat. II. The projection area 18 and 19. *Brain Res.* 39:319–35

32. Buettner-Ennever, J. A., Henn, V. 1977. An autoradiographic study of the pathways from the pontine reticular formation involved in horizontal eye movements. *Brain Res.* 108:155–64

33. Buettner, U., Buettner-Ennever, J. A., Henn, V. 1977. Vertical eye movement related unit activity in the rostral mesencephalic reticular formation of the alert monkey. *Brain Res.* 130:234–52

34. Cajal, S. B. 1909–1911. *Histologie du Systeme Nerveux de l'Homme et des Vertebres.* Paris: Maloine. 993 pp.

35. Carpenter, M. B., McMasters, R. E., Hanna, G. R. 1963. Disturbances of conjugate horizontal eye movements in the monkey. *Arch. Neurol. Chic.* 8: 231–47

36. Carpenter, M. B., Stein, B. M., Peter, P. 1972. Primary vestibulo cerebellar fibers in the monkey. *Am. J. Anat.* 135: 221–50

37. Carpenter, R. H. S. 1972. Cerebellectomy and the transfer function of the vestibulo-ocular reflex in the decere-

brate cat. *Proc. R. Soc. London Ser. B.* 181:353–74

38. Childress, D. S., Jones, R. W. 1967. Mechanics of horizontal movement in the human eye. *J. Physiol. London.* 188: 273–84

38a. Christoff, N. 1974. A clinico-pathological study of vertical eye movements. *Arch. Neurol. Chic.* 31:1–8

39. Cohen, B. 1971. Vestibulo-ocular relations. See Ref. 5, pp. 105–48

40. Cohen, B. 1974. The vestibulo-ocular reflex arc. See Ref. 126, pp. 477–550

41. Cohen, B., Feldman, M. 1968. Relationship of electrical activity in pontine recticular formation and lateral geniculate body to rapid eye movements. *J. Neurophysiol.* 31:806–17

42. Cohen, B., Komatsuzaki, A., Bender, M. B. 1968. Electrooculographic syndrome in monkeys after pontine reticular lesions. *Arch. Neurol. Chic.* 18: 78–92

43. Cohen, B., Henn, V. 1972. Unit activity in the pontine reticular formation associated with eye movements. *Brain Res.* 46:403–10

44. Cohen, B., Henn, V. 1972. The origin of quick phases of nystagmus in the horizontal plane. *Bibl. Ophthalmol.* 82: 36–55

45. Cohen, B., Komatsuzaki, A. 1972. Eye movements induced by stimulation of the pontine reticular formation: evidence for integration in oculomotor pathways. *Exp. Neurol.* 36:101–117

46. Cohen, B., Uemura, T., Takemori, S. 1973. Effects of labyrinthectomy on optokinetic nystagmus (OKN) and optokinetic after-nystagmus (OKAN). *Int. J. Equil. Res.* 3:88–93

47. Cohen, B., Matsuo, V., Raphan, T. 1977. Quantitative analysis of the velocity characteristics of optokinetic nystagmus and optokinetic after-nystagmus. *J. Physiol. London.* 270:321–44

48. Collewijn, H. 1969. Optokinetic eye movements in the rabbit: input output relations. *Vision Res.* 9:117–32

49. Collewijn, H. 1972. Latency and gain of the rabbit's optokinetic reactions to small movements. *Brain Res.* 36: 59–72

50. Collewijn, H. 1972. An analog model of the rabbit's optokinetic system. *Brain Res.* 36:71–88

51. Collewijn, H. 1976. Impairment of optokinetic (after) nystagmus by labyrinthectomy in the rabbit. *Exp. Neurol.* 52:146–56

52. Collewijn, H., Van Der Mark, F. 1972. Ocular stability in variable visual feed-

back conditions in the rabbit. *Brain Res.* 36:47–57

53. Collins, C. C. 1971. Orbital mechanics. See Ref. 5, pp. 283–325

54. Collins, C. C. 1975. The human oculomotor control system. See Ref. 17, pp. 145–80

55. Cook, G., Stark, L. 1967. Derivation of a model for the human eye positioning mechanism. *Bull. Math. Biophys.* 29: 153–74

56. Crosby, E. C. 1953. Relations of brain centers to normal and abnormal movements in the horizontal plane. *J. Comp. Neurol.* 99:437–73

57. Dallos, P. J., Jones, R. W. 1963. Learning behavior of the eye fixation control system. *IEEE Trans. Autom. Control.* AC-8:218–27

58. Daunton, N. G., Thomson, D. D. 1976. Otolith-visual interaction in single units of cat vestibular nuclei *Neurosci. Soc. Abstr.* 6:1057

59. Dichgans, J., Bizzi, E., Morasso, P., Tagliasco, V. 1973. Mechanisms underlying recovery of eye-head coordination following bilateral labyrinthectomy in monkeys. *Exp. Brain Res.* 18:548–62

60. Dodge, R. 1903. Five types of eye movements in the horizontal meridian plane of the field of regard. *Am J. Physiol.* 8:307–29

61. Duensing, F., Schaefer, K. P. 1957. Die Neuronenaktivität in der Formatio reticularis des Rhombencephalons beim vestibulären Nystagmus. *Arch. Psychiatr. Nervenkr.* 196:265–90

62. Duensing, F., Schaefer, K. P. 1958. Die Aktivität einzelner Neurone im Bereich der Vestibulariskerne bei Horizontalbeschleunigungen unter besonderer Berücksichtigung des vestibulären Nystagmus. *Arch. Psychiatr. Nervenkr.* 198:225–52

63. Duensing, F., Schaefer, K. P. 1957. Die "locker gekoppelten" Neurone der Formatio reticularis des Rhombencephalons beim vestibulären Nystagmus *Arch. Psychiatr. Nervenkr.* 196:402–20

64. Egmond, A. A. J., Van Groen, J. J., Jonkees, L. B. W. 1949. The mechanism of the semicircular canal. *J. Physiol. London* 110:1–17

65. Evarts, E. V. 1966. Pyramidal tract activity associated with conditioned hand movement in the monkey. *J. Neurophysiol.* 29:1011–27

66. Evinger, L. C., Fuchs, A. F., Baker, R. 1977. Bilateral lesions of the medial longitudinal fasciculus in monkeys. *Exp. Brain Res.* 28:1–20

67. Fender, D. 1971. Time delays in the hu-

man eye tracking system. See Ref. 5, pp. 539–43

68. Fender, D. H., Nye, P. W. 1961. An investigation of the mechanisms of eye movement control. *Kybernetik* 1: 81–88

69. Fernandez, C., Goldberg, J. M. 1971. Physiology of peripheral neurons innervating semicircular canals of the squirrel monkey. II. Response to sinusoidal stimulation and dynamics of peripheral vestibular system. *J. Neurophysiol.* 34:661–75

70. Freeman, W. 1922. Paralysis of associated lateral movements of the eyes. *Arch. Neurol. Psychiatry.* 7:454–87

71. Fuchs, A. F. 1967. Saccadic and smooth pursuit eye movements in the monkey. *J. Physiol. London* 191:609–31

72. Fuchs, A. F. 1971. The saccadic system. See Ref. 5, pp. 343–62

73. Fuchs, A. F., Luschei, E. S. 1970. Firing patterns of abducens neurons of alert monkeys in relationship to horizontal eye movements. *J. Neurophysiol.* 33:382–92

74. Fuchs, A. F., Kimm, J. O. 1975. Vestibular unit activity related to eye movements in the monkey. *J. Neurophysiol.* 38:1140–61

75. Fuchs, A. F., Lisberger, S. G. 1975. Response of flocculus purkinje cells during smooth pursuit eye movements. *Neurosci. Soc. Abstr.* 5:209

76. Gacek, R. R. 1971. Anatomical demonstration of the vestibulo-ocular projections in the cat. *Acta Oto-Laryngol. (Suppl.)* 293:1–63

77. Ghelarducci, B., Ito, M., Yagi, N. 1975. Impulse discharges from flocculus purkinje cells of alert rabbits during visual stimulation combined with horizontal head rotation. *Brain Res.* 87:66–72

78. Goebel, H., Komatsuzaki, A., Bender, M. B., Cohen, B. 1971. Lesions of the pontine tegmentum and conjugate gaze paralysis. *Arch. Neurol. Chic.* 24: 431–40

79. Gogan, P., Gueritaud, J. P., Horcholle-Bossavit, G., Tyc-Dumont, S. 1973. Inhibitory nystagmic interneurons: Physiological and anatomical identification within the abducens nucleus. *Brain Res.* 59:410–16

80. Goldberg, J. M., Fernandez, C. 1971. Physiology of peripheral neurons innervating semicircular canals of the squirrel monkey I. Resting discharge and response to constant angular accelerations. *J. Neurophysiol.* 34:635–60

81. Goldberg, J. M., Fernandez, C. 1971. Physiology of peripheral neurons innervating semicircular canals of the squir-

rel monkey III. Variations among units in their discharge properties. *J. Neurophysiol.* 34:676–84

82. Gonshor, A., Jones, G. M. 1976. Short term adaptive changes in the human vestibulo-ocular reflex arc. *J. Physiol. London* 256:361–79

83. Gonshor, A., Jones, G. M. 1976. Extreme vestibulo-ocular adaption induced by prolonged optical reversal of vision *J. Physiol. London* 256:381–414

84. Grant, K., Gueritaud, J. P., Horcholle-Bossavit, G., Tyc-Dumont, S. 1976. Horizontal vestibular nystagmus I. Identification of medial vestibular neurons. *Exp. Brain Res.* 26:67–86

85. Grant, K., Gueritaud, J. P., Horcholle-Bossavit, G., Tyc-Dumont, S. 1976. Horizontal vestibular nystagmus II. Activity patterns of medial vestibular neurons during nystagmus. *Exp. Brain Res.* 26:387–405

86. Grantyn, A. A., Grantyn, R. 1976. Synaptic actions of tectofugal pathways on abducens motoneurons in the cat. *Brain Res.* 105:269–85

87. Graybiel, A. 1977. Direct and indirect preoculomotor pathways of the brainstem: An autoradiographic study of the pontine reticular formation in the cat. *J. Comp. Neurol.* 175:37–78

88. Graybiel, A. M., Hartwieg, E. A. 1974. Some afferent connections of the oculomotor complex in the cat: An experimental study with tracer techniques. *Brain Res.* 81:543–51

89. Gresty, M., Baker, R. 1976. Neurons with visual receptive field eye movement and neck displacement sensitivity within and around the prepositus nucleus in the alert cat. *Exp. Brain Res.* 24:429–33

90. Gruettner, R. 1939. Experimentelle Untersuchungen über den optokinetischen Nystagmus. *Z. Sinnephysiol.* 68:1–48

91. Hallet, P. E., Lightstone, A. D. 1976. Saccadic eye movement towards stimuli triggered by prior saccades. *Vision Res.* 16:99–106

92. Hallet, P. E., Lightstone, A. D. 1976. Saccadic eye movements to flashed targets. *Vision Res.* 16:107–14

93. Helmholtz, H. von. 1866. Handbuch der Physiologischen Optik. Leipzig: Voss. 874 pp.

94. Henn, V., Cohen, B. 1972. Eye muscle motoneurons with different functional characteristics. *Brain Res.* 45:561–68

95. Henn, V., Cohen, B. 1973. Quantitative analysis of activity in eye muscle motoneurons during saccadic eye movements and positions of fixation. *J. Neurophysiol.* 36:115–26

96. Henn, V., Young, L. R., Finley, C. 1974. Vestibular nucleus units in alert monkeys are also influenced by moving visual fields. *Brain Res.* 71:144–49

97. Henn, V., Cohen, B. 1975. Activity in eye muscle motoneurons and brainstem units during eye movements. See Ref. 17, pp. 303–24

98. Henn, V., Cohen, B., 1976. Coding of information about rapid eye movements in the pontine reticular formation of alert monkeys. *Brain Res.* 108:307–25

99. Hering, E. 1868. *Die Lehre vom Binokularen Sehen.* Leipzig: Engelmann. 146 pp.

100. Highstein, S. M., Cohen, B., Matsunami, K. 1974. Monosynaptic projections from the pontine reticular formation to the IIIrd nucleus in the cat. *Brain Res.* 75:340–44

101. Highstein, S. M., Maekawa, K., Steinacker, A., Cohen, B. 1976. Synaptic input from the pontine reticular nuclei to abducens motoneurons and internuclear neurons. *Brain Res.* 112:162–67

102. Highstein, S. M., Baker, R. 1976. Termination of internuclear neurons of the abducens nuclei on medial rectus motoneurons. *Neurosci. Soc. Abstr.* 2:278

103. Hikosaka, O., Kawami, T. 1977. Inhibitory reticular neurons related to the quick phase of vestibular nystagmus—their location and projection. *Exp. Brain Res.* 27:377–96

104. Hikosaka, O., Maeda, M., Nakao, S., Shimazu, H., Shinoda, Y. 1977. Presynaptic impulses in the abducens nucleus and their relation to postsynaptic potentials in motoneurons during vestibular nystagmus. *Exp. Brain Res.* 27:355–76

105. Horcholle, G., Tyc-Dumont, S. 1968. Activités unitaires des neurones vestibulaires et oculomoteurs au cours du nystagmus. *Exp. Brain Res.* 5:16–31

106. Horcholle-Bossavit, G., Tyc-Dumont, S. 1969. Phénoménes synaptiques du nystagmus. *Exp. Brain Res.* 8:201–18

107. Hoyt, W. F., Daroff, R. B. 1971. Supranuclear disorders of ocular control systems in man. Clinical, anatomical, and physiological correlations. See Ref. 5, pp. 175–236

108. Hyde, J. E., Eliasson, S. G. 1957. Brainstem induced eye movements in cats. *J. Comp. Neurol.* 108:139–72

109. Ito, M. 1970. Neurophysiological aspects of the cerebellar motor control system. *Int. J. Neurol.* 7:162–76

110. Ito, M. 1972. Neural design of the cerebellar motor control systems. *Brain Res.* 40:81–85

111. Ito, M., Nisimaru, N., Yamamoto, M. 1973. Specific neural connections for the cerebellar control of vestibulo-ocular reflexes. *Brain Res.* 60:238–43

112. Ito, M., Shiida, T., Yagi, N., Yamamoto, M. 1974. Visual influence on rabbit horizontal vestibulo-ocular reflex presumably effected via the cerebellar flocculus. *Brain Res.* 65: 170–74

113. Jacobs, L., Anderson, P. J., Bender, M. B. 1973. The lesion producing paralysis of downward but not upward gaze. *Arch. Neurol. Chic.* 28:319–23

114. Jung, R. 1948. Die Registrierung des post-rotarischen und optokinetischen Nystagmus und die optisch-vestibuläre Integration beim Menschen. *Acta Oto-Laryngol.* 67:535–51

115. Jung, R., Kornhuber, H. H. 1964. Results of electronystagmography in man. See Ref. 21, pp. 428–82

116. Keller, E. L. 1974. Participation of medial pontine reticular formation in eye movement generation in monkey. *J. Neurophysiol.* 37:316–32

117. Keller, E. L. 1976. Gain of the vestibulo-ocular reflex in monkey at high rotational frequencies. *Neurosci. Soc. Abstr.* 6:279

118. Keller, E. L., Robinson, D. A. 1971. Absence of stretch reflex in the extraocular muscles on the monkey. *J. Neurophysiol.* 34:908–19

119. Keller, E. L., Robinson, D. A. 1972. Abducens unit behavior in the monkey during vergence movements. *Vision Res.* 12:369–82

120. Keller, E. L., Daniels, P. D. 1975. Oculomotor related interaction of vestibular and visual stimulation in vestibular nucleus cells in alert monkey. *Exp. Neurol.* 46:187–98

121. Keller, E. L., Kamath, B. Y. 1975. Characteristics of head rotation and eye movement related neurons in alert monkey vestibular nucleus. *Brain Res.* 100: 182–87

122. King, W. M., Lisberger, S. G., Fuchs, A. F. 1976. Responses of fibers in medial longitudinal fasciculus (MLF) of alert monkeys during horizontal and vertical conjugate eye movements evoked by vestibular or visual stimuli. *J. Neurophysiol.* 39:1135–49

123. Koempf, D., Pasik, T., Pasik, P. 1977. Critical structures for downward gaze in monkeys. *Neurosci. Abstr.* 3: 156

124. Koerner, F., Schiller, P. H. 1972. The optokinetic response under open and closed loop conditions in the monkey. *Exp. Brain Res.* 14:318–30

125. Komatsuzaki, A., Alpert, J., Harris, H. E., Cohen, B. 1972. Effect of mesencephalic reticular formation lesions on optokinetic nystagmus. *Exp. Neurol.* 34: 522–34

126. Kornhuber, H. H. 1974. *Handbook of Sensory Physiology, Vol. VI/1, Vestibular System, Part I: Basic Mechanisms.* Berlin: Springer

127. Kornhuber, H. H. 1974. *Handbook of Sensory Physiology, Vol. VI/2, Vestibular System, Part II: Psychophysics, Applied Aspects, and General Interpretations.* Berlin: Springer

128. Lisberger, S. G. *Responses of flocculus purkinje cells and mossy fibers during smooth eye movements evoked by visual and vestibular stimuli in behaving monkey.* Ph.D. Thesis. Univ. Washington. Seattle, Washington. 164 pp. 1976

129. Lisberger, S. G., Fuchs, A. F. 1974. Response of flocculus purkinje cells to adequate vestibular stimulation in the alert monkey: Fixation vs. compensatory eye movements. *Brain Res.* 69:347–53

130. Lisberger, S. G., Fuchs, A. F. 1975. Responses of flocculus purkinje cells to interactions of smooth pursuit eye movements and natural vestibular rotation. *Neurosci. Soc. Abstr.* 5:208

131. Lorente de Nó, R. 1933. Vestibulo-ocular reflex arc. *Arch. Neurol. Psychiatry* 30:245–91

132. Luschei, E. S., Fuchs, A. F. 1972. Activity of brainstem neurons during eye movements of alert monkeys. *J. Neurophysiol.* 35:455–61

133. Mach, E. 1875. *Grundlinien der Lehre von den Bewegungsempfindungen.* Leipzig: Engelmann

134. Mackensen, G. 1954. Untersuchungen zur Physiologie des optokinetischen Nystagmus. *Albrecht von Graefes Arch. Ophthalmol.* 155: 284–313

135. Mackensen, G. 1958. Die Geschwindigkeit horizontaler Blickbewegungen. *Albrecht von Graefes Arch. Ophthalmol.* 160:47–64

136. Mackensen, G., Schumacher, J. 1960. Die Geschwindigkeit der raschen Phase des optokinetischen Nystagmus. *Albrecht von Graefes Arch. Ophthalmol.* 162:400–415

137. Maeda, M., Shimazu, H., Shinoda, Y. 1971. Rhythmic activity of secondary vestibular efferent fibers recorded within the abducens nucleus during ves-

tibular nystagmus. *Brain Res.* 34:
361–65

138. Maeda, M., Shimazu, H., Shinoda, Y.
1972. Nature of synaptic events in cat
abducens motoneurons at slow and
quick phases of vestibular nystagmus. *J.
Neurophysiol.* 35:279–96

139. Maekawa, K., Natsui, T. 1973. Climbing fiber activation of purkinje cells in
rabbit flocculus during light stimulation
of the retina. *Brain Res.* 59:417–20

140. Maekawa, K., Simpson, J. I. 1973.
Climbing fiber responses evoked in vestibulo cerebellum of rabbit from visual
system. *J. Neurophysiol.* 36:649–66

141. Manni, E., Giretti, M. L. 1970. Central
eye nystagmus in the ponto mesencephalic preparation. *Exp. Neurol.* 26:
342–53

142. McMasters, R. R., Weiss, A. H., Carpenter, M. B. 1966. Vestibular projections to the nuclei of the extraocular
muscles. *Am. J. Anat.* 118:163–94

143. Meiry, J. 1971. Vestibular and proprioceptive stabilization of eye movements. See Ref. 5, pp. 483–96

144. Melvill Jones, G., Milsum, J. H. 1965.
Spatial and dynamic aspects of visual
fixation. *IEEE Trans. Biomed. Eng.*
BME-12:54–62

145. Melvill Jones, G. 1971. Organization of
neural control in the vestibulo-ocular
reflex arc. See Ref. 5, pp. 497–518

146. Melvill Jones, G., Milsum, J. H. 1971.
Frequency response analysis of central
vestibular unit activity resulting from
rotational stimulation of the semicircular canals. *J. Physiol. London* 219:191–
215

147. Miles, F. A. 1974. Single unit firing patterns in the vestibular nuclei related to
voluntary eye movements and passive
body rotation in conscious monkeys.
Brain Res. 71:215–24

148. Miles, F. A., Fuller, J. H. 1974. Adaptive plasticity in the vestibulo-ocular responses of the rhesus monkey. *Brain
Res.* 80:512–16

149. Miles, F. A., Fuller, J. H. 1975. Visual
tracking and the primate flocculus.
Science 189:1000–1002

150. Mowrer, O. H. 1937. The influence of
vision during bodily rotation upon the
duration of post-rotational vestibular
nystagmus. *Acta Oto-Laryngol.* 25:
351–64

151. Murphy, B. J., Kowler, E., Steinman,
R. M. 1975. Slow oculomotor control in
the presence of moving backgrounds.
Vision Res. 15:1263–68

152. Ohm, J. 1926. Ist der optische Drehnys-
tagmus von einem unbeweglichen Auge

auslösbar? *Klin. Monatsbl. Augen-
heilkd.* 21:330–36

153. Oyster, C. W. 1968. The analysis of im-
age motion by the rabbit retina. *J.
Physiol. London* 199:613–35

154. Oyster, C. W., Barlow, H. B. 1967. Direction selective units in the rabbit
retina: Distribution of preferred directions. *Science* 155:841–42

155. Pasik, T., Pasik, P., Bender, M. B. 1969.
The pretectal syndrome in monkeys. I.
Disturbances of gaze and body posture.
Brain 92: 521–34

156. Pasik, T., Pasik, P., Bender, M. B. 1969.
The pretectal syndrome in monkeys. II.
Spontaneous and induced nystagmus
and "lightning" eye movements. *Brain*
92:871–84

157. Peachey, L. 1971. The structure of the
extraocular muscle fibers of mammals.
See Ref. 5, pp. 47–63

158. Perenin, M. T., Maeda, T., Jeannerod,
M. 1972. Are the vestibular nuclei responsible for rapid eye movements of
paradoxical sleep? *Brain Res.* 43:
617–21

159. Plum, P., Posner, J. 1966. *Diagnosis of
Stupor and Coma.* Philadelphia: Davis.
286 pp.

160. Precht, W. 1974. The physiology of the
vestibular nuclei. See Ref. 126, pp. 353–
416

161. Precht, W. 1975. Vestibular system. In
*MTP International Review of Sciences,
Neurophysiology, Physiol. Ser. 1. Vol. 3,*
ed. A. C. Guyton, C. C. Hunt, pp. 82–
149. London: Butterworths; Baltimore:
University Park Press

162. Precht, W., Schwindt, P. C., Magherini,
P. C. 1974. Tectal influences on cat
oculomotor motoneurons. *Brain Res.*
82:27–40

163. Pola, J. 1974. MLF fiber activity in
monkey during visually elicited and vestibular eye movement. *Neurosci. Abstr.*
4:377

164. Raphan, T. 1976. *A parameter adaptive
approach to oculomotor system modeling.* Ph.D. Thesis. City Univ. New
York, New York. 220 pp.

165. Raphan, T., Cohen, B., Mekel, R. 1975.
Modeling of neuronal activity in the
pontine recticular formation (PRF) responsible for generation of rapid eye
movements. *Neurosci. Soc. Abstr.* 5:229

166. Raphan, T., Cohen, B., Matsuo, V.
1978. A velocity-storage mechanism for
optokinetic nystagmus (OKN), optokinetic after-nystagmus (OKAN) and
vestibular nystagmus. In *Control
of Gaze by Brainstem Interneurons,*

ed. A. Berthoz, R. Baker. Amsterdam: Elsevier. In press
167. Rashbass, C. 1961. The relationship between saccadic and smooth tracking eye movements. *J. Physiol. London* 159: 326–38
168. Raybourn, M., Keller, E. L. 1976. Differential colliculo reticular organization in the primate oculomotor system. *Arvo Abstr.* 2:59
169. Robinson, D. A. 1964. The mechanics of human saccadic eye movement. *J. Physiol. London* 174:245–64
170. Robinson, D. A. 1965. The mechanics of human smooth pursuit eye movement. *J. Physiol. London* 180:569–91
171. Robinson, D. A. 1968. The oculomotor control system: a review. *Proc. IEEE* 56:1032–49
172. Robinson, D. A. 1970. Oculomotor unit behavior in the monkey. *J. Neurophysiol.* 23:393–404
173. Robinson, D. A. 1971. Models of oculomotor organization. See Ref. 5, pp. 519–38
174. Robinson, D. A. 1973. Models of saccadic eye movement control system. *Kybernetik* 14:71–83
175. Robinson, D. A. 1974. Cerebellectomy and the vestibulo-ocular reflex arc. *Brain Res.* 71:215–24
176. Robinson, D. A. 1975. Oculomotor control signals. See Ref. 17, pp. 337–74
177. Robinson, D. A., Keller, E. L. 1972. The behavior of eye movement motoneurons in the alert monkey. *Bibl. Ophthalmol.* 82:7–16
178. Robinson, D. A. 1975. How signals are processed in the vestibulo-ocular reflex. *Int. J. Equil. Res.* 1 (Suppl.: Proc. Barany Society. Kyoto.):130–41
179. Ron, S., Robinson, D. A., Skavenski, A. A. 1972. Saccades and the quick phases of nystagmus. *Vision Res.* 12:2105–10
180. Sasaki, K. 1963. Electrophysiological studies on oculomotor neurons of the cat. *Jpn. J. Physiol.* 13:287–302
181. Schaefer, K. P. 1965. Die Erregungsmuster einzelner Neurone des Abducens-Kernes beim Kaninchen. *Pfluegers Arch.* 184:31–52
182. Scheibel, M. E., Scheibel, A. B. 1958. Structural substrates for integrative patterns in the brain stem reticular core. In *Recticular Formation of the Brain*, ed. H. H. Jasper et al, pp. 31–55. Boston: Little Brown
183. Schiller, P. H. 1970. The discharge characteristics of single units in the oculomotor and abducens nuclei of the unanesthetized monkey. *Exp. Brain Res.* 10:347–62

184. Schiller, P. H., Koerner, D. 1971. Discharge characteristics of single units in superior colliculus of the alert rhesus monkey. *J. Neurophysiol.* 34:920–36
185. Shanzer, S., Goto, K., Cohen, B., Bender, M. B. 1964. Median longitudinal fasciculus and vertical eye movements. *Trans. Am. Neurol. Assoc.* 89: 155–54
186. Shimazu, H. 1972. Vestibulo-oculomotor relations: Dynamic responses. *Prog. Brain Res.* 37:493–506
187. Shimazu, H., Precht, W. 1965. Tonic and kinetic responses of cats vestibular neurons to horizontal angular acceleration. *J. Neurophysiol.* 28:991–1013
188. Shimazu, H., Precht, W. 1966. Inhibition of vestibular neurons from the contralateral labyrinth and its mediating pathway. *J. Neurophysiol.* 29:467–92
189. Simpson, J. I., Alley, K. E. 1974. Visual climbing fiber input to rabbit vestibulo cerebellum: a source of direction specific information. *Brain Res.* 82:302–8
190. Skavenski, A. A., Robinson, D. A. 1973. Role of abducens motoneurons in the vestibulo-ocular reflex. *J. Neurophysiol.* 36:724–38
191. Sparks, D. L. 1975. Response properties of eye movement related neurons in monkey superior colliculus. *Brain Res.* 90:147–52
192. Sparks, D. L., Tavis, R. P. 1971. Firing patterns of reticular formation neurons during horizontal eye movements. *Brain Res.* 33:477–81
193. Sparks, D. L., Sides, J. P. 1974. Brain stem unit activity related to horizontal eye movements occuring during visual tracking. *Brain Res.* 77:320–25
194. Speigel, E. A., Price, J. B. 1939. Orgin of the quick component of labyrinthine nystagmus. *Arch. Oto-Laryngol.* 30: 576–88
195. Sperry, R. W. 1950. Neural basis of the spontaneous optokinetic response produced by visual inversion. *J. Comp. Physiol. Psychol.* 43:482–89
196. Spiller, W. G. 1924. Ophthalmoplegia internuclearis anterior: a case with necropsy. *Brain* 47:345–57
197. Stark, L., Vossius, G., Young, L. R. Predictive control of eye movements *IRE Trans. Human Factors in Electron.* HFE-3:52–57
198. Stark, L. 1971. The control system for versional eye movements. See Ref. 5, pp. 363–428
199. Steinhausen, W. 1933. Über die Beobachtung der Cupula in den Bogengangsampullen des Labyrinthes des leb-

enden Hechts. *Pflugers Arch.* 232:500–512

200. Sugie, N., Melvill Jones, G. 1971. A model of eye movements induced by head rotation. *IEEE Trans. Syst. Man Cybern.* SMC-1:251–60

201. Suzuki, J., Cohen, B. 1966. Integration of semicircular canal function. *J. Neurophysiol.* 29:981–95

202. Szentagothai, J. 1950. The elementary vestibulo-ocular reflex arc. *J. Neurophysiol.* 13:395–407

203. Szentagothai, J. 1964. Pathways and synaptic articulation patterns connecting vestibular receptors and oculomotor nuclei. See Ref. 21, pp. 205–23

204. Takemori, S. 1974. The similarities of optokinetic after-nystagmus to the vestibular nystagmus. *Ann. Otol. Rhinol. Laryngol.* 83:230–38

205. Takemori, S., Cohen, B. 1974. Visual suppression of vestibular nystagmus in rhesus monkeys. *Brain Res.* 72:203–38

206. Takemori, S., Cohen, B. 1974, Loss of visual suppression of vestibular nystagmus after flocculus lesions. *Brain Res.* 72:213–24

207. Ter Braak, J. W. G. 1936. Untersuchungen über optokinetischen Nystagmus. *Arch. Neerl. Physiol.* 21:309–76

208. Uemura, T., Cohen, B. 1973. Effects of vestibular nuclei lesions on vestibuloocular reflexes and posture in monkeys. *Acta Oto-Laryngol.* 315 (Suppl.):1–71

209. Uemura, T., Cohen, B. 1975. Loss of optokinetic after-nystagmus after dorsal medullary reticular formation (Medrf) lesions. *Int. J. Equil. Res.* 1(Suppl.: Proc. Barany Society. Kyoto.):101–85

210. Viviani, P., Berthoz, A., Tracey, D. 1977. The curvature of oblique saccades. *Vision Res.* 17:661–64

211. Von Holst, E., Mittelstaedt, H. 1950. Das Reafferenzprincip. *Naturwissenschaften* 37:464–76

212. Waespe, W., Henn, V. 1977. Neuronal activity in the vestibular nuclei of the alert monkey during vestibular and optokinetic stimulation. *Exp. Brain Res.* 27:523–38

213. Waespe, W., Henn, V. 1976. Behavior of secondary vestibular units during optokinetic nystagmus and after-nystagmus in alert monkeys. *Pfleugers Arch.* 362:R50

214. Weber, R. B., Daroff, B. 1972. Corrective movements following refixation saccades: type and control system analysis. *Vision Res.* 12:467–75

215. Westheimer, G. 1954. Mechanism of saccadic eye movement. *AMA Arch. Ophthalmol.* 52:710–24

216. Westheimer, G. 1954. Eye movement responses to a horizontally moving visual stimulus. *AMA. Arch. Ophthalmol.* 52:932–41

217. Westheimer, G. 1971. Discussion of control of eye vergence movements. See Ref. 5, 473–82

218. Wheeless, L. L., Boynton, R. M., Cohen, G. H. 1966. Eye movement responses to step and pulse step stimuli. *J. Opt. Soc. Am.* 56:956–60

219. Wilson, V. J. 1972. Physiological pathways through the vestibular nuclei. *Int. Rev. Neurobiol.* 15:27–81

220. Wilson, V. J., Maeda, M., Franck, J. I. 1975. Inputs from neck afferents to the cat flocculus. *Brain Res.* 89:133–38

221. Wurtz, R. H., Goldberg, M. E. 1971. Superior colliculus cell responses related to eye movement in awake monkeys. *Science* 171:82–84

222. Yasui, S. 1974. *Nystagmus generation, oculomotor tracking and visual motion perception.* Ph.D. Thesis. MIT, Cambridge, Mass. 525 pp.

223. Yasui, S., Young, L. R. 1975. Perceived visual motion as effective stimulus to pursuit eye movement system. *Science* 190:906–8

224. Young, L. R., Stark, L. 1963. A discrete model for eye tracking movements. *IEEE Trans. Mil. Electron.* MIL-7:2, 3

225. Young, L. R., Forster, J. D., Van Houtte, N. 1968. A revised stochastic sampled data model for eye tracking movements. *Proc. Fourth Annual NASA-University Conference on Manual Control, NASA* SP-192:489–509

226. Young, L. R. 1971. Pursuit eye tracking movements. See Ref. 5, pp. 429–46

227. Young, L. R. 1969. The current status of vestibular system models. *Automatica* 5:369–83

228. Young, L. R., Oman, C. M. 1969. Models of vestibular adaptation to horizontal rotations. *Aerosp. Med.* 40:1076–80

229. Zee, D. S., Optican, L. M., Cook, J. D., Robinson, D. A., Engel, W. K. 1976. Slow saccades in spinocerebellar degeneration. *Arch. Neurol.* 33:243–51

230. Zee, D. S., Yee, R. D., Robinson, D. A. 1976. Optokinetic responses in labyrinthine-defective human beings. *Brain Res.* 113:423–28

231. Zuber, B. L. 1971. Control of vergence eye movements. See Ref. 5, pp. 447–71

AUTHOR INDEX

SUBJECT INDEX

CUMULATIVE INDEXES

CONTRIBUTING AUTHORS   VOLUMES 36-40

CHAPTER TITLES   VOLUMES 36-40